RICHARD D. GILLIOM

Southwestern at Memphis, Tennessee

INTRODUCTION TO
PHYSICAL ORGANIC CHEMISTRY

ADDISON-WESLEY PUBLISHING COMPANY

Reading, Massachusetts . Menlo Park, California . London . Don Mills, Ontario

This book is in the

ADDISON-WESLEY SERIES IN CHEMISTRY

Consulting Editors

William Robert Moore, Frederick D. Greene

PREFACE

The striking growth of physical organic chemistry has produced a number of excellent textbooks. These normally approach the topic either from the standpoint of the empirical study of mechanisms of homogeneous organic reactions or from a theoretical viewpoint. This book attempts to relate these two complementary approaches.

Modern introductory organic textbooks now place strong emphasis upon physical principles and provide a broad introduction to the study of reaction mechanisms. Thus, the traditional third-semester survey course on organic reaction mechanisms has become largely repetitive of earlier course-work, though in greater depth. This text evolved from an attempt to teach physical organic chemistry to undergraduate seniors at a comprehensible level without covering only familiar ground. To do this, a number of compromises have been made: at times rigor has been sacrificed for clarity and principles are presented with a minimum of historical development. The principles are developed and illustrated with specific studies selected to emphasize the point to be illustrated. As this selection is highly personal, I must apologize for the vast number of alternative choices that I have omitted in the interest of brevity. It is believed that anyone teaching from this text will wish to supply examples of his own equally personal preference.

After development of the principles and techniques most frequently employed by physical organic chemists, these are applied in depth to the specific examples of electrophilic aromatic substitution and nucleophilic alkyl substitution reactions. Since these reactions have been widely studied, they serve as a good introduction to the literature of the science and together they cover all of the principles presented earlier. Finally, the student usually begins his study of these reactions with the feeling that he understands them. The shock of realizing that he does not begins, we hope, his never-ending questioning of preconceived ideas and incomplete explanations.

The use of experimental examples is graduated throughout the text. I have found that early in a student's studies he has a difficult time relating ideas and data. For this reason, few references are cited or data given in the first few chapters. As the student progresses he is faced with an increasing number of experimental examples and an increasing number of references to original literature. This "weaning" process has been quite successful in my classroom and I believe that it will be equally successful in a textbook.

The material covered can be presented in a one-semester course. Normally, the first two chapters are assigned as reading and are not covered in class, except to answer questions that may have arisen. Omission of the material on the collision theory in Chapter 7 and on group theory in Appendix B would permit time for discussion of other topics without affecting the material presented.

Extensive use of existing literature has been made and detailed acknowledgment of all sources is impossible. I am grateful to Professors Peter Gaspar and Maurice Bussey who read the manuscript and made many helpful suggestions and to the staff at Addison-Wesley for the assistance that they have afforded. Finally, I am especially appreciative to my wife, Patricia, for help throughout the preparation of the manuscript.

R.D.G.

Memphis, Tennessee
September, 1969

CONTENTS

CHAPTER 1

THE ATOM: A REVIEW

It is now accepted that matter is not continuous but is made up of particles. These "building blocks" are sometimes called *fundamental particles*, but the large number of them—there are more than twenty known now—suggests that this may be a poor choice of words. Of these various particles we will be concerned with only three, the electron, e⁻, the proton, p, and the neutron, n. In any electrically neutral atom, the number of electrons is equal to the number of protons; this is the *atomic number*, Z. The number of protons plus the number of neutrons is the *mass number*, A. Many elements have atoms of different A-values, but all the atoms of an element have the same Z-value. Atoms of varying A but constant Z are called *isotopes*.

The atom consists of two parts.

1. The *nucleus* is a very dense core consisting of protons and neutrons which are held together by forces not yet completely understood. The nucleus contains all of the positive charge of an atom and most of its mass.

2. The *electrons* are outside the nucleus; they are held there by electrostatic forces.

The radii of atoms are of the order of 10^{-8} cm. Because atoms are of such small size, it is convenient to have a unit of length other than the centimeter. This unit is the Angstrom unit, Å: 1 Å is equal to 10^{-8} cm. The nuclei have radii of the order of 10^{-4} Å.

In chemistry, with the exception of nuclear chemistry, we are concerned primarily with the nature of the electrons, the particles involved in the formation of bonds between atoms to make molecules. An understanding of how electrons form bonds is critical to an understanding of not only organic but of all chemistry.

THE BOHR ATOM

At the start of this century, physicists were not able to fully explain the details of heat radiation from incandescent bodies. They hypothesized that the source of waves was a collection of oscillators and that these oscillators when heated vibrated with increasing amplitude and emitted light. However, this hypothesis did not explain experimental observations. Max Planck then showed that theory and fact would agree if certain postulates were made. These were:

a) For each oscillator there is a quantum of energy; that is, the energy of an oscillator must be an integral multiple of the quantum. The value of the quantum

1

is related to the frequency of the oscillator by the expression $h\nu$, where ν is the frequency and h is Planck's constant, 6.6238×10^{-27} erg-sec.

b) An oscillator of energy $E = nh\nu$, where n is an integer, radiates light, or energy, in bursts containing one or more quanta. If we supply energy to one of Planck's oscillators, the amplitude will not increase continuously. The oscillator will start vibrating with an amplitude corresponding to $E = h\nu$ and will vibrate at this amplitude, even though the amount of energy supplied is increased, until enough additional energy is supplied to increase the amplitude to a value corresponding to an energy of $2h\nu$. If energy is then withdrawn, the amplitude of the oscillator does not slowly decrease to the rest position. Instead, there is an instantaneous change from an energy of $2h\nu$ to one of $h\nu$, etc.

Planck quantized only the oscillator; he believed that the light emitted as the oscillator lost energy was continuous and behaved like an ordinary wave. Soon after this, Einstein showed that the ejection of electrons from metals exposed to light (the *photoelectric effect*) was best explained if light was also considered to be corpuscular in nature. These corpuscles of light, called *photons*, were shown to have an energy of $h\nu$.

By then it was recognized that a hydrogen atom consists of a proton and an electron, but how they were held together remained a puzzle. It was known that the electron could not be whirling about the proton as the moon whirls about the earth, for, if it did, then, according to classical theory, it would give off electromagnetic radiation, i.e. light, and lose its energy. As a result, the electron would slow down and finally plunge into the nucleus. This slowing down would occur in less than one microsecond, and hence the hydrogen atom would not be the stable entity that it was known to be.

Niels Bohr discarded classical theory and suggested that there might be some orbits in which the electron could move and in which this loss of energy did not occur. The equation that describes an orbit for an electron moving about the nucleus is

$$\text{centrifugal force} = \text{Coulombic attraction}$$

or, written in physical terms,

$$mv^2/r = e^2/r^2,$$

where m is the mass of the electron moving at velocity v. The electronic charge is given by e, and the distance from the electron to the proton is r. It is convenient to restate this equation in terms of the angular momentum p_a, where $p_a = mvr$:

$$p_a^2/mr^3 = e^2/r^2.$$

The total energy of such an orbit is given by

$$E = -e^2/r + p_a^2/2mr^2.$$

Here the first term represents the potential energy of the electron relative to its potential energy when it is infinitely far away from the proton, and the second term is the kinetic energy of the electron.

These equations are for any orbit. Bohr's contribution was to describe the particular orbits in which the electron would not lose energy. He suggested that these are the ones whose angular momentum is given by

$$p_a = nh/2\pi. \tag{1-1}$$

Substituting Eq. (1–1) into the equation containing p_a above yields the radii of the stable orbits:

$$r = n^2h^2/4\pi^2me^2. \tag{1-2}$$

Substitution into the energy equation gives the energy of the stable orbits:

$$E = -2\pi^2me^4/n^2h^2. \tag{1-3}$$

If a gas is subjected to an electric discharge or is strongly heated, it often emits electromagnetic radiation. Each gaseous atom gives radiation at characteristic wavelengths only and these are called its *spectrum*. In order to explain the spectrum of hydrogen, Bohr proposed a further postulate, that light was emitted by quantum jumps from one energy level, or orbit, to a lower one. The frequency of the light was assumed to be related to the difference in energy of the two orbits by

$$\Delta E = h\nu.$$

When an electron in hydrogen is excited by the absorption of energy, it moves to an orbit of higher energy; it emits light as it drops back. On this basis, Bohr predicted most of the hydrogen spectrum.

It can be seen from Eqs. (1–2) and (1–3) that, as n increases, the electron moves farther away from the nucleus and the energy of the electron becomes a smaller negative number. The energy and radius of the ground state, the orbit of lowest energy, $n = 1$, have been calculated to be 0.529 Å and -13.60 eV, respectively. One electron volt (eV) is the energy gained by an electron falling through a potential of one volt and is equivalent to 23.06 kcal/mole. The two quantities, radius and energy, can be depicted as shown in Figs. 1–1 and 1–2.

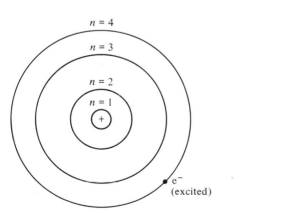
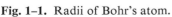

Fig. 1–1. Radii of Bohr's atom.

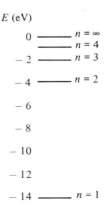

Fig. 1–2. Energy levels of Bohr's atom.

The Bohr atom looks much like the solar system with the exception that some of the orbits in the solar system are elliptical. Sommerfeld suggested that the electron also may occupy elliptical orbits (Fig. 1–3). Although this modification is mathematically difficult, its net effect was the addition of a second quantum number, l. However, the energy still depended primarily upon the principal quantum number n.

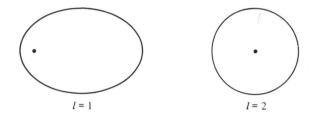

$l = 1$ $l = 2$

Fig. 1–3. Bohr-Sommerfeld hydrogen atom for $n = 2$.

The Bohr-Sommerfeld theory was very successful when applied to one-electron cases such as the hydrogen atom and ions containing only one electron such as Li(II) and Be(III). It failed when applied to systems of more than one electron.

As previously mentioned, Einstein showed that light could be considered to be corpuscular. In 1922, A. H. Compton, while studying X-rays, found that these could collide with an electron and transmit kinetic energy to it. Collision and energy transmission are behavior characteristics expected from particles of matter. Compton determined the momentum of a photon to be given by

$$p = h/\lambda,$$

where λ is the wavelength. Thus with every photon there must be associated a momentum.

Heisenberg seized upon these ideas and developed the uncertainty principle bearing his name. For our purposes, the important aspect of the principle is its statement that it is impossible to simultaneously measure the exact position and exact energy of an object. To know where an object is we must observe it; to see it we must shine a light on it; and the difficulty arises from this. If light, or photons, can transmit kinetic energy to the particle that we wish to see, then the light particles can actually move the object. However, we do not know the velocity imparted to the object, and without knowing the velocity, we cannot determine the energy. This principle is of no great importance when we deal with large objects. However, to "see" electrons, we must use light of very short wavelength, and such light carries the most momentum. The Bohr model of the atom, with its electron moving in a well-defined orbit about the nucleus, has little meaning precisely because it fixes the position of the electron so exactly that it gives rise to great uncertainty as to the energy of the electron.

Further progress was made by de Broglie, who showed that it is reasonable to expect particles to have wave character. The wavelength of a moving particle was considered to be given by the equation

$$\lambda = h/mv.$$

This equation was interpreted to mean that where there was a particle, there was a wave. Applying this expression to the Bohr atom model, we see that the electron orbits take on the appearance of the wave we would get if we tied the ends of a vibrating string together (Fig. 1–4). If each orbit did not have an integral number of waves, the waves of one cycle would be out of phase with those of other cycles, and the wave would damp itself out. If this occurred, the electron could not be in that orbit. With this restriction, the quantum conditions become simple. For an orbit of radius r the condition which ensures that an integral number of waves fit into the electron's orbit is $n\lambda = 2\pi r$. By substituting particle momentum for wavelength, using de Broglie's expression above and remembering that angular momentum is given by $p_a = mvr$, we obtain

$$p_a = nh/2\pi.$$

This is Eq. (1–1), Bohr's expression for angular momentum. De Broglie's postulate gives the same result for the hydrogen atom as that obtained by Bohr.

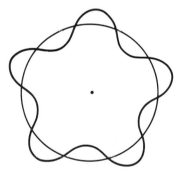

Fig. 1–4. Relationship of the wave character of the electron and Bohr's orbit.

The wave described by Eq. (1–1) can be given physical meaning. For light waves, the square of the amplitude, ψ^2, is thought to be proportional to the number of photons at the point where the value of ψ^2 is considered, that is, to the intensity of the light. This fact may be illustrated as in Fig. 1–5, where the number of photons in the region A is proportional to the value of ψ^2 at the point y. For intense light waves this interpretation presents no problem, but what if the wave is weak? Then y may correspond, mathematically, to only half (or some other fraction) of a photon. However, the photon cannot be divided into fractional parts: it is an entity. What can be done to save our simple approach? The only reasonable interpretation seems to be that y more correctly corresponds to the *probability* of finding a photon in region A. If A'

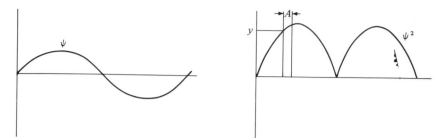

Fig. 1–5. Effect of squaring ψ.

were half as great as A, the probability of finding a photon in region A' would also be only half as great. So the probability of finding a photon in a region of size A is ψ^2 at that point times A. In three dimensions, A represents a volume and $\psi^2 A$, more commonly written as $\psi^2\,d\tau$, represents the probability of finding a photon in that volume of space. Thus ψ^2 gives the units of probability/unit-volume and is often referred to as *probability density*.

The wave associated with an electron in an atom is conveniently interpreted in the same manner. The square of the amplitude of the wave is proportional to the probability of finding an electron in the region of space $d\tau$. It is no longer possible to talk about the precise position of the electron. Instead, we talk about the probability of its being in a particular region.

It would seem appropriate at this point to ask why the probability density is given by ψ^2 and not ψ. In Fig. 1–5 it can be seen that the sign of ψ is both positive and negative. Since we are trying to describe a real physical system and a negative probability of finding an electron is an unrealistic concept, ψ^2 is chosen because it must always be positive.

What has been gained by this approach? If the indefiniteness of position of an electron is accepted, its momentum and energy can be calculated quite precisely and the uncertainty principle is satisfied. The electron appears, statistically, not as a particle whirling about a nucleus, but as an unsplittable charge cloud that has the spin, mass, and charge associated with the electron. This hazy region of space occupied by the electron is called an *orbital*. A discussion of orbitals can be very fruitful to an understanding of chemistry.

ATOMIC ORBITALS

Orbitals are identified by a series of numbers called *quantum numbers*. Only three such numbers are required to define any orbital with respect to size, shape, and orientation. A fourth number gives information about the electron itself.

These numbers are discussed below.

1. The *principal quantum number n* is restricted to the positive integers 1, 2, 3, ... describing roughly the circumference of the orbital. Electrons in an orbital designated by 1 spend more of their time near the nucleus than do those in an orbital designated by 2. Furthermore, an electron in an orbital of high principal quantum number has in most cases, more energy than one of lower number. For convenience, we can think of all electrons having the same value of n as being in the same shell. These shells have been called the K, L, M, etc. shells in the past, but it is now generally accepted practice to give them a number.

2. The *azimuthal quantum number* l is limited to integral values including zero but is always less than n. This number indicates the shape of an atomic orbital or, more precisely, it specifies the value of the angular momentum of the electron. If an orbital has an l-value of zero, its shape is that of a sphere. An l-value of 1 tells us that the orbital has the shape of a dumbbell. Although orbitals may be described in numerical terms, it is customary to use letters for l-values: thus the values 0, 1, 2, 3, and 4 of l are commonly denoted by s, p, d, f, and g, respectively.

3. The *magnetic quantum number* m_l indicates the direction or orientation of the orbital when it is placed in a magnetic field. In the absence of a magnetic field, atoms differing only in m_l value are indistinguishable. A more concise but perhaps less useful definition of m_l is that it is a measure of magnetic moment. Values of m_l are restricted to integers between l and $-l$, including 0. The magnetic quantum number is frequently given in terms of the Cartesian coordinates, x, y, and z which appear as subscripts of l.

4. The *spin quantum number* m_s, or sometimes simply s, describes the spin of the electron. The electron has a magnetic moment because, behaving like a tiny bar magnet, it spins about its own axis and interacts with the magnetic field produced by its own orbital motion as well as with any magnetic fields outside the atom. There are, of course, only two directions in which the electron can spin, and hence m_s is limited to two values, $\frac{1}{2}$ and $-\frac{1}{2}$.

The preceding may be summarized in tabular form.

Symbol	Analogy	Allowed values	Total possibilities
n	Size	1, 2, 3,...	
l	Shape	$0, 1, 2, \ldots, (n-1)$	n
m_l	Orientation	$l, l-1, l-2, \ldots, -l$	$2l+1$
m_s	Spin	$\frac{1}{2}, -\frac{1}{2}$	2

We may note that n is the number of shells, and n^2 is the number of orbitals in the nth shell.

We can draw orbitals in such a way that the drawing represents the volume of space containing approximately 90% of the electron density. The orbitals obtained for a hydrogen-like atom are shown in Fig. 1–6. The sign of the wave function (ψ) has no physical significance for the atom but will be useful when we consider chemical

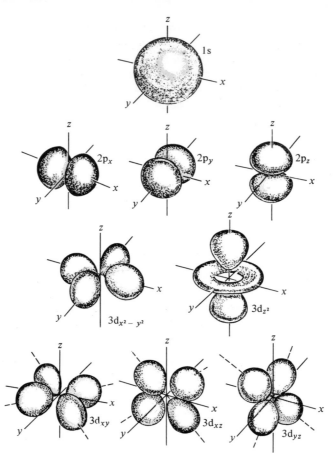

Fig. 1–6. Hydrogenic wave functions or orbitals. The d_{z^2} orbital and the p orbitals are figures of revolution about the axis of orientation, but the lobes of the remaining d orbitals are not circular in section. Note also that the two lobes of the p orbitals are of different sign, and the lobes of the d orbitals alternate in sign; i.e., opposing pairs are of the same sign. The orbitals are not drawn to scale. (Taken from K. B. Harvey and G. B. Porter, *Introduction to Physical Inorganic Chemistry*, Addison-Wesley Publishing Co., Reading, Mass., (1963), p. 68.)

bonding. The directional characteristics bear no relation to a generalized configuration of the atom but are important in describing molecular bonding.

In writing the quantum numbers to describe an atom, we first write the value of n followed by the value of l, using the s, p, d, and f notation. Thus 2s signifies the s orbital of the second shell. When doing this we need not specify the magnetic quantum number. You will recall that, in the absence of a magnetic field, atoms differing only in m_l value are indistinguishable. It is also customary to indicate the number of electrons in an orbital by a superscript; thus $3p^2$ indicates that two electrons are in the p orbital of the third shell.

It is now possible to specify the state of a complex atom simply by adding Z electrons and Z protons, one at a time, to the hydrogen atom. There are three important rules that govern the manner in which this can be done.

1. *Pauli exclusion principle.* No two electrons in an atom may have the same quantum number; that is, each orbital can contain only two electrons and these must have different spin.

2. *Aufbau principle.* Each additional electron goes into the next unfilled orbital of lowest energy. The atom will therefore be in its lowest energy state, called the *ground state.* This state is of greatest interest to the scientist studying the chemistry of atoms, while the excited states, in which an electron is in an orbital other than the lowest possible one, are of concern to the spectroscopist.

3. *Hund's rule.* When two electrons have orbitals of the same n- and l-values available to them, they occupy adjacent ones and have parallel spin. In the absence of a magnetic field, orbitals with the same n- and l-values have equal energy and are called *degenerate* orbitals. Since there are three such p orbitals, these orbitals are called triply degenerate; the d orbitals are fivefold degenerate; and the f orbitals are sevenfold degenerate.

In order to derive the structure of atoms, we must, according to the Aufbau principle, know the energy level of each orbital. One method of estimating this level is to take the sum of n and l: the higher this sum, the higher the energy of the orbital that n and l represent. (The electrons always go into the level of lowest $n + l$.) If this sum is the same for two levels, we use the orbital with the lower n-value. This method permits us to build up the electronic structure of atoms with amazing accuracy. Careful examination of Fig. 1–7 indicates that the energy levels cross and that the last electron placed in an orbital may not be the first one lost in an oxidation process such as ionization—probably because, in ionization, no proton is removed from the nucleus. Unfortunately, there is no simple way to remember the peculiar jumps observed in the process of filling orbitals; for example, vanadium with two 4s electrons and three 3d electrons is followed by chromium with one 4s and five 3d electrons.

To derive the electronic structure of the atoms of an element in the ground state, i.e. the structure atoms have at normal temperatures, we simply put the proper number of electrons in the orbitals of lowest energy. The first ten elements are shown below. Arrows represent electrons and their spin.

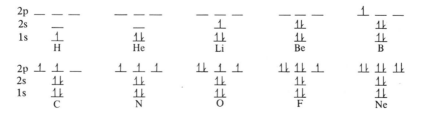

Frequently this information is given in linear notation, using the quantum numbers with a superscript to indicate the number of electrons in each orbital. For example,

carbon: $1s^2 2s^2 2p^2$,   potassium: $1s^2 2s^2 2p^6 3s^2 3p^6 4s^1$.

This notation may be shortened even further by indicating the last inert gas plus any remaining electrons:

potassium: (neon core)$4s^1$,   silver: (krypton core)$5s^1 4d^{10}$.

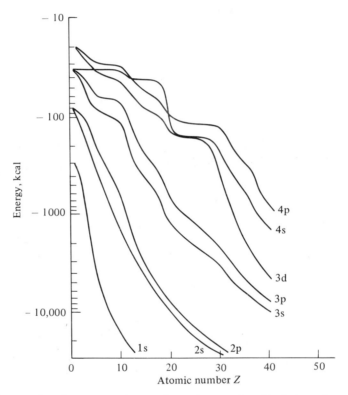

Fig. 1–7. Curves showing approximate dependence of orbital energies on atomic number. The curves are based on experimental data derived from optical and X-ray spectra. (Taken from K. B. Harvey and G. B. Porter, *op. cit.*, p. 75.)

The electronic structure of atoms is often represented in other ways, most frequently by using the symbol for the atom and dots to represent the outer shell or valence electrons:

$$\cdot\overset{\displaystyle\cdot}{\underset{\displaystyle\cdot}{\text{C}}}\cdot \qquad\qquad \text{K}\cdot$$

Finally atoms may be represented by drawing the outer orbitals using dots for electrons. This method is convenient only for elements with no more than s or p electrons but, for many purposes, such orbital diagrams are the method of choice.

Each orbital should be labeled for clarity. Hydrogen, carbon, and chlorine are represented by this method in Fig. 1–8.

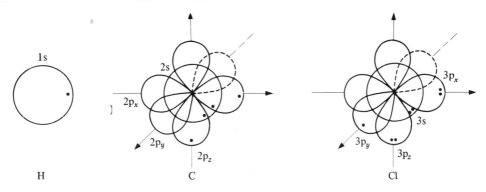

Fig. 1–8. Atomic orbital diagrams.

PROBLEMS

1. Verify the radius and energy of the first Bohr orbit of the hydrogen atom. What is the value of the ionization potential of the hydrogen atom?

2. Using linear notation, write the quantum number designation for:
   a) B   b) Ca   c) Se   d) V
   e) Zr   f) Hf   g) F⁻   h) Na⁺

3. Draw atomic orbital diagrams of the outer shell of electrons for each of the following. Clearly label all orbitals. Represent electrons by dots in the appropriate orbitals.
   a) Li   b) N   c) F   d) S

4. What elements are represented by:
   a) $1s^2 2s^2 2p^1$ b) $(Ar)3d^2 4s^2$
   c) $(Xe)4f^2 6s^2$ d) $(Xe)4f^{14} 5d^5 6s^2$

CHAPTER 2

A QUALITATIVE APPROACH
TO CHEMICAL BONDING

Atoms form ions and molecules by a process known as *bonding*. Only three distinct types of chemical bonds are of importance in organic chemistry, and it is imperative to be familiar with each.

1. Ionic bonds. These bonds are created when one or more electrons of an atom (or group of atoms) are transferred to another atom (or group of atoms). Ionic bonds are electrostatic and have no definite lengths. They are also nondirectional. An ion will attract several ions of opposite charge equally and the distance between the ions is determined solely by the packing pattern. Ionic bonding occurs in reactions between metallic and nonmetallic atoms. If two atoms of one element lose one electron each to one atom of a second element which accepts two electrons, these elements react with each other in the ratio of two atoms of the first to one atom of the second.

2. Covalent bonds. In covalent bonding, one atom shares electrons with an adjacent atom. The result is the formation of molecules. Covalent bonds are unidirectional, and the nuclei can be assigned bond lengths corresponding to their equilibrium positions. If one atom is bonded to two or more other atoms, definite bond angles are encountered across intervening atoms. These may be represented by lines drawn through the nuclei in their equilibrium positions. Bond strength, that is, the energy released when the bond is formed, can be assigned to any pair of covalently bonded atoms. This is not true of ionic bonds, since the force attracting two ions is inversely proportional to the distance separating them. Covalent bonds are formed between metalloid atoms and either metallic or nonmetallic atoms, between two metalloid atoms, and between two nonmetallic atoms.

3. Coordinate covalent bonds. These are much like covalent bonds except for the method of their formation. In the coordinate covalent bond, both electrons forming the bond are supplied by one atom, with the other atom merely "coming along for the ride."

THEORY OF LEWIS AND KOSSEL

Although many theories of bonding have been proposed, the first really valuable theory was advanced independently by Lewis and Kossel. Actually, their two theories differed somewhat, but, by combining them, one can develop a simple and frequently adequate approach, particularly for the atoms of lower atomic number. It is usually called simply the Lewis theory.

This approach recognizes that the eight-electron outer configuration of the inert gases, as well as the two-electron arrangement of helium, is a particularly stable one. The theory then proposes that all atoms tend to acquire the number of electrons necessary to bring the number of electrons in the outer or *valence* shell to eight. Kossel thought that the necessary electrons were either gained or lost (ionic bonding), while Lewis argued that the electrons are shared (covalent and coordinate covalent bonding).

In applying the Lewis and Kossel theory to the description of the bonding process in molecules, we must observe the following rules:

1. Be certain that the arrangement of the atoms is correct.

2. Be sure to use the correct number of valence electrons.

3. Use completed octets whenever possible.

4. Avoid formal charges if possible.

To see how the theory may be used to describe bonds, we shall apply it to a few simple molecules, using the short-hand method of writing the electronic structures of atoms. Fluorine is a diatomic molecule made up of two fluorine atoms. In this case, rule 1 is trivial, since two atoms can be arranged in only one way, namely, a straight line. Each fluorine atom has seven valence electrons, so 14 must be used in the molecule. These 14 electrons can be grouped in such a way that each atom is surrounded by eight as shown:

$$:\ddot{F}:\ddot{F}:$$

To determine whether rule 4 is satisfied, we count the number of unshared electrons about an atom and add to this the number of shared electrons divided by two. For each fluorine atom, our calculation gives $6 + (2/2) = 7$. This is equal to the number of electrons in the valence shell of the free atom, and hence the fluorine atom has no formal charge. The bond consists of one pair of electrons and is frequently described as a single bond. Using the same procedure for oxygen, O_2, and nitrogen, N_2, we can illustrate the double bond (O_2) and the triple bond (N_2):

$$:\ddot{O}::\ddot{O}: \qquad :N:::N:$$

Unfortunately this description of oxygen is not adequate, since this element is known to have electrons with unpaired spins. A more complicated molecule is ammonia, in which three hydrogen atoms are bonded to a central nitrogen atom. Here a total of eight valence electrons must be distributed, and, remembering that the helium arrangement will satisfy hydrogen, we find that the structure is

$$H:\ddot{N}:H$$
$$H$$

The boron trifluoride molecule introduces a new problem. It can be drawn in either of two ways:

$$A \qquad\qquad B$$

In structure A, rule 3 is violated, since boron is surrounded by only six electrons, and structure B violates rule 4. In this case, experimental evidence has proved structure A to be the correct one. In cases of this sort where a choice must be made as to the structure to choose, or the rule to break, we must work with intuition. As a guide, structures which require writing a formal positive charge on an atom that normally attracts electrons (atoms of high electronegativity) should be avoided.

The Lewis theory frequently leads to difficulties; a case in point is the structure of BF_3 discussed above. Furthermore, it fails to give any clue to the geometric arrangement of the atoms in a molecule. It is nevertheless a very useful system of representing molecular electronic structures and is widely accepted. Any student of chemistry must become familiar with Lewis structures.

In Lewis structures bonds are frequently written in a short-hand notation: each pair of bonding electrons is represented by a dash. A single bond is represented by a single dash, a double bond by two dashes, and a triple bond by three. Unshared electrons are usually omitted. Examples (fluorine, oxygen, and nitrogen) are shown below:

$$F—F \qquad O{=}O \qquad N{\equiv}N$$

There is a further problem with Lewis structures. If the Lewis structure for carbonic acid is written using the dash system, we obtain

$$\begin{array}{c} H—O—C—O—H \\ \| \\ O \end{array}$$

a structure obeying all the rules. If carbonic acid is treated with a base, for example NaOH, we get the carbonate ion, CO_3^-, which is known to exist as a discrete entity. To represent $CO_3^=$, we simply delete the H's from the structure above, retaining the dashes to indicate the two units of negative charge carried by the ion:

$$\begin{array}{c} —O—C—O— \\ \| \\ O \end{array}$$

This structure suggests that the carbonate ion has two types of carbon–oxygen bonds, two single-bonded oxygen atoms and one double-bonded. All known methods of distinguishing two types of carbon–oxygen bonds have failed, however, and all the bonds appear to be exactly alike. The structure of the carbonate ion can be represented equally well by

$$\begin{array}{ccc} —O—C{=}O & & O{=}C—O— \\ | & \text{and} & | \\ O— & & O— \end{array}$$

Although any of the above three structures may be used to represent the carbonate ion, none is adequate. They do not indicate the equivalence of all the bonds nor do they point out the observed fact that the carbonate ion is more stable than any of the structures indicate. However, Lewis structures are so convenient to use that a concept has been developed to handle this deficiency. This is known as *resonance*, an unfortunate choice of name. The concept states, quite simply, that when two (or more) reasonable Lewis structures can be drawn to represent a molecule, then the actual structure is similar to each but not like either; it is somewhere in between. It is important to note that the molecule does *not* change from one of the structures to another; it has a structure that the simple classical model cannot represent.

Returning to the carbonate ion, we wish to note that there is not *one* double-bonded oxygen atom but that *all* the carbon–oxygen bonds have some double-bond character. Since double bonds are shorter than single bonds, we might guess that the bond lengths in the carbonate ion are shorter than a normal carbon–oxygen single bond but longer than the double bond. By referring to a table of bond strengths, we could calculate the bonding energy of the total carbonate ion, using any of the three structures given above. Our calculation would be in error by about $+42$ kcal/mole. This energy difference between the observed value and the value calculated from the structures is called *resonance energy* and is always in the direction of a stabler compound than the classical structures indicate. We can see the importance of this phenomenon by comparing the stability of the carbonate ion with that of carbonic acid, where the presence of the covalently bound hydrogen precludes resonance. Carbonic acid is readily decomposed to water and carbon dioxide as anybody knows who has ever opened a bottle of soft drink and seen it fizz. Barium carbonate, which exists ionically in the solid, does not decompose until heated to 1360°C.

Structures such as the three given above to represent the carbonate ion are called *canonical formulas*, and the true structure, which cannot be drawn, is called a *resonance hybrid*. To represent a resonance hybrid, convention dictates that all the contributing canonical formulas be written and connected with double-headed arrows:

$$-O-\underset{\underset{O}{\|}}{C}-O- \leftrightarrow -O-\underset{\underset{O}{|}}{C}=O \leftrightarrow O=\underset{\underset{O}{|}}{C} \quad O-$$

Three rules may be followed in deciding whether Lewis structures are canonical formulas or not.

1. The positions of the atoms cannot change.

2. All structures must have the same number of bonds.

3. All structures must have about the same energy.

The first two rules are simple and require no explanation, but the third might cause some trouble. In most cases, high-energy structures—those in which unlike charges are widely separated or in which like charges are brought close together—may be ignored. For example, three structures may be written to represent hydrazoic acid, HN_3:

$$H—\overset{+}{N}=\overset{-}{N}=\overset{-}{N} \leftrightarrow H—\overset{-}{N}—\overset{+}{N}≡N \leftrightarrow H—\overset{+}{N}≡\overset{+}{N}—\overset{=}{N}.$$

The third structure, however, having two adjacent atoms with positive charge, is of higher energy than the first two, and therefore need not be considered a canonical formula for hydrazoic acid.

Perhaps the most serious misuse of the concept of resonance is to explain the chemistry of a compound by means of just one of its canonical formulas. Since a resonance hybrid never has the exact structure of any one of the canonical formulas, this kind of "explanation" is an obvious error, but it is one very frequently made.

ATOMIC ORBITAL APPROACH

Another approach to the description of bonds stems from the orbital picture of atoms that has been previously discussed. In this model of compounds three restrictions are placed upon the way that atomic orbitals can combine to form bonds.

1. The energies of the atomic orbitals must be of about the same magnitude. In general this means that bonds are formed only by the orbitals in the valence shells of atoms: thus, the 2p electrons of the chlorine atom do not contribute to the bond in hydrogen chloride.

2. The atomic orbitals must have the same symmetry about the bonding axis. Thus an s and a p orbital may overlap as shown in Fig. 2–1 but not as in Fig. 2–2.

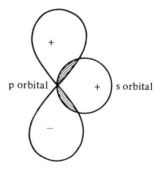

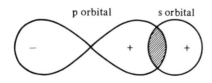

Fig. 2–1. Allowed s–p overlap.   **Fig. 2–2.** Forbidden s–p overlap.

3. The atomic orbitals will overlap as much as possible. This is the main source of bond stability and leads to the formation of bonds in the direction of greatest concentration of electron density.

The Pauli exclusion principle applies here just as it did for atoms. In this case, two overlapping atomic orbitals may have only one pair of electrons and they must have opposite spins. The individual electrons in these overlapping orbitals lose their identity and cannot be assigned to one of the bonded atoms. Thus, in this as in all schemes, bonds are formed by the pairing of electrons.

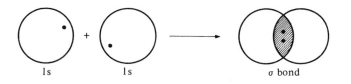

Fig. 2–3. Orbital representation of H_2.

The hydrogen molecule is pictured as a pair of overlapping 1s orbitals (Fig. 2–3). It can readily be seen that this type of bond is cylindrically symmetrical about the bonding axis. Such bonds are called *sigma* (σ) bonds and may be formed from the overlapping of two s or two p orbitals, or one of each.

A second type of covalent bond, the *pi* (π) bond, results from the overlapping of two p orbitals that are parallel to each other. Since the p orbitals are dumbbell-shaped, the bond that is formed by this overlap is antisymmetric about the bonding axis (Fig. 2–4).

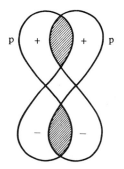

Fig. 2–4. The π bond.

Let us consider the formation of water from the combination of the 1s orbital of each of two hydrogen atoms with the 2p orbitals of an oxygen atom. Since each nucleus lies on one of the Cartesian coordinates, the bond angle between H—O—H would be expected to be 90° (Fig. 2–5). Experimentally, this angle has been found to be 105°. However, the 90° value is a reasonable guess, since 90° bond angles are also predicted for H_2S, H_2Se, H_2Te, PH_3, and AsH_3; the actual bond angles of these compounds are 90 ± 3°.

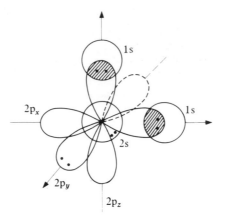

Fig. 2–5. Atomic orbital picture of H_2O.

It has been suggested that the increased bond angle in water, as in NH_3 with H—N—H angles of 107°, is caused by dipole repulsions due to the concentration of the bonding electrons between the atoms. This leaves the positive hydrogen nucleus somewhat unshielded and hence the hydrogen atom is slightly positive. It is doubtful whether such repulsions could spread the hydrogen atoms to a bond angle of more than 95°.

To accommodate such observations we must introduce another concept. It is possible for atomic orbitals within an atom to combine so as to give new orbitals with greater directional character. As a result, the orbitals move farther apart and a greater number of bonds will be formed. The process is known as *hybridization*.

The chemistry of carbon is determined almost entirely by hybrid orbitals. The carbon atom, $1s^2 2s^2 2p^2$, with two unpaired electrons, might be expected to be divalent and to form compounds of the type CH_2, with an unoccupied orbital that could possibly be involved in coordinate covalent bonding. Carbon is known to be tetravalent, however, and to form compounds of the type CH_4. This tetravalence might result from the excitation of one of the 2s electrons to the third p orbital, which would lead to the formation of three bonds by overlap with the p orbitals and a fourth bond by overlap with the s orbital. This bonding should result in two types of bonds, three similar ones from p overlap and a fourth of another type from s overlap. However, it is found that all four bonds are equivalent. The explanation is that the s and p orbitals are combined to give the same number of a new type of orbital

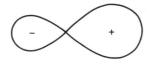

Fig. 2–6. An sp^3 hybrid orbital.

(Fig. 2–6), called sp³ hybrid orbitals because their origin is one s and three p orbitals. They are pointed toward the four corners of a regular tetrahedron around the nucleus and result in bond angles of 109°28′.

An s orbital may also be combined with either one or two p orbitals to give sp (Fig. 2–7) and sp² (Fig. 2–8) hybridization respectively. In these cases the remaining p orbitals are usually involved in π bonding. The sp and sp² hybrid orbitals have small lobes of negative sign similar to that pictured for the sp³ hybrid. Because these do not contribute to bonding, they are frequently omitted from such drawings.

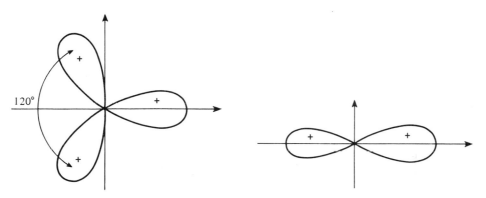

| Fig. 2–7. The three sp² hybrids. | Fig. 2–8. The two sp hybrids. |

One may ask why hybridization occurs at all. The process can be explained qualitatively as follows. Energy is required to promote an electron from an s to a p orbital so that the two can be combined. You will note from Fig. 2–6 that nearly all of a hybrid orbital extends in a single lobe from the nucleus, whereas a pure p orbital has two equal lobes on either side of the nucleus. The hybrid arrangement permits greater overlap and thus the formation of stronger bonds, resulting in the recovery of some of the energy lost by the electron's promotion to a higher orbital. Furthermore, a greater number of bonds are formed and therefore an even greater recovery of energy is made. It follows that compounds formed with hybrid orbitals are more stable than those formed with pure atomic orbitals.

To return to the examples of water and ammonia, which we were discussing, it is possible to think of water as an sp³ hybrid compound, but its bond angles are not large enough. It has been suggested that the unshared pairs of electrons that occupy two corners of a tetrahedron about the oxygen atom repel each other, with the result that the hydrogen atoms are squeezed together. This is reasonable, because the non-bonding electrons do occupy more space than the bonding pairs. Probably the best explanation for the bond angles of water and ammonia is "partial" hybridization; in other words, only a small portion of the s orbital is combined with each bonding p orbital.

This somewhat pictorial presentation is closely akin to a mathematical approach to chemical bonding known as the *valence bond method,* which was the first application of quantum theory to the problem. Although this method was widely used for a time, the newer *molecular orbital method* is rapidly replacing it in mathematical treatments. The explanation of bonding just given is very useful, however, in qualitative applications.

PROBLEMS

1. Draw Lewis structures for each of the following:

   a) F_2 b) HCN   c) $H_2C:C:CH_2$ d) $AlCl_3$ e) CH_3OCH_3
   f) H_2CO

2. Draw Lewis structures for each of the following. If more than one structure can be drawn, indicate the most stable one(s) and evaluate the importance of resonance.

   a) H_2CO_3 b) $CO_3^=$ c) NO_3^- d) NO_2^- e) NO_2 f) NO_2^+
   g) H_2CN_2 h) $H_2C:CHCN$ i) C_6H_6

3. Draw atomic orbital pictures for each of the following compounds. Indicate electrons by dots within the orbitals. Be sure to use the correct hybridized orbitals when appropriate. Label all orbitals clearly. Predict all bond angles.

   a) CH_2Cl_2 e) $H_2C:C:O$ i) CH_3^+
   b) PH_3 f) H_2CN_2 j) CH_3^-
   c) CO_2 g) naphthalene   k) pyridine
   d) HCN   h) butadiene   l) $H_2C:CHCN$

CHAPTER 3

THE WAVE EQUATION

Much of the material in the first two chapters is based on quantum theory, or, more correctly, on wave mechanics. The wave equation cannot be derived but it can be developed from analogies with classical mechanics, and an explanation of this will help the reader to obtain a proper "feel" for the chemist's approach to bonding.

THE SCHRÖDINGER EQUATION

The classical law of conservation of energy may be stated as

$$E = T + V, \tag{3-1}$$

where E represents total energy and may be calculated from some function of position and momentum, T represents the kinetic energy, and V the potential energy. For a single particle moving along the x-axis in a potential field P_x, Eq. (3–1) can be rewritten as

$$\tfrac{1}{2}m\dot{x}^2 + P_x = E, \tag{3-2}$$

where the velocity, dx/dt, is given as $\dot{x}$. Integration of Eq. (3–2) yields the classical orbit. Since momentum is given by $p = m\dot{x}$, we can substitute this in Eq. (3–2) to obtain

$$p^2/2m + P_x = E. \tag{3-3}$$

To convert (3–3) to a wave equation we make use of the rule that wherever momentum, p, appears it is replaced by $(h/2\pi i)d\,/dx$. Symbolically,

$$p \rightarrow (h/2\pi i)d\,/dx,$$

where i is $\sqrt{-1}$ and h is Planck's constant. In this notation

$$p^2 = [(h/2\pi i)d\,/dx][(h/2\pi i)d\,/dx] = -(h^2/4\pi^2)d^2\,/dx^2,$$

and, if this is substituted, Eq. (3–3) becomes

$$-(h^2/8\pi^2 m)d^2\,/dx^2 + P_x = E. \tag{3-4}$$

This description of the wave equation applies only to stationary states in which particles cannot escape to infinity, not to such experimentally observed phenomena

21

as scattering of X-rays or electrons. For these purposes a time-dependent equation is obtained by the further substitution

$$E \rightarrow -(h/2\pi i)d/dt.$$

However, for most chemical applications the stationary state is of greatest interest and we shall make use of the *amplitude equation* that can be obtained from Eq. (3–4). Really, Eq. (3–4) is no equation at all; it tells us to differentiate twice with respect to x but not what to differentiate. If we choose something to operate on, an *operand*, and call it the wave amplitude function Ψ (which in our case is a function only of x), then from Eq. (3–4) we can write the wave equation

$$[-(h^2/8\pi^2 m)d^2/dx^2 + P_x]\Psi_x = E\Psi_x. \tag{3–5}$$

This is frequently rewritten in the form

$$d^2\Psi_x/dx^2 + (8\pi^2 m/h^2)(E - P_x)\Psi_x = 0. \tag{3–6}$$

Equation (3–6) is the Schrödinger equation in one dimension for one electron in a system that does not interact with its surroundings, i.e. a conservative system. The equation may also be obtained from the classical wave equation and the de Broglie wavelength equation.

PARTICLE IN A BOX

An informative problem that can be solved with Eq. (3–5) or (3–6) is the description of a particle in a box. Let us first choose a box of one dimension only, placed so that one "edge" is at the origin of the x-axis, $x = 0$, and the box lies along the x-axis to a point $x = a$. Outside the box, that is, at all points other than $0 \leqslant x \leqslant a$, the potential energy is infinite.

The wave equation for the particle outside the box can be written using Eq. (3–5) as

$$-(h^2/8\pi^2 m)d^2\Psi/dx^2 + \infty\Psi = E\Psi \qquad (x < 0 \text{ or } > a). \tag{3–7}$$

The only solution for this is: (1) $\Psi = 0$ and $\Psi^2 = 0$ or (2) the probability of finding the particle outside the box is zero (see Chapter 1).

Within the box no forces act upon the particle. The potential energy is by definition a constant and we may set it to zero. The wave equation for the particle in the box may be written as

$$-(h^2/8\pi^2 m)d^2\Psi/dx^2 = E\Psi \qquad (0 \leqslant x \leqslant a), \tag{3–8}$$

yielding the general solution

$$\Psi = A \sin (8\pi^2 mE/h^2)^{1/2}x + B \cos (8\pi^2 mE/h^2)^{1/2}x, \tag{3–9}$$

where A and B are constants of integration. Since Ψ must not vanish identically, at least A or B must not be equal to zero.

To evaluate A and B, we make use of one of the conditions of wave mechanics, namely, that Ψ must be a continuous function throughout $-\infty \leqslant X \leqslant \infty$, or, more generally, Ψ must be continuous throughout all space. Since $\Psi = 0$ for all values of $x < 0$ and $x > a$, this condition is satisfied only if $\Psi = 0$ when $x = 0$ and $x = a$. From Eq. (3–9) it can be seen that when $x = 0$, $\Psi_0 = B$. Of course, $\Psi_0 = 0$, so $B = 0$. Hence, A must not be zero. Since Ψ must be zero when $x = a$, we may write

$$\Psi_a = A \sin (8\pi^2 mE/h^2)^{1/2}a = 0, \tag{3–10}$$

$$(8\pi^2 mE/h^2)^{1/2}a = \sin^{-1} 0 = n\pi, \tag{3–11}$$

and

$$E = n^2h^2/8ma^2. \tag{3–12}$$

In Eqs. (3–11) and (3–12) the symbol n is any positive integer. If $n = 0$, Ψ vanishes and this is not allowed. If n were any negative integer, no additional independent solutions of Ψ would result because the same values would be obtained, though of opposite sign.

The boundary condition that Ψ is everywhere continuous (and finite) does not fix the value of A, but rather determines the values of E. To evaluate A, the normalization requirement

$$\int_{-\infty}^{\infty} \Psi^2 \, dx = 1 \tag{3–13}$$

is used. A more general form of this equation is given by

$$\int_{-\infty}^{\infty} \Psi\Psi^* \, dx = 1,$$

where Ψ^* represents the complex conjugate of Ψ. The functions that we will be using do not require the use of Ψ^*, so Eq. (3–13) will be adequate. The *normalization condition* states that no waves have infinite amplitudes and that their amplitudes and slopes (variation of amplitude with distance) are continuous and single-valued at any point x. A reasonable interpretation is that the probability of finding the particle in all space is 1. Returning to Eq. (3–13), we find that substitution of Eqs. (3–10) and (3–12) gives

$$\int_{-\infty}^{\infty} \Psi^2 \, dx = A^2 \int_{-\infty}^{\infty} \sin^2 (\pi n/a)x \, dx = A^2a/2 = 1, \tag{3–14}$$

and solving, we have

$$A = (2/a)^{1/2}. \tag{3–15}$$

The solution of Eq. (3–8) is now obtained by making the proper substitutions into Eq. (3–9):

$$\Psi = (2/a)^{1/2} \sin \pi nx/a \quad (0 \leqslant x \leqslant a). \tag{3–16}$$

The number of solutions is infinite but the value of E is limited to discrete quantities determined by the value of n, and a wave function is obtained for each value of n.

In the above, we have arrived at an unrealizable limiting case, since the first derivative of the wave function, $d\Psi/dx$, is discontinuous at $x = 0$ and at $x = a$. If we allow V to be very large but not infinite outside the box, this difficulty is surmounted but there remains the probability of finding the particle outside the box. This probability can be made as small as desired if V is made increasingly larger.

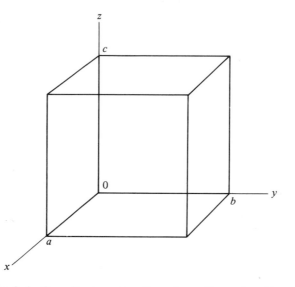

Fig. 3–1. Coordinate system for a three-dimensional box.

Of course, the cases of most interest to us are those in which the particle moves in three space coordinates. The box that was developed above can be expanded to three dimensions, with one corner placed at the origin of Cartesian coordinates and three sides of the box upon the axes (Fig. 3–1). The length of the box along the x-axis is a, along the y-axis is b, and along the z-axis is c. As before, if the potential energy is set equal to infinity outside the box, Ψ is found to vanish, and we may write

$$\Psi = 0 \quad \begin{cases} -\infty \leqslant x \leqslant 0 & \text{or} \quad a \leqslant x \leqslant \infty, \\ -\infty \leqslant y \leqslant 0 & \text{or} \quad b \leqslant y \leqslant \infty, \\ -\infty \leqslant z \leqslant 0 & \text{or} \quad c \leqslant z \leqslant \infty. \end{cases} \quad (3\text{--}17)$$

The probability of finding the particle outside the box is again zero.

Within the box, the potential energy is a constant and can be set equal to zero as before. The kinetic energy of the particle is given by

$$T = (m/2)(\dot{x}^2 + \dot{y}^2 + \dot{z}^2) = (p_x^2 + p_y^2 + p_z^2)/2m. \quad (3\text{--}18)$$

If we make the substitutions

$$p_{x(y)(z)} \rightarrow (h/2\pi i)d \, /dx(y)(z),$$

remembering that $V = 0$, the wave equation becomes

$$-(h^2/8\pi^2m)(d^2\Psi/dx^2 + d^2\Psi/dy^2 + d^2\Psi/dz^2) = E\Psi \tag{3-19}$$

between the limits $0 \leqslant x \leqslant a, 0 \leqslant y \leqslant b$, and $0 \leqslant z \leqslant c$. This sort of equation is often written as

$$-(h^2/8\pi^2m)\nabla^2\Psi = E\Psi. \tag{3-19a}$$

This second form of the equation makes use of the Laplacian operator, ∇^2, which is given by

$$\nabla^2 \equiv d^2/dx^2 + d^2/dy^2 + d^2/dz^2.$$

There are rules for converting ∇^2 into an equivalent operator by using other variables such as spherical polar coordinates, but we will not be particularly concerned with these operations.

Equation (3–19) may be simplified by separation of the variables. Let us assume that Ψ can be expressed as the product of a function of x alone, X_x, a function of y alone, Y_y, and a function of z alone, Z_z:

$$\Psi = X_x Y_y Z_z. \tag{3-20}$$

By combining Eqs. (3–19) and (3–20) and then dividing by Ψ, we obtain

$$-(h^2/8\pi^2m)\left(\frac{1}{X}d^2X/dx^2 + \frac{1}{Y}d^2Y/dy^2 + \frac{1}{Z}d^2Z/dz^2\right) = E. \tag{3-21}$$

On the left is a sum of three terms, each of which is a function of only one independent variable, x, y, or z. For Eq. (3–21) to be valid, each term must be a constant, since the sum of the terms is a constant that does not involve x, y, or z. This is expressed by Eqs. (3–22) through (3–25):

$$-(h^2/8\pi^2mX)d^2X/dx^2 = E_x, \tag{3-22}$$

$$-(h^2/8\pi^2mY)d^2Y/dy^2 = E_y, \tag{3-23}$$

$$-(h^2/8\pi^2mZ)d^2Z/dz^2 = E_z, \tag{3-24}$$

$$E_x + E_y + E_z = E. \tag{3-25}$$

Equation (3–22) is identical with Eq. (3–7) except that the wave function is now called X and not Ψ and the energy term is called E_x and not E. Using Eqs. (3–16) and (3–12), we can write

$$X = (2/a)^{1/2} \sin \pi n_x x/a \qquad (0 \leqslant x \leqslant a) \tag{3-26}$$

and

$$E_x = n_x^2 h^2/8ma^2, \tag{3-27}$$

where n_x is again any positive integer. Similarly, we can write the other two pairs of equations:

$$Y = (2/b)^{1/2} \sin \pi n_y y/b \qquad (0 \leqslant y \leqslant b), \tag{3-28}$$

$$E_y = n_y^2 h^2/8mb^2, \tag{3-29}$$

and

$$Z = (2/c)^{1/2} \sin \pi n_z z/c \qquad (0 \leqslant z \leqslant c), \tag{3-30}$$

$$E_z = n_z^2 h^2/8mc^2. \tag{3-31}$$

Using Eq. (3–20), we can now write the wave function for the particle:

$$\Psi_{n_x n_y n_z} = X_x Y_y Z_z$$
$$= (8/abc)^{1/2} \sin (\pi n_x x/a) \sin (\pi n_y y/b) \sin (\pi n_z z/c). \tag{3-32}$$

The energy expression can be obtained from Eq. (3–25):

$$E = E_x + E_y + E_z$$
$$= (h^2/8m)(n_x^2/a^2 + n_y^2/b^2 + n_z^2/c^2). \tag{3-33}$$

These two equations, (3–32) and (3–33), are valid only when x lies between zero and a, y between zero and b, and z between zero and c. The energy is purely kinetic, because $V = 0$.

There are three points of interest that are valid throughout quantum mechanics and are well illustrated by the "particle in a box" problem. First, there is the importance of the quantum numbers n_x, n_y, and n_z. These appear as a natural consequence of the conditions for acceptable solutions of the wave equation. Second, since the lowest allowed value of each of these quantum numbers is 1, the lowest kinetic energy of the particle must be

$$E_{111} = (h^2/8m)(1/a^2 + 1/b^2 + 1/c^2).$$

This means that, if the particle is in the box, it must be in motion. Finally, the energy increases with a decrease in mass (m), or in any of the dimensions of the box. Although the energy value is small for large objects or large boxes, it is appreciable at the atomic level. For a particle with the mass of an electron placed in a box whose sides have the dimension of 1 Å, the energy amounts to approximately 1.8×10^{-10} erg or 2.6 kcal/mole.

This increase in kinetic energy accompanying a decrease in volume has many important chemical effects. The repulsive forces that keep atoms from approaching each other too closely arise, as least in part, from this increase, and hence bond lengths and bond energies are influenced by it. Also Eq. (3–33) is valid for any particle in any box. Thus we could apply "the particle in a box" approach to a perfect gas and would arrive at the same conclusions reached by using kinetic theory.

THE HYDROGEN MOLECULE

For another example of the use of quantum mechanics, let us look at the hydrogen molecule. It is necessary to establish a coordinate system before proceeding. In Fig. 3–2, the two nuclei of the molecule are indicated by A and B, the two electrons by 1 and 2, and distances by r, to obtain the coordinates.

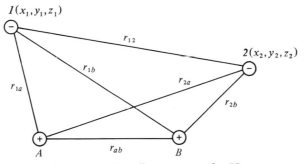

Fig. 3–2. Coordinate system for H_2.

Referring to Eq. (3–1), terms must be written for T and V; these are given in Eqs. (3–34) and (3–35):

$$T = (1/2m)(p_{x1}^2 + p_{y1}^2 + p_{z1}^2) + (1/2m)(p_{x2}^2 + p_{y2}^2 + p_{z2}^2), \qquad (3\text{–}34)$$

$$V = -e^2/r_{1a} - e^2/r_{2a} - e^2/r_{1b} - e^2/r_{2b} + e^2/r_{12} + e^2 r_{ab}. \qquad (3\text{–}35)$$

Making the substitutions previously described, we obtain the wave equation:

$$(\nabla_1^2 + \nabla_2^2)\Psi + (8\pi^2 m/h^2)(E - V)\Psi = 0. \qquad (3\text{–}36)$$

Equation (3–36) is analogous to Eq. (3–19a) but the terms have been rearranged: V is as in Eq. (3–35) and not zero, and there are now six variables.

Equations such as (3–36) are frequently written in a more convenient form. As stated before (see Eq. 3–1), the expression $T + V$ is a constant and is equal to E for stationary states. For the problems that concern us, V is independent of time and $T + V$ is identical with the Hamiltonian function of classical mechanics. The classical conservation of energy can thus be written

$$H = E. \qquad (3\text{–}37)$$

In wave mechanics this becomes

$$H\Psi = E\Psi. \qquad (3\text{–}38)$$

The Hamiltonian is simply an operator telling us what to do just as the symbol $+$ tells us to add. The constant E is called an *eigenvalue* and can assume several values, as we have already seen. The function Ψ is called an *eigenfunction*. In general, the kinetic energy portion of H is expressed in a form involving the momenta of the various particles, and the operator substitution

$$p_x \rightarrow (h/2\pi i)d/dx, \text{ etc.,}$$

is made. For the hydrogen molecule, the complete Hamiltonian is

$$\{-(h^2/8\pi^2 m)[(d^2/dx_1^2 + d^2/dy_1^2 + d^2/dz_1^2) + (d^2/dx_2^2 + d^2/dy_2^2 + d^2/dz_2^2)]$$
$$+ (-e^2/r_{1a} - e^2/r_{2a} - e^2/r_{1b} - e^2/r_{2b} + e^2/r_{12} + e^2/r_{ab})\}.$$

Fortunately, it is not necessary to solve such equations. In fact, they can be solved only for rather special cases. For example, let us consider the case of methane, which has five nuclei and 10 electrons. The complete wave equation takes account of three degrees of freedom for each particle, so that we would have a partial differential equation in 45 independent variables. For ethane, the wave equation involves 78 independent variables. However, by using an approximation based upon the greater mass of the nuclei, we can reduce this number of variables. Since the nuclei move much more slowly than the electrons, they can be considered to be stationary in calculations of electron energies. This was done in writing the H_2 wave equation. Of course, for any given positions of the nuclei a definite energy is obtained for the electrons. Thus E denotes the electron energy together with a nuclear repulsion term and is a function of the relative nuclear positions. This is our justification for drawing

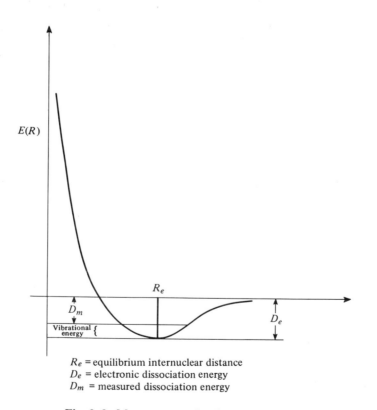

R_e = equilibrium internuclear distance
D_e = electronic dissociation energy
D_m = measured dissociation energy

Fig. 3–3. Morse curve of a diatomic molecule.

the familiar Morse curves for molecules, where $E(R)$ plotted against R (internuclear distance) gives the potential energy curve of a molecule (Fig. 3–3).

The use of the term "potential energy curve" is somewhat misleading because it includes Coulombic attractions and repulsions as well as the kinetic energies of the electrons. It is a potential energy curve only in that it represents potential energy in calculations determining nuclear vibrations.

The fixed nuclei model simplifies the wave equation but, unfortunately, not enough. For methane, it still has 30 variables, for ethane, 54, and for hydrogen, as we have seen, 6. The approach using linear combinations of atomic orbitals developed in the following section gives a simple approximate solution to this problem.

LINEAR COMBINATION OF ATOMIC ORBITALS

Before continuing, we should examine the implications and assumptions of a molecular orbital approach to chemical bonding:

1. Each electron in a molecule is described by a wave function which identifies the orbital encompassing two or more nuclei.

2. Each wave function is described by certain quantum numbers.

3. Each wave function has a definite energy value.

4. Each electron has a spin of $\frac{1}{2}$ or $-\frac{1}{2}$.

5. The Pauli exclusion principle, the Aufbau principle, and Hund's rule apply to molecules and may be used to describe their electronic structure.

The description of a molecule, then, is very much like that of an atom.

The problem is to write wave functions in a form that can be solved for molecular orbitals. To do this, we assume that we can obtain approximate molecular orbital functions by treating molecular orbitals as linear combinations of the atomic orbitals (LCAO), χ_i, involved in bond formation. The molecular orbital Ψ is then approximated by

$$\Psi = c_1\chi_1 + c_2\chi_2 + c_3\chi_3 \cdots$$

To see how this LCAO system works, let us examine the simplest of all possible cases of bonding, the ionized hydrogen molecule H_2^+. Here both atoms are the same, that is, the species is symmetrical, and we can expect that $c_1 = c_2$. (In a nonsymmetrical molecule such as HF we would expect that $c_1 \neq c_2$.)

Now c_1 and c_2 are parameters for which we shall want to determine values. The energy value will be obtained in terms of the coefficients c_1 and c_2 and the energies of the atomic orbitals. To do this, we start with Eq. (3–38):

$$H\Psi = E\Psi.$$

Multiplication by Ψ gives

$$\Psi H\Psi = E\Psi^2. \tag{3–39}$$

(Recall that H denotes an operation to be performed upon Ψ, so we must not write $H\Psi^2$.) By integrating Eq. (3–39) over all space we obtain

$$\int \Psi H \Psi \, d\tau = E \int \Psi^2 \, d\tau$$

$$E = \int \Psi H \Psi \, d\tau \Big/ \int \Psi^2 \, d\tau. \qquad (3\text{–}40)$$

In this manner E is obtained in a form that simplifies the coordinate problem. By substituting $c_1\chi_1 + c_2\chi_2$ for Ψ,

$$E = \frac{\int (c_1\chi_1 + c_2\chi_2) H (c_1\chi_1 + c_2\chi_2) \, d\tau}{\int (c_1\chi_1 + c_2\chi_2)^2 \, d\tau}$$

$$= \frac{\int (c_1\chi_1 H c_1\chi_1 + c_1\chi_1 H c_2\chi_2 + c_2\chi_2 H c_1\chi_1 + c_2\chi_2 H c_2\chi_2) \, d\tau}{\int (c_1^2\chi_1^2 + 2c_1c_2\chi_1\chi_2 + c_2^2\chi_2^2) \, d\tau} \qquad (3\text{–}41)$$

$$= \frac{\left(c_1^2 \int \chi_1^2 H\chi_1 \, d\tau + 2c_1c_2 \int \chi_1 H\chi_2 \, d\tau + c_2^2 \int \chi_2 H\chi_2 \, d\tau \right)}{\left(c_1^2 \int \chi_1^2 \, d\tau + 2c_1c_2 \int \chi_1\chi_2 \, d\tau + c_2^2 \int \chi_2^2 \, d\tau \right)}.$$

For values of E that correspond to physical reality it can be shown that $\int \chi_1 H\chi_2 \, d\tau = \int \chi_2 H\chi_1 \, d\tau$. Equation (3–41) was simplified by use of this fact, and further simplification can be achieved with several definitions:

$$H_{11} = \int \chi_1 H\chi_1 \, d\tau, \qquad\qquad S_{11} = \int \chi_1^2 \, d\tau,$$

$$H_{12} = H_{21} = \int \chi_1 H\chi_2 \, d\tau = \int \chi_2 H\chi_1 \, d\tau, \qquad S_{12} = \int \chi_1\chi_2 \, d\tau,$$

$$H_{22} = \int \chi_2 H\chi_2 \, d\tau, \qquad\qquad S_{22} = \int \chi_2^2 \, d\tau.$$

If these are substituted, Eq. (3–41) becomes

$$E = (c_1^2 H_{11} + 2c_1c_2 H_{12} + c_2^2 H_{22})/(c_1^2 S_{11} + 2c_1c_2 S_{12} + c_2^2 S_{22}). \qquad (3\text{–}42)$$

We are usually interested in the ground states of the molecules, that is, the minimum values for E. The *variation principle* states that E must be a minimum with respect to c_1 and c_2 in the ground state, and that the value of E so obtained will not be less than the energy of the true ground state (see Appendix C for development of this principle). Thus we can state that

$$dE/dc_1 = 0 \qquad \text{and} \qquad dE/dc_2 = 0.$$

Minimizing Eq. (3–42) in this manner gives

$$0 = \frac{dE}{dc_1} = \frac{(c_1^2 S_{11} + 2c_1c_2 S_{12} + c_2^2 S_{22})(2c_1 H_{11} + 2c_2 H_{12})}{(c_1^2 S_{11} + 2c_1c_2 S_{12} + c_2^2 S_{22})^2}$$

$$- \frac{(c_1^2 H_{11} + 2c_1c_2 H_{12} + c_2^2 H_{22})(2c_1 S_{11} + 2c_2 S_{12})}{(c_1^2 S_{11} + 2c_1c_2 S_{12} + c_2^2 S_{22})^2}.$$

Rearranging and eliminating like terms yields

$$c_1 H_{11} + c_2 H_{12} = \frac{(c_1^2 H_{11} + 2c_1 c_2 H_{12} + c_2^2 H_{22})(c_1 S_{11} + c_2 S_{12})}{(c_1^2 S_{11} + 2c_1 c_2 S_{12} + c_2^2 S_{22})}.$$

Substituting Eq. (3–42) into this expression, we have

$$c_1 H_{11} + c_2 H_{12} = E(c_1 S_{11} + c_2 S_{12})$$

or, by rearrangement,

$$c_1(H_{11} - ES_{11}) + c_2(H_{12} - ES_{12}) = 0. \qquad (3\text{–}43)$$

Similarly, $dE/dc_2 = 0$ gives

$$c_1(H_{12} - ES_{12}) + c_2(H_{22} - ES_{22}) = 0. \qquad (3\text{–}44)$$

Equations (3–43) and (3–44) are called the *secular equations*. The permitted values of E can be obtained for this system of simultaneous equations by finding the roots of the secular determinant:

$$\begin{vmatrix} H_{11} - ES_{11} & H_{12} - ES_{12} \\ H_{12} - ES_{12} & H_{22} - ES_{22} \end{vmatrix} = 0.$$

In the more general case of $\Psi = c_1\chi_1 + c_2\chi_2 \cdots c_n\chi_n$, the secular determinant is

$$\begin{vmatrix} H_{11} - ES_{11} & H_{12} - ES_{12} \cdots H_{1n} - ES_{1n} \\ H_{21} - ES_{21} & H_{22} - ES_{22} \cdots H_{2n} - ES_{2n} \\ H_{31} - ES_{31} & H_{32} - ES_{32} \cdots H_{3n} - ES_{3n} \\ \vdots & \vdots \\ H_{n1} - ES_{n1} & H_{n2} - ES_{n2} \cdots H_{nn} - ES_{nn} \end{vmatrix} = 0.$$

The values of E obtained in this manner are not necessarily the true energy of the system, because they depend on the wave function chosen. The advantage of the variation process is that the value obtained for E with this approach is always larger than the true E but is usually closer to it than is the trial wave function to the true wave function. Also, it should be pointed out that the LCAO wave functions are convenient but by no means the only wave functions to which the variation principle may be applied.

Before continuing we must make our first major approximations, known as the *Hückel approximations*. Although this approach is not a general LCAO treatment, it is convenient for simple calculations.

1. The integrals

$$S_{ij} = \int \chi_i \chi_j \, d\tau$$

are called *overlap integrals* and measure the probability of finding electrons at atoms i and j (see Eq. 3–13). If $i = j$, for example S_{11}, S_{22}, then $S_{ij} = 1$ if normalized atomic orbitals are employed. When $i \neq j$, we are using orbitals from two different atoms. If the atoms are not close together, the overlap integral approaches zero. In this first approximation we assume that the overlap integral is zero and the atomic orbitals are orthogonal:

$$i \neq j, \qquad S_{ij} = \int \chi_i \chi_j \, d\tau = 0.$$

Of course, when atoms are bonded to each other they are close together and $S_{ij} \neq 0$. As we shall see later, we *can* make this correction but if we ignore it and assume that $S_{ij} = 0$ even for bonded atoms, the consequences are not very serious.

2. The integrals

$$H_{ij} = \int \chi_i H \chi_j \, d\tau = \int \chi_j H \chi_i \, d\tau = H_{ji},$$

when $i = j$, are called *Coulomb integrals* and are a rough representation of the energy of an electron isolated in an atomic orbital. In this treatment we will regard this energy as being unaffected by any other nuclei. The Coulomb integral is denoted by α:

$$H_{ii} = \alpha,$$

where α is a function of nuclear charge and the type of orbital involved.
When $i \neq j$, the integral

$$H_{ij} = \int \chi_i H \chi_j \, d\tau = \beta,$$

where β is called the resonance integral. It represents the energy of an electron in the fields of the atoms i and j, and its value depends on the distance between the atoms. When the two atoms are not bonded in a classical structure, the interaction must be small and we will assume that it is 0:

$$H_{ij} = 0 \quad \text{(atoms } i \text{ and } j \text{ not bonded).}$$

If all bonds of a polyatomic molecule are to have the same resonance integral, all bond lengths must be equal and all nuclei identical, and all bonds must be formed from the same type of atomic orbitals, which must share the same nodal plane.

Relative to the energy of an electron at infinity, both α and β are negative quantities. The term $\alpha - E$ is the negative binding energy.

Returning to the problem of the H_2^+ ion and using the above assumptions to make suitable substitutions, we find that the secular determinant becomes

$$\begin{vmatrix} \alpha_1 - E & \beta \\ \beta & \alpha_2 - E \end{vmatrix} = 0.$$

Since the nuclei are identical, $\alpha_1 = \alpha_2$. It is frequently convenient to divide all terms of the determinant by β:

$$\begin{vmatrix} (\alpha - E)/\beta & 1 \\ 1 & (\alpha - E)/\beta \end{vmatrix} = 0.$$

If $(\alpha - E)/\beta$ is replaced by x, the determinant becomes

$$\begin{vmatrix} x & 1 \\ 1 & x \end{vmatrix} = 0.$$

Expanding this gives

$$x^2 - 1 = 0, \qquad x^2 = 1, \qquad x = \pm 1 = (\alpha - E)/\beta, \qquad E = \alpha \pm \beta.$$

We find two possible energy levels for the H_2^+ ion; now we must determine the wave functions to find which is the more stable.

Making the substitutions just described into the secular equations (3–43) and (3–44), we obtain the analogous equations (3–45) and (3–46):

$$c_1(\alpha - E) + c_2\beta = 0, \tag{3–45}$$

$$c_1\beta + c_2(\alpha - E) = 0. \tag{3–46}$$

From Eq. (3–45) we obtain

$$c_1/c_2 = -\beta/(a - E).$$

When $E = \alpha + \beta$,

$$c_1/c_2 = -\beta/-\beta = 1,$$

and when $E = \alpha - \beta$,

$$c_1/c_2 = -\beta/\beta = -1.$$

For the energy level of $\alpha + \beta$ we can take

$$\Psi_1 = c(\chi_1 + \chi_2), \qquad \text{since } c_1 = c_2,$$

and for the energy level $\alpha - \beta$,

$$\Psi_2 = c(\chi_1 - \chi_2), \qquad \text{since } c_1 = -c_2.$$

To determine values for c_1 and c_2 we use the normalization condition, since the molecular orbital, as well as the component atomic orbitals, must be normalized:

$$\int \Psi^2 \, d\tau = 1.$$

For $\Psi_1 = c(\chi_1 + \chi_2)$ we have

$$\int \Psi^2 \, d\tau = \int [c(\chi_1 + \chi_2)]^2 \, d\tau = c^2 \int \chi_1^2 \, d\tau + c^2 \int \chi_2^2 \, d\tau + 2c^2 \int \chi_1\chi_2 \, d\tau = 1. \tag{3–47}$$

If χ_1 and χ_2 are both normalized and mutually orthogonal functions,

$$\int \chi_1^2 \, d\tau = 1, \qquad \int \chi_2^2 \, d\tau = 1, \qquad \text{and} \qquad \int \chi_1\chi_2 \, d\tau = 0.$$

Substituting these values into Eq. (3–45) gives

$$c^2 + c^2 + 0 = 1, \qquad 2c^2 = 1, \qquad c = 1/\sqrt{2}.$$

Now we can write the normalized wave equations as

$$\Psi_1 = (1/\sqrt{2})(\chi_1 + \chi_2) \qquad \text{for } E = \alpha + \beta,$$

$$\Psi_2 = (1/\sqrt{2})(\chi_1 - \chi_2) \qquad \text{for } E = \alpha - \beta.$$

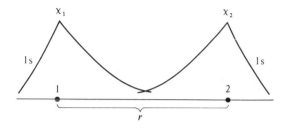

Fig. 3–4. Amplitude diagram of the bonding orbital $\Psi_1 = \chi_1 + \chi_2$.

To calculate the absolute binding energy to the accuracy determined by the approximations and assumptions, the appropriate values of α and β must be known. Even without knowing these, useful information can be obtained from the relative values and in particular from the signs associated with the various chi's in the wave functions Ψ.

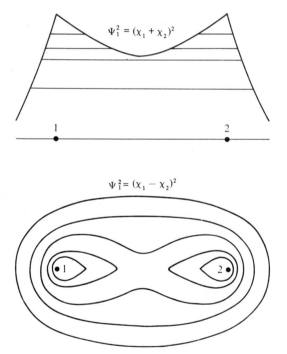

Fig. 3–5. Probability diagrams of the bonding orbital.

For Ψ_1 both chi's are positive and their cross-sections can be represented as in Fig. 3–4. The square of Ψ_1—the total probability of finding the electron—is illustrated in Fig. 3–5, where the lines represent equal probabilities. The electron

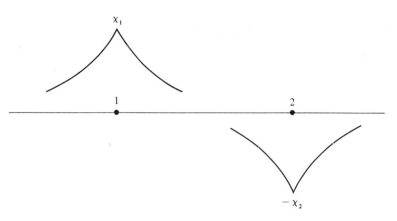

Fig. 3–6. Amplitude diagram of the antibonding orbital $\Psi_2 = \chi_1 - \chi_2$.

is likely to be found between the two nuclei and will tend to hold them together. The wave function Ψ_1 is called a *bonding orbital*.

For Ψ_2 the same features are shown in Figs. 3–6 and 3–7. It should be noted that the probability of the electron being midway between the two nuclei is zero. The electron, being outside the nuclei most of the time, will not hold them together; in fact, the nuclear charges will tend to push the nuclei apart. The wave function Ψ_2 is an *antibonding orbital*.

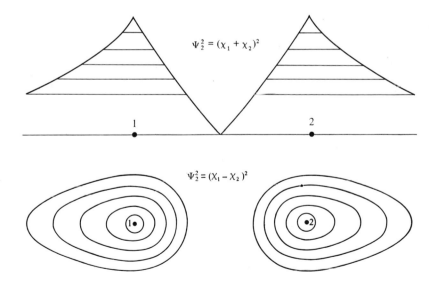

Fig. 3–7. Probability diagrams of the antibonding orbital.

Wave functions are frequently represented as cells to indicate the energy level of each:

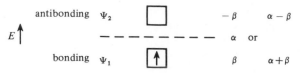

We are not justified in simply adding another electron to obtain the energy of the hydrogen molecule, because the internuclear distances are different and the Coulombic repulsion of the two electrons is ignored. These problems can be corrected, however, by choosing different values for α and β. It is common practice to use one-electron orbitals such as those obtained for H_2^+ to describe molecules, just as the one-electron orbitals of the hydrogen atom are used to describe atoms.

It should be noted that the result for H_2^+ can be generalized; that is, when two atomic orbitals are combined two molecular orbitals result, combination of four atomic orbitals gives four molecular orbitals, and so forth. For diatomic molecules, we frequently can predict interesting results by keeping this in mind. Figure 3–8

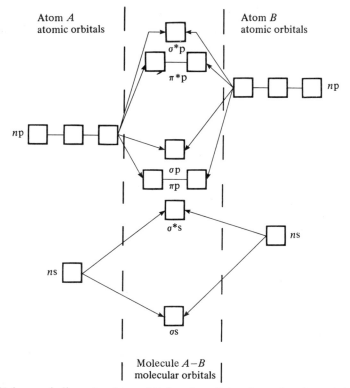

Fig. 3–8. Valence shell molecular orbitals of a diatomic molecule. A is the more electro-negative atom.

indicates how molecular orbitals are formed. Of course, when atoms A and B are of the same element, their atomic orbitals are at the same energy level.

Oxygen was mentioned earlier as a particular problem. In Lewis terminology, it is described as having a double bond with all electrons paired, but it is known to have two unpaired electrons, and this could be predicted from Fig. 3–8. The linear notation used for atoms can also be applied to molecular electronic structures. For the oxygen molecule it is

$$\sigma 1s^2 \sigma^* 1s^2 \sigma 2s^2 \sigma^* 2s^2 \pi 2p^4 \sigma 2p^2 \pi^* 2p^2.$$

It should be noted that in this treatment all the electrons are placed in molecular orbitals. Normally we can treat the electrons in all but the valence shell as if they remained in the atomic orbitals. Thus the description of oxygen is not altered by considering the $\sigma 1s$ and $\sigma^* 1s$ electrons as remaining in the 1s atomic orbitals, since these electrons make no important contribution to the electronic character of the bond.

PROBLEMS

1. Obtain the wave function and energy expression for a particle constrained to move in a circle of radius r.
2. Obtain the wave functions and an expression for the energy of the hydrogen molecule ion, using $S_{12} = 0.3$.
3. Calculate the energy of the hydrogen molecule ion if the electron is localized on one atom, that is $H_{12} = H_{22} = 0$.
4. Using diagrams such as that given in Fig. 3–8, explain the following order of bond lengths: O_2^+, 1.123 Å; O_2, 1.207 Å; O_2^-, 1.26 Å; $O_2^=$, 1.49 Å. Which would have the shorter bond length, N_2 or N_2^+? Explain.

SUGGESTED READING FOR CHAPTERS 1–3

COULSON, C. A., *Valence*, 2nd Ed., Oxford University Press, London (1961).

GRAY, H. B., *Electrons and Chemical Bonding*, W. A. Benjamin, New York (1964).

LINNETT, J. W., *Wave Mechanics and Valency*, John Wiley & Sons, New York (1960).

ROBERTS, J. D., *Notes on Molecular Orbital Calculations*, W. A. Benjamin, New York (1962).

STREITWIESER, A., Jr., *Molecular Orbital Theory for Organic Chemists*, John Wiley & Sons, New York (1961).

WIBERG, K. B., *Physical Organic Chemistry*, Part I, John Wiley & Sons, New York (1964).

The following are at a somewhat more difficult level:

DAUDEL, R., R. LeFEBVRE and C. MOSER, *Quantum Chemistry Methods and Applications*, Interscience Publishers, New York (1959).

EYRING, H., J. WALTER and G. E. KIMBALL, *Quantum Chemistry*, John Wiley & Sons, New York (1944).

PAULING, L., *The Nature of the Chemical Bond*, 3rd Ed., Cornell University Press, Ithaca, N. Y. (1960).

PITZER, K. S., *Quantum Chemistry*, Prentice-Hall, Englewood Cliffs, N. J. (1959).

CHAPTER 4

THE Π APPROXIMATION

To deal with molecules more complicated than the hydrogen molecule ion, we can use combinations of all the atomic orbitals in the molecule. This process rapidly becomes complex and the absolute numbers obtained may be of no more value than simple comparisons between molecules of the same type. Therefore, organic chemists frequently assume that all of the σ bonds are localized and contribute little to the electronic character of any remaining π bonds. Although this simplification limits us to π systems, it is worth it because we can treat a relatively large number of compounds by a simple approach.

THE PROPENYL RADICAL (ALLYL)

To see how the approach works, let us examine the propenyl radical, CH_2=CH—CH_2. Since we are concerned only with the π system of electrons, we shall concentrate on the overlapping p orbitals (Fig. 4–1). The wave function will take the form $\Psi = \sum c_i \chi_i = c_1 \chi_1 + c_2 \chi_2 + c_3 \chi_3$, where χ_i is the normalized atomic p orbital of the ith atom.

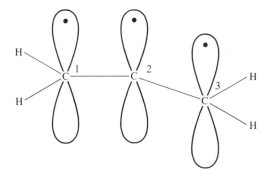

Fig. 4–1. Overlapping p orbitals for allyl.

As we did in Chapter 3, we may write the secular equations and then the secular determinant, which is set equal to zero to determine the roots. To the assumptions made in Chapter 3, we will add another, that $\alpha_1 = \alpha_2 = \alpha_3$. This is not overly unrealistic because the electrical surroundings of each carbon atom are at least similar.

If we wish, we can take a shortcut by writing our shorthand form of the determinant using $x = (\alpha - E)/\beta$. (Recall that we write x when considering a specific atom in the series, 1 when an atom is bonded to the one we are considering, and 0 when an atom is not bonded to the atom under consideration.) To do this, let us consider the determinant in the following form:

Atom considered in relation
to main atom

$$
\begin{array}{c}
\quad\quad\quad 1 \quad 2 \quad 3 \\
\text{Main atom under}\quad \begin{array}{c} 1 \\ 2 \\ 3 \end{array}
\begin{vmatrix} - & - & - \\ - & - & - \\ - & - & - \end{vmatrix}
\end{array}
$$

consideration

We draw the σ system and number the atoms with p orbitals consecutively (see Fig. 4–1). When considering atom number 1, we work with row number 1. The first column represents atom 1, so we write x; the second column represents atom 2, which is bonded to the atom under consideration, so we write 1; the third column represents atom 3, which is not bonded to atom 1, so we write 0. Proceeding in the same manner for atom 2 in the second row and for atom 3 in the third row, we easily write the secular determinant:

$$
\begin{vmatrix} x & 1 & 0 \\ 1 & x & 1 \\ 0 & 1 & x \end{vmatrix} = 0.
$$

Solving this, we obtain the values of x:

$$x^3 - 2x = 0, \qquad x(x^2 - 2) = 0,$$
$$x = 0, \qquad x = \pm\sqrt{2}.$$

Using the relationship $x = (\alpha - E)/\beta$ and rearranging this as $E = \alpha - x\beta$, we obtain the values of E for each value of x:

$$E = \alpha - x\beta;$$
$$\text{for } x = \sqrt{2}, \qquad E_3 = \alpha - \sqrt{2}\beta,$$
$$\text{for } x = 0, \qquad E_2 = \alpha,$$
$$\text{for } x = -\sqrt{2}, \qquad E_1 = \alpha + \sqrt{2}\beta.$$

We now have the π energy levels, in units of α and β, for the molecular orbitals. To obtain the total π energy for the propenyl radical in terms of α and β, we multiply each energy level by the number of electrons occupying that level and add them together. Since α represents the energy of an electron on the atom, the bonding energy can be considered as the β term:

$$
\begin{array}{cl}
\underline{\quad} & E_3 = \alpha - \sqrt{2}\beta, \\
\uparrow & E_2 = \alpha, \\
\uparrow\downarrow & E_1 = \alpha + \sqrt{2}\beta;
\end{array}
$$

$$E_{\text{total}} = 2E_1 + E_2 = 2(\alpha + \sqrt{2}\beta) + \alpha = 3\alpha + 2\sqrt{2}\beta.$$

With the π energy values for Ψ_n, we can now evaluate the coefficients c_i in the wave function $\Psi_n = c_1\chi_1 + c_2\chi_2 + c_3\chi_3$. To do this we may proceed as we did for H_2^+. The method of cofactors is easier, however, and also gives normalized values but it works only for nondegenerate molecular orbitals. For cofactors A_i along the first, or any, row the coefficient of the ith atom is proportional to the ith cofactor:

$$c_i \sim A_i = (-1)^{i+1} \quad \text{(minor of } a_i\text{)}.$$

We obtain

$$A_1 = (-1)^{1+1}\begin{vmatrix} x & 1 \\ 1 & x \end{vmatrix} = x^2 - 1,$$

$$A_2 = (-1)^{2+1}\begin{vmatrix} 1 & 1 \\ 0 & x \end{vmatrix} = -\begin{vmatrix} 1 & 1 \\ 0 & x \end{vmatrix} = -x,$$

$$A_3 = (-1)^{3+1}\begin{vmatrix} 1 & x \\ 0 & 1 \end{vmatrix} = 1.$$

Since the coefficient can be evaluated by using $c_i = A_i/(\sum A_i^2)^{1/2}$, the values of c_i can be obtained for each energy level with the appropriate values of x. Tabulation of the work in the following form is insurance against computational error. Let us first evaluate the coefficients for Ψ_3.

$$\Psi_3: E_3 = \alpha - \sqrt{2}\beta, \quad x = \sqrt{2}$$

Atom i	A_i	A_i^2	$C_i = A_i/(\sum A_i^2)^{1/2}$
1	1	1	1/2
2	$-\sqrt{2}$	2	$-\sqrt{2}/2 = -1\sqrt{2}$
3	1	1	1/2
		$\sum A_i^2 = 4$	
		$(\sum A_i^2)^{1/2} = 2$	

Now we can write the wave function for E_3 in terms of the p atomic wave functions, χ_i:

$$\Psi_3 = \tfrac{1}{2}\chi_1 - 1/\sqrt{2}\chi_2 + \tfrac{1}{2}\chi_3.$$

Similarly, we can obtain the wave functions for E_2 and E_1.

$$\Psi_2: E_2 = \alpha, \quad x = 0$$

i	A_i	A_i^2	C_i
1	-1	1	$-1/\sqrt{2}$
2	0	0	0
3	1	1	$1/\sqrt{2}$
		$\sum A_i^2 = 2$	
		$(\sum A_i^2)^{1/2} = \sqrt{2}$	

$$\Psi_2 = -1/\sqrt{2}\,\chi_1 + 1/\sqrt{2}\chi_3$$

$$\Psi_1: E = \alpha + \sqrt{2}\beta, \quad x = -\sqrt{2}$$

i	A_i	A_i^2	C_i
1	1	1	1/2
2	$\sqrt{2}$	2	$\sqrt{2}/2 = 1/\sqrt{2}$
3	1	1	1/2

$$\Sigma A_i^2 = 4$$
$$(\Sigma A_i^2)^{1/2} = 2$$

$$\Psi_1 = \tfrac{1}{2}\chi_1 + 1/\sqrt{2}\chi_2 + \tfrac{1}{2}\chi_3$$

These wave functions can be represented schematically as in Fig. 4–2.

Knowing the energy of the propenyl radical, we might inquire whether this radical has gained any stability by the delocalization of the electrons over the three atoms. A reasonable model, against which to compare the energy calculated above, is an ethylene bond and an isolated electron on the third atom. If we calculate the energy of this model, by setting β_{23} equal to zero, we obtain the shorthand secular determinant:

$$\begin{vmatrix} x & 1 & 0 \\ 1 & x & 0 \\ 0 & 0 & x \end{vmatrix} = 0 = x^3 - x = x(x^2 - 1), \qquad x = 0, \qquad x = \pm 1;$$

$$\text{for } x = -1, \quad E_1 = \alpha + \beta,$$
$$\text{for } x = 0, \quad E_2 = \alpha,$$
$$\text{for } x = 1, \quad E_3 = \alpha - \beta.$$

The total π energy for this localized model E_L is obtained as before, as $2(\alpha + \beta) + \alpha = 3\alpha + 2\beta$. The difference between the energy calculated for the delocalized model and that calculated for the localized model will indicate whether any additional stability is afforded by delocalization. This difference is known as the *delocalization energy*, DE:

$$\text{DE} = E_\pi - E_L(3\alpha + 2\sqrt{2}\beta) - (3\alpha + 2\beta) = 0.828\beta. \qquad (4\text{–}1)$$

Thus, the propenyl radical is stabilized by 0.828β energy units. Had a negative β value been obtained, we would have concluded that the localized electron model was the better model for the propenyl radical.

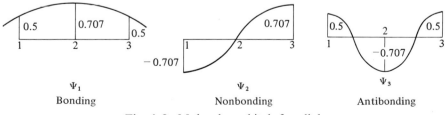

Fig. 4–2. Molecular orbitals for allyl.

The delocalization energy thus calculated is obtained in units of β, which is adequate if we merely wish to compare the effects of resonance upon a series of molecules. An absolute value of β, in kilocalories per mole, is obtained by comparing calculated delocalization energies with those obtained by "experimental" methods. For example, the usual experimental value given for benzene is 36 kcal/mole, and the above method gives a value of 2β for the calculated delocalization energy, suggesting that β is equal to 18 kcal/mole. For several aromatic compounds, an average value of 16 kcal is obtained (see Fig. 4–3). Although this value of β allows us to predict experimental resonance energies fairly accurately for benzenoid aromatic compounds, it does not work well for alicyclic π systems, for which a β value of 7 kcal/mole gives better results. Table 4–1 compares experimental resonance energies (RE) with (calculated) delocalization energies for some representative compounds, and Fig. 4–3 graphically illustrates this correlation.

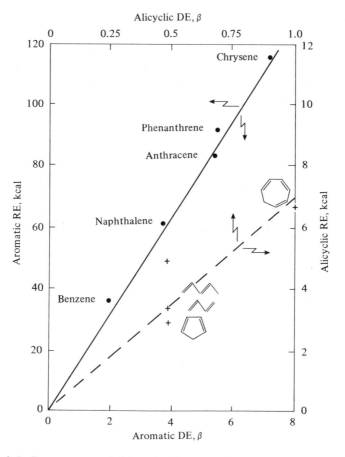

Fig. 4–3. Resonance and delocalization energies of some hydrocarbons.

Table 4–1. Resonance and Delocalization Energies

Compound	Exp. RE*, kcal	Calc. DE, β	RE/DE, kcal/β
1,3-Butadiene	3.5	0.47	7.4
1,3-Cyclopentadiene	2.9	0.47	6.1
1,3-Pentadiene	4.2	0.47	8.9
1,3,5-Cycloheptatriene	6.7	0.99	6.8
Benzene	36.0	2.0	18.0
Naphthalene	61.0	3.68	16.6
Anthracene	83.5	5.31	15.7
Phenanthrene	91.3	5.45	16.8
Chrysene	116.5	7.19	16.2

* From G. W. Wheland, *Resonance in Organic Chemistry*, John Wiley & Sons, New York (1955), pp. 80, 98.

The problem of resonance energy is discussed more fully in Chapter 5. For the present, since the values of β arrived at above were obtained by comparison with empirical resonance energies, it is not safe to use them for other purposes.

We have seen how to calculate the π bonding energy of the propenyl radical. If we neglect electron repulsions, we may also obtain bonding energies for the allyl (propenyl) cation and anion, by simply adding the appropriate number of electrons to the energy diagram found for the radical. In this manner, the π bonding energies of the cation, anion, and radical are all found to have the same β value, owing to the fact that the highest occupied orbital in each case is nonbonding. Examination of the dianion shows that the bonding energy is decreased, since an antibonding orbital is now occupied.

	Cation	Radical	Anion	Dianion
$\alpha - \sqrt{2}\beta$				↑
α		↑	↑↓	↑↓
$\alpha + \sqrt{2}\beta$	↑↓	↑↓	↑↓	↑↓

$$E_\pi^+ = 2\alpha + 2\sqrt{2}\beta \quad E_\pi^{\cdot} = 3\alpha + 2\sqrt{2}\beta \quad E_\pi^- = 4\alpha + 2\sqrt{2}\beta \quad E_\pi^= = 5\alpha + \sqrt{2}\beta$$

As with the hydrogen molecule, this approach cannot be justified; not only are we using one-electron orbitals, but we are also ignoring repulsions between electrons in different orbitals. This deficiency of the simple π approximation should always be kept in mind.

Having determined the π bonding energy, the delocalization energy, and the wave function (albeit in terms of the atomic wave functions), can we determine any other quantities of interest? Yes, we can. Recalling that the probability of finding an electron in the volume of space $d\tau$ is $\int \Psi\Psi^* \, d\tau$ or (dropping the complex conjugate notation, since we are concerned with real functions) $\int \Psi^2 \, d\tau$, we obtain

$$\int \Psi^2 \, d\tau = \int [\Sigma (c_i\chi_i + c_j\chi_j)]^2 \, d\tau = \int \Sigma c_i^2\chi_i^2 + \int \Sigma c_ic_j\chi_i\chi_j \, d\tau + \int \Sigma c_j^2\chi_j^2 \, d\tau.$$

The zero overlap approximation, $\int \chi_i\chi_j \, d\tau = 0$ when i and j are different, allows us to write

$$\int \Psi^2 \, d\tau = \int \Sigma c_i^2\chi_i^2 \, d\tau + \int \Sigma c_j^2\chi_j^2 \, d\tau$$

$$= \Sigma c_i^2 \int \chi_i^2 \, d\tau + \Sigma c_j^2 \int \chi_j^2 \, d\tau.$$

Because normalized atomic wave functions, χ, have been used, that is $\chi^2 d\tau = 1$, c_i^2 indicates the probability that an electron in a molecular orbital is associated with the atomic orbital component χ_i. The value of c_i^2 may be taken as simply the electron density of the orbital at atom i and c_j^2 as the electron density at atom j. The total electron density at any atom will be the sum of the densities contributed by each electron (whose number cannot exceed two) in each occupied molecular orbital:

$$\pi \text{ electron density} = q_i = \overset{\psi_{occ}}{\Sigma} nc_i^2. \tag{4–2}$$

If a carbon atom forms three sp^2 bonds, it will be electrically neutral provided that there is one electron in the remaining p orbital. Because q_i is a measure of the number of electrons in the p orbital, we can obtain the *charge density*, Z_i, at atom i:

$$Z_i = 1.00 - q_i = 1.00 - \overset{\psi_{occ}}{\Sigma} nc_i^2. \tag{4–3}$$

For the allyl radical, we obtain the following values:

$$Z_1 = Z_3 = 1.00 - [2(\tfrac{1}{2})^2 + 1(-1/\sqrt{2})^2] = 0.0,$$
$$Z_2 = 1.00 - [2(1/\sqrt{2})^2 + 1(0)^2] = 0.0.$$

The charge density at each atom is zero. The total charge for the allyl radical, obtained by adding the charge densities at each atom, must equal the charge of molecule, which in this case is zero. This requirement provides an easy check for the values of c_n. For the allyl anion, atoms 1 and 3 carry all of the charge, and the total charge is -1, which is just what it should be if the values of c_n are correct:

$$Z_1 = Z_3 = 1.00 - [2(\tfrac{1}{2})^2 + 2(-1/\sqrt{2})^2] = -\tfrac{1}{2},$$
$$Z_2 = 1.00 - [2(1/\sqrt{2})^2 + 2(0)^2] = 0,$$
$$Z_1 + Z_2 + Z_3 = -1.$$

The result obtained for the charge distribution of the allyl radical illustrates the results for a large group of radicals and hydrocarbons. Conjugated hydrocarbons and radicals whose carbon atoms can be alternately starred (so that all starred atoms have only unstarred neighbors and all unstarred atoms have only starred neighbors) are called *alternant hydrocarbons* (AH). Some examples of these are:

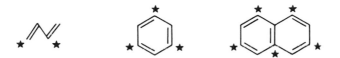

These hydrocarbons and radicals always have the same number of π electrons on each carbon atom, which lends some credence to our assumptions that $\alpha_i = \alpha_j$ and that all β's are equal. We might expect that our results will be less reliable for non-alternant hydrocarbons—α_i would not be expected to be equal to α_j if they do not have the same π-electron densities.

There is another point of interest with the allyl radical. An electron is removed from a nonbonding molecular orbital to form the allyl carbonium ion, and, similarly, an electron is placed into a nonbonding molecular orbital to form the anion. Thus, the coefficients of the atomic orbitals composing the nonbonding molecular orbital alone determine the charge density of singly charged ions. All alternant hydrocarbon radicals with an odd number of conjugated carbon atoms have a nonbonding molecular orbital, and the charge density of the singly charged ion is similarly determined. (Chapter 12 gives a simple method of determining the coefficients of odd alternant hydrocarbon radicals without solving the secular determinants.)

Another quantity that we may attempt to calculate is the π-electron density *between* two atoms. We might expect that if the space between two atoms has a greater electron density than that between two other atoms, the first pair would be more strongly bonded. To attempt to evaluate this, an expression similar to that used for electron density may be employed:

$$p_{ij} = \overset{\psi_{occ}}{\underset{}{\sum}} nc_i c_j. \tag{4-4}$$

This quantity, the *total mobile bond order*, p_{ij}, will be positive when a given molecular orbital is bonding between atoms i and j. It will be zero for a given nonbonding molecular orbital and negative for an antibonding orbital. Of course, it is the sum of all occupied orbitals that is of most interest. Since the values of p_{ij} give at least a relative measure of π bond strength, and since bond lengths are inversely related to bond strengths, a correlation of p_{ij} with bond lengths is expected. Although there is a definite trend of shorter bond lengths with increasing p_{ij} values, the correlation is not very good (Fig. 4–4).

Note that benzene, by this approach, has a p_{cc} value of 0.667 and not 0.500. The solid line in Fig. 4–4 is frequently employed to estimate bond lengths from total mobile bond orders, but the dashed line appears to be a somewhat better fit of the data given here. Either line may be used to estimate bond lengths to an accuracy of about 0.02 Å. We might inquire which of the two lines is the more significant. The solid line assumes that ethane is a good model for a bond with zero mobile π bond order, but this may be a bad assumption because all the other bonds are between carbons with sp² hybridization, whereas ethane has a bond between carbons in the sp³ hybrid state. There is no compelling reason to believe that a "single" sp²—sp² bond should have the same bond length as an sp³—sp³ bond. In fact, the single (σ) $C(sp^2)$—$3(sp^2)$ bond has been estimated at several values between 1.46 and 1.52 Å, and a value of 1.51 Å seems reasonable.

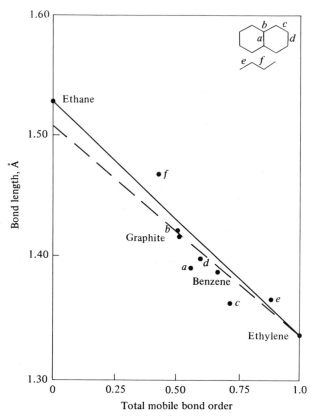

Fig. 4–4. Bond order–bond distance relationship.

To compute p_{ij} for the allyl radical we must use the wave functions obtained above:

$$\psi_3 = \tfrac{1}{2}\chi_1 - 1/\sqrt{2}\chi_2 + \tfrac{1}{2}\chi_3,$$
$$\psi_2 = -1/\sqrt{2}\chi_1 + 1/\sqrt{2}\chi_3,$$
$$\psi_3 = \tfrac{1}{2}\chi_1 + 1/\sqrt{2}\chi_2 + \tfrac{1}{2}\chi_3.$$

Since the radical is symmetrical, $p_{12} = p_{23}$:

$$p_{12} = p_{23} = \sum nc_1c_2 = 2(\tfrac{1}{2})(1/\sqrt{2}) + 1(-1/\sqrt{2})(0) = 1/\sqrt{2} = 0.707.$$

For the allyl anion and cation, the same bond order is obtained. Why?

An alternative method of reporting p_{ij} values is frequently employed. If the σ portion of a double bond is taken as a 1.0 bond, the *total bond order* can be written as

$$N_{\pi ij} = 1.0 + p_{ij}.$$

Thus for allyl we obtain $N_{\pi 12} = N_{\pi 23} = 1.707$.

As we have seen, mobile bond orders are frequently obtained as fractional values. If we assume that a carbon atom has some maximum bonding power, we can easily calculate how far any particular atom is from the maximum and, hence, its capacity for further bonding. To obtain the maximum mobile bond order of a carbon atom we pick a model compound with a carbon atom bonded to three other atoms with π bonds. Trimethylenemethane has such a carbon atom and none of the three bonded atoms are involved in other π bonds, so it is a model in which maximum bonding can occur at the central carbon.

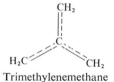
Trimethylenemethane

Calculation gives a bond order of $\sqrt{3}/3$ for each bond. Thus the central atom in trimethylenemethane is involved in $3(\sqrt{3}/3)$, 1.732, π bonds. Taking this value as the maximum π-bond involvement of any carbon atom, we can write the equation for the difference between the sum of all of the bond orders in which an atom is involved, $\sum p_{ij}$, and the maximum that is possible, 1.732. This is known as the *free valence index*, F_i; F_i gives a quantitative meaning to Thiele's partial valence theory and to Werner's residual affinity:

$$F_i = 1.732 - \sum p_{ij}. \qquad (4\text{--}5)$$

For the allyl radical, we obtain free valence indices by the following technique:

$$\overset{1}{C}\text{--}\overset{2}{C}\text{--}\overset{3}{C}, \qquad p_{12} = p_{23} = 0.707.$$

Due to the symmetry of allyl, $F_1 = F_3$, so

$$F_1 = F_3 = 1.732 - 0.707 = 1.025,$$
$$F_2 = 1.732 - (0.707 + 0.707) = 0.318.$$

Values of F_i of about 1.0 are expected for free radicals, for example F_1 and F_3 for allyl. The values obtained for the terminal atoms of a chain are about 0.8 and for atoms of an aromatic system are usually about 0.4. These roughly correlate with free radical reactivities, and F_i has been taken as a measure of reactivity toward neutral, nonpolar reactants.

We can now calculate a number of quantities and need a convenient method of reporting them. The following scheme is generally used:

$$DE_\pi$$

Thus, the values calculated for allyl are reported as

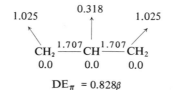

$$DE_\pi = 0.828\beta$$

The principal uses of the calculations we have just carried out are summarized below.

1. Bond orders may be used to estimate bond lengths.

2. Bond orders may be used to crudely compare bond strengths.

3. Bond orders suggest the π-electron mobility. Total bond orders near the value of 2.0 indicate bonds that are like ethylene, i.e. isolated; values near 1.0 indicate bonds with little double-bond character. When such high and low values alternate, delocalization is not very important.

4. Charge densities suggest the most likely atoms to be attacked by ionic reagents. Cations generally react with atoms of high electron density and anions with atoms of low electron density.

5. Charge densities permit the prediction of the presence of dipole moments. In fact, bond angles and bond lengths, along with net charge values, may be used to calculate dipole moments, although the values obtained by this method are usually too large.

6. Free valence indices suggest the atoms most likely to react with uncharged reactants such as free radicals.

7. Energies of the lowest unoccupied molecular orbitals suggest relative electron affinities.

8. Energies of the highest occupied molecular orbitals suggest relative ionization potentials.

9. Delocalization energies permit prediction of the most stable, hence favored, product in equilibrium reactions.

The calculations illustrated above for allyl are not difficult. They become quite laborious, however, when larger molecules are considered. Solving the secular determinant for benzene, with only six rows, requires considerable patience, and for naphthalene, with a ten-row determinant, it is extremely tedious. With a large digital computer nearly all π systems are easily handled; unfortunately, computers are not generally available. Group theory may also be applied to the problem and the secular determinants can be considerably simplified. For those interested in handling medium-sized molecules with pencil and paper, this method is illustrated in Appendix B.

SIMPLE IMPROVEMENTS AND COMPLICATIONS

Before continuing, we should examine the theoretical significance of the approach we have just developed. We began with one-electron molecular orbitals and then proceeded to put two electrons in each molecular orbital, ignoring any electron-electron repulsion effects, likewise any repulsions between electrons in different orbitals, both π and σ. This probably has the greatest effect upon α. Because α depends upon the net charge of an atom, as well as on several other factors, calculations made on ionic species should not be used carelessly. The simplifying assumptions made for each of the integrals are, at best, drastic, and lead to difficulties and errors. These assumptions are: that H_{ij} is β for all bonds, even though the integral varies with bond length; that H_{ij} is zero for all nonbonded interactions (although the importance of this assumption is not clear); that S_{ij} is zero when atoms i and j are different. Nevertheless, all of these assumptions can be handled within the framework of the π approximation. The justification of this method lies not in its theoretical significance but rather in its actual success in predicting molecular properties, which is doubtless due to the use of empirical values of α and β. Because of this, the validity of any application of the approach must be demonstrated.

We may improve on the approximation that the integral S_{ij} is zero when $i \neq j$. The value of 0.25 is generally accepted for adjacent orbitals in a carbon–carbon π bond at a bonding distance of 1.40 Å (Fig. 4–5). We may include this overlap for allyl radical without great difficulty. Inclusion of S_{ij} for adjacent atoms changes the secular determinant:

$$\begin{vmatrix} \alpha - E & \beta - SE & 0 \\ \beta - SE & \alpha - E & \beta - SE \\ 0 & \beta - SE & \alpha - E \end{vmatrix} = 0.$$

The solution of this determinant can be simplified. By making the substitutions

$$\alpha - E = A, \qquad \beta - SE = B,$$

we obtain

$$\begin{vmatrix} A & B & 0 \\ B & A & B \\ 0 & B & A \end{vmatrix} = 0 \qquad \text{and} \qquad A^3 - 2AB^2 = 0,$$

$$A = 0, \qquad A = \pm\sqrt{2}B.$$

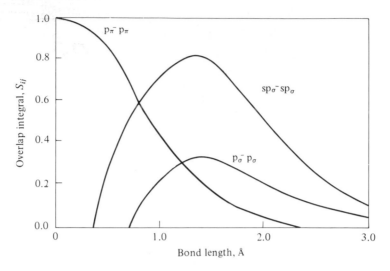

Fig. 4–5. Values for overlap integrals of C—C bonds. (Based upon data from R. S. Mulliken, C. A. Rieke, D. Orloff and H. Orloff, *J. Chem. Phys.*, **17**, 1248, 1949.)

By replacing the values of A and B, the values of the π energies are obtained in terms of α, β, and S:

$$E = \alpha, \qquad E = (\alpha - \sqrt{2}\beta)/(1 - \sqrt{2}S), \qquad E = (\alpha + \sqrt{2}\beta)/(1 + \sqrt{2}S).$$

Since we are especially interested in the energy levels above and below the non-bonding level α, we may set $\alpha = 0$ and substitute the appropriate value of S; here $S = 0.25$. Making the substitution gives the values

$$E = 0.0\beta$$
$$= 1.04\beta$$
$$= -2.19\beta.$$

Although the spacing of the energy levels is strikingly different when overlap is considered, and inclusion of it appears to be justified, it is seldom used.

The approximation that all sp² carbon atoms have the same Coulomb integral α may also be corrected. When the π-electron density, q, is less than 1, we might expect that Coulombic attraction of the nucleus for an electron will be greater than for a standard atom with $q = 1$. Thus the value of the Coulomb integral will be more negative than the standard α. Similarly, a carbon atom with a negative charge, $q > 1$, will effectively screen the electron from the nucleus and the electron will not be as strongly attracted as in the standard atom. This will result in a value less negative than the standard α. We might then expect that the most significant changes in our calculations will result when $q \neq 1$, that is, with nonalternant hydrocarbons and with ionic species.

To allow for differences in the value of the Coulomb integral, we might consider that the value of α for some particular atom i is proportional to the standard value α_0 for some particular carbon atom, usually a carbon atom in benzene. In practice, changes in α are expressed in terms of β units:

$$\alpha_i = \alpha_0 + h_i\beta_0. \tag{4-6}$$

We are left with the problem of evaluating h_i. A convenient method of doing this, known as the ω-technique, consists of successive approximations. First, we obtain the values of q. These are used to calculate new values for α, which in turn are used to calculate revised values of q. The process is continued until successive computations give the same charge distribution. To do this, a linear relationship of q and α is assumed:

$$\alpha_i = \alpha_0 + (1 - q_i)\omega\beta. \tag{4-7}$$

In this equation ω is a parameter chosen to give the best experimental agreement, usually 1.4.

To see how the ω-technique operates, let us apply it to the allyl cation. We have already calculated $q_1 = q_3 = 0.50$ and $q_2 = 1.0$ for the first approximation. Using these values and $\omega = 1.4$, we evaluate new α's in terms of the standard α_0 and β:

$$\alpha_1 = \alpha_3 = \alpha_0 + (1 - 0.5)1.4\beta = \alpha_0 + 0.7\beta,$$
$$\alpha_2 = \alpha_0 + (1 - 1)1.4\beta = \alpha_0.$$

We then write the new secular determinant:

$$\begin{vmatrix} (\alpha_0 + 0.7\beta - E) & \beta & 0 \\ \beta & \alpha_0 - E & \beta \\ 0 & \beta & (\alpha_0 + 0.7\beta - E) \end{vmatrix} = 0.$$

Dividing all terms by β and substituting $x = (\alpha_0 - E)/\beta$ gives the shorthand determinant

$$\begin{vmatrix} x + 0.7 & 1 & 0 \\ 1 & x & 1 \\ 0 & 1 & x + 0.7 \end{vmatrix} = 0.$$

Solving this gives $x = -0.7, -1.81, +1.11$.

To determine the charge distribution, we must evaluate the coefficients but this is not necessary for all three energy levels. Since the allyl cation has only two electrons in the π system, we need evaluate only the coefficients of the most stable orbital, which will contain both these electrons. Calculation by the method of cofactors gives the coefficients for this orbital:

$$E_1 = \alpha_0 + 1.81\beta, \qquad \psi_1 = 0.558(\chi_1 + \chi_3) + 0.615\chi_2.$$

From these values we determine the revised electron density for each atom in the second approximation:

$$q_1 = q_3 = 2(0.558)^2 = 0.622,$$
$$q_2 = 2(0.615)^2 = 0.756.$$

A similar use of these gives the third approximation:

$$q_1 = q_3 = 0.533, \qquad q_2 = 0.934.$$

The procedure of using q to obtain new values for α and the revised α values to obtain new values for q will finally lead to repeating values. We may, of course, calculate all other quantities by using the values of E, c_i and q_i thus obtained.

The assumption that the resonance integral is equal for all nearest neighbors may also be improved. The resonance integral is a function of the degree of overlap and hence may be related to bond length. We shall find it convenient to relate the value of the resonance integral to a standard value, again taking that for benzene, β_0, as our standard. In this manner we obtain β for any bond distance in units of β_0 and a proportionality parameter, k:

$$\beta_{ij} = k_{ij}\beta_0. \tag{4–8}$$

We may use Fig. 4–6 to evaluate k for various π-bond distances relative to the bond distance of benzene, 1.39 Å.

Unfortunately we cannot apply this correction of the resonance integral to our example. The bond lengths of the allyl radical are not known and, in any event, are probably identical. Butadiene offers an example in which carbon-carbon double bonds have different lengths:

$$H_2C \overset{1.34\text{Å}}{=\!=\!=} CH \overset{1.48\text{Å}}{-\!\!-\!\!-} CH =\!=\!= CH_2.$$

From Fig. 4–6 we obtain $k_{12} = k_{34} = 1.10$ and $k_{23} = 0.87$. Using these in the secular determinant for butadiene, we can see how this improvement is made:

$$\begin{vmatrix} x & 1.1 & 0 & 0 \\ 1.1 & x & 0.87 & 0 \\ 0 & 0.87 & x & 1.1 \\ 0 & 0 & 1.1 & x \end{vmatrix} = 0.$$

$$x^4 - 3.067x^2 + 1.331 = 0,$$
$$x = \pm 0.748; \pm 1.618.$$

The total bonding energy is $4\alpha + 4.732\beta$. To obtain the delocalization energy, we use the same value of 1.10 for k_{12} and k_{34} in the localized model, the value of k_{23} being, of course, zero. These values give an energy of $4\alpha + 4.40\beta$, from which we can obtain the delocalization energy, DE_π, of 0.332β. [Compare this to the value of DE_π obtained when all β's are equal (Problem 2).]

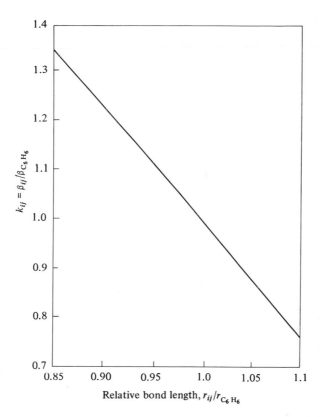

Fig. 4–6. Variation of k with bond length. (Based upon data from R. S. Mulliken, *J. Phys. Chem.*, **56,** 295, 1952.)

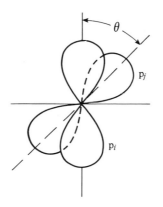

Fig. 4–7. Coordinate system for twisted p orbitals.

We can also use this approach when the p orbitals are twisted so that they are not coplanar (Fig. 4–7). Here the value of β_{ij} would be β_0 when $\theta = 0°$ and would be zero when $\theta = 90°$. For other angles, $\beta = k\beta_0$, as above, where $k = \cos \theta$:

$$\beta_{ij} = \beta_0 \cos \theta. \tag{4–9}$$

The approach is exactly the same as for those cases in which we allow the resonance integral to vary with bond distance.

HETEROATOMS

The treatment of heteroatoms in the Hückel method follows the pattern established above for varying α and β. We attempt to vary these empirical parameters in units of the standards for benzene, so that the calculated values fit experimental data as accurately as possible, and therefore values for h_i of Eq. (4–6) and k_{ij} of Eq. (4–8) must be determined. Of course, values of h_i and k_{ij} evaluated for the simple π approximation should not be used either for the improvements made in the above section or for more advanced approaches, since the parameters are adjusted to fit *only* the simple π approximation with the appropriate assumptions.

Table 4–2 gives values (suggested by Streitwieser as "useful to suggest trends and in semiquantitative work") that may be used for heteroatom systems. Because of the semiquantitative nature of the entire Hückel approach, these values are adequate for crude comparisons.

Table 4–2. Heteroatom Integral Values for Hückel Molecular Orbital Theory*

Atom X	Sample compound	Coulomb integral	Resonance integral	Coulomb integral of C adjacent to X
C	Benzene	α	β	α
N(1)	Pyridine	$\alpha + 0.5\beta$	β	$\alpha + 0.05\beta$
N(2)	Pyrrole	$\alpha + 1.5\beta$	0.8β	$\alpha + 0.075\beta$
O(1)	Acrolein	$\alpha + \beta$	β	$\alpha + 0.1\beta$
O(2)	Furan	$\alpha + 2\beta$	0.8β	$\alpha + 0.1\beta$
F	Fluorobenzene	$\alpha + 3\beta$	0.7β	$\alpha + 0.3\beta$
Cl	Chlorobenzene	$\alpha + 2\beta$	0.4β	$\alpha + 0.2\beta$
Br	Bromobenzene	$\alpha + 1.5\beta$	0.3β	$\alpha + 0.15\beta$
CH_3	Toluene	$\alpha - 0.5\beta$	0	α

* After A. Streitwieser, Jr., *Molecular Orbital Theory for Organic Chemists*, John Wiley & Sons, New York (1961), Chap. 5.

Table 4–2 lists two values for both N and O. The O(1) value should be used when oxygen contributes one electron to the π system, as in acrolein or formaldehyde, and the O(2) value when it contributes two electrons to the π system, as in furan or phenol.

The values for N are used in the same way. The value given for methyl permits inclusion of "hyperconjugation" by considering the effect of a methyl group as purely inductive. The hyperconjugative effect of a methyl group has been treated by several methods but this simple approach seems to give adequate results. It is not meant to imply that π-σ conjugation does or does not occur but only that we can include the effect within the calculations of the Hückel molecular orbital theory.

The last column of Table 4–2 gives values for the Coulomb integral of all carbon atoms bonded to the heteroatom. What is the purpose of this last parameter? The Coulomb integral of the heteroatom could not be assigned the same value as that of a carbon atom because the heteroatom has a different nuclear charge and must attract electrons more (or less) than the carbon nucleus. We know that the atom adjacent to a heteroatom is also influenced by its presence. The last column in Table 4–2 is an attempt to correct for this, the inductive, effect.

Now that we have the necessary parameters to treat heteroatoms, let us see how they are used to set up the secular determinant, taking acrolein as an example. We write the secular determinant as before, using parameters as necessary:

$$\begin{vmatrix} \alpha - E & \beta & 0 & 0 \\ \beta & \alpha - E & \beta & 0 \\ 0 & \beta & (\alpha + 0.1\beta) - E & \beta \\ 0 & 0 & \beta & (\alpha + \beta) - E \end{vmatrix} = 0.$$

Dividing by β and substituting $x = (\alpha - E)/\beta$ gives the shorthand determinant

$$\begin{vmatrix} x & 1 & 0 & 0 \\ 1 & x & 1 & 0 \\ 0 & 1 & x + 0.1 & 1 \\ 0 & 0 & 1 & x + 1 \end{vmatrix} = 0.$$

From this point on the calculation proceeds as previously described. To calculate E_L and ultimately DE_π, we use the same determinant with $H_{23} = 0$.

The calculations that can be performed within the π approximation have been illustrated. Later chapters will deal with the use of these results to solve chemical problems, but in the next section we shall examine one novel approach utilizing the molecular orbitals which we are now able to describe.

THE WOODWARD-HOFFMANN APPLICATION

Woodward and Hoffmann [1] have employed the symmetry of molecular orbitals to explain and predict a number of stereochemical and reactivity observations. As an example of this approach let us consider the electrocyclic reaction

When *cis*-3,4-dimethylcyclobutene is heated it is converted to *cis,trans*-2,4-hexadiene, while the *trans*-isomer gives the *trans,trans*-hexadiene exclusively [2]. This stereospecificity is strong evidence that the ring-opening reaction occurs by a concerted mechanism, rather than step by step as in a diradical process. The two stereochemical ways for the ring opening to occur are shown in Fig. 4–8. In conrotatory motion the methyls rotate in the same direction; in disrotatory motion they rotate in opposite directions. Clearly, the thermal ring fission of cyclobutenes occurs by a conrotatory process.

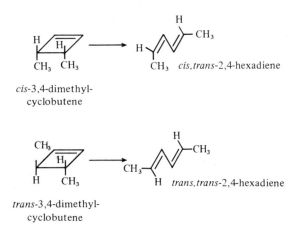

In the ring fission of cyclobutenes, four molecular orbitals—the bonding and antibonding orbitals of the σ bond that is broken and the bonding and antibonding

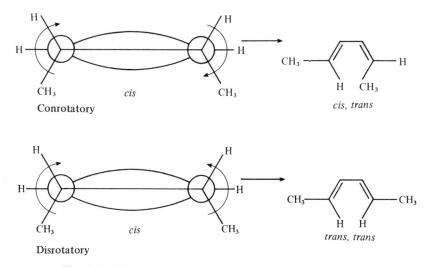

Fig. 4–8. Alternative modes of cyclobutene ring cleavage.

π orbitals of the cyclobutene double bond—undergo dramatic change and become the π molecular orbitals of the butadiene. Woodward and Hoffmann used the principle of the *conservation of orbital symmetry* to predict the direction of ring openings. This principle may be stated as: *a σ bond opens so that the resulting p orbitals will have the same symmetry as the highest occupied π orbital of the product.* In the case of butadiene the highest occupied orbital, ψ_2, has the symmetry†

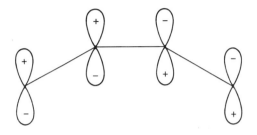

The σ orbital of cyclobutene has the symmetry

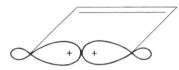

Conrotatory motion will move one of the positive lobes of the σ bond up and the other positive lobe down, so that the resulting p orbitals are oriented like those of ψ_2 in butadiene. Disrotatory motion would lead to both positive lobes being up (or down), a result different from that required for the electrons to go into ψ_2 of butadiene.

    To apply the Woodward-Hoffmann rule we need examine only the occupied σ orbital of the cyclobutene and the highest occupied orbital of the product, butadiene. For the more complete explanation of why the rule leads to the prediction of the favored product, given by Longuet-Higgins and Abrahamson [3], we must examine all four orbitals mentioned earlier. In Fig. 4–9 we can see that conrotatory motion preserves a twofold axis of symmetry throughout the reaction, and the orbitals are classified according to this symmetry: A is antisymmetric, S is symmetric. Disrotatory motion preserves a plane of symmetry and the orbitals are classified as A or S in relation to this plane. For conrotatory motion the σ and π^* orbitals are S and

† The molecular orbital wave functions of butadiene are:

$$\psi_1 = 0.37\chi_1 + 0.60\chi_2 + 0.60\chi_3 + 0.37\chi_4,$$
$$\psi_2 = 0.60\chi_1 + 0.37\chi_2 - 0.37\chi_3 - 0.60\chi_4,$$
$$\psi_3 = 0.60\chi_1 - 0.37\chi_2 - 0.37\chi_3 + 0.60\chi_4,$$
$$\psi_4 = 0.37\chi_1 - 0.60\chi_2 + 0.60\chi_3 - 0.37\chi_4.$$

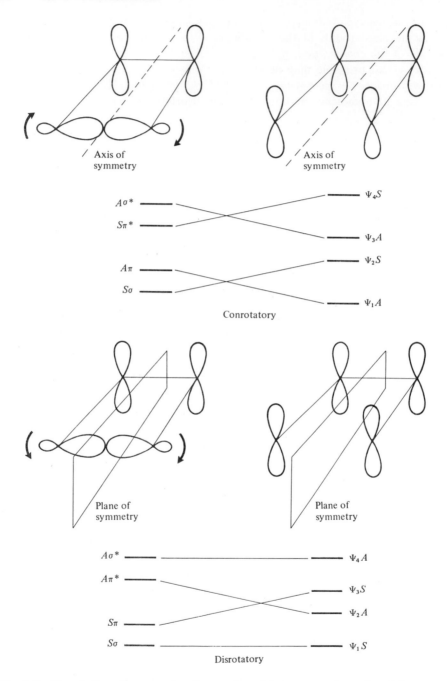

Fig. 4–9. Correlation diagrams for the modes of interconversion of cyclobutene and butadiene.

the σ^* and π orbitals are A about the axis of symmetry. The ψ_2 and ψ_4 orbitals of butadiene are S while ψ_1 and ψ_3 are A. The σ orbital correlates with ψ_2 (both are S). Similarly, π^* correlates with ψ_4 and σ^* with ψ_3. The ground state of the reactant has the electronic configuration $\sigma^2\pi^2$ and produces the *ground* state of butadiene, $\psi_1^2\psi_2^2$. For the disrotatory mode the σ and π orbitals are S and the σ^* and π^* orbitals are A about the symmetry plane. The ψ_1 and ψ_3 orbitals are S and the ψ_2 and ψ_4 orbitals are A so that σ correlates with ψ_1, π with ψ_3, π^* with ψ_2, and σ^* with ψ_4. The ground state configuration of cyclobutene would lead to the *excited* state, $\psi_1^2\psi_3^2$, of butadiene. Thus, conrotatory motion is predicted to be the favored process.

Application of the principle to the reverse reaction, the cyclization of butadienes, also predicts conrotatory motion, even though cyclization does not generally occur by a thermal process. The principle can also be applied to the photochemical ring openings and closures. The first excited state of cyclobutene has the electronic configuration $\sigma^2\pi^1\pi^{*1}$. The ring opening of this state leads to the excited state of butadiene in the $\psi_1^2\psi_2^1\psi_4^1$ configuration by the conrotatory process, whereas the disrotatory process leads to the more stable $\psi_1^2\psi_2^1\psi_3^1$ configuration. Thus, the favored mode of ring opening by a photochemical process is disrotatory. Similarly, the photochemical cyclization of butadienes is predicted to occur by disrotatory motion, a prediction borne out by experiment. For photochemical processes the modes of rotation (conrotatory *vs.* disrotatory) are reversed relative to thermal processes because in each case a higher orbital of inverted symmetry is occupied.

When the principle of orbital symmetry is applied to the thermal cleavage of cyclohexadienes, the predicted rotation is disrotatory. This result is opposite to that for the cyclobutene-butadiene thermal interconversion because of the different symmetry of the highest occupied orbital of a hexatriene. To get the positive lobes of the p orbitals on the same side of the plane determined by the atoms requires disrotatory motion.

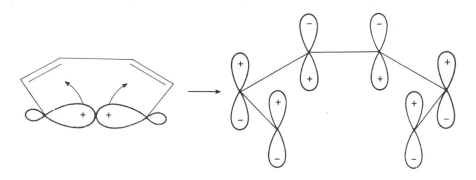

The conservation of orbital symmetry has been used to explain other reactivity relationships. For example, the thermal dimerization of olefins to give cyclobutanes generally gives very poor results while the apparently similar Diels-Alder reaction proceeds smoothly. For these cases, the principle of orbital symmetry must be restated to say that reaction is permitted when all overlaps between the highest occupied orbital of one reactant and the lowest unoccupied orbital of the other reactant occur in such a way that positive lobes overlap only with positive lobes and negative lobes overlap only with negative ones. Thus for the cyclization of ethylene we must examine the lowest unoccupied orbital of one ethylene with the highest

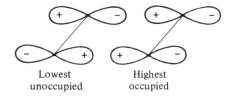

Lowest
unoccupied

Highest
occupied

occupied orbital of another. Clearly the concerted cyclization of two mono-olefins (a 2 + 2 reaction) is not allowed. For this reaction to occur a positive lobe must overlap with a negative lobe. The Diels-Alder reaction (a 2 + 4 reaction) is allowed, whether we consider the lowest unoccupied orbital of the dienophile and the highest occupied orbital of the diene or *vice versa*. The reverse reactions follow the same

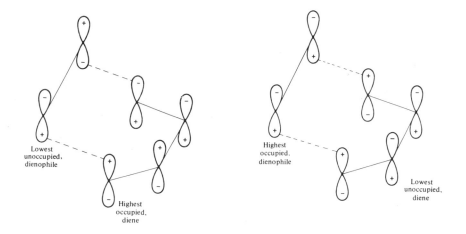

Lowest
unoccupied,
dienophile

Highest
occupied,
diene

Highest
occupied,
dienophile

Lowest
unoccupied,
diene

rules; indeed, the reverse Diels-Alder reaction is well known. The opening of cyclo-butanes requires strenuous conditions, as predicted, even though there is consid-erably more ring strain. The reverse predictions are made when photochemical cyclizations are considered because one of the reactants has an electron promoted into a vacant orbital before reaction occurs. The 4 + 2 ring closure is not allowed but the 2 + 2 cyclization is.

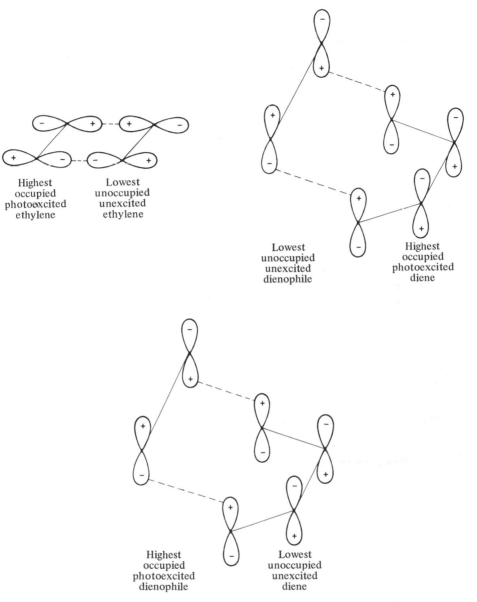

Highest
occupied
photoexcited
ethylene

Lowest
unoccupied
unexcited
ethylene

Lowest
unoccupied
unexcited
dienophile

Highest
occupied
photoexcited
diene

Highest
occupied
photoexcited
dienophile

Lowest
unoccupied
unexcited
diene

Using the principle of orbital symmetry we can show that 2 + 2, 4 + 4, and 2 + 6 ring openings and closures are forbidden for a thermal process but will occur photochemically. On the other hand, 2 + 4, 4 + 6, and 2 + 8 ring openings and closures will occur thermally but are forbidden during photochemical processes. One further condition must be mentioned: the rule applies only when the mechanism is cyclic, never when one bond is broken or formed before the other.

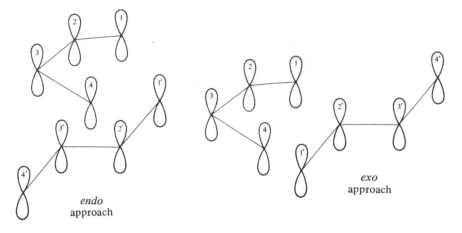

Woodward and Hoffmann have also attempted to explain the predominant *endo* addition observed in the Diels-Alder reaction. The approach during the addition may be either *endo* or *exo* for the addition of butadiene to itself. The *endo* approach

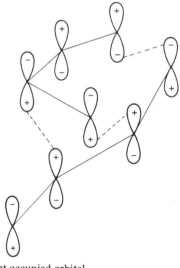

Highest occupied orbital of diene (top); lowest unoccupied orbital of dienophile (bottom) (*endo* approach)

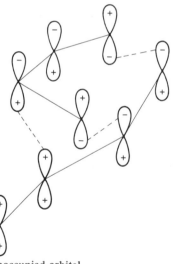

Lowest unoccupied orbital of diene (top); highest occupied orbital of dienophile (bottom) (*endo* approach)

is distinguished by the proximity of the orbitals on carbon atoms 3 and 3'. Any secondary interaction occurring between these orbitals will contribute little to the total energy of the system if both orbitals are occupied; such interaction would lower the energy of some orbitals but would raise the energy of others. The interaction can lower the energy of the system and thus tend to stabilize the *endo* approach transition state if mixing occurs between an occupied and an unoccupied orbital. It is easily seen that whether the highest occupied molecular orbital of the diene overlaps with the lowest unoccupied molecular orbital of the dienophile or *vice versa*, the symmetry is correct for mixing. No such mixing can occur during *exo* addition because of the distance between atoms 3' and 4' and the diene.

At the start of this discussion of Diels-Alder type reactions we restated the principle of orbital symmetry. To see that the principle actually remains the same let us examine correlation diagrams for the cyclization of ethylene with itself (Fig. 4–10) and with butadiene (Fig. 4–11).

For the correlation diagram of the cyclization of ethylene to cyclobutane the two ethylene molecules are placed on a plane so that the lobes of the p orbitals face each other. There are two planes of symmetry throughout the reaction, one perpendicular to the axis of the π bonds of the two ethylenes, P_1, and the other parallel with the axis of the π bonds, P_2. To determine the symmetry we project the possible orientations of the molecular orbitals upon the plane passing through the four carbon atoms, as shown in the middle of Fig. 4–10, along with the symmetry assignment, first in relation to P_1 then in relation to P_2. At the bottom of the figure is the correlation diagram, from which we see that one of the π bonding orbitals correlates with one of the σ antibonding orbitals of cyclobutane. Thus, electrons in the SA orbital of one of the ethylenes will end up in the SA antibonding orbital of the product, and we must predict that the thermal reaction is unlikely to occur, but that the photochemical reaction appears to be possible.

In Fig. 4–11 we see that there is one plane of symmetry maintained throughout the cyclization of ethylene with butadiene, and the symmetry assignments are made relative to this plane. The symmetry orbital assignments are: ψ_1, S; ψ_2, A; ψ_3, S; ψ_4, A; those for ethylene are: ψ_1, S; ψ_2, A; and the orbitals of cyclohexene have the symmetry given in the figure. According to the correlation diagram, the ground state of the reactants flows smoothly into the ground state of the products so the reaction should take place under thermal conditions, and the photochemical reaction is not expected to occur. In similar fashion it can be shown that 6 + 4 and 8 + 2 cyclizations should proceed under thermal conditions while 4 + 4 and 6 + 2 cyclizations should proceed photochemically. These conclusions are based on the reasonable postulate that thermal reactions yield correlation diagrams with no correlations between bonding and antibonding orbitals, whereas photochemical reactions do yield such correlations.

In closing, one important feature of the principle of orbital symmetry must be emphasized. The selection rules predicted by the principle are permissive, not obligatory. Steric hindrance may prevent a reaction from occurring that is predicted

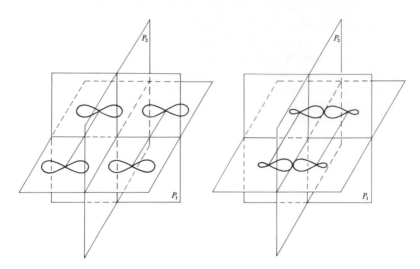

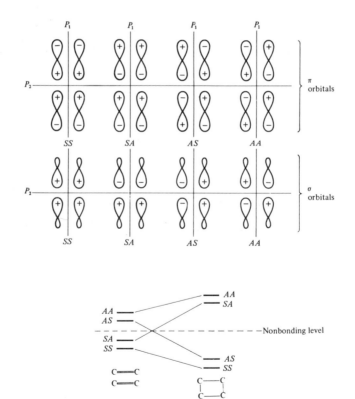

Fig. 4–10. Correlation diagram for the cyclization of ethylene to cyclobutane.

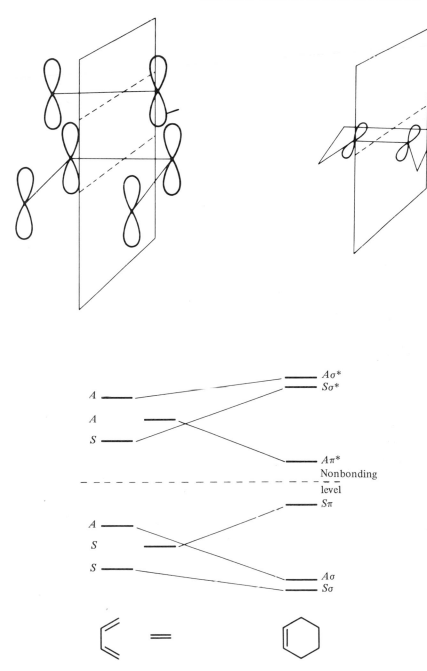

Fig. 4–11. Correlation diagram for the Diels-Alder reaction of ethylene with butadiene.

by the principle. More importantly the predictions are based upon the assumption of concerted mechanisms. Should a reaction proceed by a multistep mechanism involving discrete intermediates we should not expect the principle to be able to predict the products.

PROBLEMS

1. Calculate the π bonding energy of: a) ethylene; b) cyclopropenyl radical; c) trimethylenemethane.

2. Obtain the π bonding energy and the delocalization energy of butadiene.

3. Calculate the coefficients for each energy level and sketch the complete wave functions of butadiene.

4. Calculate the electron density and the charge at each carbon atom for butadiene and its cation.

5. Calculate the bond order of each bond and the free valence at each carbon atom in butadiene.

6. Write the secular determinant for cyclobutadiene. Solve for the allowed energy values. Compute the bonding energy and delocalization energy for the cation, molecule, and anion in units of β.

7. Calculate the π bonding energy and the delocalization energy for acrolein.

8. Apply the ω-technique, with $\omega = 1.4$, to the allyl cation and determine electron densities.

9. Draw a correlation diagram for the cyclization of butadiene to give cycloocta-1,5-diene.

10. Even though thermal 2 + 2 cyclizations are not allowed by the principle of orbital symmetry several olefins are known to dimerize to cyclobutanes, for example, the dimerization of acrylonitrile to 1,2-dicyanocyclobutane. What conclusion about the mechanism can be drawn?

11. Predict the product obtained from the thermal cleavage of cis-5,6-dimethylcyclohexa-1,3-diene.

REFERENCES

1. R. B. WOODWARD and R. HOFFMANN, *J. Am. Chem. Soc.*, **87**, 395, 2046, 2511, 4388, and 4389 (1965).
2. R. E. K. WINTER, *Tetrahedron Letters*, **1965**, 1207.
3. H. C. LONGUET-HIGGINS and E. W. ABRAHAMSON, *J. Am. Chem. Soc.*, **87**, 2045 (1965).

SUGGESTED READING

LIBERLES, A., *Introduction to Molecular-Orbital Theory*, Holt, Rinehart and Winston, New York (1966).

ROBERTS, J. D., *Notes on Molecular Orbital Calculations*, W. A. Benjamin, New York (1962).

SALEM, L., *The Molecular Orbital Theory of Conjugated Systems*, W. A. Benjamin, New York (1966).

STREITWIESER, A., JR., *Molecular Orbital Theory for Organic Chemists*, John Wiley & Sons, New York, 1961.

CHAPTER 5

RESONANCE ENERGY
AND AROMATICITY

In the preceding chapter we introduced the terms resonance and delocalization energies. The common practice of using them as synonyms blurs an essential distinction that we wish to retain. We shall use the term *resonance* when the empirical data on a substance suggest that it cannot be adequately represented by a single Lewis structure and, therefore, must be considered a hybrid. On the other hand, the term *delocalization energy* will be used when the calculated total π energy of a delocalized molecular model is less (a greater positive value) than that of a localized model. In other words, we shall use resonance energy to indicate an observed phenomenon and reserve the term delocalization energy for a theoretically derived stabilization energy. The method employed in Chapter 4 to find absolute values for the delocalization energy obtained by the Hückel method equates delocalization and resonance energies.

EMPIRICAL RESONANCE ENERGIES

To obtain an empirical resonance energy directly we must compare the energy of the resonance hybrid with that of a hypothetical compound of the same gross structure as the hybrid but without electron delocalization. This is impossible for two reasons: first, we cannot measure the energy of a hypothetical structure; second, the determination of the energy of the hybrid itself is impractical in the case of complicated organic structures. We *could* measure either the energy released when the molecule is formed from its isolated atoms or the energy consumed when the molecule is dissociated into its atoms, but neither method is useful for any but the simplest of organic molecules. Therefore, an indirect method must be used to determine resonance energies. Both heat of hydrogenation and heat of combustion have been generally used to obtain the necessary thermochemical data. We can compare the heat of hydrogenation (or combustion) of a compound with that of the hypothetical localized structure but, since no molecule of the latter exists, we must estimate its heat of hydrogenation (or combustion) by comparison with the data obtained from closely related compounds that do exist.

Kistiakowsky and coworkers have provided the most accurate data on *heats of hydrogenation* [1–8]. Table 5–1 collects many of their results for compounds where no resonance is expected [9]. The application of them to the determination of resonance energies is straightforward. The heat of hydrogenation of the substance in question is measured [10,11], and compared with a suitable model chosen from the compounds in Table 5–1. This model is used to estimate the heat of hydrogenation of the compound without resonance stabilization.

Table 5–1. Heats of Hydrogenation
(Gas Phase, 82°C, 1 atm)*

Compound	− kcal/mole
Ethene	32.8
Allene	71.3
Propene	30.1
1-Butene	30.3
1-Pentene	30.1
1-Heptene	30.1
cis-2-butene	28.6
trans-2-butene	27.6
cis-2-pentene	28.6
trans-2-pentene	27.6
Isobutylene	28.4
2-Methyl-1-butene	28.5
Trimethylethene	26.9
Tetramethylethene	26.6
Cyclopentene	26.9
Cyclohexene	28.6
Cycloheptene	26.5
Cyclooctene	23.5

* From Kistiakowsky *et al.* [1–8].

The treatment of benzene will be used to illustrate the procedure. The hydrogenation of benzene affords 49.8 kcal/mole of heat under the conditions used in Table 5–1. As a model for benzene, we might choose cyclohexene. The hydrogenation of this compound produces cyclohexane, which is also obtained from the hydrogenation of benzene. A Kekule structure of benzene has three double bonds and the stoichiometry of the hydrogenation requires three moles of hydrogen. Since only one double bond and one mole of hydrogen are involved in the hydrogenation of cyclohexene, we might expect that the measured heat of hydrogenation of cyclohexene would be a third of that for benzene. We would, therefore, predict 3×28.6 kcal/mole $= 85.8$ kcal/mole as the heat of hydrogenation of benzene, which is 36.0 kcal/mole too high. Since the same product results from both reactions, we must ascribe the difference to differing stabilities of the reactants, as is shown schematically in Fig. 5–1.

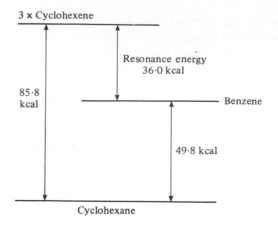

Fig. 5–1. Diagram of available data from heats of hydrogenation and their relationship to the resonance energy of benzene.

Table 5–2 lists heats of hydrogenation for several compounds with more than one double bond and the resonance stabilization of each obtained in the manner described above for benzene. The models chosen for substituted benzenes in Table 5–2 are not as obvious as the cyclohexene model for benzene. As an illustration, if styrene is drawn as the structure

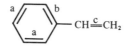

we can see that cyclohexene is not the best model for the benzene ring. Cyclohexene will serve as a model for the two double bonds labeled a, but trimethylethene might be a better model for bond b, being trisubstituted, and 1-butene is a good model for

Table 5–2. Heats of Hydrogenation (Gas Phase, 82°C, 1 atm)

Compound	− kcal/mole*	RE (kcal/mole)
1,3-Butadiene	57.1	3.5
1,3-Pentadiene	54.1	4.2
1,3-Cyclopentadiene	50.9	2.9
1,3-Cyclohexadiene	55.4	1.8
1,3-Cycloheptadiene	51.3	1.7
1,3,5-Cycloheptatriene	72.8	6.7
Benzene	49.8	36.0
ortho-xylene	47.3	35.1
Styrene	77.5	36.9

* From Kistiakowsky *et al.* [1–8].

bond c. If these models are selected, the predicted heat of hydrogenation of styrene is $2 \times 28.6 + 26.9 + 30.3 = 114.4$ kcal/mole. Of course, this choice of a model is somewhat arbitrary and small deviations of quoted resonance energies can be expected. For example, a small change in the resonance energy of styrene is made by selecting either propene or 1-pentene for the terminal double bond.

It may be argued correctly that, in using heats of hydrogenation, we have replaced an energy term with an enthalpic term. It has been found, however, that $T\Delta S$ is very nearly a constant and is self-canceling [12]. The estimated values of ΔG, $T\Delta S$, and ΔH for the hydrogenation of several compounds are given in Table 5–3.

Table 5–3. Thermodynamic Values for the Addition of One Mole of H_2 at 298°K*

Compound	$-\Delta H$	$-\Delta G$	$-T\Delta S$
Ethene	32.6	24.4	8.2
Propene	29.9	21.0	8.2
cis-2-butene	28.2	19.4	8.9
Tetramethylethene	26.4	17.5	8.9
Butadiene to trans-2-butene	29.2	20.3	8.9
Benzene to 1,3-cyclohexadiene	− 5.8	− 13.6	7.8

* From Conant and Kistiakowsky [12].

The gaseous heats of hydrogenation data are unfortunately scanty, but their usefulness has been extended somewhat by Williams [10] and by Turner and co-workers [11, 13–21], employing an acetic acid solution, which has the advantage of not being restricted to volatile compounds. These liquid phase data (Table 5–4) should not be used with the gas phase data of Kistiakowsky without appropriate corrections.

Although heats of hydrogenation provide the most accurate method of obtaining resonance energies, the lack of sufficient data frequently forces us to use a second approach. *Heats of combustion* have been measured for a large number of substances and therefore are very useful in this application. We are again faced with the problem of estimating the heat of combustion for the hypothetical model involving no resonance. Several methods have been used but we shall examine only that of Klages [22]. Values are assigned to each bond in the model compound, and the sum of these values is corrected for certain structural features of the molecule, to give a value for the heat of combustion of the gaseous substance at 25°C. This calculated heat of combustion is then compared with the measured value to obtain the resonance energy. Values for several bond contributions given by Wheland [9] are listed in Table 5–5

Table 5–4. Heats of Hydrogenation (Acetic Acid, 25°C)

Compound	− kcal/mole	Reference
1-Methylcyclopentene	23.0	13
Methylenecyclopentane	26.8	13
1-Ethylcyclopentene	23.6	13
Ethylidenecyclopentene	24.9	13
Cyclohexene	27.1	11
1-Methylcyclohexene	25.7	13
Methylenecyclohexane	27.8	13
1-Ethylcyclohexene	25.1	13
Ethylidenecyclohexane	26.3	13
Cycloheptene	25.9	11
1-Methylcycloheptene	24.0	13
Methylenecycloheptane	26.3	13
Cycloheptatriene	70.5	11
cis-cyclooctene	23.0	14
trans-cyclooctene	32.2	14
1,3,5-Cyclooctatriene	72.4	15
Cyclooctatetraene	98.0	15
cis-cyclononene	23.6	14
trans-cyclononene	20.7	14
cis, cis, cis-1,4,7-cyclononatriene	76.9	16
trans-cyclodecene	24.1	14
Bicyclo[2.2.1]heptene	33.1	11
Bicyclo[2.2.1]heptadiene	68.1	11
Bicyclo[2.2.2]octene	28.3	11
Bicyclo[2.2.2]octadiene	56.2	11
Bicyclo[2.2.2]octatriene	93.8	17
Diethyl fumarate	28.9	11
1-Hexene	29.0	18
2,4-Dimethyl-1-pentene	26.7	19
2,4-Dimethyl-2-pentene	25.2	19
2,4,4-Trimethyl-1-pentene	25.5	19
2,4,4-Trimethyl-2-pentene	26.8	19
4-Methyl-*cis*-2-pentene	27.3	19
4-Methyl-*trans*-2-pentene	26.4	19
4,4-Dimethyl-*cis*-2-pentene	30.8	19
4,4-Dimethyl-*trans*-2-pentene	26.5	19
2,2,5,5-Tetramethyl-*cis*-3-hexene	36.2	19
2,2,5,5-Tetramethyl-*trans*-3-hexene	26.9	19
cis-3-penten-1-yne	94.4	18
trans-3-penten-1-yne	94.8	18
cis-3-decen-1-yne	93.6	18
trans-3-decen-1-yne	93.9	18

Table 5–4—*continued*

Compound	− kcal/mole	Reference
Cholest-1-ene	27.3	20
Cholest-2-ene	25.9	20
Cholest-3-ene	28.0	20
Cholest-5-ene	25.9	20
Cholest-6-ene	27.4	20
3-α-Hydroxy-Δ^{11}-cholenic acid	28.9	15
Azulene	99.0	15
Heptafulvene	92.6	15
Heptafulvalene	130.8	15
Dihydroheptafulvalene	138.8	15
Tropone	67.6	15
Tropylium (chloride)	86.2	21

Table 5–5. Parameters for Calculating Heats of Combustion by Klages' Method*

Bond	kcal
C—H	54.0
C—C	49.3
RC=C	119.1
cis-RC=CR	117.4
trans-RC=CR	116.4
R_2C=C	115.5
R_2C=CR	114.0
R_2C=CR$_2$	112.0
RC≡C	197.7
RC≡CR	193.6
O—H	7.5
C—O	10.0
RC=O	19.8
R_2C=O	13.5
N—H	30.5
C—N	33.0
C≡N	97.0
Corrections	
Aliphatic tertiary carbon atom	− 1.7
Quaternary carbon atom	− 4.2
Tertiary alcohol	− 8.8
Five-membered ring	+ 6.0
Six-membered ring	+ 1.0

* Selected values from Wheland [9].

To illustrate the use of Klages' values in determining resonance energies, we will again look at styrene, using the same structure as a model that we used for the heat of hydrogenation method:

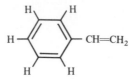

From Table 5–5 we obtain the bond contributions:

8 C—H	54.0 × 8 =	432.0 kcal
4 C—C	49.3 × 4 =	197.2
1 RC=C		119.1
2 *cis*-RC=CR	117.4 × 2 =	234.8
1 R$_2$C=CR		114.0
1 Six-membered ring		1.0
	Total	1098.1

Thus, at 25°C we would expect the heat of combustion of styrene to be 1098.1 kcal/mole. The reaction is

$$C_8H_8(g) + 10O_2(g) \rightarrow 8CO_2(g) + 4H_2O(l)$$

and if this is carried out, the observed heat of combustion is 1060.0 kcal/mole [22]. A resonance stabilization energy of 1098.1 − 1060.0 = 38.1 kcal is obtained, which can be compared with that of 36.9 kcal obtained by the heat of hydrogenation method. We might ask which is the better value. With Klages' method, we were forced to subtract a large number from another large number to obtain the resonance energy, whereas, with the heat of hydrogenation data, smaller numbers were employed. Therefore, an experimental error of 0.1% in the measured heat of combustion would be reflected in the resonance energy as 1.1 kcal/mole, while the same error in the measured heat of hydrogenation would amount to only 0.07 kcal/mole. Thus, the same percentage error in measurement leads to an absolute error for Klages' method that is nearly sixteen times greater than that for the heat of hydrogenation method. Since thermochemical data cannot generally be relied upon to an accuracy of 0.1%, we should use Klages' method only for compounds with large resonance stabilization energies or when other data are not available.

Heats of combustion may be calculated from Table 5–5 when the gaseous material at 20°C is being oxidized to the products in an experimentally convenient state, such as H$_2$O(l) or N$_2$(g). To convert data from states other than the gaseous one is not difficult for nonpolar liquids. We need only correct the heat of combustion for the liquid being measured to that for the compound in the gas phase at 25°C. To do this, we can imagine heating the liquid to its boiling point, converting it to the gas phase, and finally cooling the gases to 25°C. To obtain the heat of vaporization of the liquid at its boiling point we can use Trouton's rule,

$$\Delta H_v = 0.021 T_b \text{ kcal/mole}, \tag{5-1}$$

where T_b is the boiling point in Kelvin degrees. The heat required to raise the liquid from 25°C to its boiling point is obtained by using the molar heat capacity, $C_p(l)$, of the liquid:

$$\Delta H = C_p(l)\Delta T = C_p(l)(T_b - 298). \tag{5-2}$$

The heat released in cooling the gas from the boiling point to 25°C is similarly obtained:

$$-\Delta H = -C_p(g)\Delta T = -C_p(g)(T_b - 298). \tag{5-3}$$

Combining these equations gives the heat of vaporization at 25°C:

$$\Delta H_v(25°) = \Delta H_v + C_p(l)(T_b - 298) - C_p(g)(T_b - 298). \tag{5-4}$$

The measured heat of combustion, $\Delta H(l)$, can then be corrected to give $\Delta H(g)$, as needed for Klages' approach:

$$\begin{aligned}
\Delta H(g) &= \Delta H(l) + \Delta H_v(25°) \\
&= \Delta H(l) + 0.021\, T_b + [C_p(l) - C_p(g)](T_b - 298). \tag{5-5}
\end{aligned}$$

The value of $C_p(l) - C_p(g)$ has been estimated to be 0.015 kcal/mole-degree [9]. Using this value and substituting $T_b = t + 273$, where t is the boiling point of the liquid in Centigrade degrees, gives the equation for correcting measured heats of combustion of nonassociated liquids:

$$\Delta H(g) = \Delta H(l) + 5.4 + 0.036t. \tag{5-6}$$

Equation (5–6) may be used to estimate $\Delta H(g)$ from $\Delta H(l)$ with an accuracy better than 1 kcal/mole. The relationships used in this derivation are shown graphically in Fig. 5-2.

A less direct method of obtaining resonance energies, using bond energies, may also be employed. It leads to no information that cannot be obtained by Klages' heat of combustion method but bond energies are valuable characteristics of covalent bonds. For this reason, the method will be discussed briefly.

We might ask the question: "What is a bond energy?" For diatomic molecules it is defined as the *enthalpy change* when one mole of the molecule is converted into its constituent atoms, in the gas phase at 25°C and 1 atm, rather than an energy. This terminology of bond energy is incorrect because $\Delta H°$ contains a pressure-volume term and terms for rotational, vibrational, and translational energies, as well as the electronic bond strength, but we will accept this definition, while recognizing its inadequacy.

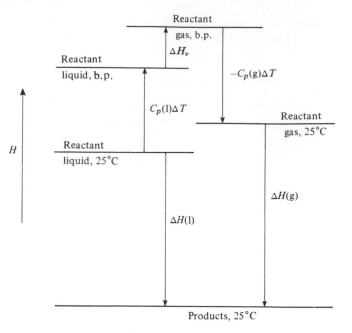

Fig. 5-2. Thermochemical cycle for conversion of heats of combustion of liquids to those of gases.

The bond energy of H_2, $DH°(H—H)$, is simply the enthalpy change at 25°C for the reaction:

$$H_2(g) \rightarrow 2H(g).$$

Since the bond energy $DH°$ is the same as the heat of reaction and since the heat of reaction may be obtained from the heats of formation, $\Delta H_f°$, we can obtain $DH°$ from tables of $\Delta H_f°$:

$$\Delta H_r = DH° = \sum \Delta H_f°(\text{products}) - \sum \Delta H_f°(\text{reactants}).$$

Excellent thermochemical tables are now available and values quoted in this discussion are taken from these tables, using $\Delta H_f° = 0$ for all elements in their standard state [23].

For polyatomic molecules, there are two possible definitions for bond energy. For methane we might completely dissociate the molecule into atoms and then assign $\frac{1}{4}$ of the enthalpy change to each of the four C—H bonds, which gives an average bond energy, $\Delta H_{avg}°$. Alternatively, we might determine the enthalpy change for removal of just one of the hydrogen atoms at a time, which gives four different values for four C—H bond energies, called the bond dissociation energies, $DH°$. For methane, the average bond energy is 99.3 kcal/mole while the bond dissociation energies are 104, 106, 106, and 81 kcal/mole for the successive steps.

Table 5–6. Bond Dissociation Energies (in kcal/mole)*

Single Bonds

	H	F	Cl	Br	I	CH_3	C_2H_5	C_6H_5
H	104.2	135.8	103.0	87.5	71.3	104	98	103
F	135.8	38	61	60	58	108	106	116
Cl	103.0	61	58	52	50	83.5	81.5	
Br	87.5	60	52	46.0		70	69	72
I	71.3	58	50		36.1	56	53.5	
CH_3	104	108	83.5	70	56	88	85	93
CH_3CO	87.5	119	83.5		52.5	82	79	89
$CH_2{=}CH$	103		84			92	89	99
HO	119		60		56	91.5	91.5	103
NH_2	103						79	78	91

Multiple Bonds

	N	O	CH_2	CH
N	226	151		224
O	151	119.2		
H_2C		175	163	
HC	224			230
HN		115		
OC		127		
C		257		

* Taken from Benson [25].

The application of bond dissociation energies to the problem of evaluating resonance energies is restricted by the lack of data, and so average bond energies must be employed. The technique is to estimate an enthalpy change for a reaction using a model. Comparison of this value with the measured ΔH for the reaction gives the resonance energy. Since the heat of combustion is an easily measured quantity, we might choose combustion as the reaction, in which case nothing is gained by not using Klages' method.

Table 5–6 lists some bond dissociation energies. The methods of obtaining both bond dissociation energies and average bond energies have recently been reviewed [24, 25]. These sources should be consulted for details of measurements [24], for other applications [25], and for further references.

DELOCALIZATION ENERGIES

In computing delocalization energies we obtained values for stabilization due to the delocalization of π electrons. Delocalization leads to bond strengths greater than those in the localized model [26]. Setting the delocalization energy equal to the empirically obtained resonance energy is a convenient but misleading practice. We have already considered the fact that delocalization energies are true energies whereas resonance energies are obtained as changes in enthalpy. Unfortunately, the difficulty does not stop there.

To obtain the resonance energy for benzene, we used thermochemical data obtained from cyclohexene, which has bond lengths different from those of benzene; that is, we obtained resonance energies from a model with alternating single and double bond lengths:

The model used to obtain delocalization energies, on the other hand, was a Kekule structure with all bond lengths the same:

As we might expect, it is necessary to stretch the double bonds and compress the single bonds of the resonance energy model so that the resonance energy values correspond to the phenomenon used in obtaining delocalization energies. This deformation requires an energy term, the *distortion energy*. Having made this correction, we obtain the true stabilization energy caused by the delocalization of electrons, the *vertical resonance energy*. These relationships are illustrated in Fig. 5–3. The correction for distortion energy is, at best, a crude estimate and we will not consider here the values used for the computation. It suffices to say that the vertical resonance energy obtained in this manner must be greater than the empirical resonance energy because deformation of the model requires energy.

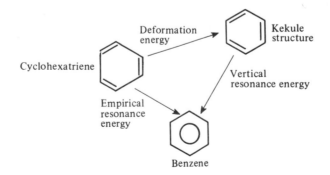

Fig. 5–3. Relationship of resonance energies of benzene using deformation energy.

To review briefly, we first considered that the difference between $3 \times \Delta H$ for hydrogenation of cyclohexene and the ΔH for hydrogenation of benzene was the resonance energy of benzene and that this might be duplicated by a theoretical calculation based upon the π electron system. We then added a distortion energy term to account for variations of bond strength with bond length. Dewar and Schmeising [27, 28] have pointed out a further change that has occurred in the thermochemical system. When cyclohexene is hydrogenated, two C—C bonds are converted from a bond between sp^2 and sp^3 hybrid carbon atoms to one between sp^3—sp^3 atoms. When benzene is hydrogenated, this change in hybridization is from sp^2—sp^2 to sp^3—sp^3 bonds. If these two types of σ bonds, sp^2—sp^3 and sp^2—sp^2, have different bond strengths, we must adjust the vertical resonance energy for this change, the hybridization energy. If an sp^2—sp^2 σ bond is stronger than the corresponding sp^2—sp^3 bond, a portion of the stabilization energy of benzene is due to the σ hybrid orbital bonds. Dewar and Schmeising [28] have calculated the π electron delocalization or vertical resonance energy using both of the corrections (distortion energy and hybridization energy) to be as low as 8.7 kcal/mole for benzene.

Although the details of this approach have been criticized [29, 30], it does point out the difficulty of relating delocalization energies to resonance energies. The correlation of these two quantities (see Fig. 4–1) is remarkably good, and, since it exists, we will continue to rely upon it, always keeping in mind the above theoretical problems.

Calculations of the above type reveal two features. First, π delocalization energies do exist for molecules with conjugated π systems but probably in an amount less than the empirical resonance energies suggest. Secondly, this stabilization is far more important for benzenoid aromatic hydrocarbons than for conjugated alkenes, like butadiene, for which only one classical structure can be drawn [27, 28].

THE $4N + 2$ RULE AND AROMATICITY

It was noted above that the benzenoid aromatic compounds have significantly greater resonance energies than conjugated alkenes. Hückel [31] offered a possible explanation for this based upon simple molecular orbital theory. He noted that when monocyclic conjugated π systems have $4N + 2$ π electrons all the bonding orbitals are just filled. On the other hand, those cyclic neutral conjugated systems with only $4N$ electrons have half-filled, nonbonding molecular orbitals. Examples of these two states are benzene with six π electrons $(4 \times 1 + 2)$ and cyclooctatetraene with eight π electrons $(4 \times 2 + 0)$. The energy levels for these are

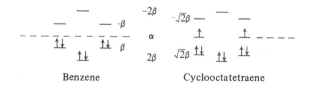

Benzene   Cyclooctatetraene

If each energy level is considered as a shell, the $4N + 2\,\pi$ systems are filled while the $4N$ systems are not. The filled shell configuration must be of considerable importance. The delocalization energy of cyclooctatetraene is less than that of benzene but it is still a rather large negative value. The simple molecular orbital treatment incorrectly predicts that all annulenes larger than cyclobutadiene are resonance-stabilized, and even correcting for distortion and hybridization energies does not markedly improve the prediction [32]. It is interesting to note, however, that the delocalization energy is more important for the $4N + 2$ systems (see Fig. 5–4).

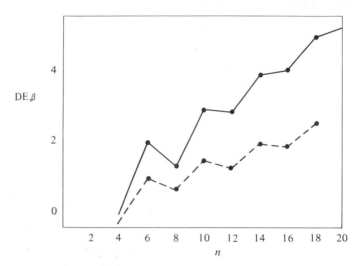

Fig. 5–4. Plot of delocalization energy of $(C—H)_n$ as a function of ring size. ———, Simple π approximation; – – – –, corrected for distortion and hybridization energies. (From Chung and Dewar [32].)

The closed or filled shell idea provided considerable stimulation for research on aromatic systems, which has led to the synthesis of several interesting systems. The simplest cyclic system fitting the $4N + 2$ rule is the cyclopropenyl cation. Although this particular cation has not been isolated, several substituted cyclopropenyl cations have been prepared, the simplest of these being the dipropylcyclopropenyl cation [33]. Systems with six π electrons have been known for a long time. Cyclopentadiene forms a potassium salt when treated with the metal giving the six-electron cyclopentadienyl anion [34], and benzene, of course, is isoelectronic with the cyclopentadienyl anion as well as with the cycloheptatrienyl cation. This remarkably stable cation, called the tropylium ion, is well known and has been thoroughly studied [35]. Other closed shell cyclic systems that have recently been prepared are the cyclooctatetraenyl dianion [36] and the cyclononatetraenyl anion [37, 38].

The annulenes are an interesting series of compounds with which to test the $4N + 2$ rule. Cyclooctatetraene, [8]annulene, does not fit the rule: it exists in a nonplanar conformation and has normal olefinic properties. [10]Annulene has not been prepared even though it has $4N + 2\pi$ electrons [39]. The bridged structures

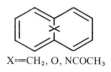

X=CH₂, O, NCOCH₃

have been prepared and appear to exhibit aromatic properties [40–43]. [12]Annulene does not fit the rule and attempts to prepare it have produced equivocal results [44]. Although [14]annulene fits the rule and has been prepared [45], it is not aromatic. The compound is not planar as required by Hückel's rule, presumably because of crowding of the internal hydrogen atoms:

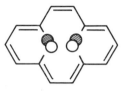

Both dehydro-[14]annulene and bisdehydro-[14]annulene have been prepared [46, 47] and exhibit aromatic character [48] even though the dehydro compound has internal hydrogens.

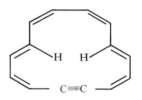

By replacing the internal hydrogen atoms of [14]annulene, the unstrained, planar, stable compound

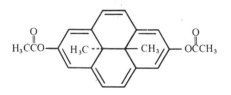

has been prepared [49]. Although several other annulenes have been studied, perhaps the most significant results are that the [18] and [22]annulenes are aromatic but the larger [30]annulene is not [48]. Of course, [30]annulene fits the $4N + 2$ rule, so our simple theory has again failed but not without opening a whole new area of organic chemistry. It is pertinent to add that an advanced molecular orbital calculation [50] successfully predicts that the $4N + 2$ annulenes up to and including [22]annulene are aromatic while the larger rings are not. This method also successfully predicts that the $4N$ annulenes are nonaromatic.

The $4N + 2$ rule was not intended for polycyclic systems and should not be expected to apply to them. Many stable polycyclic aromatics are known with only $4N$ electrons, e.g. biphenylene and fluoranthene. Considerable success has been achieved by considering only the peripheral π electrons as those of an annulene, or groups of annulenes, linked by σ bonds. If the perturbations caused by these cross-links are small, the $4N + 2$ rule can be applied to the peripheral π system. In this manner, biphenylene can be considered as two benzene rings and fluoranthene as a six- and a ten-electron system connected together.

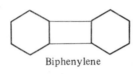

Biphenylene

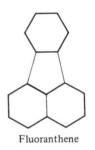

Fluoranthene

PROBLEMS

1. Compute the heats of reaction for each of the following:
   a) $H_2 + F_2 \rightarrow 2HF$
   b) $CH_4 + Cl_2 \rightarrow CH_3Cl + HCl$
   c) $C_6H_6 + Br_2 \rightarrow C_6H_5Br + HBr$

2. Compute the resonance energy of naphthalene from the gas phase heat of hydrogenation value of 82 kcal/mole.

3. a) Compute the resonance energy of cyclooctatetraene from the heat of combustion of 1095 kcal at 25°C.
   b) Is this value consistent with the geometry of the molecule? Explain.

4. Dimethylfulvene has a greater resonance energy than an acyclic triene and has a large dipole moment. Predict the direction of the dipole and explain.

Dimethylfulvene

5. a) Suggest several reasons why the resonance energy of biphenylene (59 kcal) is less than twice the value for benzene.

b) The bond distances for biphenylene are

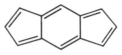

Explain these in the terms used in 5a.

6. Would *s*-indacene exhibit aromatic properties? Predict the products when *s*-indacene is treated with: a) methyl lithium; b) sodium in liquid ammonia.

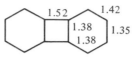

s-Indacene

7. Would pentalene be a stable aromatic system? Explain. The pentalenyl dianion has been prepared and is found to be stable. How can this be explained?

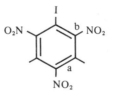

Pentalene

8. Compute the π bonding energy for the cyclopropyl cation, radical, and anion by the HMO procedure.

9. The bond length of bond a in picryl iodide is 1.35 Å, that of bond b is 1.45 Å. Explain

Picryl iodide

REFERENCES

1. G. B. KISTIAKOWSKY, H. ROMEYN, J. R. RUHOFF, E. A. SMITH, and W. E. VAUGHAN, *J. Am. Chem. Soc.*, **57**, 65 (1935).
2. G. B. KISTIAKOWSKY, J. R. RUHOFF, E. A. SMITH, and W. E. VAUGHAN, *J. Am. Chem. Soc.*, **57**, 876 (1935).
3. G. B. KISTIAKOWSKY, J. R. RUHOFF, E. A. SMITH, and W. E. VAUGHAN, *J. Am. Chem. Soc.*, **58**, 137 (1936).
4. G. B. KISTIAKOWSKY, J. R. RUHOFF, E. A. SMITH, and W. E. VAUGHAN, *J. Am. Chem. Soc.*, **58**, 146 (1936).
5. M. A. DOLLIVER, T. L. GRESHAM, G. B. KISTIAKOWSKY, and W. E. VAUGHAN, *J. Am. Chem. Soc.*, **59**, 831 (1937).
6. M. A. DOLLIVER, T. L. GRESHAM, G. B. KISTIAKOWSKY, E. A. SMITH, and W. E. VAUGHAN, *J. Am. Chem. Soc.*, **60**, 440 (1938).
7. J. B. CONN, G. B. KISTIAKOWSKY, and E. A. SMITH, *J. Am. Chem. Soc.*, **60**, 2764 (1938).

8. J. B. Conn, G. B. Kistiakowsky, and E. A. Smith, *J. Am. Chem. Soc.*, **61**, 1868 (1939).
9. For complete tables see: G. W. Wheland, *Resonance in Organic Chemistry*, John Wiley & Sons, New York (1955), Chap. 3.
10. R. B. Williams, *J. Am. Chem. Soc.*, **64**, 1395 (1942).
11. R. B. Turner, W. R. Meador, and R. E. Winkler, *J. Am. Chem. Soc.*, **79**, 4116 (1957).
12. J. B. Conant and G. B. Kistiakowsky, *Chem. Revs.*, **20**, 181 (1937).
13. R. B. Turner and R. H. Garner, *J. Am. Chem. Soc.*, **80**, 1424 (1958).
14. R. B. Turner and W. R. Meador, *J. Am. Chem. Soc.*, **79**, 4133 (1957).
15. R. B. Turner, W. R. Meador, W. von E. Doering, L. H. Knox, J. R. Mayer, and D. W. Wiley, *J. Am. Chem. Soc.*, **79**, 4127 (1957).
16. W. R. Roth, W. B. Bang, P. Goebel, R. L. Sass, R. B. Turner, and A. P. Yue, *J. Am. Chem. Soc.*, **86**, 3178 (1964).
17. R. B. Turner, *J. Am. Chem. Soc.*, **86**, 3586 (1964).
18. H. A. Skinner and A. Snelson, *Trans. Faraday Soc.*, **55**, 404 (1959).
19. R. B. Turner, D. E. Nettleton, Jr., and M. Perelman, *J. Am. Chem. Soc.*, **80**, 1430 (1958).
20. R. B. Turner, W. R. Meador, and R. E. Winkler, *J. Am. Chem. Soc.*, **79**, 4122 (1957).
21. R. B. Turner, H. Prinzbach, and W. von E. Doering, *J. Am. Chem. Soc.*, **82**, 3451 (1960).
22. F. Klages, *Chem. Ber.*, **82**, 358 (1949).
23. JANAF Interim Thermochemical Tables (1960–1965).
24. T. L. Cottrell, *The Strengths of Chemical Bonds*, Butterworth and Co., London (1958).
25. S. W. Benson, *J. Chem. Ed.*, **42**, 502 (1965).
26. A. Streitwieser, Jr., *Molecular Orbital Theory for Organic Chemists*, John Wiley & Sons, New York (1961).
27. M. J. S. Dewar and H. N. Schmeising, *Tetrahedron*, **5**, 166 (1959).
28. M. J. S. Dewar and H. N. Schmeising, *Tetrahedron*, **11**, 96 (1960).
29. R. S. Mulliken, *Tetrahedron*, **6**, 68 (1959).
30. W. F. Yates, *J. Phys. Chem.*, **65**, 185 (1961).
31. E. Hückel, *Z. Physik*, **70**, 204 (1931).
32. A. L. H. Chung and M. J. S. Dewar, *J. Chem. Phys.*, **42**, 756 (1965).
33. R. Breslow, H. Hover, and H. W. Chang, *J. Am. Chem. Soc.*, **84**, 3168 (1962).
34. J. Thiele, *Chem. Ber.*, **34**, 68 (1901).
35. See N. C. Deno, "Carbonium Ions," in *Progress in Physical Organic Chemistry*, Vol. 2 (Eds. S. G. Cohen, A. Streitwieser, Jr., and R. W. Taft), Interscience Publishers, New York (1964).
36. T. J. Katz, *J. Am. Chem. Soc.*, **82**, 3784 and 3785 (1960), and subsequent papers by this author.
37. T. J. Katz and P. J. Garratt, *J. Am. Chem. Soc.*, **85**, 2852 (1963).
38. E. A. LaLancette and R. E. Benson, *J. Am. Chem. Soc.*, **85**, 2853 (1963).
39. E. E. vanTamelen and B. Pappas, *J. Am. Chem. Soc.*, **85**, 3296 (1963).
40. E. Vogel and H. D. Roth, *Angew. Chem., Int. Ed.*, **3**, 228 (1964).
41. E. Vogel and W. A. Boll, *Angew. Chem., Int. Ed.*, **3**, 642 (1964).

42. E. VOGEL, M. BISKUP, W. PRETZER, and W. A. BOLL, *Angew. Chem., Int. Ed.*, **3,** 642 (1964).
43. F. SONDHEIMER and A. SHANI, *J. Am. Chem. Soc.*, **86,** 3168 (1964).
44. Y. GAONI and F. SONDHEIMER, *Proc. Chem. Soc.*, 299 (1964).
45. R. WOLOVSKY and F. SONDHEIMER, *J. Am. Chem. Soc.*, **87,** 5720 (1965).
46. F. SONDHEIMER and Y. GAONI, *J. Am. Chem. Soc.*, **82,** 5765 (1960).
47. F. SONDHEIMER, Y. GAONI, L. M. JACKMAN, N. A. BAILEY, and R. MASON, *J. Am. Chem. Soc.*, **84,** 4595 (1962).
48. L. M. JACKMAN, F. SONDHEIMER, Y. AMIEL, D. A. BEN-EFRIAM, Y. GAONI, and A. A. BOTHNER-BY, *J. Am. Chem. Soc.*, **84,** 4307 (1962).
49. V. BOEKELHEIDE and J. B. PHILLIPS, *J. Am. Chem. Soc.*, **85,** 1545 (1963).
50. M. J. S. DEWAR AND G. J. GLEICHER, *J. Am. Chem. Soc.*, **87,** 685 (1965).

CHAPTER 6

PHENOMENOLOGY OF CHEMICAL KINETICS

Chemical kinetics is the study of systems whose properties are a function of time. The field is concerned with the rates of reactions, with all the factors that affect them, and with the explanation of both in terms of the reaction mechanism.

For the organic chemist, an understanding of chemical kinetics is of twofold importance. Since most organic reactions involve several competing reactions, if the chemist understands the variables controlling them, he can frequently direct the course of the reaction and thereby obtain a desired product. A typical case of this control is the well-known sulfonation reaction of naphthalene, in which the position of substitution is highly temperature-dependent. Of perhaps greater immediate interest to the physical organic chemist is the fact that chemical kinetics provides one of the best general methods of determining a reaction mechanism. Although kinetics cannot be used alone to determine a reaction mechanism, neither can a mechanism be determined fully without a detailed kinetic investigation (see Chapter 11).

In this chapter we will examine chemical kinetics from a purely experimental viewpoint, looking at the mathematical forms commonly used to describe the kinetic system and the experimental determination of these forms.

ORDER OF REACTION AND MOLECULARITY

In investigating reaction rates, we attempt to isolate all of the variables affecting the rate of the reaction and to study each factor separately. Because temperature is an easily controlled variable, rate studies are normally made at a constant temperature. Trace impurities may cause marked changes in rates so that pure materials must be used and the role of any impurities that are present, e.g. water, oxygen, carbon dioxide, should be determined. The ionic strength of the solution and the pH of the medium may also play important roles in determining the reaction rate, and, to further complicate the study, these factors may vary as a reaction proceeds. To minimize any changes in ionic strength or pH, salts and buffers can be added and the reaction carried out at low reactant concentrations. Even these precautions are not enough. We must also know the exact stoichiometric equation that describes the reaction. If it is a single stoichiometric equation, we can define a unique reaction rate. If not, the reaction is complex and must be treated as such. For the moment, let us work with simple reactions.

The *reaction rate* is usually defined as the rate of change of the concentration of a reactant or product. This is written with a minus or plus sign to indicate disappearance or appearance of the particular material so that the rate will always have a positive value. If a simple stoichiometric reaction may be written as

$$aA + bB = cC + dD,$$

the rate is expressed as

$$-d[A]/dt, \qquad -d[B]/dt, \qquad d[C]/dt, \qquad \text{or} \qquad d[D]/dt,$$

where $[A]$, $[B]$, $[C]$, and $[D]$ are in concentration units and t is time. It is apparent that $-d[A]/dt$ is not equal to $-d[B]/dt$ unless they react in a one-to-one ratio, that is, $a = b$. So that the rate of reaction will have the same value no matter what species we discuss, we can divide each term by its stoichiometric coefficient. The rate of reaction is then defined as

$$\text{rate} = -\frac{1}{a}d[A]/dt = -\frac{1}{b}d[B]/dt = \frac{1}{c}d[C]/dt = \frac{1}{d}d[D]/dt.$$

Empirically, we find that most reactions fit a rate equation of the form

$$\text{rate} = k[A]^m[B]^n. \tag{6-1}$$

The values of m and n, the exponents of the concentrations of A and B, must be determined experimentally. For this type of rate equation, the sum of the exponents $m + n$ is called the *order of reaction*. We may also talk about the order in any reactant. Thus the reaction is $m + n$ order, mth order in A and nth order in B. The stoichiometry of the reaction does not determine the reaction order and we will usually find that $a \neq m$ and $b \neq n$. If the rate study is carried out in such a manner that one (or more) of the concentration factors does not change or changes only insignificantly, this unchanging factor may be included in the proportionality constant k and the reaction is said to be of a pseudo order. If, for example, reactant B is present in large concentration relative to A in our general reaction or if B is a catalyst at constant concentration, Eq. (6-1) may be rewritten as

$$\text{rate} = k'[A]^m$$

and the reaction is pseudo mth order. Such a case is the acid-catalyzed esterification reaction

$$CH_3CO_2H + CH_3CH_2OH \xrightarrow{H^+} CH_3CO_2CH_2CH_3 + H_2O.$$

The complete rate expression obtained experimentally is

$$d[CH_3CO_2C_2H_5]/dt = k[CH_3CO_2H][CH_3CH_2OH][H^+],$$

which is a third-order reaction, but because ethanol is normally used as the solvent, its concentration is essentially constant, and because the acid concentration does not change, the reaction is pseudo first-order.

The values of the exponents in Eq. (6–1) are usually small whole numbers. Because of this, it is easy to get the order of reaction and the molecularity of the reaction confused. The *molecularity of a reaction* is a theoretical concept that describes the number of particles taking part in a collision. A bimolecular reaction is frequently also a second-order reaction but the reverse statement is not necessarily true. Similarly, a termolecular process is usually a third-order one but most third-order reactions are not termolecular. The acid-catalyzed esterification reaction, for example, is a third-order reaction; it occurs, however, in a series of steps none of which is termolecular.

To obtain a value for the rate of reaction, we normally follow the change in concentration of one or more of the materials present as a function of time. The concentration data do not give the rate of reaction directly, but from them we can obtain the value of k, the specific rate constant, using integrated forms of the rate expressions. Because simple-order kinetic expressions are so frequently observed, we will first examine several of these in detail.

Zero-Order Reactions

According to our convention, a zero-order reaction is one whose rate is independent of the concentrations of the reactants, so that their rate of change is a constant. The rate expression is given by

$$\text{rate} = -d[A]/dt = k. \tag{6–2}$$

Zero-order kinetics are very rarely observed. The known cases involve reactions where the rate is determined by some limiting factor other than concentration. If, for example, a reaction occurs on a metal surface which becomes saturated, further addition of material will not change the surface concentration and the reaction rate will appear to be independent of the concentration.

First-Order Reactions

The rate expression for a first-order reaction is given by Eq. (6–3) where, as usual, $[A]$ refers to the concentration of A:

$$\text{rate} = -d[A]/dt = k[A]. \tag{6–3}$$

Rearrangement of the terms of Eq. (6–3) gives

$$d[A]/[A] = -kdt,$$

which can be integrated to give

$$-\ln [A] = kt + \text{constant}, \tag{6–4}$$

and

$$-2.303 \log [A] = kt + \text{constant}. \tag{6–5}$$

It is apparent that a plot of ln $[A]$ or 2.303 log $[A]$ against t will give a straight line whose slope is equal to $-k$. Thus, if we measure the concentration of the reactant at known times, we can obtain a value of k by graphical methods. The value of the integration constant is determined by the experimental conditions.

Equations (6–4) and (6–5) can be modified to eliminate the constant of integration by integrating between limits which are selected in a straightforward manner. If the concentration of A is $[A_1]$ at some time t_1, it will have some other value $[A_2]$ at a later time t_2. Employing these limits in the integration of Eq. (6–3) yields the convenient forms

$$- \int_{A_1}^{A_2} d[A]/[A] = k \int_{t_1}^{t_2} dt$$
$$- \ln [A_2] - (-\ln [A_1]) = k(t_2 - t_1)$$
$$\ln [A_1]/[A_2] = k(t_2 - t_1). \tag{6-6}$$

and

$$2.303 \log [A_1]/[A_2] = k(t_2 - t_1). \tag{6-7}$$

If we set the initial time $t_1 = 0$, the concentration of A at $t = 0$ will be the initial concentration $[A_0]$ and $t_2 - t_1$ will simply be the elapsed time t. Equation (6–6) is thus reduced to

$$\ln [A]/[A_0] = -kt. \tag{6-6a}$$

The integrated rate expression for first-order kinetics may be obtained in yet another form. We will let A_0 be the initial number of moles of A in a given volume and define a quantity X as the number of moles of A reacting in time t so that the concentration of A at time t is given by $[A_0 - X]$. Equation (6–3) may be rewritten in these terms as

$$- d[A]/dt = -d[A_0 - X]/dt = dX/dt = k[A_0 - X]. \tag{6-8}$$

Integration of Eq. (6–8) between the limits of $[A] = [A_0 - X_1]$ at t_1 and $[A_2] = [A_2 - X_2]$ at any other time t_2 gives

$$\ln [A_0 - X_1]/[A_0 - X_2] = k(t_2 - t_1). \tag{6-9}$$

This equation may be simplified by the condition that $X = 0$ at $t = 0$:

$$\ln A_0/[A_0 - X] = kt. \tag{6-10}$$

Equations (6–9) and (6–10) are particularly useful when the experimental rate determination is made by following the formation of a product.

The equations developed above are all in the form of linear equations. Three methods of plotting experimental data for a first-order reaction are shown in Fig. 6–1.

Second-Order Reactions

The rate law for a second-order reaction may take two forms. One form is observed when the reaction is first-order in each of two reactants. The rate equation is given

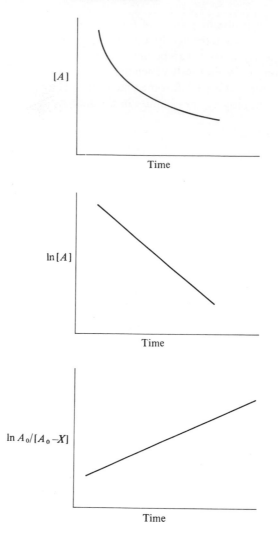

Fig. 6–1. Three ways of plotting data for a first-order reaction.

by Eq. (6–11), where $[A]$ and $[B]$ are the concentrations of the two reactants A and B for the reaction $A + B \rightarrow$ products, i.e. one-to-one stoichiometry:

$$\text{rate} = -d[A]/dt = -d[B]/dt = k[A][B]. \tag{6–11}$$

Again, if A_0 and B_0 are the initial molar concentrations of A and B and X is the number of moles per liter that react in time t, Eq. (6–11) can be rewritten as

$$dX/dt = k[A_0 - X][B_0 - X]. \tag{6–12}$$

Integration of Eq. (6–12) yields

$$(1/[A_0 - B_0]) \ln B_0[A_0 - X]/A_0[B_0 - X] = kt. \tag{6–13}$$

The use of Eq. (6–13) is, of course, limited to those reactions that involve a stoichiometry of 1:1. A reaction of different stoichiometry must be accounted for in Eq. (6–12), by writing $[A] = [A_0 - 2X]$ if the two moles of A react with one of B, and so forth.

The integrated expression for the second-order rate, Eq. (6–13), can be simplified if the two substances are present in stoichiometric concentration, i.e., $A_0 = B_0$ if 1:1, $2A_0 = B_0$ if 2:1, etc. For our case of 1:1 stoichiometry, the rate equation becomes

$$dx/dt = k[A_0 - X]^2. \tag{6–14}$$

Integration and elimination of the integration constant affords the special expression Eq. (6–15), where the usual notation applies:

$$1/[A_0 - X] - 1/A_0 = kt. \tag{6–15}$$

This equation is also appropriate for the second type of second-order reaction, in which the reaction rate depends upon the square of the concentration of a single reagent, A:

$$\text{rate} = -d[A]/dt = k[A]^2.$$

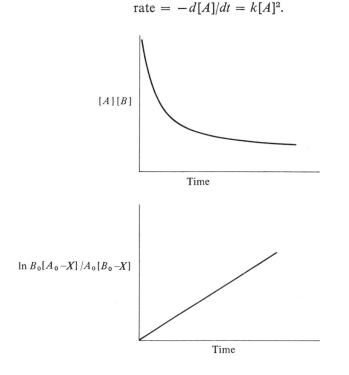

Fig. 6–2. Two ways of plotting data for a second-order reaction

For most purposes Eqs. (6–13) or (6–15) may be used to determine the rate constant of a second-order reaction; both are in the form of a linear equation and a graphical solution may be used. They are not appropriate, however, when the stoichiometric concentration of A is near, but not equal to, that of B. In this case, Eq. (6–13) is not useful because the logarithmic term will not vary much with time and the equation becomes insensitive. For this special case, the reader should consult any standard text on chemical kinetics. Two methods of plotting experimental data for a second-order reaction are shown in Fig. 6–2.

Third-Order Reactions

Third-order rate expressions may also take more than one form. From our definition of reaction order we can see that third-order reactions may depend upon a single reactant raised to the third power, upon two reactants of which one is first-order and the other second-order, or upon three reactants all raised to the first power. The respective rate expressions for these three cases are given by

$$-d[A]/dt = k[A]^3, \tag{6–16}$$

$$-d[A]/dt = k[A][B]^2, \tag{6–17}$$

$$-d[A]/dt = k[A][B][C]. \tag{6–18}$$

These equations are treated exactly like those for first- and second-order reactions. For the simplest case, Eq. (6–16), the integrated equations are given by Eq. (6–19) without further development, and the reader will recognize that Eq. (6–18) can be reduced to Eq. (6–16) by arranging the experiment so that the concentrations of A, B, and C are stoichiometrically equal:

$$1/2[A]^2 - 1/2[A_0]^2 = kt,$$
$$1/2[A_0 - X]^2 - 1/2[A_0]^2 = kt. \tag{6–19}$$

In summary, the equations developed above are for those reactions that show a 1:1 stoichiometric ratio for the reactants. If another ratio is followed, an appropriate allowance must be made in the differential rate equation before it is integrated. The equations may be used to obtain the value of the specific rate constant provided we know the order of the reaction. As has been shown, we can sometimes obtain this by plotting the data and obtaining a straight line, the slope of which gives the value of k.

The units of the specific rate constant depend upon the reaction order, as shown by examination of the integrated rate equations. Since concentrations are normally expressed in moles per liter, the units normally used for specific rate constants are moles and liters. Time is expressed as seconds, minutes, or hours, and any of these may be used for the specific rate constant. Any value can be converted from one set of units to another by means of appropriate conversion factors. Common units of specific rate constants for several different orders of reaction are given in Table 6–1.

The kinetics just discussed are for reactions that can be described in terms of the reaction order. In practice, however, there are many reactions that cannot be described by such a simple method. In general, these *complex reactions* proceed to

Table 6-1. Units of Specific Rate Constants

	Total Reduction Reaction Order			
	Zero	First	Second	Third
Units of k	moles / liter-sec	1/sec	liters / mole-sec	liters^2 / mole^2-sec

completion by more than one process and take several forms. The reaction may be reversible so that an equilibrium mixture is obtained upon completion, leading to an apparent decrease in rate: the concentrations of the products increase as the reaction proceeds and the rate of the reverse reaction increases as a result until the rates become equal at equilibrium. Again, we can expect complex kinetics if the reaction under study proceeds step by step—i.e., the reactants do not form the products directly but rather produce an intermediate that undergoes a further reaction—a very common situation. Finally, if the reactants can combine in more than one way to give different products, the competing reactions may appear to change from one kinetic expression to another as conditions are altered. We will examine only a few of the more common examples of complex kinetics.

Reversible Reactions

Many reactions proceed to an equilibrium mixture of reactants and products. To evaluate the rate constant of such reactions we must consider the rate of both the reverse and the forward reaction. In the simplest case the reaction is first-order in each direction:

$$A \underset{k_{-1}}{\overset{k_1}{\rightleftharpoons}} B.$$

The rate of this reaction can be written as

$$-d[A]/dt = d[B]/dt = k_1[A] - k_{-1}[B]. \tag{6-20}$$

If at the start of the reaction only species A is present, the concentration of B at any time will be

$$[A_0] - [A] = [B]$$

and Eq. (6-20) can be written entirely in terms of the initial, $[A_0]$, and the instantaneous, $[A]$, concentrations of A:

$$-d[A]/dt = k_1[A] - k_{-1}([A_0] - [A])$$
$$= (k_1 + k_{-1})[A] - k_{-1}[A_0].$$

Integration gives

$$\ln k_1[A_0]/[(k_1 + k_{-1})[A] - k_{-1}[A_0]] = (k_1 + k_{-1})t. \tag{6-21}$$

At equilibrium the rates of the two reactions are equal, so that

$$k_1[A_e] = k_{-1}[B_e] = k_{-1}([A_0] - [A_e]),$$

where the subscript e refers to the equilibrium concentration. Equation (6–21) is then simplified to

$$\ln ([A_0] - [A_e])/([A] - [A_e]) = (k_1 + k_{-1})t. \tag{6–22}$$

Thus, the reaction appears to be a first-order process as it approaches equilibrium but the rate constant being evaluated is actually the sum of the constants for the forward and reverse reactions. Equation (6–22) permits evaluation of the individual rate constants since the sum $k_1 + k_{-1}$ can be measured and the ratio $k_1/k_{-1} = K$, the equilibrium constant, is also known.

A similar treatment will also resolve two higher-order equilibrium reactions, which will not be developed here. In the case of a first-order reaction opposed by a second-order one, Eq. (6–23) results:

$$A \underset{k_{-1}}{\overset{k_1}{\rightleftharpoons}} B + C,$$
$$-d[A]/dt = k_1[A] - k_{-1}[B][C]. \tag{6–23}$$

By using the same symbols as for the first-order reversible reaction, we can obtain the integrated form of Eq. (6–23):

$$\frac{[A_0] - [A_e]}{[A_0] + [A_e]} \ln \left[\frac{[A_0]^2 - [A_e][A]}{[A_0][A] - [A_0][A_e]} \right] = k_1 t. \tag{6–24}$$

The equilibrium condition gives:

$$k_{-1} = k_1[A_e]/([A_0] - [A_e])^2.$$

For opposing second-order reactions the equations become more difficult to work with:

$$A + B \underset{k_{-1}}{\overset{k_1}{\rightleftharpoons}} C + D,$$
$$-d[A]/dt = k_1[A][B] - k_{-1}[C][D].$$

Although the integrated rate equation for this case is quite lengthy, the data can be plotted and the values of k_1 and k_{-1} obtained if the equilibrium constant is known.

Consecutive Reactions

A commonly observed kinetic system is one in which two successive first-order reactions form a product. In general terms, the overall observed reaction is

$$A \rightarrow C,$$

but it occurs in two steps by forming the reactive intermediate, B:

$$A \xrightarrow{k_1} B$$
$$B \xrightarrow{k_2} C.$$

We can write the rate equations based upon each material:

$$-d[A]/dt = k_1[A], \tag{6-25}$$

$$d[B]/dt = k_1[A] - k_2[B], \tag{6-26}$$

$$d[C]/dt = k_2[B]. \tag{6-27}$$

Equation (6–25) is simply that of a first-order reaction. Its solution is given by Eq. (6–6a) and can be written in exponential form and solved for $[A]$:

$$\ln [A]/[A_0] = -k_1t, \tag{6-6a}$$

$$[A] = [A_0] \exp (-k_1t). \tag{6-28}$$

This equation may be substituted into Eq. (6–26):

$$d[B]/dt = k_1[A_0] \exp -k_1t - k_2[B].$$

Integration of this linear first-order equation, with the usual condition of $[B_0] = 0$, affords

$$[B] = \frac{([A_0]k_1)}{(k_2 - k_1)} [\exp (-k_1t) - \exp (-k_2t)]. \tag{6-29}$$

To obtain $[C]$, we use the stoichiometric relationship that the sum of the concentrations must equal $[A_0]$ if only A is present initially:

$$[C] = [A_0] - [A] - [B].$$

The behavior of the concentrations of each species is shown in Fig. 6–3. The particular shape of each curve will depend upon the values of k_1 and k_2. This is easily seen by obtaining the maximum concentration of the intermediate, B. We set the first derivative of Eq. (6–29) equal to zero:

$$d[B]/dt = \frac{A_0k_1}{k_2 - k_1} (k_2 \, e^{-k_2t} - k_1 \, e^{-k_1t}) = 0.$$

Because $[A_0]k_1/(k_2 - k_1)$ will normally not be zero, we can set

$$k_2 \, e^{-k_2t} - k_1 \, e^{-k_1t} = 0,$$

and solve for t:

$$\ln k_2/k_1 = k_2t - k_1t,$$

$$t = [1/(k_2 - k_1)] \ln k_2/k_1.$$

It is readily noted that as k_1 decreases in respect to k_2, the time for the maximum concentration of B decreases. If $k_1 \gg k_2$, the reaction occurs in two distinct steps whereas if $k_1 \ll k_2$, the concentration of B becomes negligible. We shall make use of this latter fact shortly.

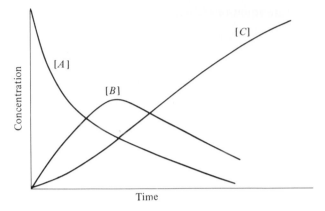

Fig. 6–3. Changes in concentrations for consecutive first-order reactions.

Competitive Reactions

A reactant may undergo more than one reaction under a given set of conditions. Similarly, it may undergo reaction with more than one other reactant, producing different products, or an intermediate formed during a reaction may react further by more than one path. These competitive reactions can be a serious problem to a synthetic organic chemist or to a chemist attempting an analysis by functional group methods, but for the physical organic chemist they can frequently be used to answer problems that are otherwise experimentally very difficult or impossible to deal with. Reactions that are too fast or whose kinetics are too complex to permit accurate evaluation of absolute rate constants can be studied by competitive methods, for example, the nitration of reactive aromatic compounds (see Chapter 12). The chemical properties of reactive intermediates such as carbonium ions and free radicals have also been studied by competitive methods. Kinetic isotope effects (Chapter 8) are frequently examined by competitive methods. Because of the applications that have been developed for mechanistic studies, we will spend somewhat more time on competitive rates than we have on other complex situations.

The simplest case of a competitive reaction is a reactant that decomposes by two paths:

$$A \xrightarrow{k_1} B$$

$$A \xrightarrow{k_2} C.$$

If the rate is followed by the disappearance of A, the rate equation is given by

$$-d[A]/dt = k_1[A] + k_2[A] = (k_1 + k_2)[A] = k_{obs}[A]. \qquad (6–30)$$

This is simply a first-order reaction and Eq. (6–6a) applies. The observed rate constant is the sum of the specific rate constants $k_1 + k_2$. If the formation of B can be followed experimentally, we can obtain a value for k_1 and hence for k_2 as well:

$$d[B]/dt = k_1[A].$$

Of course, if absolute rates can be determined there is no point in obtaining a ratio of rate constants, k_1/k_2. If we wish to study reactions for which this is impossible or impractical, we might ask how to obtain the relative rates for the system we are discussing. The method is straightforward. We write the rate expressions for each path:

$$d[B]/dt = k_1[A],$$
$$d[C]/dt = k_2[A].$$

Rearrangement affords two equations that can be set equal:

$$d[B]/k_1 = [A]dt,$$
$$d[C]/k_2 = [A]dt,$$
$$d[B]/k_1 = d[C]/k_2$$

Integration, with the restriction that B and C are not initially present, shows that the rate constants are related in the same way as the product concentrations:

$$[B]/k_1 = [C]/k_2,$$
$$k_1/k_2 = [B]/[C].$$

Since both concentration terms are in moles per liter and both reactions occur in the same solution, the ratio k_1/k_2 is simply equal to the moles of A/moles of B produced.

A second case of competitive reactions involves parallel first-order (or pseudo first-order) and second-order reactions such as competition between solvolytic and displacement reactions:

$$A \xrightarrow{k_1} C$$
$$A + B \xrightarrow{k_2} C.$$

For this case we write the rate expression as

$$-d[A]/dt = k_1[A] + k_2[A][B], \tag{6--31}$$

which can be integrated to give the complex equation

$$\ln \frac{[A_0]}{[A]} \cdot \frac{k_1 + k_2[B]}{k_1 + k_2[B_0]} = (k_1 + k_2[B_0 - A_0])t,$$

but it is not very useful for determining values of k_1 and k_2. Taking another approach, we write the rate expression for disappearance of B as

$$-d[B]/dt = k_2[A][B]. \tag{6--32}$$

If we divide Eq. (6--31) by (6--32) we get

$$d[A]/d[B] = \frac{k_1 + k_2[B]}{k_2[B]} = k_1/k_2[B] + 1,$$

which can be integrated to give Eq. (6–33), relating initial and instantaneous concentrations to the ratio of the rate constants:

$$[A] - [A_0] = (k_1/k_2) \ln [B]/[B_0] + [B] - [B_0]. \qquad (6\text{–}33)$$

The ratio of k_1/k_2 can be obtained simply by knowing the concentrations of the reactants initially and at some later time.

The last case we will consider is that of competitive second-order reactions in which two reagents are competing for a third:

$$A + B \xrightarrow{k_1} D$$
$$A + C \xrightarrow{k_2} E$$

This system is commonly used in mechanistic studies, especially where A represents a reactive intermediate so that its concentration is not known. This, of course, precludes evaluation of the absolute rate constants and we must be satisfied with relative values.

The differential rate expressions for the two reactions may be written as

$$-d[B]/dt = k_1[A][B],$$
$$-d[C]/dt = k_2[A][C].$$

Division of the first by the second gives

$$d[B]/d[C] = \frac{k_1[B]}{k_2[C]},$$

and integration, with the initial conditions of $[B] = [B_0]$ and $[C] = [C_0]$, yields

$$k_1/k_2 = \frac{\ln [B]/[B_0]}{\ln [C]/[C_0]}, \qquad (6\text{–}34)$$

Since $[B] = [B_0] - [D]$ and $[C] = [C_0] - [E]$, we can rewrite Eq. (6–34) in terms of concentrations of the initial reactants and products:

$$k_1/k_2 = \frac{\ln ([B_0] - [D])/[B_0]}{\ln ([C_0] - [E])/[C_0]} = \frac{\ln (1 - [D]/[B_0])}{\ln (1 - [E]/[C_0])}. \qquad (6\text{–}35)$$

Thus, for this competitive situation we can evaluate the ratio k_1/k_2 if we know the initial concentrations of the reactants and the concentrations of either the reactants or the products at any later time, usually taken as when the reaction is completed. Because the equations are extremely sensitive as $[B]$ and $[C]$ approach zero or as $[D]$ approaches $[B_0]$ and $[E]$ approaches $[C_0]$, the relative rates are normally determined by using a large (fivefold or greater) excess of each of the competing reagents. The sensitivity of the function Eq. (6–34) is shown in Fig. 6–4; if the rates are very different and excess reagents are not used, one of them will react completely (within practical limits) before the common reagent is consumed.

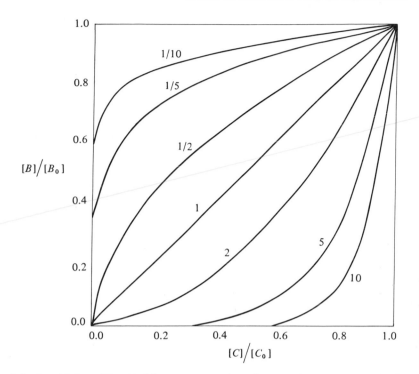

Fig. 6–4. Sensitivity of Eq. (6–34) to consumption of competing reactants. The figures on the curves are values of k_1/k_2.

Autocatalytic Reactions

Reactions that are catalyzed by one of the products of the reaction are called autocatalytic. They exhibit a stoichiometry of the type

$$A \rightarrow B + C.$$

The rate expression, on the other hand, is second-order:

$$-d[A]/dt = k[A][B].$$

Before integrating this expression, it is convenient to put the concentration terms in another form. If X moles of A have reacted, the concentration of A will be $([A_0] - X)$, but when X moles of A react, X moles of B are produced, so that the instantaneous concentration of B will be given by $([B_0] + X)$. The rate equation can be written as

$$-d[A]/dt = dx/dt = k([A_0] - X)([B_0] + X).$$

Integration affords

$$\frac{1}{[A_0] + [B_0]} \ln \frac{([B_0] + X)[A_0]}{([A_0] + X)[B_0]} = kt,$$

which can be rewritten as

$$\frac{1}{[A_0] + [B_0]} \ln \frac{[A_0 B]}{[AB_0]} = kt. \qquad (6\text{--}36)$$

The value of k can again be obtained graphically.

By solving Eq. (6–36) for $[B]$ and plotting $[B]$ as a function of time, we find a sigmoid curve typical of autocatalytic reactions (Fig. 6–5).

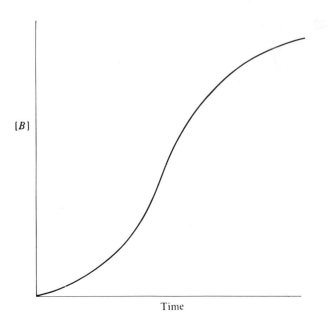

$[B]$

Time

Fig. 6–5. Changes in catalyst concentration with time for autocatalytic reactions.

EXPERIMENTAL METHODS

Now that we have developed mathematical equations that express rates, we must decide how to obtain data. Actually, we do not determine rates of reaction directly but rather concentrations as a function of time. The measurement of time is usually not a problem; for most purposes, a stopwatch or electronic timer will provide sufficiently accurate measurement. The measurement of concentrations, however, must be carefully done so that the results are accurate and can be obtained quickly.

The analytical part of any kinetic experiment is limited only by the investigator's imagination. Any property of the system that changes as reaction proceeds may be employed so long as it provides accurate, precise results that can be related to changes in concentration. The many analytical methods that have been employed may be divided into two general classifications; chemical and physical.

Chemical methods of determining concentrations utilize the classical tests of analytical chemistry. If, for example, an acid is produced during a reaction we can analyze for it by standard titration procedures. To get a sample of the reaction mixture for analysis, we might simply remove a portion of the mixture, but there are two problems connected with this. First, we do not want to upset the reaction conditions. If opening the vessel and inserting a pipette to withdraw a sample does not affect the reaction mixture, this method is perfectly acceptable. If, on the other hand, this method does upset the conditions, perhaps by introduction of oxygen or loss of a vapor, we cannot use it. The second problem is that the reaction is still continuing in the pipette after the sample has been removed and, to increase the difficulty, the temperature control has been lost. A method of stopping the reaction rapidly, *quenching*, is required. The procedure will vary with the reaction being studied. Rapid cooling in dry ice or liquid nitrogen may be effective, or removal of one of the reactants, for example, by pouring an acidic solution into excess base, which will remove the acid and allow titration of the remaining base. Once quenching has been carried out, the subsequent analysis may be done at any convenient time.

To avoid upsetting the system when the sample is removed, one can analyze the complete system. The procedure for this is to prepare several small samples, initiate the reaction, and periodically quench one of the samples. Normally several vessels, usually test tubes, are prepared at one time from the same batch of solutions. The "run" consists of the series of individual identical reactions that are interrupted at different times.

Both these methods are capable of giving good results where they can be used. Analysis by gas chromatography and mass spectroscopy work well with this approach and previously unobtainable analytical separations are now routine.

Although *physical methods* have certain advantages over chemical analysis, they also have their disadvantages. Instruments must be calibrated and cannot be more accurate than the procedure used for the calibration. This is sometimes tedious but is offset by the fact that measurements can frequently be made without withdrawing samples from the system.

Among the physical methods of analysis are absorption spectroscopy, refractive index measurements, and polarimetry. With all of these a reaction may continue in the sample cell and a continuous automatic recording of the readings is possible. These methods require careful calibration of the instruments but are convenient to use.

Dilatometry, the measurement of volume changes of liquids, is highly sensitive and enables very precise measurements to be made but requires exact temperature control. Similarly, pressure and volume changes in gaseous reactions have been widely used to study rates and are convenient when a gas is evolved from a liquid system. Difficulties may be introduced if the liquid has a high vapor pressure or the gas is soluble in the liquid phase.

Measurement of electrical properties such as conductance, pH, dielectric constant, and redox potentials permit analysis without concomitant upset of the system, although the use of electrodes *may* introduce a catalytic agent into the system, in which case it must be ruled out.

EXPERIMENTAL DETERMINATION OF REACTION ORDER

Having obtained data for the dependence of concentration upon time, we must determine the order of reaction before we can evaluate the rate constant. Several methods are available and we shall consider a number that are applicable to simple systems. The reader will recognize as he proceeds that the method of determining the reaction-order will necessarily determine the readings that are taken.

Integrated Rate Equations

Probably the simplest and perhaps the most useful approach to determining reaction-order is to plot the data in the forms of the integrated rate expressions developed above. In this manner we plot the concentration terms of the integrated rate expression for each reaction-order against time and find which set of points lies nearest to a straight line.

An analogous method is to calculate the value of k for each point (*vide infra*), using each of the integrated rate equations. This gives a series of values that will be the same for all points only for the equation of the correct order.

In either of these methods, it must be recognized that experimental data are not exact and scatter of the points must be expected. Also, since the data will nearly fit any of the equations in the early part of the reaction, points must be taken as late as during the last 10 to 20% of the entire reaction, because these late points will indicate deviations from an assumed rate equation.

As an example of the application of the determination of reaction order, we will look at the study of the nitrosation of N-methylaniline.* To find the kinetic order of this reaction

$$C_6H_5NHCH_3 + HONO \xrightarrow{\text{HClO}_4} C_6H_5NCH_3NO$$

at low concentrations of $HClO_4$ (<0.1 M), the data were found to fit a second-order rate equation,

$$\text{rate} = k[HNO_2]^2,$$

at any initial concentration of $HClO_4$ (Table 6–2). It is only fair to mention at this point, however, that the value of k was also dependent upon initial $[HClO_4]$.

The integrated rate expression method, in either graphic or analytical form, permits estimation of reaction order from a single experiment. Of course, any such determination of reaction orders should be carefully checked by repeating the experiment at different initial concentrations. If more than one reactant is involved in the rate expression, the ratio of initial concentrations should be varied without

---

* E. Kalatzis and J. H. Ridd, *J. Chem. Soc.*, **1966**, 529.

affecting the value of k. Also we are able to spot deviations from linearity easily if the random errors of the measurements are not so large as to obscure trends.

Table 6–2. Second-Order Rate-Dependence for $C_6H_5NHCH_3$ + $HNO_2 \rightarrow$ as Shown by Constancy of k at Varying Times*

Time (min)	Reaction (%)	k_2 (l.mole^{-1} sec^{-1})
3	15.2	
10	34.7	0.888
15	43.7	0.862
20	51.0	0.868
30	60.7	0.859
40	67.5	0.864
50	72.4	0.862
60	75.5	0.860

* Initial concentrations are: $C_6H_5NHCH_3$, 0.01 M; HNO_2, 0.001 M; $HClO_4$, 0.01 M (temperature, 0°C).

Half-Lives

The half-life of a reaction is the time required to consume one-half of the starting materials. The dependence of this time upon the initial concentration of reactants is determined by the order of the reaction. To illustrate this, let us consider a first-order reaction. Equation (6–6), one form of the integrated first-order rate expression, will be useful:

$$\ln [A_1]/[A_2] = k(t_2 - t_1). \tag{6–6}$$

At the half-life, $t_2 - t_1 = t_{1/2}$, the relationship $[A_1] = 2[A_2]$ must be correct (by definition). Substituting this into Eq. (6–6) gives the relationship that expresses $t_{1/2}$ in terms of reactant concentrations:

$$\ln 2[A_2]/[A_2] = \ln 2 = kt_{1/2},$$
$$\text{(first-order)} \quad t_{1/2} = \ln 2/k. \tag{6–37}$$

From Eq. (6–37), it can be seen that the half-life of a first-order reaction is not dependent upon the initial concentration. The half-lives for reactions of other order can be obtained in a similar manner. The equations for zero-order (Eq. 6–38), second-order (Eq. 6–39), and third-order reactions (Eq. 6–40) are given below for rate expressions of the type $k[A]^n$:

$$\text{(zero-order)} \quad t_{1/2} = [A_0]/2k, \tag{6–38}$$

$$\text{(second-order)} \quad t_{1/2} = 1/k[A_0], \tag{6–39}$$

$$\text{(third-order)} \quad t_{1/2} = 3/2k[A_0]^2. \tag{6–40}$$

Expressions for any fractional life can be obtained in a similar way. Similarly, expressions can be obtained for second- and third-order reactions when they are dependent upon two or three reactants, not just a single one. These expressions are somewhat complicated, however, and it is frequently more convenient to use equal concentrations of all reagents and Eqs. (6–37) through (6–40). To use these equations, we must measure $t_{1/2}$ at different initial concentrations of reactants. The equation that correctly describes the behavior of $t_{1/2}$ as a function of initial concentration is the one derived from the appropriate differential rate expression.

Examination of Eqs. (6–37) through (6–40) reveals that $t_{1/2}$ is proportional to the initial concentration raised to the $1 - n$ power where n is the reaction-order:

$$t_{1/2} \propto [A_0]^{(1-n)}.$$

For two different values of $[A_0]$ the ratio of half-lives can be written thus:

$$t_{1/2}/t'_{1/2} = [A_0]^{(1-n)}/[A'_0]^{(1-n)}.$$

Taking the logarithm and rearranging gives

$$n = \frac{\log t'_{1/2}/t_{1/2}}{\log [A_0]/[A'_0]} + 1. \tag{6-41}$$

This equation can also be used to determine the value of n. Also, although we derived Eq. (6–41) for the half-life, it is a general relationship for any fractional life, e.g., third-life. In the previously cited work of Kalatzis and Ridd this method was used to demonstrate that, although the nitrosation reaction was second-order in nitrous acid at low $[HClO_4]$, the order changed as $[HClO_4]$ increased, going through a maximum of third-order and decreasing again to second-order at high $[HClO_4]$ (> 1–5 M). Their results are shown in Table 6–3.

This result was consistent with a rate expression

$$\text{rate} = k_3[\text{amine}][\text{HONO}]^2$$

for intermediate $HClO_4$ concentrations. This relationship was proved by studying the rate at varying initial concentrations of reagents and applying the integrated rate expression to demonstrate the constancy of k_3.

Reduction of Order

In either of the above methods, the calculations become tedious when the rate expression involves two or more different concentrations. If it is possible to adjust the concentrations so that all of the reactants but one are greatly in stoichiometric excess, their concentrations do not change significantly and the order of the reaction will be reduced. For the reaction

$$A + B \rightarrow C,$$

with a second-order rate expression

$$\text{rate} = k[A][B],$$

we can see that, if $[A] \gg [B]$,

$$\text{rate} \cong k[A_0][B] \cong k'[B].$$

Table 6–3. Use of Half-Life Method to Determine Reaction-Order for the Reaction of N-methylaniline and Nitrous Acid

[HClO$_4$]	10^3[A$_0$]*	$t_{1/2}$ (min)	n
0.02	1.0	36.0	
0.02	1.5	18.8	2.6
0.02	2.0	12.8	
0.1	1.0	108	
0.1	1.5	45.5	3.0
0.1	2.0	25.3	
1.0	1.5	250	
1.0	2.0	145	2.8
1.0	2.5	98	
1.5	1.5	137	
1.5	2.0	102	2.2
1.5	2.5	80	
2.5	1.0	49.0	
2.5	1.5	30.5	2.06
2.5	2.0	23.0	

* Equal concentrations of $C_6H_5NHCH_3$ and HONO were used (temperature, 0°C).

If the concentration of A is so large that it does not change much, the equation is reduced to a pseudo-first-order equation. The above methods for determining reaction order can be applied to find the experimental order in B, and by reversing the concentration ratios, the order in A is also found. If we divide k' by the initial concentration of the excess reagent, we get an approximate value for the true rate constant k.

Differential Rate Equations

The reaction order can also be determined directly from the differential rate equations in two ways. One method depends upon measuring the initial rate of reaction: we start with the initial concentrations, let the reaction proceed for a short period, and determine the concentrations. If the period is short enough, say less than one-tenth of the total reaction, the change in concentration divided by the change in time is a close approximation to the rate. The rate so obtained is the average rate during the time period $t_1 - t_0$. The algebraic relationship showing this is

$$-d[A]/dt = \frac{[A_0] - [A_1]}{t_1 - t_0} = \frac{\Delta[A]}{\Delta t}. \qquad (6\text{–}42)$$

If we make several runs at varying initial concentrations of A, with all other initial concentrations maintained constant throughout the series, we can obtain the order in A. This is effectively making the reaction a pseudo-order reaction. We can then determine the order for each reactant in the same experimental manner, by taking the log of the differential rate equation

$$-d[A]/dt = k'[A]^n,$$
$$\ln(-d[A]/dt) = \ln k' + n \ln [A].$$

$(6\text{--}43)$

If we substitute Eq. (6–42) into this, we find

$$\ln(\Delta[A]/\Delta t) = \ln k' + n \ln [A],$$

$(6\text{--}44)$

and a plot of $\ln(\Delta[A]/\Delta t)$ against $\ln [A]$ will give a line whose slope is the order-of-A.

A similar approach can give the order of each reactant in one run. Again, the time interval must be very short relative to the total reaction time, but now the concentrations of *all* of the reactants will change. Equation (6–44) will be applicable if the rate depends only upon $[A]$ but not if it depends upon other reagents as well. To see how we can determine the order of each reactant, let us begin with a differential rate expression of mixed order,

$$-d[A]/dt = k[A]^m[B]^n.$$

The logarithm of this,

$$\ln - d[A]/dt = \ln k + m \ln [A] + N \ln [B],$$

is rearranged to give

$$\ln -d[A]/dt = \ln k + m \ln [A] + \frac{n}{m} \ln [B].$$

$(6\text{--}45)$

Using Eq. (6–42) for the value of $\ln -d[A]/dt$, we again plot that term against $\ln [A]$. If the reaction rate depends only upon $[A]^m$, we will get a straight line of slope m. If a straight line is not obtained, we guess at the ratio n/m and plot the entire equation. This is not too difficult as only three or four points need to be tried for each guess and n/m must be a ratio of small whole number, 1/1, 2/1, 1/2, etc. After finding the ratio that gives a straight line, slope m, the rest of the points should be tested.

EXPERIMENTAL DETERMINATION OF RATE CONSTANTS

The determination of the specific rate constant in the rate equation has necessarily been mentioned several times in the preceding sections. However, it cannot be evaluated until after the order of reaction is determined, or perhaps concurrently with it.

We evaluate the rate constant for each point from the appropriate integrated rate expressions, using kinetic equations such as (6–6) or (6–6a) in the case of a first-order reaction. This gives a value for k for each experimental determination, and the arithmetic mean is then computed as the best value of k. We should note, however, that the individual values are all obtained by using the initial concentration. In experiments where this is known more accurately than the succeeding values, the approach is reasonable, but this is rarely the case. The error in the initial concentration is frequently as large as that in any other value and repeated use gives it a disproportionately large importance, which cannot be justified.

To compensate for this overemphasis on the initial concentrations, rate constants are frequently calculated from equations of the form of Eq. (6–6). The values of t_1, t_2, $[A_1]$, and $[A_2]$ are obtained for each successive pair of measurements; the results at t_1 and t_2 are used to calculate a value of k, then t_2 and t_3 are used to obtain a second value of k, and again a series of values for k is obtained. If the time intervals are equal, that is, $t_2 - t_1 = t_3 - t_2$, the use of the average value of k as the "best" value is far from justified because it is totally dependent upon the initial and final measurements and all others are lost in the computation. (The reader may wish to demonstrate this.) Even when the time intervals are only *nearly* equal the greatest weight is thrown upon the initial and final concentrations. This difficulty is avoided if readings are made at time periods corresponding to the disappearance of a constant amount of reactant, but most kinetic experiments do not make measurements in this way.

Probably the best method is to plot the data, using an appropriate expression, and obtain the value of k from the slope of the line that best represents the points. The drawing of this line is somewhat subjective but results can be obtained that are as good as is justified by the experimental error of most rate studies.

To eliminate the subjective aspects of drawing the line of best fit through the plotted points, the *method of least squares* is frequently used. This numerical approach is also used when the accuracy of the data precludes the use of a convenient scale. The method of least squares will be developed in the following section.

If readings of physical properties are to be used in place of concentrations in the first-order rate equation, these must be related to the concentration by a simple function. The most common case is that the physical property being measured (e.g., gas pressure, optical density and rotation, electrical conductance, refractive index, vapor pressure) is related to concentration by a linear function. This linearity must be demonstrated for the conditions under which the measurement is made. Having demonstrated this experimentally we can write the function in the form

$$r = a + b[A], \tag{6–46}$$

where r is the measurement, a and b are constants, and $[A]$ is the concentration of material A. The constants can be eliminated from this equation by recognizing that $[A]$ at infinite time $[A]_\infty$ will be zero for a reaction going to completion. We write Eq. (6–46) for some initial concentration of A as

$$r_0 = a + b[A_0]$$

and also for the infinity reading, when $[A_\infty] = 0$,

$$r_\infty = a.$$

By subtracting the second from the first we obtain

$$r_0 - r_\infty = a + b[A_0] - a = b[A_0]. \tag{6-47}$$

An analogous equation can be written for the concentration of A at some other time:

$$r_i - r_\infty = b[A_i]. \tag{6-48}$$

To eliminate the constant b, we divide Eq. (6–48) by (6–47):

$$(r_i - r_\infty)/(r_0 - r_\infty) = [A_i]/[A_0], \tag{6-49}$$

and substitute it into the first-order rate equation, Eq. (6–6a), to give

$$\ln (r_i - r_\infty)/(r_0 - r_\infty) = -kt. \tag{6-50}$$

If we can fix the values of r_0 and r_∞ by experiment, this equation can be handled as any first-order reaction expression. In the special case where r_0 and r_∞ cannot be determined, some other method must be used.

When the initial concentration or its equivalent—the concentration reacted at infinite time—is unknown for a first-order reaction the method of Guggenheim* is convenient. The method is applicable where concentrations are measured directly or where a physical measurement is used to follow the reaction. In this latter case, the physical readings, $r_1, r_2, \ldots, r_n$, may be used without the conversion to concentration terms described above. Instead, the method involves making a series of readings at $t_1, t_2, \ldots, t_n$, followed by a second series made after a period of time t', so that the second series corresponds to the first but is made after at least two half-lives. This time period t' should also be longer than t_n. The times for the second set of readings, r_1, r_2, and r_3, are then $t' + t_1, t' + t_2, \ldots, t^1 + t_n$.

It is convenient to restate Eq. (6–50) in exponential form, solve for r_i, and introduce the observed times and readings:

$$r_i = r_\infty - (r_0 - r_\infty) \exp (-kt_i),$$

$$r_i' = r_\infty - (r_0 - r_\infty) \exp [-k(t' + t_i)].$$

Subtracting the second equation from the first gives

$$r_i - r_i' = (r_0 - r_\infty)[\exp (-kt_i)][1 - \exp (-kt')],$$

which in logarithmic form is

$$kt_i + \ln (r_i - r_i') = \ln (r_0 - r_\infty)[1 - \exp (-kt')]. \tag{6-51}$$

The right-hand side of Eq. (6–51) contains no term that is not constant, and therefore we can write

$$kt_i + \ln (r_i - r_i') = \text{constant}. \tag{6-52}$$

This is simply a linear equation and k can be evaluated by plotting $\ln (r_i - r_i')$ against t_i or, of course, by arithmetic curve-fitting, e.g. the least-squares method.

* E. A. Guggenheim, *Phil. Mag.*, **2**, 538 (1926).

This method is frequently more convenient than measuring r_∞ and can be used even when r_∞ is obtainable. Some care must be used, however, in demonstrating first-order kinetics before applying the Guggenheim method because certain complex kinetic systems will give apparent rate constants by this method.

CURVE-FITTING BY THE LEAST-SQUARES METHOD

Although graphical curve-fitting is usually accurate enough for determining a value of k, these values are more often obtained by the method of least squares. Although this is the simplest statistical method of adjusting parameters to fit a set of measured points, it has certain disadvantages. All measured points are weighted equally even though some of them may involve greater error than others. Also, errors are assumed to follow a Gaussian distribution, but a kinetic determination can easily involve systematic error. Finally, we must know the function that is to be fitted. If, for example, we are fitting data to an integrated rate equation and the relationship is not quite linear, we will not observe the non-linearity. For this reason all kinetic experiments should be plotted on graph paper even if k is evaluated by the least-squares procedure. Trends that may be otherwise overlooked become obvious visually.

The least-squares procedure is based upon the postulate that the best values for the adjustable parameters of an equation are those that make the sum of the squares of the residuals, S, a minimum. When experimental values, Y_{obs}, are expected to fit some analytical function,

$$Y = f(a, b, \ldots, X),$$

this method says that the best values of $a, b, \ldots,$ are those for which

$$S = \sum (Y_{obs} - f(a, b, \ldots, X_i)]^2$$
$$= \sum (Y_{obs} - Y_{calc})^2 = \text{minimum}.$$

(6–53)

To minimize, we set the first derivative equal to zero so that

$$\partial S/\partial a = \partial S/\partial b \cdots = 0.$$

As an illustration of the least-squares method, let us take a very simple case. We weigh an object several times. Our observed values are simply the individual weighings, $Y_1, Y_2, \ldots, Y_n$. If we want to know the "best" value of Y, that is Y_{calc}, using the least-squares method to find it, we take Eq. (6–53) as our starting point:

$$\sum (Y_{obs} - Y_{calc})^2 = \text{minimum}$$
$$\partial(Y_{obs} - Y_{calc})^2/\partial Y_{calc} = 0$$
$$\sum 2(Y_{obs} - Y_{calc})/(-1) = 0$$
$$\sum (Y_{obs} - Y_{calc}) = 0.$$

weighings were made, $\sum Y_{calc}$ is equal to nY_{calc}. Substituting this in the last ation we get

$$\sum Y_{obs} - nY_{calc} = 0$$

$$Y_{calc} = \sum Y_{obs}/n. \tag{6-54}$$

ius, for this rather trivial example, we obtain the result that the "best" value is the ithmetic mean, a solution that the reader probably expected.

Because in general we attempt to fit kinetic data to a straight line for evaluation f the rate constant and because many other experimental equations take a linear orm, we will apply the least-squares technique to a general linear equation. Then, or any specific application, we can use the general result obtained. Equation (6–55) is our linear equation, where a and b are the adjustable parameters and X and Y are measured values such that we have sets of data $X_1Y_1, X_2Y_2, \ldots, X_nY_n$ when n measurements have been made:

$$Y = aX + b. \tag{6-55}$$

Applying (6–53) to this equation affords

$$\sum [Y_{obs} - (aX_{obs} + b)]^2 = \text{minimum}.$$

Then

$$\partial S/\partial a = \partial \sum [Y_{obs} - (aX_{obs} + b)]^2/\partial a = 0,$$

so that

$$a \sum X_{obs}^2 + b \sum X_{obs} = \sum X_{obs} Y_{obs} \tag{6-56}$$

and

$$\partial S/\partial b = \partial \sum [Y_{obs} - (aX_{obs} + b)]^2/\partial b = 0$$
$$a \sum X_{obs} + nb = \sum Y_{obs}. \tag{6-57}$$

The simultaneous equations (6–56) and (6–57) may be solved for a and b either by elimination of one of these or by the method of determinants. If we choose the latter method, we obtain

$$a = \frac{\begin{vmatrix} \sum XY & \sum X \\ \sum Y & n \end{vmatrix}}{\begin{vmatrix} \sum X^2 & \sum X \\ \sum X & n \end{vmatrix}} = \frac{n \sum XY - \sum X \sum Y}{n \sum X^2 - (\sum X)^2} \tag{6-58}$$

and

$$b = \frac{\begin{vmatrix} \sum X^2 & \sum XY \\ \sum X & \sum Y \end{vmatrix}}{\begin{vmatrix} \sum X^2 & \sum X \\ \sum X & n \end{vmatrix}} = \frac{\sum X^2 \sum Y - \sum X \sum XY}{n \sum X^2 - (\sum X)^2}. \tag{6-59}$$

For convenience, the subscripts have been removed from Eqs. (6–58) and (6–59). It is understood that the summation is for all points taken so that, for example, $\sum X = X_1 + X_2 + \cdots + X_n$.

One advantage of the least-squares method of obtaining rate constants is that it permits determination of the uncertainty of a derived quantity in terms of the random errors of any measured quantities. Although a text on statistical treatment of data should be referred to for the development, several equations for finding the uncertainties follow. One of the more commonly reported estimates of error is the standard deviation, σ_Y. For a series of n measurements of a single point, that is, where Eq. (6–54) is applicable, the standard deviation may be obtained by

$$\sigma_Y = [\sum (Y_{obs} - Y_{calc})^2/(n - 1)]^{1/2}.$$

The probability of error in a value of Y_{obs} within the limit of $\pm \sigma_Y$ is 68.3%.

Other measurements of error are also used. The average deviation η sets a limit within which the probability of error is 55%:

$$\eta = \sum | Y - \bar{Y}|/n = 0.798\sigma_Y.$$

The probability of error within the limits of the probable error Q is 50%:

$$Q = 0.6745\sigma_Y.$$

Finally, the limit of error λ is sometimes reported. It will include 95% of the measurements if

$$\lambda = \pm 1.96\sigma_Y(n)^{1/2}$$

is used and 99% if 2.58 is substituted for 1.96. This is frequently called the 99% confidence limit.

When a linear equation is applicable (Eq. 6–55), we use

$$\sigma_Y = [\sum (Y_{obs} - Y_{calc})^2/(n - 2)]^{1/2}$$
$$= [\sum (Y_{obs} - aX - b)^2/(n - 2)]^{1/2}$$

to obtain the standard error in a and b for the linear expression

$$\sigma_a = [n\sigma_Y^2/(n \sum X^2 - (\sum X)^2)]^{1/2},$$
$$\sigma_b = [(\sum X^2)\sigma_Y^2/(n \sum X^2 - (\sum X)^2)]^{1/2}.$$

To apply the least-squares method to kinetic data, we simply write the appropriate kinetic expression, compare it with Eq. (6–55), and make the necessary substitutions in Eqs. (6–58) and (6–59). Thus, the integrated first-order rate expression, Eq. (6–6), may be written in the form

$$\ln [A] = -kt + \ln [A_0],$$
$$Y = aX + b.$$

The measured values $\ln [A]$ and t correspond to Y and X, and the adjustable parameters are $-k$ and $\ln [A_0]$. If $[A_0]$ is known with good accuracy, this parameter can be eliminated. One problem is immediately obvious—the values of $[A]$ were measured, not $\ln [A]$ as is needed. Because $\ln [A]$ is a function of $[A]$ and does not vary linearly with $[A]$, a more general treatment would weigh each term in $\ln [A]$ to account for this variation.

THE STEADY-STATE APPROXIMATION

Many, indeed most, reactions are complex, and frequently they are more complex than those we have already discussed. Therefore certain simplifying assumptions are necessary to make these very complex systems mathematically tractable. For reactions that involve the formation and destruction of unstable intermediates, the steady-state approximation is extremely useful. When the intermediates are so unstable or reactive that their concentrations are always very small, the assumption is made that the concentration of the intermediate does not change during the course of reaction; that is, a "steady state" is achieved by the intermediate. If this is so, the rate of change of the concentration of the intermediate is negligibly small and the rate expressions for formation and consumption may be set equal to zero.

Let us examine a relatively simple reaction sequence:

$$A + B \underset{k_{-1}}{\overset{k_1}{\rightleftharpoons}} C$$

$$C + D \xrightarrow{k_2} E.$$

The rate of formation of E is given by the expression

$$d[E]/dt = k_2[C][D]. \tag{6-60}$$

We do not know the concentration of C, however, so this equation is not very useful at present, but we can write a rate expression for the appearance of C:

$$D[C]/dt = k_1[A][B] - k_{-1}[C] - k_2[C][D] = 0.$$

We set this equal to zero, using the steady-state assumption, and we can then solve for $[C]$:

$$[C] = k_1[A][B]/(k_{-1} + k_2[D]).$$

Substitution of this into Eq. (6–60) yields a new rate expression for the formation of E:

$$d[E]/dt = k_1 k_2[A][B][D]/(k_{-1} + k_2[D]). \tag{6-61}$$

We might examine this expression for its application to special cases. If $k_{-1} \gg k_2[D]$, Eq. (6–61) is reduced to

$$d[E]/dt = k_1 k_2[A][B][D]/k_{-1}.$$

The rate of formation of E is third-order dependent upon $[A]$, $[B]$, and $[D]$ and the observed rate constant is a composite, $k_1 k_2/k_{-1}$. If, on the other hand, $k_2[D] \gg k_{-1}$, Eq. (6–61) reduces to

$$d[E]/dt = k_1[A][B].$$

The rate equation is second-order and $k_2[D]$ has dropped out. The observed rate constant is equal to k_1. Of course, if $k_{-1} \cong k_2[D]$, the full expression must be employed. The differential rate expressions obtained by using the steady-state approximation may be integrated and handled like any other rate expression to determine the concentrations as functions of time.

EFFECT OF TEMPERATURE ON REACTION RATES

Having examined the role of concentrations in chemical kinetics rather closely, we shall now turn our attention to the role played by temperature. It has long been known that for most reactions the temperature dependence of the rate constant is given by the Arrhenius equation:

$$k = A \exp(-E_a/RT), \qquad (6-62)$$

where A is the pre-exponential factor and is temperature-independent and T is absolute temperature.

By writing Eq. (6–62) in logarithmic form (Eq. 6–63) we see that a plot of $\ln k$ against $1/T$ will give a straight line, whose slope is $-E_a/R$:

$$\ln k = \ln A - E_a/RT. \qquad (6-63)$$

If data are available at several temperatures, the method of least squares is preferable for evaluating E_a. Frequently, data at only two temperatures are used to evaluate E_a. Although this is not ideal procedure, when it is done it is convenient to use the Arrhenius equation in the form where k_1 and k_2 are rate constants at T_1 and T_2 respectively:

$$\ln k_2/k_1 = (E_a/R)(T_2 - T_1)/T_1 T_2.$$

The Arrhenius equation is adequate for most experimental work. By very exact determinations, however, it has been found to be only a first approximation. A more accurate equation is

$$k = AT^n \exp(-E_a/RT),$$

which also has theoretical justification, as will be pointed out in the following chapter. Further discussion of the Arrhenius equation will be postponed until we examine the theory of chemical kinetics.

PROBLEMS

1. Derive a relationship for k_1/k_2 and the concentrations of C and D for the scheme

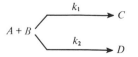

2. Write a differential rate equation for the reversible reaction

$$A \underset{k_{-1}}{\overset{k_1}{\rightleftharpoons}} B$$

Let the initial molarity of A be a, the initial molarity of B be b, and the molarity of A converted to B at any time t be X. Define any other symbols used. Integrate this equation and eliminate the constant of integration by using $X = 0$ at $t = 0$. Combine terms where possible. By use of an equation that expresses the fact that the forward and reverse rates are equal at equilibrium, eliminate the term $k_1 a - k_2 b$ by introducing X_∞ (X at infinite time).

3. Although in long-chain free radical reactions initiation and termination steps occur infrequently and can be ignored in product studies, the termination step has a profound effect upon the kinetic order of the reaction. Predict the reaction order in P expected for the following schemes. [*Hint:* use reasonable approximations.]

a) $P \xrightarrow{k_1} 2R$ (initiation)

   $R + HS \xrightarrow{k_2} S + RH$

   $S + P \xrightarrow{k_3} R$

   $2R \xrightarrow{k_4} R_2$ (termination)

b) $P \longrightarrow 2R$

   $R + HS \longrightarrow S + RH$

   $S + P \longrightarrow R$

   $2S \xrightarrow{k_5} S_2$

c) $P \longrightarrow 2R$

   $R + HS \longrightarrow S + RH$

   $S + P \longrightarrow R$

   $R + S \xrightarrow{k_6} RS$

4. Determine the reaction order and evaluate the rate constant for the reaction of iodine with 1,3-dicarbethoxy-2,4-dimethyl pyrrole in aqueous dioxane at 43°C. The initial concentration of the pyrrole was 0.00851 M and of iodine 0.0119 M.

	Concentration	
Time (min)	Iodine	Pyrrole
0.5	0.01013	0.00673
14.5	0.00476	0.00135
24.7	0.00402	0.00062

5. From the following data calculate k_H, k_0, standard deviation, and the standard error of k_H. The data fit the equation $k_1 = k_0 + k_H[H^+]$.

[H$^+$], M	$k_1 \times 10^6$ (sec^{-1})
0.0600	1.609
0.0400	1.053
0.0200	0.520

6. a) Obtain the rate expression for the formation of C for the system:

$$A \underset{k_{-1}}{\overset{k_1}{\rightleftharpoons}} B \overset{k_2}{\longrightarrow} C.$$

Use the steady-state assumption.

b) If the first step of this reaction is rapid and reversible, the rate expression can be simplified. What is the rate expression for this special case?

c) What is the rate expression if $k_2 \gg k_{-1}$?

7. The chlorination of a mixture of 0.04763 mole of cylohexane and 0.04878 mole of toluene was carried out in benzene at 40°C, using *tert*-butyl hypochlorite as the chlorinating agent. Aliquots of the resulting mixture were analyzed by solvolytic methods for total chloride, 0.00801 mole, and for benzyl chloride, 0.00137 mole.

a) Compute the relative rate of chlorination of cyclohexane to toluene, k_{cyclo}/k_{tol}.

b) The relative rate of chlorination of cyclohexane to *m*-xylene was found to be 4.44. Compute the value of $k_{m-xylene}/k_{tol}$.

c) Correct the value obtained in (b) for the differing numbers of benzylic hydrogens in the two reactants.

d) The value of $k_{m-xylene}/k_{tol}$ was also measured by analyzing the reactants after chlorination by gas chromatography. An initial mixture of 0.0161 mole of *m*-xylene and 0.0188 mole of toluene was found to contain 0.0116 mole and 0.0162 mole of these reactants, respectively, upon completion of the reaction. From these data compute $k_{m-xylene}/k_{tol}$.

e) Compare the value obtained in (b) with that in (d). Cyclohexyl chloride was not analyzed in either technique. What errors might be involved in the values obtained?

SUGGESTED READING

BENSON, S. W., *The Foundations of Chemical Kinetics*, McGraw-Hill Book Co., New York (1960).

FRIESS, S. L., E. S. LEWIS, and A. WEISSBERGER (Eds.), *Investigation of Rates and Mechanisms of Reactions*, Interscience Publishers, New York, Part I (1961), Part II (1962).

FROST, A. A., and R. G. PEARSON, *Kinetics and Mechanism*, 2nd Ed., John Wiley & Sons, New York (1961).

JOHNSTON, H. S., *Gas Phase Reaction Rate Theory*, Ronald Press, New York (1966).

KING, E. L., *How Chemical Reactions Occur*, W. A. Benjamin, New York (1963).

KONDRAT'EV, V. N., *Chemical Kinetics of Gas Reactions*, Pergamon Press, London (1964).

CHAPTER 7

THEORY OF CHEMICAL KINETICS

There are advantages and drawbacks to both the important theories dealing with rates of reactions. Of the two, the *collision theory* can be expressed in simpler terms. It is based on the kinetic theory of gases and employs a mechanical model which gives an intuitively satisfying description of reaction rates. The *transition state theory*, sometimes called the theory of absolute rates, is based on thermodynamics and employs a potential energy surface as a model. This theory is more generally applicable to reactions involving complex organic molecules in solution. We shall examine both theories only as they apply to bimolecular reactions.

COLLISION THEORY

The simplest model that can be employed in the collision theory of reaction rates involves molecules that are assumed to be spherical and that undergo only perfectly elastic collisions. There are several other models which might be employed. We might, for example, consider the molecules to be point particles of mass equal to the molecular weight and undergoing perfectly elastic collisions. This dimensionless model is quite capable of describing properties of monatomic gases at low pressures and at temperatures well above their liquefaction point, but we will not use it to treat chemical kinetics, because it is impossible to account for molecular collisions with such a model. It is reasonable to assume that two molecules must collide for reaction to occur, and therefore our model provides for collisions by adding the dimension of diameter. Even so, the hard-sphere model does not permit a detailed description of the reaction because it includes no time period during which changes can occur at the collision. Also, the only energy transfer permitted by a hard-sphere collision is that of translational kinetic energy. Rotational and vibrational energies require the use of a multidimensional molecular model. We can, however, make our hard-sphere model more acceptable by treating the diameter as an adjustable parameter. The ideal model would be a molecule-shaped object capable of exerting both repulsive and attractive forces. This exact treatment is impossible but has been approximated with both spherical and symmetrical molecular models with central force fields. The central force field approach is necessary to treat the properties of a condensed phase but is mathematically difficult.

In developing the collision theory for bimolecular reactions, we shall choose the elementary reaction

$$A + B \rightarrow C.$$

116

For the reaction to occur, we assume that a molecule of A must collide with one of B. From the kinetic theory of gases, the expression for the number of times molecules of A and B collide per cubic centimeter per second is given by

$$Z_{AB} = n_A n_B \left(\frac{\sigma_A + \sigma_B}{2}\right)^2 \sqrt{\frac{8\pi \mathbf{k}T(m_A + m_B)}{m_A m_B}}, \tag{7-1}$$

where σ_A and σ_B are the molecular diameters, m_A and m_B are the molecular masses, and n_A and n_B are the molecules of A and B per cubic centimeter. If reaction occurred with every collision, the collision frequency would also be the reaction rate.

If we now assume that reaction will not occur unless the energy of the colliding pair exceeds some minimum value, ϵ^*, we must obtain the collision frequency $z_{AB}(\epsilon^*)$ for encounters with $\epsilon \geq \epsilon^*$. The number of collisions between molecules A and B with $\epsilon \geq \epsilon^*$ will be proportional to the fraction of molecules with $\epsilon \geq \epsilon^*$ (obtained by use of the Maxwell distribution function). For a system of two colliding hard-sphere molecules the energy of collision arises from the translational energy of each molecule along the line of centers of the two spheres. The appropriate Maxwell distribution law gives the fraction of molecules with $\epsilon \geq \epsilon^*$ as

$$n_{\epsilon*}/n = e^{-\epsilon^*/\mathbf{k}T}. \tag{7-2}$$

The quantity $\exp(-\epsilon^*/\mathbf{k}T)$ represents the probability of a molecule having $\epsilon \geq \epsilon^*$ but we are interested in collisions with $\epsilon \geq \epsilon^*$. That Eq. (7-2) still applies is shown in the following manner. For the collision of two molecules we can say that molecule A must have an energy $\geq \epsilon^A$ and B must have an energy $\epsilon \geq \epsilon^B$. For a reaction to occur, however, requires that $\epsilon^A + \epsilon^B = \epsilon^*$. Using Eq. (7-2), the probability of an A molecule having $\epsilon \geq \epsilon^A$ is $\exp(-\epsilon^A/\mathbf{k}T)$ and, similarly, that of a B molecule having $\epsilon \geq \epsilon^B$ is $\exp(-\epsilon^B/\mathbf{k}T)$. The probability of a collision with the necessary energy is the product of these two probabilities and is equal to Eq. (7-2):

$$e^{-\epsilon^A/\mathbf{k}T} e^{-\epsilon^B/\mathbf{k}T} = e^{-(\epsilon^A + \epsilon^B)/\mathbf{k}T} = e^{-\epsilon^*/\mathbf{k}T}.$$

Combining Eq. (7-2) with Eq. (7-1) affords an expression for the number of collisions with $\epsilon \geq \epsilon^*$ per cubic centimeter per second:

$$Z_{AB}(\epsilon^*) = Z_{AB} n_{\epsilon*}/n = n_A n_B \left(\frac{\sigma_A + \sigma_B}{2}\right)^2 \sqrt{\frac{8\pi \mathbf{k}T(m_A + m_B)}{m_A m_B}} e^{-\epsilon^*/\mathbf{k}T}. \tag{7-3}$$

If reaction occurs with every collision of sufficient energy, Eq. (7-3) is then equal to the rate of disappearance of either A or B per cubic centimeter:

$$-dn_A/dt = -dn_B/dt = Z_{AB}(\epsilon^*) = Z_{AB} e^{-\epsilon^*/\mathbf{k}T}. \tag{7-4}$$

The empirical rate law of a second-order reaction is given in units of moles/liter/second:

$$-dN_A/dt = -dN_B/dt = k_2 N_A N_B. \tag{7-5}$$

Since N_i (moles/liter) $= 10^3 n_i/N_0$, where N_0 is Avogadro's number, we can write

$$-dN_A/dt = -(10^3/N_0)dn_A/dt, \tag{7-6}$$

and from Eq. (7–5)

$$-dN_A/dt = k_2 N_A N_B = k_2(10^6/N_0^2)n_A n_B. \tag{7-7}$$

Thus, equating (7–6) and (7–7), we get

$$k_2 = (-dn_A/dt)N_0/10^3 n_A n_B. \tag{7-8}$$

By substitution of (7–4) into (7–8) we obtain the observed bimolecular rate constant in terms of the collision theory as

$$k_2 = (N_0/10^3 n_A n_B)Z_{AB}\, e^{-\epsilon^*/kT} = \frac{N_0}{10^3}\left(\frac{\sigma_A + \sigma_B}{2}\right)^2 \sqrt{\frac{8\pi kT(m_A + m_B)}{m_A m_B}}\, e^{-\epsilon^*/kT}. \tag{7-9}$$

By converting molecular mass to molecular weights (M), $\mathbf{k}$ to the gas constant R, and evaluating all constants, we obtain

$$k_2 = 2.74 \times 10^{25}\left(\frac{\sigma_A + \sigma_B}{2}\right)^2 \sqrt{\frac{T(M_A + M_B)}{M_A M_B}}\, e^{-E^*/RT}. \tag{7-10}$$

Equation (7–10) does not apply for reactions involving like molecules $(A = B)$. In this case, we have counted each collision twice, once when A hits B and once when B hits A, and since these two processes are indistinguishable, we must reduce the collision frequency term by $1/2$. Also the term $(M_A + M_B)M_A M_B$ reduces to $2/M$ when $M = M_A = M_B$ and $(\sigma_A + \sigma_B)/2$ becomes σ when $\sigma = \sigma_A = \sigma_B$. Thus Eq. (7–10) becomes

$$k_2 = 1.94 \times 10^{25}\sigma^2\sqrt{T/M}\, e^{-E^*/RT} \tag{7-11}$$

for bimolecular reactions between like molecules. Equations (7–10) and (7–11) may be shortened to the form

$$k_2 = \bar{Z}\, e^{-E^*/RT}. \tag{7-12}$$

In this form, we can compare collision theory predictions with the pre-exponential term of the Arrhenius equation (Eq. 6–62):

$$k_{obs} = A\, e^{-E_\alpha/RT}.$$

Although $\bar{Z}$ is dependent upon $\sqrt{T}$ whereas A in Eq. (6–62) is not, we can directly compare the predicted values of k from Eqs. (7–10) and (7–11) with the observed value by dividing the observed A value by $\sqrt{T}$ where T is some mean temperature for the experimental range shown. Table 7–1 shows some typical results.

From Table 7–1, we can see that the rates predicted by the collision theory are nearly always too high. For reactions involving relatively simple molecules, the agreement with experimental values is satisfactory but, as the molecules become more

Table 7–1. Comparison of Experimental and Collision Theory
Pre-exponential Values

Reaction	E_a (kcal/mole)	$\log A/\sqrt{T}$ (l/mole·sec)	$\log \bar{Z}/\sqrt{T}$ (l/mole·sec)	$A/\bar{Z}$
$H + Br_2 \rightarrow HBr + Br$	0.9	9.83	10.65	0.15
$Br + H_2 \rightarrow HBr + H$	17.6	9.31	10.23	0.12
$CH_3 + CH_3CH{=}CH_2 \rightarrow$ $CH_4 + CH_2CH{=}CH_2$	7.7	6.48	7.14	0.22
$CH_3 + CH_3CH{=}CHCH_3 \rightarrow$ $CH_4 + CH_3CH{=}CHCH_2$	7.7	6.88	7.20	0.48
$CH_3 + H_2 \rightarrow CH_4 + H$	10.0	7.25	10.72	9.5×10^{-4}
$CH_2{=}CH_2 +$ $CH_2{=}CHCH{=}CH_2 \rightarrow$	26.7	5.80	10.20	4×10^{-5}
$CH_2{=}CHCH{=}CH_2 +$ $CH_2{=}CHCH{=}O \rightarrow$	19.3	4.65	10.17	3×10^{-6}

complicated, the deviations become quite large. Because of this, an additional factor must be added to Eq. (7–12), called the *steric factor* or, more satisfactorily, the *probability factor*, *P*:

$$k_2 = P\bar{Z}\,e^{-E^*/RT}. \qquad (7\text{–}13)$$

The need to add the probability factor suggests that even those collisions with sufficient energy to produce a reaction may not do so. At first, this was attributed to the need for a particular orientation of the molecules during a collision. The third and fourth entries in Table 7–1 might be used to support this interpretation: for either of those reactions to occur, it is reasonable to assume that the methyl radical must collide with the alkene at one of the allylic hydrogen atoms. Since 2-butene has twice as many allylic hydrogens as propene, we would expect the value of *P* for propene to be one-half that of butene—which, indeed, is found to be the case. This kind of reasoning led to the name steric factor. It is now recognized that the deviation of *P* from unity is even more complex. Molecules are not the hard spheres we postulated in our theory, and, although a collision may occur with sufficient energy to bring about reaction, the energy may be siphoned off into nonreactive portions of the molecules by vibrational and rotational energy conversions. As the molecules become more complex, we can expect these processes to be more important and hence our theory will be inadequate. Because it is impossible to calculate the value of P within the frame of the collision theory, it must be seen as simply a measure of the discrepancy between the theory and the experimental results. (It should be mentioned that P can be calculated by a theory that supplements the collision theory without affecting the assumptions made.)

TRANSITION STATE THEORY

This theory attempts to treat reaction kinetics in terms of thermodynamic equilibrium and rests upon three postulates: (1) the reacting molecules must acquire potential energy greater than that of the reactants or products; (2) the species with sufficient potential energy are in statistical equilibrium with the reactants; and (3) the rate of reaction is proportional to the number (concentration) of the "activated" species. In this theory, then, the rate of reaction is the product of the number of species with sufficient energy for reaction to occur times the frequency with which they decompose into products.

A simple approach to obtaining the frequency assumes that decomposition into products will occur when enough energy is supplied to a bond to rupture it and the activated complex can fly apart. Thus one vibrational degree of freedom becomes a translational motion. The average vibrational energy is given in terms of the frequency, ν, by Planck's equation (see Chapter 1), for the quantum energy

$$E = h\nu. \tag{7–14}$$

At temperatures at or above room temperature, i.e. relatively high T, vibrational energy may also be treated as classical vibrational energy:

$$E = kT. \tag{7–15}$$

Equating Eqs. (7–14) and (7–15) and solving for ν gives the frequency of decomposition of the activated complex into products or the rate at which the activated complexes pass over the energy barrier:

$$h\nu = kT,$$
$$\nu = kT/h. \tag{7–16}$$

To calculate the number (or concentration) of the activated complexes, we employ postulate 2. By assuming a statistical equilibrium between the complex and reactants we can write

$$A + B \rightleftharpoons AB^\ddagger \rightarrow C. \tag{7–17}$$

We will use a double dagger ($\ddagger$) to indicate the activated complex or any quantity associated with it. Now we can define an equilibrium constant for the first step of Eq. (7–17):

$$K^\ddagger = [AB^\ddagger]/[A][B]. \tag{7–18}$$

From this we obtain the number of activated complexes, in concentration terms

$$[AB^\ddagger] = K^\ddagger[A][B].$$ (7-r

Since the rate of reaction is given by the product of the concentration of the activated complex and the rate at which the complex decomposes, we can write the rate expression

$$\text{rate} = \nu[AB^\ddagger] = (kT/hK)^\ddagger[A][B].$$ (7–20)

In arriving at Eq. (7–20), we have assumed that any activated complex will decompose to products, but this may not happen if through some peculiarity the complexes are reflected back to reactants. To correct for this, another term can be added to Eq. (7–20). The correction term, κ, is called the transmission coefficient and for normal reactions may be considered to have a value of one. An exception is the combination of two atoms to form a diatomic molecule. Because collisions of atoms are elastic, the two atoms fly apart after collision and the value of K is zero. For the diatomic process to occur, a third body must be present at the collision to carry off energy in the forms of translations and vibrations. In any event, Eq. (7–20) can be corrected for this occurrence by using the transmission coefficient to give

$$\text{rate} = \kappa(kT/h)K^\ddagger[A][B].$$ (7–21)

Since $K^\ddagger$ is similar to an equilibrium constant, we can define terms analogous to the thermodynamic functions employed in ordinary equilibrium development. By defining a free energy of activation as

$$-\Delta G^\ddagger = RT \ln K^\ddagger$$ (7–22)

we obtain

$$K^\ddagger = e^{-\Delta G^\ddagger/RT}.$$ (7–23)

Substitution of (7–23) into (7–21) affords

$$\text{rate} = \kappa(kT/h) e^{-\Delta G^\ddagger/RT}[A][B].$$ (7–24)

This can be further expanded by defining

$$\Delta G^\ddagger = \Delta H^\ddagger - T\Delta S^\ddagger$$

so that enthalpy of activation and entropy of activation are introduced. Equation (7–24) becomes

$$\text{rate} = \kappa(kT/h) e^{-\Delta H^\ddagger/RT} e^{\Delta S^\ddagger/R}[A][B].$$ (7–25)

From this equation, we can see that the rate constant, k_r, is given by

$$k_r = \kappa(kT/h) e^{\Delta S^\ddagger/R} e^{-\Delta H^\ddagger/RT}.$$ (7–26)

This may be compared with the Arrhenius equation (Eq. 6–62):

$$k_2 = A e^{-E_a/RT} = (\kappa kT/h) e^{\Delta S^\ddagger/R} e^{-\Delta H^\ddagger/RT}.$$ (7–27)

difference is that $\Delta H^{\ddagger}$ appears in place of E_a. It can be shown that, for reactions occurring in solution with the concentration units employed in (7-26), $\Delta H^{\ddagger} = E_a - RT$, for gaseous reactions in which concentrations are used, $\Delta H^{\ddagger} = E_a - RT + p\Delta V$, and, if pressures are employed, again $\Delta H^{\ddagger} = E_a - RT$. Of greater interest is the comparison of the Arrhenius pre-exponential term:

$$A \cong (\kappa kT/h) \, e^{\Delta S^{\ddagger}/R}. \tag{7-28}$$

A negative value for the entropy of activation will result in a low value for A while a positive value will have the opposite effect. In general, a negative value for $\Delta S^{\ddagger}$ is observed when the activated complex is more "ordered" than are the reactants. This is frequently the case for association reactions. The experimental value of $\Delta S^{\ddagger}$ obtained from the empirical values of the rate constant and the energy of activation affords a good indication of the nature of the activated complex.

We should also note that it is the free energy of activation, not the enthalpy (heat) of activation, that determines the rate of a chemical reaction. Equations (7-25) and (7-26) bring out the essential point that a large value of $T\Delta S^{\ddagger}$ can compensate for a high $\Delta H^{\ddagger}$. The energy of activation, which differs from $\Delta H^{\ddagger}$ by only about 600 cal at normal temperatures, is frequently quite large even though reaction may proceed at a high rate, owing to a large increase in entropy. Similarly, a reaction with a low energy of activation may proceed quite sluggishly if there is a large decrease in entropy.

To use the equations developed above for calculating theoretical reaction rates, the methods of quantum mechanics and statistical mechanics must be employed. Statistical mechanics can be used to obtain a value for $K^{\ddagger}$ if enough information is available about the reactants and the activated complex, e.g., moments of inertia and vibrational frequencies. These quantities are not experimentally available for the activated complex but, in principle, can be obtained theoretically—if we know the distance between the nuclei and also how potential energy varies with this distance. By assuming that the electronic energy can be calculated with the nuclei at rest (the *adiabatic assumption*), we can compute the energy for a collection of particles at varying configurations, so generating a multidimensional surface called a *potential-energy surface*. Complete representation of the potential energy requires a coordinate for each independent variable that is employed to specify the relative positions of all particles (nuclei) in the system. At the present time, drastic simplifications are required in any but the simplest of systems. Nevertheless, a qualitative examination of potential-energy surfaces is very useful in developing an understanding of chemical reaction mechanisms.

Let us begin by considering a potential-energy surface for three atoms. Each atom has three coordinates, giving us a total of nine, of which three may be used to determine orientation in space and another three to determine the center of mass. We are left with three coordinates to determine the relative positions of the three nuclei, the three internuclear distances. Since it is difficult to visualize a surface in four dimensions (the fourth being potential energy), we arbitrarily limit the nuclei to a linear configuration which needs only two coordinates. The potential energy for the system is computed by means of quantum mechanics and the results are presented graphically in a contour diagram.

Figure 7–1 shows such a potential-energy surface. The curves are lines of equal potential energy. The surface has two valleys separated by a saddle-shaped pass. The valley on the upper side represents molecule B–C when A is far enough away not to interact and the valley in the lower-right corner represents molecule A–B with C removed. A section taken from the surface at the right-hand side of the figure is the potential-energy curve for the diatomic molecule A–B (Fig. 7–2).

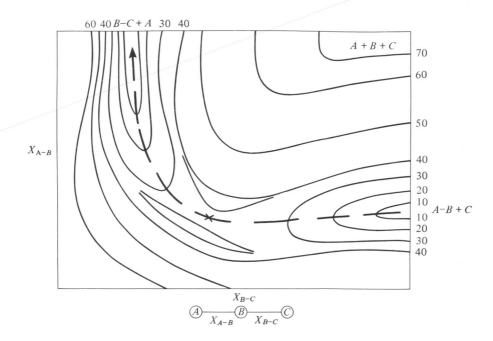

Fig. 7–1. Potential-energy surface for a three-atom linear system.

When atom C approaches molecule A–B there is an increase in the energy of the system. If meanwhile the A–B distance at minimum potential energy increases, the energy reaches some maximum value and then begins to decrease while atom A and molecule B–C are formed. This, of course, is the reaction

$$A–B + C \rightarrow A + B–C.$$

The dashed line in Fig. 7–1 corresponds to this change, with the reasonable assumption that the energy of the system will be at its lowest for any given nuclear configuration. At point X along this path (Fig. 7–1) the path crosses a saddle point, which represents the activated complex or, as it is frequently called, the *transition state*. It is apparent that the transition state is the least likely configuration of nuclei, or alternatively the most energetic, occurring as the reactants are converted to products. The transition state also represents the lowest maximum energy that the reactants can have and still become products. However, the energy difference between the saddle point and the reactants is obviously the activation energy (see below).

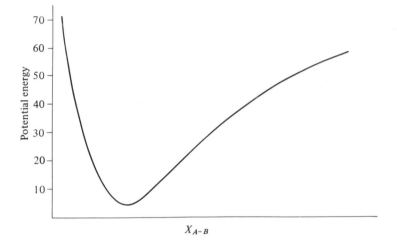

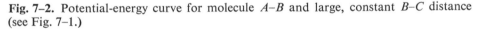

Fig. 7–2. Potential-energy curve for molecule A–B and large, constant B–C distance (see Fig. 7–1.)

If we take a section of the potential-energy surface along the dashed line and redraw it in a plane, we have a curve of the energy requirements for the reaction. This section is called the *reaction profile* and the dashed line the *reaction coordinate*. In Fig. 7–3 such a section is drawn from Fig. 7–1. This concept of the reaction coordinate is certainly one of the most important contributions of the transition state theory. It leads to the realization that the transition state is an activated complex that may be treated like any other molecule except that it has a fourth translational degree of freedom, the reaction coordinate, and correspondingly one less internal degree of freedom. It should be noted that the activated complex is stable with regard to any motion other than that along the reaction coordinate.

For reactions in which A and C are the same atoms, the potential-energy surface and, obviously, the reaction profile are symmetrical.

In the more general case where the atoms differ, the reaction will result in either liberation or consumption of energy. The reaction profile represents this by different levels for the stable reactants and products (Fig. 7–4). In this figure E represents the activation energy and Q the heat of reaction if the atoms are classical. Any atomic system capable of vibrational energy has a zero-point energy, below which the system cannot fall. Thus the actual activation energy and heat of reaction must include these energy values. The activated complex also has a zero-point energy and must be included. Figure 7–5 shows the role of this nonclassical energy factor. (See Chapter 8 for an interesting result caused by zero-point energy differences.)

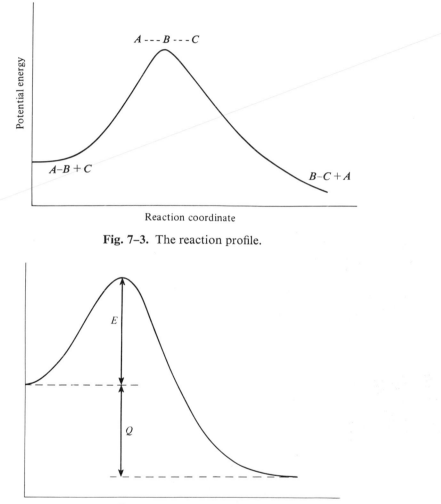

Fig. 7–3. The reaction profile.

Reaction coordinate

Fig. 7–4. Reaction profile for the exothermic reaction $A–B + C \rightarrow A + B–C$ when $A \neq C$.

Although representation of the potential-energy surface for reactions involving more than three atoms requires multidimensional space, a simplification can facilitate visualization of the surface. We assume that molecular fragments can be considered as atoms. For example, in the reaction of methane with a chlorine atom we would consider the CH_3— fragment of methane as atom A and the remaining H as atom B in the above figures. This is certainly drastic but it does permit visualization of potential-energy surfaces and of reaction coordinates in a convenient form.

The exact solution of the quantum mechanical problem, required to generate potential-energy surfaces and, hence, to calculate reaction rates, is not currently possible in any but the simplest cases, although many potential-energy surfaces have been drawn by making severe assumptions. Nevertheless, this theory has led to significant gains in our understanding of how reactions occur in solution and has given us a convenient framework within which to discuss reaction mechanisms.

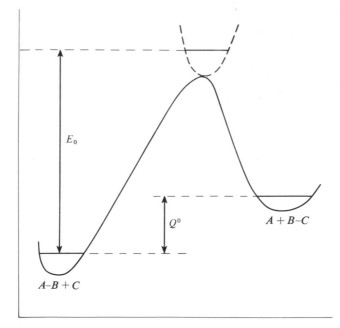

Fig. 7–5. True activation energy E_0 and heat of reaction $Q°$ for an endothermic reaction.

PRINCIPLE OF MICROSCOPIC REVERSIBILITY

Another point is immediately obvious from Fig. 7–1. If $A–B$ and C react by passing over the potential barrier at point X, then $B–C$ and A will react by passing through the same transition state. The configuration of lowest energy in one direction must also be the configuration of lowest energy in the reverse direction—the principle of *microscopic reversibility*. This is of great importance because it permits us to know the mechanism of a reverse reaction if we know the mechanism for the forward reaction. With this approach, reactions that involve unfavorable equilibrium can be studied by examining the reverse step only.

It would appear that the principle of microscopic reversibility would be applicable to all situations. Actually it is not. In our examination of potential-energy surfaces we have examined only one surface for any reaction, but to be complete we must examine several. In general, our approach of considering the surface of only the electronic ground state is reasonable for thermal reactions. If, however, the reaction involves excitement to an excited state, the excited molecule may undergo reaction and the products decay back to the ground state by processes other than radiation. In such a case we cannot expect the principle of microscopic reversibility to apply. Although radiationless decay to the ground state from excited levels is well known, this is not a problem in thermal reactions.

PROBLEMS

1. From the postulates of the transition state theory write an expression for the free energy of activation in terms of k_2, the rate constant, and the activity coefficients of the reactants A and B and the transition state X.

2. What change in the free energy of activation is necessary for a tenfold change in k_2 at 25°C? For a hundredfold change?

3. What is the maximum rate constant at 25°C for a second-order reaction? Assume that the activity coefficients are one.

4. What is the value of E_a for a second-order reaction that has a k_2 value of 0.0380 l/mole-sec at 26.5°C and 0.285 l/mole-sec at 42.6°C? Evaluate the Arrhenius pre-exponential term A.

SUGGESTED READING

BENSON, S. W., *The Foundations of Chemical Kinetics*, McGraw-Hill Book Co., New York (1960).

FROST, A. A. and R. G. PEARSON, *Kinetics and Mechanism*, 2nd Ed., John Wiley & Sons, New York (1961).

GLASSTONE, S., K. J. LAIDLER, and H. EYRING, *The Theory of Rate Processes*, McGraw-Hill Book Co., New York (1941).

KONDRAT'EV, V. N., *Chemical Kinetics of Gas Reactions*, Pergamon Press, London (1964).

MOELWYN-HUGHES, E. A., *The Kinetics of Reactions in Solution*, 2nd Ed., Oxford University Press, London (1947).

CHAPTER 8

KINETIC ISOTOPE EFFECTS

The role of chemical kinetics in determining reaction mechanisms is an important one. Kinetics frequently permit us to determine the number and kinds of species (e.g. molecules, ions, free radicals, and carbenes) that must collide for a reaction to occur. The effect of temperature gives information on the energy requirements of the reaction, from which we can sometimes make intelligent guesses about the conformation of the nuclei of the transition state. In principle, we could use these possible transition state configurations to calculate the absolute rates for each assembly of nuclei and to test the predicted rates by experiment; in practice, however, we must know all of the physical parameters extremely accurately in order to obtain calculated results reliable enough for a meaningful comparison. At the present time we do not have sufficient information to permit us to take this approach. Therefore, other methods, which will be discussed in this and the following chapter, must be employed.

One easier and more practical approach to the study of reaction mechanisms is to make comparisons between two similar transition states. Thus, many unknown physical parameters are canceled in the rate ratios and our conclusions need not be based on estimates of these factors. The more subtle the change that we employ in determining the relative rates, the more factors will tend to cancel. The subtlest change that we can make in a reaction is in the isotopic composition of the reactants and, hence, of the transition state. Isotopic change has no effect upon the potential-energy surface and we can thus eliminate the largest source of inaccuracy in any theoretical calculation of absolute rates. The kinetic isotope effect, nevertheless, is dependent directly upon the shape of the potential-energy surface and can be used to gain insight into the structure of the activated complex. As we shall see, different models of the transition state frequently lead to different predictions of the magnitude of the isotope effect.

There is an inherent limitation to the use of kinetic isotope effects that cannot be overcome. Because the transition state theory requires the reactants and the transition state to be in thermodynamic equilibrium, we can learn only the free energy of activation. In complex reactions, the transition state examined by kinetic methods is that involved in the rate-determining step. If any fast steps precede it, kinetic methods can give no information about them. Similarly, we cannot tell what happens *after* the transition state has been reached. This limitation, of course, is of general significance in any kinetic approach to determining reaction mechanisms.

In the following discussion, we shall examine several kinds of isotope effects and their origins. The most important factor for the organic chemist, their interpretation in terms of reaction mechanisms, will be taken up in later chapters. Although we shall consider only the isotopic substitution of deuterium for hydrogen, the same ideas may be applied to any atom, e.g. C^{12} and C^{14}, although the observed differences in rate will be much smaller and, therefore, experimentally more demanding.

PRIMARY ISOTOPE EFFECTS

Reactions that proceed by breaking the bond between the reacting molecule and an isotopic atom during the rate-determining step exhibit *primary isotope effects*. In this situation isotopic substitution is of most importance and sizable rate differences may be observed. We shall now examine the origin of the primary isotope effect, using a simplified approach—although the detailed theory is well advanced [1, 2].

Let us consider a diatomic molecule X—H. This molecule will be vibrating and the simplest model is that X—H behaves like a harmonic oscillator with potential energy $V = \frac{1}{2}kX^2$ and kinetic energy $T = \frac{1}{2}\mu\dot{X}^2 = p^22\mu$, where k is the force constant (Hooke's Law), X is displacement, and μ is the reduced mass $m_x m_H/(m_x + m_H)$. The Schrödinger equation for the harmonic oscillator is given by

$$\partial^2\psi/\partial X^2 + \frac{8\pi^2\mu}{h^2}(E - \tfrac{1}{2}kX^2)\psi = 0. \tag{8-1}$$

The solution of Eq. (8–1) is

$$E = h\nu(n + \tfrac{1}{2}) \qquad (n = 0, 1, 2, \ldots), \tag{8-2}$$

$$\nu = \frac{1}{2\pi}\sqrt{k/\mu} = 1303\sqrt{k/\mu}\ \text{cm}^{-1}, \tag{8-3}$$

where k is 10^5 dynes/cm.

Thus, the lowest energy level for any diatomic molecule is $\frac{1}{2}h\nu$, the zero-point energy (E^0) mentioned in the previous chapter. The above approximation is illustrated in Fig. 8–1 (cf. Fig. 3–2). We can see that the parabolic curve is a good representation of the dissociation-energy curve when the bond is neither stretched nor compressed greatly.

The zero-point energy is the vibrational energy at $0°K$. The vibrational energy levels are generally spaced far enough apart for nearly all the molecules (*ca*. 99%) to be at their zero-point levels at room temperature. We should note that, since isotopic substitution will not affect the potential-energy surface and therefore k is unchanged when H is changed to D, there will be a difference in the value of E^0 for X—H and X—D. This change is in μ in Eq. (8–3). The ratio E_H°/E_D° is given by

$$E_H^\circ/E_D^\circ = \left[\frac{h}{4\pi}(k/\mu_H)^{1/2}\right]\bigg/\left[\frac{h}{4\pi}(k/\mu_D)^{1/2}\right] = (\mu_D/\mu_H)^{1/2} \cong \sqrt{2}. \tag{8-4}$$

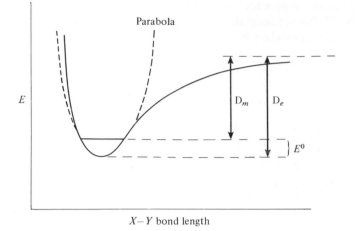

X–Y bond length

Fig. 8–1. Relationship of assumed parabolic curve and actual dissociation-energy curve.

The familiar useful relationships,

$$E = h\nu,$$
$$\nu = c/\lambda$$
$$E/hc = 1/\lambda = cm^{-1},$$
$$349.6 \ cm^{-1} = 1 \ kcal/mole$$
$$1000 \ cm^{-1} = 2.86 \ kcal/mole,$$

where c is velocity of light in centimeters per second and λ is wavelength in centimeters, permit us to compute the zero-point energy difference for X—H and X—D bonds if we know the vibrational frequencies, ν. Let us assume $\nu_H = 3000 \ cm^{-1}$ and $\nu_D = 2200 \ cm^{-1}$. The zero-point energy difference $\Delta E°$ is $(3000 - 2200)/2$ or $400 \ cm^{-1}$, *ca.* 1.15 kcal/mole—which means that it is more difficult to rupture an X—D than an X—H bond (see Fig. 8–2).

The case illustrated in Fig. 8–2 is an extreme situation and represents a maximum isotope effect. The frequencies chosen in the illustration are approximately those of a C—H and a C—D bond. Thus, if we assume there are no other effects, we can compute the maximum isotope effect (k_H/k_D) for rupture of a C—H bond by writing the Arrhenius equation for the reaction of X—H and of X—D:

$$k_H = A_H \ e^{-E_H^*/RT},$$
$$k_D = A_D \ e^{-E_D^*/RT}.$$

Dividing one by the other gives the ratio we are seeking:

$$k_H/k_D = A_H \ e^{-E_H^*/RT}/A_D \ e^{-E_D^*/RT}.$$

Assuming A_H/A_D is unity gives

$$k_H/k_D = e^{-E_H^*/RT}/e^{-E_D^*/RT}$$
$$= e^{(E_D^* - E_H^*)/RT}.$$

But the difference $E_D^* - E_H^*$ is totally derived from the zero-point energy difference, which is 1.15 kcal/mole in the case we are considering. At 300°K the value of k_H/k_D is easily obtained:

$$k_H/k_D = e^{1150/1.98 \times 300} = e^{1.94} = 7.$$

The source of this isotope effect is the zero-point energy difference that exists in the original molecules but not when the atoms are separated, because no vibrational degree of freedom remains. The value obtained is for a C—H bond. We must not expect it to be more than the crudest approximation since we have ignored both the fact that the C atom will have other groups bonded to it and the consequent bending vibrations. We have also ignored any changes in vibrational frequency for the rest of the molecule. Certainly we have been crude but, nevertheless, our approximation has found the principal source of the kinetic isotope effect.

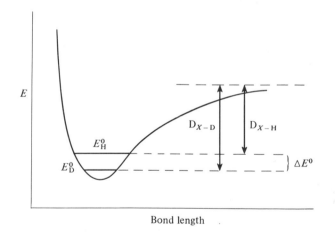

Fig. 8–2. The role of the zero-point energy difference in bond breaking.

Of more general interest is the isotope effect when a *three-center transition state* is operative, as in reactions involving transfer of a hydrogen atom or ion from one species to another. The treatment that we shall use closely follows that of Westheimer [3].

Let us consider the reaction

$$A—B + C \rightleftharpoons A\text{---}B\text{---}C \rightarrow A + BC,$$

where B is either hydrogen or deuterium. We will treat the transition state as a linear, one-dimensional species, thereby ignoring bending vibrations. We can describe the displacements of the nuclei from their equilibrium positions by X_A, X_B, and X_C. The transition state is held together by forces, described by force constants, that tend to return the atoms to an equilibrium position during a displacement. The force constant for stretching the A—B bond will be termed $\mathbf{k}_1$, that for the B—C bond $\mathbf{k}_2$. A third, the coupling constant, $\mathbf{k}_{12}$, will be used to account for interaction of the A—B bond when the B—C bond distance changes or of the B—C bond when A—B changes:

$$A \overset{\mathbf{k}_1}{\underset{X_{\vec{A}}}{-\!\!-\!\!-}} B \overset{\mathbf{k}_2}{\underset{X_{\vec{B}}}{-\!\!-\!\!-}} C. \\ \quad \phantom{X_{\vec{A}}} \quad \quad \phantom{X_{\vec{B}}} \quad X_{\vec{C}}$$

The potential energy of a stretched spring (bond) is given by the expression $\frac{1}{2}(\mathbf{k}X^2)$. For a system in which there are three masses and coupling of the stretching vibrations occurs, the potential energy is given by

$$V = \tfrac{1}{2}\mathbf{k}_1(X_B - X_A)^2 + \tfrac{1}{2}\mathbf{k}_2(X_C - X_B)^2 + \mathbf{k}_{12}(X_B - X_A)(X_C - X_B). \quad (8\text{–}5)$$

We are interested, however, not in V but rather in the forces exerted on A, B, and C. Since force, $\mathbf{F}$, is given by the negative partial derivative of the potential energy, we can obtain it easily:

$$\partial V/\partial X_A = -\mathbf{F}_A = -\mathbf{k}_1(X_B - X_A) - \mathbf{k}_{12}X_C + \mathbf{k}_{12}X_B, \quad (8\text{–}6)$$

$$\partial V/\partial X_B = -\mathbf{F}_B = \mathbf{k}_1(X_B - X_A) - \mathbf{k}_2(X_C - X_B) + \mathbf{k}_{12}X_C - 2\mathbf{k}_{12}X_B + \mathbf{k}_{12}X_A, \quad (8\text{–}7)$$

$$\partial V/\partial X_C = -\mathbf{F}_C = \mathbf{k}_2(X_C - X_B) + \mathbf{k}_{12}X_B - \mathbf{k}_{12}X_A. \quad (8\text{–}8)$$

If we consider the forces to be classical, we can also write Eq. (8–9), where m is the mass of any atom and a is the acceleration:

$$\mathbf{F} = ma = m\partial^2 X/\partial t^2. \quad (8\text{–}9)$$

If we assume the motion is that of a harmonic oscillator we can relate displacement X to time t by writing the expression that gives displacement at any time for harmonic motion:

$$X = A \cos 2\pi\nu t. \quad (8\text{–}10)$$

Differentiating with respect to time gives

$$dX/dt = -2\pi\nu A \sin 2\pi\nu t,$$
$$d^2 X/dt^2 = -4\pi^2\nu^2 A \cos 2\pi\nu t, \quad (8\text{–}11)$$

and substituting Eq. (8–10) into Eq. (8–11) gives

$$d^2 X/dt^2 = -4\pi^2\nu^2 X. \quad (8\text{–}12)$$

We obtain the force on each atom by substituting Eq. (8–12) into Eq. (8–9):

$$\mathbf{F}_A = -4\pi^2\nu^2 X_A m_A, \quad (8\text{–}13)$$

$$\mathbf{F}_B = -4\pi^2\nu^2 X_B m_B, \quad (8\text{–}14)$$

$$\mathbf{F}_C = -4\pi^2\nu^2 X_C m_C. \quad (8\text{–}15)$$

To obtain a set of simultaneous equations we substitute the previous values of $\mathbf{F}$ into these equations and use $\lambda = 4\pi^2\nu^2$ to simplify:

$$(m_A\lambda - \mathbf{k}_1)X_A + (\mathbf{k}_1 - \mathbf{k}_{12})X_B + \mathbf{k}_{12}X_C = 0,$$

$$(\mathbf{k}_1 - \mathbf{k}_{12})X_A + (m_B\lambda - \mathbf{k}_1 - \mathbf{k}_2 + 2\mathbf{k}_{12})X_R + (\mathbf{k}_2 - \mathbf{k}_{12})X_C = 0,$$

$$\mathbf{k}_{12}X_A + (\mathbf{k}_2 - \mathbf{k}_{12})X_{AB} + (m_C\lambda - \mathbf{k}_2)X_C = 0.$$

The solution to this set of equations is obtained by the method of determinants:

$$\begin{vmatrix} m_A\lambda - \mathbf{k}_1 & \mathbf{k}_1 - \mathbf{k}_{12} & \mathbf{k}_{12} \\ \mathbf{k}_1 - \mathbf{k}_{12} & m_B\lambda - \mathbf{k}_1 - \mathbf{k}_2 - 2\mathbf{k}_{12} & \mathbf{k}_2 - \mathbf{k}_{12} \\ \mathbf{k}_{12} & \mathbf{k}_2 - \mathbf{k}_{12} & m_C\lambda - \mathbf{k}_2 \end{vmatrix} = 0.$$

Expansion gives

$$m_A m_B m_C \lambda^3 - (m_A m_B \mathbf{k}_2 + m_A m_C \mathbf{k}_1 + m_A m_C \mathbf{k}_2 + m_B m_C \mathbf{k}_1 - 2m_A m_C \mathbf{k}_{12})\lambda^2$$
$$+ (m_A + m_B + m_C)(\mathbf{k}_1\mathbf{k}_2 - \mathbf{k}_{12}^2)\lambda = 0. \quad (8\text{--}16)$$

Equation (8–16) can be factored to give a value of $\lambda = 0$. (This solution corresponds to the translation of the entire molecule and is not of special interest to us.) After factoring λ out of Eq. (8–16), we obtain

$$m_A m_B m_C \lambda^2 - (m_A m_B \mathbf{k}_2 + m_A m_C \mathbf{k}_1 + m_A m_C \mathbf{k}_2 + m_B m_C \mathbf{k}_1 - 2m_A m_C \mathbf{k}_{12})\lambda$$
$$+ (m_A + m_B + m_C)(\mathbf{k}_1\mathbf{k}_2 - \mathbf{k}_{12}^2) = 0. \quad (8\text{--}17)$$

To continue, we must apply the transition-state theory. Two solutions for λ remain and, since by definition $\lambda = 4\pi^2\nu^2$, these correspond to vibrations of the transition state. If we were discussing a linear molecule, it would have two stretching frequencies, a symmetrical and an asymmetrical vibration:

$\leftarrow A\ B\ C \rightarrow$ $\leftarrow A\ B \rightarrow \leftarrow C$
Symmetric vibration   Asymmetric vibration

It is readily seen that the asymmetric vibration represents movement along the reaction coordinate, which is not a vibration at all but corresponds to translational motion. The potential-energy surface is concave along the reaction coordinate at the transition state and consequently not only is there no restoring force operative but there is a *negative* force constant. This would yield an imaginary vibrational frequency ν^* for the asymmetric stretching. A more detailed theory of kinetic isotope effects would take ν^* into consideration, but in our simplified approach we will consider that this frequency, and hence another value of ν^*, is zero. For this to be so, the last term in Eq. (8–17) must equal zero†:

$$\mathbf{k}_1\mathbf{k}_2 - \mathbf{k}_{12}^2 = 0. \quad (8\text{--}18)$$

---

† Examination will show that if $\mathbf{k}_{12}^2 > \mathbf{k}_1\mathbf{k}_2$, i.e. $\mathbf{k}_{12}$ is large, one of the roots of the quadratic equation (8–17) must be negative and an imaginary frequency is obtained. If $\mathbf{k}_1\mathbf{k}_2 > \mathbf{k}_{12}^2$, i.e. $\mathbf{k}_{12}$ is small, both roots are positive and ABC corresponds to a stable molecule.

When Eq. (8–18) is valid, Eq. (8–17) may be reduced to

$$m_A m_B m_C \lambda^2 - (m_A m_B \mathbf{k}_2 + m_A m_C \mathbf{k}_1 + m_A m_C \mathbf{k}_2 + m_B m_C \mathbf{k}_1 - 2 m_A m_C \mathbf{k}_{12}) \lambda = 0,$$

and the value of $\lambda = 0$ may be factored out. This affords

$$m_A m_B m_C \lambda -- (m_A m_B \mathbf{k}_2 + m_A m_C \mathbf{k}_1 + m_A m_C \mathbf{k}_2 + m_B m_C \mathbf{k}_1 - 2 m_A m_C \mathbf{k}_{12}) = 0,$$

which may be rearranged to give Eq. (8–19) after substitution of Eq. (8–18):

$$\lambda = 4\pi^2 \nu^{\ddagger 2} = \frac{\mathbf{k}_1}{m_A} + \frac{\mathbf{k}_1 + \mathbf{k}_2 - 2\sqrt{\mathbf{k}_1 \mathbf{k}_2}}{m_B} + \frac{\mathbf{k}_2}{m_C}. \tag{8–19}$$

This equation is the solution for the frequency of the symmetrical vibration of the transition state. This stretching frequency corresponds to motion at right angles to the reaction coordinate. The real vibration is not related to the stretching vibration in the reactant AB but results from the formation of a new bond. These results are illustrated in Fig. 8–3.

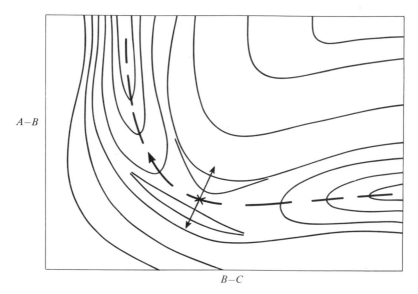

$A-B$

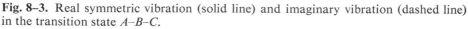

$B-C$

Fig. 8–3. Real symmetric vibration (solid line) and imaginary vibration (dashed line) in the transition state $A–B–C$.

Equation (8–19) gives the relationship of the isotopic mass (recall that B is H or D) to the vibrational frequency of the symmetric vibration. Since the zero-point energy is related to the frequency by $\frac{1}{2}h\nu$, we also have the relationship for the influence of isotopic substitution on the zero-point energy. We shall consider two extreme cases to see what can be learnt from Eq. (8–19).

First, when the two force constants are equal ($\mathbf{k}_1 = \mathbf{k}_2 = \mathbf{k}$), the transition state is perfectly symmetrical and Eq. (8–19) becomes

$$\lambda = 4\pi^2 \nu^{\ddagger 2} = \mathbf{k}/m_A + \mathbf{k}/m_C. \tag{8–20}$$

We note that m_B does not appear, so that substitution of D for H will have no effect upon the zero-point energy of the transition state. The kinetic isotope effect will be determined by the zero-point energy difference between the reactants A—H and A—D. This situation will lead to a maximum isotope effect, as illustrated in Fig. 8–4 (*cf.* Fig. 8–2).

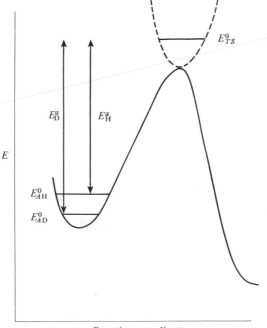

Fig. 8–4. Origin of the intermolecular kinetic isotope effect in a symmetrical transition state.

Next, let us consider the case when $\mathbf{k}_1 \gg \mathbf{k}_2$ and the transition state is far from symmetrical. If we apply this inequality to Eq. (8–19), we obtain

$$\lambda = 4\pi^2\nu^{\ddagger 2} = \mathbf{k}_1/m_A + \mathbf{k}_1/m_B. \qquad (8\text{–}21)$$

Now the mass of B is important in determining the zero-point energy of the vibration labeled "symmetrical" earlier. If m_A is large relative to the mass of H or D, Eq. (8–21) is further reduced to

$$\lambda = 4\pi^2\nu^{\ddagger 2} = \mathbf{k}_1/m_B,$$

and it is apparent that both the frequencies and the zero-point energies will differ by a factor of $\sqrt{2}$, exactly as in Eq. (8–4). Thus, in this extreme case, the difference in zero-point energies of the symmetrical stretching frequency of AHC and ADC may equal the difference between that of AH and AD, and the kinetic isotope effect will vanish (Fig. 8–5).

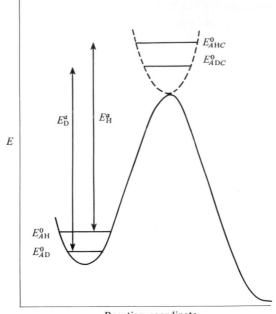

Fig. 8–5. Origin of vanishing intermolecular kinetic isotope effect in a nonsymmetric transition state.

We have examined two extreme cases for a three-center transition state. In the first, with equal force constants, a maximum isotope effect is observed. In the second, when $k_1 \gg k_2$, a vanishingly small isotope effect is expected. Examination of Eq. (8–19) will show that when $k_1 \ll k_2$ the kinetic isotope effect is again vanishingly small. When k_1 and k_2 differ but not greatly, a kinetic isotope effect is observed whose value lies between the two limiting cases. Many reactions exhibit intermediate values for the isotope effect. Table 8–1 lists some typical values, and the review article by Wiberg [4] is another valuable source.

Table 8–1. Typical Values of the Primary Kinetic Isotope Effect

Reaction	$T(°C)$	k_H/k_D	Reference
$C_6H_5CH_3(D_3)$ + *tert*-BuO $\rightarrow$	40	2.4	5
$C_6H_5CH_2$ + *tert*-BuOH	80	1.9	6
$H_3CNO_2(D_3)$ + $CH_3CO_2^-$ $\rightarrow$	25	6.5	7
$H_3CNO_2^-$ + CH_3CO_2H			
$C_6H_5CH_2D$ + Cl $\rightarrow$ $C_6H_5CH_2$ + DCl	77	1.3	8
$C_6H_5CH_2D$ + Br $\rightarrow$ $C_6H_5CH_2$ + DBr	77	4.6	8

The first two entries in Table 8–1 were studied by examining the rate of reaction (or relative rate) when the reactive position either contained no deuterium or was completely deuterated. The ratio k_H/k_D is, therefore, a comparison of the rates of reaction of two different reactants:

$$A\!-\!H + C \xrightarrow{\ k_H\ } A + H\!-\!C,$$

$$A\!-\!D + C \xrightarrow{\ k_D\ } A + D\!-\!C.$$

Because different reactants are used, this effect, examined above, is called an *intermolecular isotope effect*. The last entries in Table 8–1 were determined differently: the same reactant contained both hydrogen and deuterium in equivalent positions and reaction occurred selectively at the two positions (k_H/k_D is statistically corrected for differing numbers of H and D atoms). This is known as an *intramolecular isotope effect* and the ratio k_H/k_D is a measure of the rates for the reaction

$$H\!-\!A\!-\!D + C \left[\begin{array}{l} \xrightarrow{\ k_H\ } (D\!-\!A\text{---}H\text{---}C) \to DA + HC \\[1em] \xrightarrow{\ k_D\ } (H\!-\!A\text{---}D\text{---}C) \to HA + DC. \end{array} \right.$$

The origin of the intramolecular kinetic isotope effect differs from that of the intermolecular effect. For the former there is no difference between the zero-point energies of the reactants—there is only one reactant—but there is a difference in the activated complex and this is the principal source of the effect. In our model reaction, $HAD + C$, the activated complex for removal of H contains a normal $A\!-\!D$ bond, and the transition state for removal of D contains a normal $A\!-\!H$ bond. This leads to a zero-point energy difference for the transition states, which is the principal source of the intramolecular isotope effect (see Fig. 8–6). The effect will be modified by any residual zero-point energy difference associated with breaking the bond, just as in the case of the intermolecular effect. This modification is not large, however, if the force constants for the symmetrical stretching vibration are approximately equal ($\mathbf{k_1 = k_2}$). If $\mathbf{k_1 \gg k_2}$ or $\mathbf{k_2 \gg k_1}$, the modification does become important and the observed isotope effect will be decreased.

The foregoing discussion has ignored several factors that are important only in a more sophisticated treatment. We have not considered bending frequencies that must change in going to the transition state, since these will have only a small effect upon the zero-point energy difference. We assumed that the transmission coefficients of the transition state theory are the same for H and D—which is probably correct at normal temperatures. We have not felt it necessary to treat the proton by quantum mechanical methods that allow for leakage or *tunneling* across the energy barrier by hydrogen. (Because of mass differences deuterium is much less likely to tunnel.) This tunneling effect, leading to an observed high activation energy difference and a low pre-exponential factor difference, seems to be unimportant in most reactions that have been investigated, although there are some reactions in which it does play an important role [9]. Finally, we have considered only linear transition states. In reactions having nonlinear transition states, such as hydrogen migration

we cannot assign the transfer of hydrogen to a corresponding stretching frequency. We should not expect our linear model to predict the magnitude of the isotope effect for this transition state, but a corresponding treatment using a bending frequency can be employed with some success.

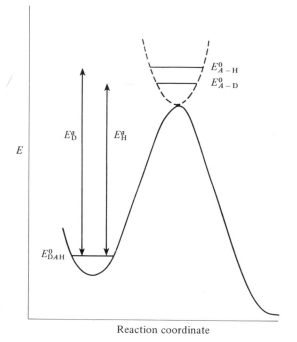

Reaction coordinate

Fig. 8–6. Origin of the intramolecular kinetic isotope effect.

The primary isotope effect is a very useful tool to determine whether a C—H bond is broken in the rate-determining step of a reaction. The observance of an isotope effect suggests such bond breakage while the value of the isotope effect suggests the symmetry, in terms of force constants, of the transition state. If no isotope effect is observed, the C—H bond is broken in some step other than the slow one, or else the transition state is highly asymmetric. Bond breaking prior to the slow step will normally occur in an equilibrium step and will lead to hydrogen-deuterium scrambling. If bond breaking occurs after the slow step, we can learn nothing by the isotope effect method. (This is illustrated in Chapter 12, in which the lack of an isotope effect is used to substantiate other chemical evidence that bond breaking does not occur before or during the slow step in the nitration of several aromatic reactants.)

SECONDARY ISOTOPE EFFECTS

Reactions that proceed by breaking a bond other than an isotopically substituted bond within a reacting molecule during the rate-determining step may also show kinetic isotope effects and are called *secondary isotope effects*. They are not as well understood as primary effects and consequently our discussion will be limited. Although our discussion of primary isotope effects was limited to the role of stretching vibrations, it should be clear to the reader that loss of any degree of freedom in going from reactants to the transition state might lead to zero-point energy changes, which will in turn lead to an isotope effect upon reaction rate.

Streitwieser *et al.* [10] have pointed out that an isotope effect is observed when the hybridization of carbon changes from sp^3 to sp^2, as in the formation of a carbonium ion in solvolytic reactions. Using an aldehydic C—H bond as his model for a carbonium ion (sp^2 hybrid), Streitwieser has shown that the change from sp^3 to sp^2 hybridization causes a change in the stretching frequency of about 100 cm^{-1} (2900 → 2800), no change in the in-plane bending frequency, and a large change in the out-of-plane bending frequency (1340 → 800):

Out-of-plane bending vibration

The change in zero-point energy for this vibration is the principal origin of the isotope effect observed when deuterium replaces hydrogen on a carbon atom undergoing ionization. The resulting α isotope effect, k_H/k_D of 1.4, is smaller than predicted by basing the origin on the out-of-plane bending frequency change. Table 8–2, which gives values for the isotope effect, shows that the effect can even become a reverse isotope effect, $k_H/k_D < 1$. The article by Streitwieser *et al.* [10] gives a perfectly reasonable explanation of the lower observed values. If the out-of-plane bending vibration is inhibited in the transition state by the presence of some other group, the frequency will be raised and consequently the zero-point energy change will be lowered. In an ionization process, the back side of the molecule may be free but the front side must have a group leaving close by. This will inhibit the vibration and lower the observed k_H/k_D.

Inhibition of out-of-plane bending vibration by a leaving group

Should the change in hybridization occur by an S_N2 process, the back side of the molecule will also be occupied and the vibration will be further inhibited.

$$Y \text{---} \overset{\nearrow}{\underset{\underset{H}{|}}{C}} \text{---} X$$

Inhibition of out-of-plane bending vibration by entering and leaving groups

In this case the frequency might well be higher than in the free reactant and an inverse isotope effect would be expected. A second effect undoubtedly plays a role in lowering the observed k_H/k_D below that calculated with the aldehydic model transition state. Any developing positive charge in the transition state would weaken the force constants for both stretching and bending vibrations of the α—H. If the positive charge is greater than in the model transition state, the value of k_H/k_D will be increased. On the other hand, if the positive charge is less than in the model, a carbonyl carbon atom, the force constants will be larger than those in the model and the resulting increase in the frequency will give a low value for k_H/k_D. A delicate balance of the effects is indicated by the data for ethyl compounds (Table 8–2).

Table 8–2. α-Deuterium Isotope Effects for the Solvolytic Reaction
$$R\text{---}X + Y \rightarrow R\text{---}Y + X$$

Compound	Solvent	$T(°C)$	k_H/k_D	Reference
Methyl chloride	Water	90	0.97	11
Methyl bromide	Water	80	0.96	11
Methyl iodide	Water	70	0.95	11
Methyl tosylate	Water	70	0.985	11
Ethyl bromide	Water	80	0.995	12
Ethyl iodide	Water	80	0.99	12
Ethyl tosylate	Water	54	1.02	12
1-Propyl bromide	Water	80	0.99	12
1-Propyl iodide	Water	90	1.00	12
2-Propyl bromide	Water	60	1.07	12
2-Propyl iodide	Water	90	1.05	12
2-Propyl tosylate	Water	30	1.13	12
Cyclopentyl tosylate	AcOH	50	1.15	10
Cyclohexyl tosylate	AcOH	75	1.19	13

Substitution of deuterium for hydrogen on a carbon atom adjacent to a reacting center may also cause a change in rate, known as a β isotope effect. Explanation of this effect is a matter for debate but at present the experimental evidence appears to support the theory of hyperconjugation, which holds that, when an electron-deficient p orbital exists on a carbon atom, an adjacent C—H bond may overlap with the orbital. The overlap shifts electrons toward the deficient p orbital and the H atom moves with the electrons. Thus, a bending vibration of the ground state becomes a C—H deformation while the adjacent carbon atom becomes electron-deficient in the transition state. The restoring force is lowered and so is the vibrational frequency. Again we have a change in zero-point energy in going from reactants to the transition state, resulting in a rate difference when H is replaced by D. Table 8–3 shows the magnitude of β isotope effects.

Table 8–3. β-Deuterium Isotope Effects for the Solvolytic Reaction $R—X + Y \rightarrow R—Y + X$

Compound	Solvent	$T(°C)$	k_H/k_D	Reference
CD_3CH_2OTs	Water	60	1.02	12
CD_3CH_2Br	Water	80	1.03	12
CD_3CH_2I	Water	80	1.04	12
$(CD_3)_2CHOTs$	Water	30	1.55	12
$(CD_3)_2CHBr$	Water	60	1.34	12
$(CD_3)_2CHI$	Water	60	1.31	12
$(CD_3)_3CCl$	Water	20	2.45	15
$(CD_3)_3CCl$	Methanol	56	2.27	15

The explanation for the β isotope effect given above has been challenged [14]. Secondary β isotope effects upon the hydrolysis rates of several isopropyl-d_6 compounds were found to be nearly independent of temperature [14]. In this case the isotope effect is due principally to *entropy* of activation effects rather than the *enthalpy* expected in a zero-point energy difference explanation. In the hydrolysis of *tert*-butyl-d_9 chloride, however, the temperature dependence is that expected for the zero-point energy difference explanation offered above [15]. The lack of temperature dependence for the β isotope effects of isopropyl derivatives is said to involve reasonable compensating changes in force constants and, hence, zero-point energy differences. In S_N2 reactions, a strong interaction between the nucleophile and the reacting carbon atom increases *bending* frequencies of the methyl group; at the same time, electronic changes associated with formation of the new bond and concomitant breaking of the old bond tend to decrease *stretching* frequencies [15]. The dependence of the β isotope effect upon temperature may become a new tool in distinguishing between S_N2 (temperature-independent) and S_N1 (temperature-dependent) mechanistic pathways (see Chapter 13 for others).

Because the rates for either of the secondary isotope effects differ only slightly, experimental precision is of the utmost importance. The methods employed to obtain any isotope effect parallel those to obtain any rate (see Chapter 6). An excellent review of both theory and experimental approach is available [16]. For an alternative explanation of the origin of secondary isotope effects, the reader should consult the work of Halevi [17].

Two additional uses of isotopes have been employed in mechanistic studies. The use of isotopes as tracers is well-known and this can occasionally give information about steps preceding the rate-determining step. A discussion of the second, the *solvent isotope effect*, will be postponed until Chapter 10.

The importance of isotope effects in mechanistic studies cannot be overstated. They provide us with a highly sensitive tool for the examination of transition states. The application of isotope effects to the study of reaction mechanisms will be illustrated in later chapters.

PROBLEMS

1. The bromination of toluene, ethylbenzene, and cumene with N-bromosuccinimide at 77°C gives k_H/k_D of 4.9, 2.7, and 1.8 respectively.
   a) For which substrate is the difference $E_H^a - E_D^a$ the greatest?
   b) For which substrate is the transition state the least symmetrical?
   c) Make a reasonable prediction whether the ratio of force constants k_{CH}/k_{HBr} is increased or decreased when toluene is compared with cumene.

2. a) Compute the ratio of zero-point energies E_H^0/E_T^0 for the diatomic hydrogen- and tritium-substituted compounds XH and XT.
   b) From this and the C—H stretching frequency of 3000 cm^{-1} compute the C—T stretching frequency.
   c) What is the zero-point energy difference $E_H^0 - E_T^0$ in kcal?
   d) Predict the value of k_H/k_T at 300°K.
   e) What is the ratio of k_D/k_T?

3. a) A mixture of 13.83 mmoles of toluene and 13.26 mmoles of trideuterotoluene was chlorinated with *tert*-butyl hypochlorite. The benzyl chloride isolated, 6.27 mmoles, was found to be 12.9% dideuterobenzyl chloride, the rest being un-deuterated. What is the value of k_H/k_D?
   b) The initial mixture also contained 0.94 mmole of $C_6H_5CHD_2$. Derive an expression for the millimoles of this compound present at completion of the reaction in terms of k_H, k_D, and millimoles of toluene and toluene-d_3. Assuming the value of k_H/k_D obtained above applies, what is the value for the final mmoles of $C_6H_5CHD_2$?
   c) Some of the $C_6H_5CD_2Cl$ formed came from $C_6H_5CHD_2$. How many millimoles of $C_6H_5CD_3$ remained at the completion of the reaction?
   d) Using this value for the final millimoles of trideuterotoluene, calculate k_H/k_D for the reaction. From this compute the final concentration of di- and trideutero-toluene and again evaluate k_H/k_D. In this problem we have used the method of successive approximations to solve an otherwise very difficult problem.

REFERENCES

1. J Bigeleisen and M. Wolfsburg, *Advances in Chemical Physics*, Vol. 1 (Ed. I. Prigogine), Interscience Publishers, New York (1958), p. 15.
2. H. S. Johnston, *Advances in Chemical Physics*, Vol. 3 (Ed. I. Prigogine), Interscience Publishers, New York (1961), p. 131.

3. F. H. WESTHEIMER, *Chem. Revs.*, **61,** 265 (1961).
4. K. B. WIBERG, *Chem. Revs.*, **55,** 713 (1955).
5. B. R. KENNEDY and K. U. INGOLD, *Can. J. Chem.*, **44,** 2381 (1966).
6. R. D. GILLIOM, Ph.D. Thesis, Massachusetts Institute of Technology, Cambridge, Mass., 1960.
7. O. REITZ, *Z. Physik. Chem.*, **A176,** 363 (1936).
8. K. B. WIBERG and L. H. SLAUGH, *J. Am. Chem. Soc.*, **80,** 3033 (1958).
9. R. P. BELL, *The Proton in Chemistry*, Cornell University Press, Ithaca, N. Y. (1959), pp. 202–214.
10. A. STREITWIESER, R. H. JAGOW, R. C. FAHEY, and S. SUZUKI, *J. Am. Chem. Soc.*, **80,** 2326 (1958).
11. J. A. LLEWELLYN, R. E. ROBERTSON, and J. M. W. SCOTT, *Can. J. Chem.*, **38,** 222 (1960).
12. K. T. LEFFEK, J. A. LLEWELLYN, and R. E. ROBERTSON, *Can. J. Chem.*, **38,** 1505 (1960).
13. K. MISLOW, S. BORCIC, and V. PRELOG, *Helv. Chim. Acta*, **40,** 2477 (1957).
14. K. T. LEFFEK, R. E. ROBERTSON, and S. SUGAMORI, *Can. J. Chem.*, **39,** 1989 (1961).
15. L. HAKKA, A. QUEEN, and R. E. ROBERTSON, *J. Am. Chem. Soc.*, **87,** 161 (1965).
16. L. MELANDER, *Isotope Effects on Reaction Rates*, Ronald Press Co., New York (1960).
17. E. A. HALEVI, *Progress in Physical Organic Chemistry*, Vol. 1, (Eds. S. G. Cohen, A. Streitwieser, and R. W. Taft), Interscience Publishers, New York (1963), p. 109.

CHAPTER 9

LINEAR FREE ENERGY
RELATIONSHIPS

The material to be covered in this chapter is based upon one of the underlying concepts of modern organic chemistry, the *reaction series*. This is a group of reactions involving small changes from one reaction to another. The changes may be structural, such as a series of primary, secondary, and tertiary halides, or may involve a single reaction carried out in a series of solvents. Organic chemists make the definition that all of the reactions in a series involve mechanisms similar enough to be classified together as a single mechanism or that a single mechanistic change occurs somewhere within the series. It has frequently been demonstrated that such series, based upon mechanistic integrity, can be assembled. Furthermore, it has been found that the changes in rates and in equilibrium constants occurring in one series can often be related to those occurring in another, closely related series. This reasoning by analogy—applying our knowledge of the mechanism of one reaction to another reaction—has become very important.

GENERAL DEVELOPMENT

The relationship between the equilibrium constant for a reaction and the difference between the standard free energies, $\Delta G°$, of the products and reactants is given by

$$\ln K = -(G_p° - G_r°)/RT = -\Delta G°/RT. \tag{9-1}$$

A similar expression for the rate constant of a reaction can be written from Eq. (7–26), using the free energy of activation $\Delta G^{\ddagger}$:

$$\ln k = -\Delta G^{\ddagger}/RT + \ln \kappa \mathbf{k}T/h. \tag{9-2}$$

Thus, if we could estimate the standard free energies of organic compounds and transition states, calculation of equilibrium constants and reaction rate constants would be possible. Unfortunately, this estimation cannot be carried out with the accuracy needed for useful computations involving Eqs. (9–1) and (9–2). It is experimentally known, however, that plotting $\ln k$ or $\ln K$ for one reaction series against $\ln k$ or $\ln K$ for a second, closely related, series frequently gives a straight line [1].

This linear relationship can be expressed in the form

$$\ln k_1 = A \ln k_2 + B, \tag{9-3}$$

where A and B are constants. This kind of correlation, found when the free energy of activation or change of one reaction is related linearly to the free energy of activation or change of a second reaction, is shown by substitution of Eqs. (9–1) and (9–2) into Eq. (9–3) for the case when rates of one series are linearly related to equilibrium constants of another:

$$-\Delta G^{\ddagger}/RT + \ln \kappa kT/h = A(-\Delta G^{\circ}/RT) + B,$$
$$\Delta G^{\ddagger} = A\Delta G^{\circ} + BRT - RT \ln \kappa kT/h. \tag{9-4}$$

The last two terms in Eq. (9–4) are constants at any given temperature so that this equation is in linear form. These linear free energy relationships give predictions of much greater precision than can be obtained by the estimation of standard free energies.

If we specify some compound (or condition) within a series as a "standard" with equilibrium constant K_0 and some second compound (or condition) with equilibrium constant K, we can relate the constants through the free energy changes, where the operator δ represents the effect of a substituent (or medium) change:

$$\ln K - \ln K_0 = -\Delta G/RT - (-\Delta G_0/RT) = \delta \Delta G/RT.$$

Using the same two compounds (or conditions) for a second reaction with K' and K_0', we get a similar relationship:

$$\ln K' - \ln K_0' = \delta \Delta G'/RT.$$

The observed linearity between the two reaction series implies that the differences in free energy changes are also linear, so that

$$\ln K/K_0 = A \ln K'/K_0'. \tag{9-5}$$

A similar expression can be written for rate constants.

Let us consider the reaction series represented by the primed quantities in Eq. (9–5) as a standard series. The value of $\ln K'/K_0'$ will be characteristic of the particular factor (structure, solvent, etc.) that changes when the standard compound (or condition) is changed to another in the series; we can call it a *substituent constant* (or medium constant). The value of the constant A depends upon the particular reaction series (K) that is being compared with the standard reaction and it is frequently called a *reaction constant*. Its value for the standard reaction series is, of course, 1.00.

In thermodynamics we are dealing with macroscopic properties. Although linear free energy relationships are outside the scope of formal thermodynamic analysis, the approach employed resembles that of thermodynamics. There is no need to consider a detailed specific interaction as causing an equilibrium or a rate change. We need only consider that whatever causes a change within a standard series also causes a similar change in any subsidiary series. Thus any linear free energy relationship that is observed is valid. If we draw a conclusion that later proves to be incorrect from a relationship, it will be the conclusion and not the relationship that is wrong. But, the reader might ask, if our approach is thermodynamically oriented, how can conclusions be drawn about mechanisms involving specific molecules? How can we obtain microscopic information from macroscopic data? The answer lies in our microscopic knowledge of the model, i.e. the standard, reaction. If we know that the effect of substituting some group, e.g. a chlorine atom, for another group, usually hydrogen, on the standard compound of the model reaction is caused by some specific interaction, perhaps an inductive effect or resonance, we can anticipate a similar interaction in a related reaction series. Similarly, a deviation from the correlation will suggest other specific interactions. The value of the proportionality constant A in Eq. (9–5) may also give microscopic information by analogy. If we know specifically what causes changes within the standard reaction series and we have another series related to the standard by a linear free energy equation, the magnitude of A may be taken as a measure of the sensitivity of the related series to the specific cause. A large value of A suggests a sensitivity to the particular interaction greater than in the standard series.

Linear free energy relationships are useful in two ways. The first, and by far the most important, use is in the study of reaction mechanisms. The correlation of data for a new reaction series by means of a linear free energy equation establishes a similarity between the new series and all others that obey the equation; the effect of the particular variable correlated is regular. The values of the parameters may suggest deductions about transition state structures. The second use of linear free energy equations is to predict reaction rates or equilibrium constants.

Equations have been found for many types of reaction series. The effects of *meta* and *para* substituents on rates and equilibria of side-chain reactions of benzene have been correlated, as have rates of nucleophilic substitution reactions and solvent effects in solvolytic reactions. Some of these correlations are developed in this chapter, while the correlation of the catalytic effect of acids and bases to their ionization constants is discussed in the following chapter.

THE HAMMETT EQUATION

Of the many linear free energy relationships, the best known is the Hammett equation [1]. It correlates reaction rates and equilibrium constants for side-chain reactions of *meta*- and *para*-substituted benzene derivatives. Because of the availability of data, the standard reaction was chosen to be the dissociation equilibrium of benzoic acids in water at 25°C.

For any substituent, the value of $\log K'/K_0'$ was defined as σ, where K' is the ionization constant of the substituted benzoic acid and K_0' is that for benzoic acid. The proportionality constant A in Eq. (9–5) was given the symbol ρ. The Hammett equation has the form

$$\log K/K_0 \text{ (or } \log k/k_0) = \rho\sigma. \qquad (9\text{–}6)$$

Since electron-withdrawing groups increase the strength of the benzoic acids, these substituents have positive σ-values, whereas electron-releasing groups have negative σ-values. The value of σ for a particular group is now considered to be a measure of the ability of the particular group to supply or withdraw electrons. When the logarithms of rate or equilibrium constants for a reaction series are plotted against σ, a straight line of slope ρ is obtained if the electronic interactions involved resemble those in the ionization of benzoic acids. The ρ-value measures the sensitivity of the reaction to electron supply or withdrawal.

In an important review article [2], Jaffe re-examined the Hammett equation and redefined σ. He used Hammett's original values to compute a value of ρ for a reaction, and from this ρ-value he calculated σ-values for substituents not on the original list. He then averaged the σ-values obtained from several reactions to get the "best" value. Although this is a good approach for calculating unknown rate and equilibrium constants, it creates difficulties in interpreting deviations from a Hammett plot because of the loss of a model reaction. For this reason, McDaniel and Brown [3] advocated a return to the original definition of σ and their values are now customarily employed (Table 9–1).

Table 9–1. Hammett σ-Values*

Substituent	Meta-σ	Para-σ
CH_3	−0.07	−0.17
C_6H_5	0.06	−0.01
$COCH_3$	0.38	0.50
CN	0.56	0.66
$CO_2C_2H_5$	0.37	0.45
NO_2	0.71	0.78
$N(CH_3)_2$		−0.83
NH_2	−0.16	−0.66
OCH_3	0.12	−0.27
SO_3^-	0.05	0.09
$N(CH_3)_3^+$	0.88	0.82
CO_2^-	−0.10	0.00
OH	0.12	−0.37
F	0.34	0.06
Cl	0.37	0.23
Br	0.39	0.23
I	0.35	0.18
SH	0.25	0.15
SO_2CH_3	0.60	0.72
H	(0.00)	(0.00)

* From McDaniel and Brown [3].

The values of σ in Table 9–1 are all for the standard reaction conditions. Those substituents that can interact with the solvent might change values as the solvent is changed. This is shown by data of Bright and Briscoe [4], who measured equilibrium constants for the ionization of benzoic acids in a series of aqueous ethanol

Table 9–2. Solvent Dependence of σ-Values for the OH Group in Aqueous Ethanol*

Ethanol (%)	Meta-σ	Para-σ
100	−0.134	−0.442
95	−0.129	−0.429
90	−0.126	−0.414
80	−0.111	−0.384
70	−0.102	−0.350
40	−0.014	−0.285

* From Jaffe [2].

mixtures. Table 9–2 gives some σ-values for the hydroxyl group. No effect of temperature change upon σ-values has been observed.

Literally hundreds of applications of the Hammett equation are known. A few of these, taken from the review of Jaffe [2], are given in Table 9–3.

A brief examination of Table 9–3 reveals several facts about the value of ρ. As is shown by the data for the saponification of methyl benzoates, the value of ρ is temperature-dependent. This temperature effect will be discussed later. The first

Table 9–3. Values of ρ from Hammett Correlations*

Reaction	Solvent	$T(°C)$	ρ
Equilibria			
ArOH	Water	25	2.113
$ArCO_2H$	Water	25	1.000
$ArCH_2CO_2H$	Water	25	0.489
$ArCH_2CH_2CO_2H$	Water	25	0.212
$ArCH{=}CH_2CO_2H$	Water	25	0.466
$ArNH_2 + HCO_2H{=}$	67% C_5H_5N	100	−1.429
$ArNHCHO + H_2O$			
Rates			
$ArCO_2H + (C_6H_5)_2CN_2$	EtOH	30	0.940
$ArCO_2CH_3 + OH^-$	60%	50	1.920
	Acetone	0	2.460
$ArSO_2OCH_3 + H_2O$	50% EtOH	50	1.248
$ArCONH_2 + OH^-$	60% EtOH	53	1.364
$ArCONH_2 + H_3O^+$	60% EtOH	52	−0.483
$Ar(C_6H_5)CHCl + C_2H_5OH$	EtOH	25	−5.090

* From Jaffe [2].

four entries in the table show that, the closer the reacting center is to the ring, the larger the ρ-value. If our interpretation of ρ as a measure of sensitivity to electron supply is correct, this behavior is expected. Certainly, electron supply and withdrawal is less important as the reacting center is removed from the interacting group. The addition of a CH_2 group between the interacting centers removes any possibility of transmitting resonance effects, and inductive effects are known to fall off rapidly with chain length. If a $-CH_2CH_2-$ unit is replaced by a double bond, ρ increases— as is evident from the fifth entry. Also, the value of ρ may be either positive or negative. From the nature of the standard reaction we assume that electron-withdrawing groups increase the equilibrium constant by dispersing and thus stabilizing the negative charge developed in the product, $ArCO_2-$. A change in sign of ρ suggests that electron withdrawal is decreasing the equilibrium or rate constant. The last entry in Table 9–3 almost certainly involves generation of positive charge in the transition state leading to an intermediate carbonium ion. Electron-supplying substituents stabilize this incipient intermediate (the transition state), speeding the reaction, and we observe a negative ρ-value. Finally, the value of ρ changes sign for the catalyzed hydrolysis of benzamides. Basic catalysis leads to a positive ρ-value, so we may conclude that the transition state for this reaction involves a greater negative charge on the carbonyl carbon than does the starting material. Similarly, the negative ρ-value observed for acid catalysis suggests an increased positive charge density on the carbonyl carbon of the transition state for this reaction. This sort of reasoning has been useful in developing an understanding of reaction mechanisms.

Let us examine this in somewhat more detail. It is apparent from the preceding discussion that the particular interaction mechanism involved in the ionization of benzoic acids, the model, is believed to be of electronic origin. The mechanisms of electronic effects are not yet completely understood but there appear to be at least three modes of interaction: field effects, inductive effects, and resonance effects.

Field Effects

Electronic effects that are transmitted through space are called field effects. In terms of our model reaction, we must consider the interaction of a dipole (or charge) of the substituent with the negative charge of the carboxylate ion. The laws of electrostatics may be applied to the problem to calculate a potential-energy change, but this presents certain problems. First, because groups may undergo relatively free rotation, it is not always possible to set a unique distance for charge separation. Secondly, when a substituent leads to a dipole because of electronegativity differences, the value for the charge on the substituent must be estimated. Although these two approximations can be made with some confidence, a third, serious problem remains. To compute a potential-energy change when a substituent is introduced requires a knowledge of the dielectric constant of the medium through which the charge separation is "felt." Some of the interaction will occur through the solvent system and some through the carbon skeleton of the molecule itself. Therefore, an estimate must be made of the dielectric constant of the carbon chain of the molecule.

These problems have been considered and calculations have led to fair agreement with observed effects [5]. On a qualitative basis, we can see the field or some similar effect operating by examination of Table 9–1. The effect of introducing a positively charged substituent, NMe_3^+, is to increase the acidity of benzoic acid, and this increase is greater in the closer *meta* position than in the *para* position. Similarly, introduction of a negatively charged substituent, SO_3^- or CO_2^-, in the *para* position has less effect than in the *meta*; i.e., *meta*-substituted acids are less acidic than *para*-substituted. We should note, however, that the introduction of the negative SO_3^- substituent in either position increases the ionization constant, an effect that we would not have predicted. Although the field effect must be operative in controlling acidities, there must also be one or more other interactions.

Inductive Effects

Electronic effects that are transmitted through bonds are called inductive effects. They arise by reason of the different electron-withdrawing powers of two different atoms when bonded. If atom X is more electronegative than atom Y, X will withdraw electrons from Y. This in turn makes Y more electronegative and it withdraws electrons from any other atoms bonded to it. The effect falls off rapidly with chain length. If the inductive effect is operative in the ionization of carboxylic acids, substitution of a —CH_2— group between the reaction center and the substituent should not cause a breakdown of the linear free energy relationship. That no such breakdown occurs has already been pointed out. The ionization of phenylacetic and phenylpropionic acids does fit the Hammett equation (see Table 9–3). The value of ρ is small and decreases by a factor of approximately 2 for each —CH_2— group. Since each additional —CH_2— would further separate the reaction center from the substituent, a similar fall-off of sensitivity might be expected for the field effect. This is correct but there is a large error in the predicted magnitude of this decrease when a field-effect model is used.

    Separation of field and inductive effects has not been experimentally practical although it is an area of active interest. We will accept both of these polar effects as methods of electronic interaction.

Resonance Effects

The resonance effect has been discussed in several earlier chapters. We will, therefore, examine the resonance effect only as it applies to the ionization of benzoic acids.

    The correlation between the acidities of benzoic and phenylacetic acids suggests that resonance effects are not important in the model reaction. Certainly, the presence of the CH_2 group between the ring and the carboxyl group precludes resonance in the parent acids of the phenylacetic acid series. In going to the anion, however, the presence of the charge changes the Coulomb integral for the ring carbon nearest the carboxyl group, and the effect is greater for benzoate anions than for the phenylacetate anions. This will lead to a change in the π-electron density around the ring with the greatest change occurring at the *ortho* and *para* positions.

Thus, an *ortho* or *para* substituent will interact more strongly than a *meta* group will. The resonance effect, then, may be operative in the ionization of benzoic acids. For further evidence of this electronic mechanism, we can recognize that the *meta-σ*-values probably represent only inductive and field effects whereas *para*-values also include resonance effects. If it is assumed that the inductive and field effects are the same in both positions, $\sigma_m - \sigma_p$ should be a measure of the resonance effect. Table 9-4 shows that groups arranged according to increasing values of $\sigma_m - \sigma_p$ are also arranged in order of increasing electron-releasing resonance effects.

Table 9-4. Values of $\sigma_m - \sigma_p$

Substituent	$\sigma_m - \sigma_p$
$COCH_3$	-0.12
CN	-0.10
NO_2	-0.07
CH_3	0.10
Cl	0.14
F	0.28
OCH_3	0.39
OH	0.49
NH_2	0.50

The importance of this kind of resonance is not great but it undoubtedly exists. The conclusion that we must draw about the ionization of *meta*- and *para*-substituted benzoic acids is that all three of the electronic effects are operative. Any reaction that can be correlated by the Hammett equation is expected to have a similar balance of these electrical effects.

When the reaction center adjacent to the aromatic ring involves an atom with unshared electron pairs, the Hammett equation breaks down for some substituents. For example, the *para*-nitro group has a much greater influence on the ionization constant of phenols in water at 25°C than it does on that of benzoic acids. The same observation can be made for reactions of anilines. In both cases, groups that can stabilize negative charge by strong electron-withdrawing resonance effects require the use of *enhanced σ-values*, σ^-. This need is undoubtedly caused by an additional or enhanced resonance effect of a type impossible with the benzoates:

Table 9-5 compares some of the values of σ^- (denoted by σ^* in the original article) given by Jaffe [2] with values of *para-σ* from Table 9-1. For all *meta* groups and for *para* groups that do not strongly withdraw electrons, normal σ-values are used. The σ^--values will presumably give a better correlation than normal σ-values whenever direct conjugation of a pair of electrons at the reaction site is possible with the substituent. Such conjugation may occur in either the reactants or the product (transition state in the case of a kinetic series) but not in both. Thus, when a reaction is found to fit the Hammett equation using σ^--values, the assumption is usually made that conjugation of the type described is occurring.

Table 9–5. *para*-Substituent
Constants, σ^- and σ

Substituent	σ^-	σ
NO_2	1.27	0.78
CHO	1.13	
SO_2CH_3	1.05	0.72
CN	1.00	0.66
$COCH_3$	0.87	0.50
CO_2H	0.73	
$CO_2C_2H_5$	0.68	0.45
CO_2CH_3	0.64	
$CONH_2$	0.63	

A second group of reactions was found that did not fit the Hammett relationship well. As we might expect, if reactions involving *high* electron density do not fit Eq. (9–6), this same equation is unlikely to be applicable to those involving very *low* electron density at the reaction site. The groups that can supply electrons can also be given modified σ-values to obtain a good correlation. The modified σ-values for reactions involving high electron demand have been put on a sound basis by adopting another model reaction, which we shall now discuss.

THE OKAMOTO-BROWN EQUATION

Reactions involving generation of positive charge in a position capable of direct resonance interaction with a substituent are best fitted to Eq. (9–7). This equation has exactly the same form as the Hammett equation but a new standard reaction defines the substituent constants, which are given the symbol σ^+:

$$\log K/K_0 \text{ (or } \log k/k_0) = \rho\sigma^+. \tag{9–7}$$

The standard reaction used to establish this equation was the solvolysis in 90% acetone of cumyl chlorides at 25°C [6, 7]. This reaction almost certainly involves the generation of a carbonium ion intermediate and a transition state with considerable positive charge.

So that the σ- and σ^+-scales would be as similar as possible, σ-values of *meta* substituents unlikely to undergo resonance interactions were used to establish a ρ-value for the solvolytic reaction. The σ^+-value for all other substituents was then determined using this ρ-value. As a result, most *meta* substituents have similar values on the two scales (Table 9–6).

Table 9–6. Okamoto-Brown σ^+-Values*

Substituent	*Meta*	*Para*
CH_3O	0.047	−0.778
CH_3	−0.066	−0.311
C_2H_5	−0.064	−0.295
$(CH_3)_2CH$	−0.060	−0.280
$(CH_3)_3C$	−0.059	−0.256
H	0.00	0.00
F	0.352	−0.073
Cl	0.399	0.114
Br	0.405	0.150
I	0.359	0.135
$CO_2C_2H_5$	0.366	0.482
CN	0.562	0.659
NO_2	0.674	0.790
CO_2^-	−0.028	−0.023
$N(CH_3)_3^+$	0.359	0.408

* From Brown and Okamoto [7].

Reactions that fit Eq. (9–7) are all expected to resemble the standard reaction, that is, to involve significant developing positive charge. Since electron-supplying substituents have negative values for σ^+, we expect, and indeed find, that ρ is nearly always negative, but at least one σ^+-plot has been reported with a positive ρ-value. The reaction of the malonitrile anion with substituted benzaldehydes affords a ρ-value of +1.45 [8]. A reasonable interpretation of this is that resonance occurs in the reactant benzaldehydes and is destroyed when the anion attacks the benzaldehyde. The more stabilized reactants react more slowly, so that a positive ρ-value is to be expected.

At this point we might review briefly. Many reactions involving side-chains of substituted benzenes show polar effects, which are frequently correlated by linear free energy relationships. We have three such relationships, any one of which may give a superior correlation. The one giving the best correlation suggests, by analogy, certain characteristics of the particular reaction. A plot with σ^- is interpreted to mean that a negative charge is stabilized by a strong resonance interaction, while a σ^+ plot suggests the same stabilization for a positive charge. A Hammett correlation suggests that resonance is much less important but is not totally excluded. The following resonance structures will illustrate the differences between the three model reactions:

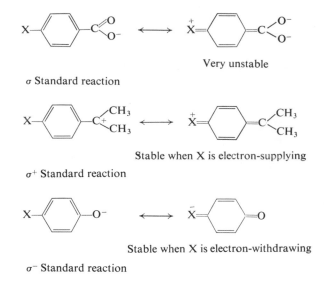

Very unstable

σ Standard reaction

Stable when X is electron-supplying

σ^+ Standard reaction

Stable when X is electron-withdrawing

σ^- Standard reaction

OTHER HAMMETT-TYPE EQUATIONS

We might question the idea of three distinct σ-scales, since this implies that resonance and polarization always occur in the same ratio. We might also ask whether a σ-scale involving no resonance at all might not better replace the Hammett scale if we want to keep the three-scale system. However, the three-scale system has been seriously questioned and has been found inadequate [9–11]. The σ-values for groups capable of resonance interactions have been shown to vary widely, with the σ^-- and σ^+-scales serving as limiting values for the variation.

Van Bekkum et al. developed a method for attempting to eliminate resonance effects from σ [9]. To do this they plotted some eighty reactions by the Hammett equation, using only substituents believed to involve no resonance interactions. These were m-methyl, m-fluoro, m-chloro, m-bromo, m-iodo, m-acetoxy, and m-nitro as well as hydrogen. In addition, p-acetoxy and p-nitro groups were used in reactions where para-resonance effects were considered out of the question. After obtaining ρ-values by the least-squares method, all other substituents were placed on the line obtained to get new σ^n-values. These latter values were found to involve considerable variation, particularly for para substituents. Many of the groups examined in this manner fell within a rather narrow range of σ-values and an average value was taken as a representative, non-resonance σ-value. For $p\text{-}NH_2$, $p\text{-}NMe_2$, p-OH, and p-OMe the values were found to fall into two groups, one involving reactions of substituted anilines that gave more negative σ-values than the values obtained from all other reactions. The average value for the last grouping was taken as the "best" measure of the inductive and field effect for these substituents. These workers showed that the σ-value can vary by as much as 1.237 units (for $p\text{-}NMe_2$) depending on the particular reaction series employed to evaluate the "constant." The conclusions to be drawn from this work are that resonance interactions are variable and any attempt to establish a constant resonance factor is doomed to failure, and that direct resonance interactions are of some importance in the ionization of benzoic acids —a conclusion we have already reached by other means.

The values for σ obtained in the above-mentioned work have been given the symbol σ^n. They are considered by these authors to be free of any resonance effects. Similar scales and conclusions have been reached by others. Taft [10] evaluated a σ-scale, to which he assigned the symbol σ°, by studying four reactions that he considered to be free of resonance effects, i.e., in which the reaction site is insulated from the aromatic ring so that there should be a minimum and constant resonance effect. The specific reactions employed were the ionization of phenylacetic and phenylpropionic acids, the saponification of ethyl phenylacetates and the saponification of benzyl acetates. Norman et al. [11] introduced a third "normal" σ-scale, σ_G, using rate data for the saponification of ethyl phenylacetates as the standard reaction. All three of these scales are similar to the Hammett scale and to each other, with the exception of para substituents that supply electrons by resonance. For these groups, the scales differ somewhat even among themselves. The data of

Table 9–7. Values of σ° and σ^n

Substituent	Meta		Para	
	σ°*	σ^n†	σ°*	σ^n†
H	0.00	0.00	0.00	0.00
F	0.35	0.337	0.17	0.056
Cl	0.37	0.373	0.27	0.238
Br	0.38	0.391	0.26	0.265
I	0.35	0.352	0.27	0.299
CH_3	−0.07	−0.069	−0.15	−0.129
OH		0.095		−0.178
OCH_3	0.13	0.076		−0.111
NH_2	−0.14	−0.038		−0.172
$N(CH_3)_2$	−0.15	−0.049		−0.172
CF_3		0.467		0.532
CO_2H				0.406
CO_2CH_3	0.36	0.321	0.46	0.385
SO_2CH_3		0.678		0.686
CN	0.62	0.613	0.69	0.674
$COCH_3$	0.34	0.376	0.46	0.502
NO_2	0.70	0.710	0.82	0.778
$N(CH_3)_3^+$		0.855		0.800

* From Taft [10].
† From Van Bekkum et al. [9].

Van Bekkum *et al.* [9] are most complete; these are given in Table 9–7 together with the values of Taft [10].

Because resonance effects have been demonstrated to vary from one reaction to another, several approaches have been taken to account for this variation in correlations. Perhaps the most interesting is that of Yukawa and Tsuno [12], who proposed a linear combination of the two models to handle reactions in which the role of resonance in stabilizing positive charge differs from that in either of the two standard scales, σ and σ^+. Their equation is in the form

$$\log k/k_0 = \rho[\sigma + r(\sigma^+ - \sigma)], \tag{9-8}$$

where the term $(\sigma^+ - \sigma)$ is assumed to represent the contribution of resonance above that in the Hammett model. Since the value of this term for "normal" *meta* substituents (those used by Van Bekkum *et al.*) is zero, or nearly so, these can be used to establish the value of the reaction constant ρ. If $[(1/\rho) \log (k/k_0) - \sigma]$ is plotted against $(\sigma^+ - \sigma)$, the slope of the line obtained is r, as can be seen by dividing Eq. (9–8) by ρ. If the use of Eq. (9–8) does not improve the correlation, the r-value will be 1 and the equation reduces to Eq. (9–7); if Eq. (9–6) is more appropriate, the r-value obtained will be zero. Typical r-values are 2.29 for the brominolysis of benzeneboronic acids and 0.323 for the epoxidation of *cis*-dimethylstilbenes [13]. The value of r is taken to indicate the importance of resonance interactions in the reaction series being investigated and the value of ρ is taken to be a measure of the sensitivity of the reaction to electron withdrawal. Perhaps surprisingly, the r-value is not a function of ρ and a large ρ-value in no way implies a correspondingly large r-value. An analogous equation has been proposed for reactions involving a negative site. It successfully correlates the acidities of the benzenesulfonanilides [14]:

$$\log k/k_0 = \rho[(\sigma + r(\sigma^- - \sigma)]. \tag{9-9}$$

There are several other substituent constant scales for *meta* and *para* groups. Because the most important use of the correlations is to offer a model that can be employed by analogy in mechanistic reasoning, we believe that the σ-, σ^+-, and σ^--scales are to be preferred. The use of equations like (9–8) should also be considered.

THE TAFT EQUATION

The above equations have dealt specifically with *meta*- and *para*-substituted aromatics. If *ortho* substitution is to be considered, we must recognize that the presence of groups so close to the reaction center can lead to another interaction mechanism, that of *steric effects*. Following a suggestion of Ingold [15], Taft [16] has shown that the polar and steric terms can be treated separately.

The hydrolysis reaction of *ortho*-substituted benzoate esters was used as a model reaction. When this reaction is catalyzed by acids and the substituents are *meta* and *para*, Hammett ρ-values range between -0.2 and $+0.5$. Similarly, the base-catalyzed saponification leads to ρ-values between $+2.2$ and $+2.8$. Since both of these reactions have activated complexes that are nearly the same (differing by only two protons), any steric effect should be constant:

$$\left(R'-\underset{\underset{OH}{|}}{\overset{\overset{OH}{|}}{C}} \cdots \overset{H}{\underset{}{O}}-R \right)^{+} \quad \left(R'-\underset{\underset{OH}{|}}{\overset{\overset{O}{\|}}{C}} \cdots OR \right)$$

Acidic Activated Complex   Basic Activated Complex

If we now assume that the relative ΔG^* for these reactions may be treated as a sum of independent factors, we can write

$$\log k/k_0 = \rho^* \sigma^* - SE_s. \tag{9-10}$$

This has the same form as the Hammett equation (9–6) but another term has been added. The polar parameter, σ^*, is a measure of the polar effect of a substituent while ρ^* measures the sensitivity of the reaction to the polar effect. Similarly, E_s is a measure of the steric effect introduced by the presence of a substituent while S measures the sensitivity of the reaction to this steric effect. If we can separate the polar and steric effects so that Eq. (9–10) applies to the hydrolysis reactions, we can write the following equations, where the subscripts A and B refer to acid and base catalysis respectively:

$$\log (k/k_0)_B = \rho_B^* \sigma^* + S_B E_s,$$
$$\log (k/k_0)_A = \rho_A^* \sigma^* + S_A E_s.$$

In these two equations, no subscripts are written to identify σ^* and E_s, as these are not, we hope, dependent upon the reaction. Subtracting the second from the first affords

$$\log (k/k_0)_B - \log (k/k_0)_A = (\rho_B^* - \rho_A^*)\sigma^* + (S_B - S_A)E_s. \tag{9-11}$$

This equation may be simplified. As has been pointed out previously, the steric effect is the same in both reactions, so that $(S_B - S_A) = 0$. Also, the polar effect of the acid-catalyzed reaction is very small and we may set $\rho_A^* = 0$. If we use ρ_B^* obtained from the Hammett expression (ca. 2.48), the polar effects measured by σ^* should be on about the same scale as Hammett's σ-values. Substitution of these values in Eq. (9–11) followed by rearrangement gives the equation used by Taft to define the polar substituent constant σ^*:

$$\sigma^* = (1/2.48)[\log (k/k_0)_B - \log (k/k_0)_A]. \tag{9-12}$$

To evaluate σ^*, it would be ideal to have rate data for both acidic and basic hydrolysis reactions at a single set of conditions. Since such data are not available, averages of σ^*-values obtained at various conditions have been used. This approach appears to be justified by the small deviations of the values so obtained, except when pure water is used as solvent.

Equation (9–12) and the approach described have been used to obtain values for substituents in the *ortho* position, as well as to define and obtain values for substituents in aliphatic compounds. For the latter series, CH_3CO_2R' was chosen as the standard compound, k_0. Some values of σ^* for the two series are given in Table 9–8.

Table 9–8. Polar and Steric Substituent Constants†

R	σ^*	E_s	R	σ^*	E_s
			Substituents in Aliphatic Series R—Y‡		
Cl_3C	2.65	-2.06	$(C_6H_5)_2CH$	0.41	-1.76
Cl_2CH	1.940	-1.54	$C_6H_5CH_2$	0.215	-0.33
$ClCH_2$	1.05	-0.24	$C_6H_5(CH_2)_2$	0.080	-0.38
FCH_2	1.10	-0.24	$C_6H_5(CH_2)_3$	0.02	-0.45
$BrCH_2$	1.00	-0.27	CH_3	0.000	0.00
ICH_2	0.85	-0.37	C_2H_5	-0.100	-0.07
$NCCH_2$	1.300		$nor\text{-}C_3H_7$	-0.115	-0.36
CH_3CO	1.65		$iso\text{-}C_4H_9$	-0.125	-0.93
C_6H_5	0.600	—§	$nor\text{-}C_4H_9$	-0.130	-0.39
H	0.490	1.24	$iso\text{-}C_3H_7$	-0.190	-0.47
$HOCH_2$	0.555		$sec\text{-}C_4H_9$	-0.210	-1.13
CH_3OCH_2	0.520	-0.19	$tert\text{-}C_4H_9$	-0.300	-1.54
			ortho Substituents		
OCH_3	-0.39	0.99	Cl	0.20	0.18
OC_2H_5	-0.35	0.90	Br	0.21	0.00
CH_3	-0.17	0.00	I	0.21	-0.20
H	0.00	—§	NO_2	0.78	-0.75
F	0.24	0.49			

† From Taft [17].
‡ Y is a functional group.
§ Cannot be evaluated because of resonance factors.

To evaluate the steric constant E_s we make use of the fact that polar effects in the acid-catalyzed hydrolysis reaction are unimportant. Equation (9–10) is then reduced to

$$\log k/k_0 = SE_s. \tag{9–13}$$

By setting $S = 1$ for this reaction, we obtain the values of E_s given in Table 9–8.

When the complete Taft equation, Eq. (9–10), is employed for a series of kinetic data for *ortho*-substituted benzene derivatives or aliphatics, we must try several "equations." If $\log k$ gives a linear plot against σ^*, the implication is that steric effects do not cause rate differences. If the first plot is not linear, we may try plotting log k against E_s. If this is linear, Eq. (9–13) applies and we conclude that electronic effects are not important. If neither of these gives a linear plot, we can try log $(k/k_0) - E_s$ against σ^*. Linearity in this plot suggests that both steric and electronic effects play a role in determining the rate and that $S = 1$. Should even this last try not be linear, it is still possible that the complete Eq. (9–10) will give a good correlation of the data. If a correlation is expected, deviation of a point from the correlation may indicate a change in mechanism. Reaction series are known that fit each of the four "equations" (see reference 17). Equations with four adjustable parameters (Taft) nearly always give a better correlation of data than an equation with two (Hammett).

4-X-bicyclo[2.2.2]octane-1-carboxylic acid

The σ^* values for aliphatic compounds should be a measure of inductive and field effects with no interaction due to resonance. Resonance interaction between the substituent and the reactive center is eliminated by the intermediate methylene group, as shown by comparing the σ^* values of Taft with those obtained in another study. Roberts and Moreland [18] studied the ionization of 4-substituted bicyclo-[2.2.2]octane-1-carboxylic acids in 50% ethanol at 25°C. They found that the ionization constants could be used to define a value σ':

$$\sigma' = (1/1.464) \log (K/K_0). \tag{9–14}$$

The value of 1.464 in Eq. (9–14) is that of ρ for the ionization of benzoic acids in 50% ethanol and is used so that σ and σ' are on about the same scale. The values of σ' may be used to correlate other reactions of this system, e.g. ester hydrolyses, by

$$\log k/k_0 = \rho'\sigma'. \tag{9–15}$$

It is clear that any polar effect measured by σ' cannot include resonance interactions. If σ' includes only inductive and/or field effects and σ^* for aliphatics is a measure of the same effects, there should be a correlation between the two. Indeed, the ratio σ'/σ^* is found to have an almost constant value of 0.45, as is shown in Table 9–9 [18].

The close correlation of σ' and σ^* (aliphatic) has led to the development of another σ-scale, σ_I, considered to be a measure of polar effects exclusive of resonance. It corresponds to the σ'-scale and, because of the similar geometry of the bicyclooctyl and aromatic series, is taken to be a measure of aromatic polar effects exclusive of resonance:

$$\sigma_I = 0.45\sigma^* \text{ (aliphatic)} \cong \sigma'.$$

Table 9–9. Comparison of σ'- and σ^*-Values

Substituent	σ'^a	σ^{*b} for XCH_2	σ'/σ^*
H	0.00	0.00	
OH	0.28	0.56	0.50
CO_2ET	0.30	0.71	0.42
Br	0.45	1.00	0.45
CN	0.58	1.30	0.45

[a] From Roberts and Moreland [18].
[b] From Taft [17].

The use of the σ_I-scale for aromatic compounds appears to be justified: the chemical shifts in the NMR spectra of *meta*-substituted fluorobenzenes are correlated by σ_I better than by Hammett's σ constants [19].

Taft [17] has achieved a further separation of polar effects in substituent constants. On the assumption that inductive (and/or field) effects are the same in the *meta* and *para* positions, the resonance effect can be obtained by subtracting σ_I from σ:

$$\sigma_R = \sigma - \sigma_I. \tag{9–16}$$

Two problems immediately arise in the application of Eq. (9–16). First, it is not clear from which substituent constant scale σ_I should be subtracted, but, whatever scale is used, it will be analyzed into resonance and other polar effects. Secondly, because the importance of resonance effects depends upon the particular reaction, the use of σ_R in correlations of reaction rates is doubtful, though sometimes helpful in understanding deviations from a normal correlation. Taft [17] has given an example of this by examining the p-nitro group in a reaction series where resonance is inhibited by steric crowding. From the data of Westheimer and Metcalf [20] on the saponification rates of ethyl 4-substituted-3,5-dimethylbenzoates, the p-nitro group must be assigned a substituent constant of $+0.68$. Because of the adjacent methyl groups, the necessary coplanarity of the ring and the nitro group cannot be achieved and any resonance interaction is thus inhibited. This would reduce the electronic effect to one described by σ' (or σ_I). The value observed, $+0.68$, is in reasonable agreement with the value of σ' for NO_2, $+0.63$ [17].

From the foregoing discussion, it is apparent that the effect of substituents upon equilibria and reaction rates can frequently be understood or at least predicted to be relatively constant from one reaction series to another. One might reasonably ask whether other variables can be similarly correlated, and therefore we shall now look at such correlations, *albeit* in less detail. In general, the approach is the same as for substituent constants and the mechanistic conclusions are similarly reached.

THE SWAIN-SCOTT EQUATION

Swain and Scott [21] have studied the nucleophilicity of a number of substrates in nucleophilic substitution reactions (see Chapter 13). For their model they chose the nucleophilic displacement of bromide from methyl bromide by water at 25°C. A linear free energy relationship was found to correlate the reactivities of several nucleophiles:

$$\log k/k_0 = sn, \qquad (9\text{--}17)$$

where k is the second-order rate constant for the reaction of a substrate with some nucleophile and k_0 is the second-order rate constant for reaction of the same substrate with water obtained by dividing the experimental pseudo-first-order rate constant by the concentration of water. The value of s is 1.00 for reactions of methyl bromide and the value of n is 0.00 for pure water. Values of n may be used as a measure of relative nucleophilicities of attacking groups and are given in Table 9–10. Values of s measure the sensitivity of the particular substrate to changes in nucleophilicity and are given in Table 9–11.

Table 9–10. Swain-Scott n-Values*

Nucleophile	n	Nucleophile	n
H_2O	0.0	$(NH_2)_2CS$	4.1
NO_3^-	1.0	HO^-	4.2
$SO_4^=$	2.5	SCN^-	4.4
Cl^-	2.7	$C_6H_5NH_2$	4.5
$CH_3CO_2^-$	2.7	I^-	5.0
HCO_2^-	2.8	HS^-	5.1
$C_6H_5O^-$	3.5	$SO_3^=$	5.1
Br^-	3.5	CN^-	5.1
C_5H_5N	3.6	$S_2O_3^=$	6.4
N_3^-	4.0	$HPSO_3^=$	6.6

* From Wells [22].

The Swain-Scott equation will work for those nucleophilic reactions where the methyl bromide-water reaction is a good model. However, it is *not* always an adequate model, as rather large deviations have been observed. The reaction of hydroxide ion with ethylene-β-chloroethylsulfonium ion (mustard ion), for example, is about 40 times faster than predicted by the correlation with other nucleophiles. Similarly, triethylamine is 26 times more reactive than pyridine toward methyl iodide, but it is only one-sixth as reactive with 2-iodopropane. The latter deviation may be explained on steric grounds—an interaction not expected in the model reaction. The former deviation and others cannot be so easily rationalized. There must be at least two interactions (excluding steric effects) involved in nucleophilic

Table 9–11. Swain-Scott s-Values*

Substrate	s	Substrate	s
CH_3Br	1.00	$\begin{array}{c}CH_2-O\\ \| \qquad \|\\ CH_2-C=O\end{array}$	0.77†
CH_3I	1.15	$\begin{array}{c}CH_2\\ \|\quad \overset{+}{\diagdown}\\ \quad\; SCH_2CH_2Cl\\ \diagup\\ CH_2\end{array}$	0.95†
$ClCH_2\overset{\displaystyle O}{\overset{\diagup\diagdown}{CHCH_2}}$	1.00†	$C_6H_5CH_2Cl$	0.87
$HOCH_2\underset{\diagdown\diagup}{\underset{O}{CHCH_2}}$	0.96†	$C_2H_5OSO_2C_7H_7$	0.66
$ClCH_2CO_2^-$	1.0	C_6H_5COCl	1.43
$BrCH_2CO_2^-$	1.1	$C_6H_5SO_2Cl$	1.25
$ICH_2CO_2^-$	1.33	$(C_6H_5)_3CF$	0.61

* From Wells [22].
† Ring-opening reactions.

reactivities whose relative importance varies with the substrate. This situation may be treated by a four-parameter equation. Swain and Scott [21] suggested Eq. (9–18), where the new term e is an electrophilic constant characteristic of the electrophile that helps remove the leaving group and s' is a measure of the sensitivity of the substrate to this "pulling":

$$\log k/k_0 = sn + s'e. \tag{9–18}$$

Equation (9–17) is simply a special case of Eq. (9–18), where $s'e$ is very small compared to sn. Rather than discuss this equation, let us turn to another four-parameter equation that employs two different models.

THE EDWARDS EQUATION

Nucleophilic reactivity is also correlated by an equation developed by Edwards [23]:

$$\log k/k_0 = \alpha E_n + \beta H, \tag{9–19}$$

where the rate constants are the same as those used by Swain and Scott, E_n is a parameter measuring the nucleophilicity of the reagent, and α is a measure of the sensitivity of the substrate to nucleophilicity. The model for evaluating E_n is the standard electrode potential, E_0, of the reagent in the reaction

$$2X^- = X_2 + 2e^-,$$

relative to that of the standard potential, $-2.60v$, of water for the reaction

$$2H_2O = H_4O_2^{++} + 2e^-.$$

Thus, E_n is defined by

$$E_n = E^0 + 2.60,$$

so that E_n is zero for water. The parameter H is a measure of the basicity of the reagent and β is a measure of the sensitivity of the substrate to this factor. The model for evaluating H is the pK_a of the conjugate acid of the reagent in water relative to the pK_a of hydronium ion (1.74), so that H is defined by

$$H = pK_a + 1.74.$$

Some values of the parameters used in Eq. (9–19) are given in Tables 9–12 and 9–13.

Table 9–12. Edwards' Reagent Parameters*

Reagent	E_n	H
NO_3^-	0.29	0.4
$SO_4^=$	0.59	3.74
$CH_3CO_2^-$	0.95	6.46
C_5H_5N	1.20	7.04
Cl^-	1.24	-3.0
$C_6H_5O^-$	1.46	11.7
Br^-	1.51	-6.0
N_3^-	1.58	6.5
OH^-	1.65	17.5
$C_6H_5NH_2$	1.78	6.3
I^-	2.06	-9.0
$(NH_2)_2CS$	2.18	0.8
$S_2O_3^=$	2.52	3.6
$SO_3^=$	2.57	9.0
CN^-	2.79	10.9

* Selected from Wells [22].

Although the Edwards equation frequently gives a more general and better correlation than that of Swain and Scott, the models used by Edwards contribute little to the understanding of reaction mechanisms. Both equations employ a measure of nucleophilicity but, whereas the n factors of Swain and Scott are determined for a specific reaction believed to be a good model for other nucleophilic reactions, the E_n terms of Edwards are based upon a fundamental property of the nucleophiles, the

Table 9–13. Edwards' Substrate
Parameters*

Substrate	α	β
CH_3Br	2.50	0.006
ClCH$_2$CHCH$_2$ (O)	2.46†	0.035†
HOCH$_2$CHCH$_2$ (O)	2.52†	0.000†
$ICH_2CO_2^-$	2.59	−0.052
CH$_2$ $\overset{+}{S}$CH$_2$CH$_2$Cl CH$_2$	2.45†	0.074
$C_6H_5CH_2Cl$	3.53	−0.128
$C_2H_5OSO_2C_7H_7$	1.68	0.014
C_6H_5COCl	3.56	0.008
$C_6H_5SO_2Cl$	2.56	0.046

* From Wells [22].
† Ring-opening reactions.

standard electrode potentials. If both equations measure the same thing there should be some relationship between them and, indeed, Fig. 9–1 shows a fair correlation of the two parameters. That the electrode potential for the oxidation reaction is a pretty good model, if not a mechanistically useful one, is not surprising, since the nucleophile is oxidized in the displacement reaction.

Davis [24] has suggested the use of Eq. (9–19) to correlate the effect of leaving groups from saturated carbon atoms: if the leaving group is considered a nucleophile leaving the reaction center, it can be correlated with Edwards' oxidation and basicity parameters. He further suggests that Eq. (9–19) be called the *oxibase scale* and demonstrates (see Fig. 9–2) that α for carbon substrates is linearly related to the

Table 9–14. β-Values for $C-Y$
Bonds*

$C-Y$	β
C—I	−0.0134
C—Br	+0.002
C—Cl	+0.008
C—OSO$_2$C$_7$H$_7$	+0.013

* From Davis [24].

electrode potential of the leaving ion of strong acids. In this approach α is thought to be a reduction term. Values of β for various $C—Y$ bonds were also obtained and are given in Table 9–14. The β parameter is called an *acidity term* and is considered to be a measure of positive charge on the carbon atom, as well as being related to the square of the electro-negativity difference between the leaving group and the carbon. Although data are still scarce, this approach permits estimation of E_n for very poor nucleophiles [24] and prediction of the leaving group in complex reactions [25].

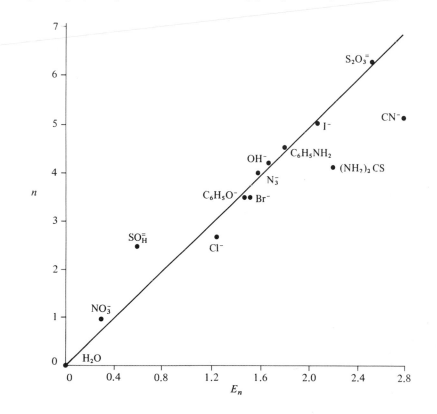

Fig. 9–1. Relationship between Swain-Scott and Edwards nucleophilic parameters.

THE WINSTEIN-GRUNWALD EQUATION

Swain and Scott [21] attempted to measure nucleophilicity using a reaction believed to proceed by an S_N2 mechanism. Grunwald and Winstein [26] chose a reaction believed to proceed by an S_N1 mechanism and suggested the following equation for correlation of reactions of this type:

$$\log k/k_0 = mY, \tag{9–20}$$

where Y is a measure of the ionizing power of the solvent, m measures sensitivity to

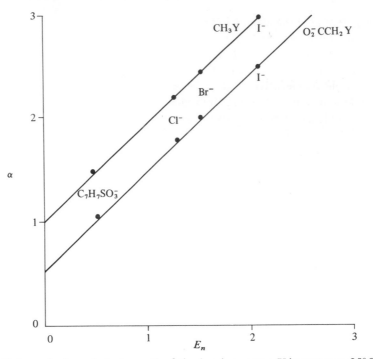

Fig. 9–2. Values of α for substrate $vs.$ E_n of the leaving group Y in water at 25°C. (Data from Davis [24].)

solvent changes, k is the rate constant for the solvolytic reaction of a compound in the medium being studied, and k_0 is the solvolytic rate constant of the same compound in 80% ethanol. To evaluate Y, the standard reaction chosen was the solvolysis of *tert*-butyl chloride. Values of Y and m are given in Tables 9–15 and 9–16.

From Table 9–16 we can note that reactions proceeding by an S_N1 mechanism show m-values close to unity, while compounds reacting by an S_N2 mechanism exhibit much lower values, e.g. methyl bromide, 0.26, and ethyl bromide, 0.34 [27]. Some of the primary halides also exhibit considerable curvature when Eq. (9–20) is plotted. We should not expect the Grunwald-Winstein equation to work well for these latter compounds since it has no term representing nucleophilicity. This point will be discussed in more detail in Chapter 13 but it is surprising that Eq. (9–20) works at all with S_N2 reactions. It is clear that primary substrates are less sensitive to Y than are tertiary, which is to be expected if Y really is a measure of ionizing power.

Because the term "ionizing power" undoubtedly includes a number of interaction mechanisms it is not surprising to find that Eq. (9–20) frequently fails. For one thing, different solvent systems frequently give different m-values. Benzhydryl bromide, for example, gives an m-value of 1.687 in aqueous acetic acid mixtures and of 0.954 in aqueous dioxane [27]. This dispersion of points suggests that there must be more than one interaction for stabilizing the positive charge developed in the

Table 9–15. Values of Y for the Winstein-Grunwald Equation
at 25°C*

Solvent†	Y	Solvent†	Y
100% EtOH	−2.03	100% MeOH	−1.09
90% EtOH	−0.75	50% MeOH	1.97
80% EtOH	0.00	90% Dioxane	−2.03
70% EtOH	0.60	50% Dioxane	1.36
60% EtOH	1.12	90% Acetone	−1.86
50% EtOH	1.66	50% Acetone	1.40
40% EtOH	2.20	100% Acetic acid	−1.64
30% EtOH	2.72	50% Acetic acid	1.40
20% EtOH	3.05	100% Formic acid	2.05
10% EtOH	3.31	50% Formic acid	2.64
Water	3.49	100% Formamide	0.60
		100% tert-Butyl alcohol	−3.26

* From Wells [22].
† Volume %.

ionizing substrates. The breakdown of the correlation for S_N2 reactions can be easily explained (*vide supra*), but the failure to correlate data in different solvent systems is not yet completely understood. Nevertheless, the Grunwald-Winstein equation is of considerable use in reaction mechanism studies.

We have seen how linear relationships in a reaction series lead to certain mechanistic conclusions. We might now ask what the limitations are on such an approach. Certainly, any given relationship is limited by the model used for its development, as has been discussed. There is one more important limitation of a general nature, which we shall now examine.

Table 9–16. Values of m for the Winstein-
Grunwald Equation*

Substrate	$T(°C)$	m	$\log k°$
tert-C_4H_9Cl	25	1.00	−5.03
tert-C_4H_9Br	25	0.94	−3.47
$CH_3CHBrC_6H_5$	50	1.20	−3.81
tert-$C_5H_{11}Br$	25	0.90	−3.21
$(C_6H_5)_2CHCl$	25	0.76	−2.78

* From Grunwald and Winstein [26].

THE ISOKINETIC RELATIONSHIP

As we have seen, both equilibrium and rate constants can be expressed in terms of free energy changes (Eqs. 9–1 and 9–2). Free energies, however, are functions of temperature, enthalpy, and entropy (Eq. 7–25a). Since both the standard free energy changes and the free energy of activation can be treated alike, we will use the symbol ΔG to represent either; similarly, we will use ΔH and ΔS as general symbols:

$$\ln k = -\Delta G/RT, \tag{9-1}$$

$$\Delta G = \Delta H - T\Delta S,$$

$$\partial \Delta G = \partial \Delta H - T\partial \Delta S. \tag{7-25a}$$

For a large number of reaction series, it is found that $\partial \Delta H$ and $\partial \Delta S$ are proportional [28]. This experimental observation is expressed by Eq. (9–21), where β is the constant of proportionality, the slope of the line obtained when $\partial \Delta H$ is plotted against $\partial \Delta S$:

$$\partial \Delta H = \beta \partial \Delta S. \tag{9-21}$$

Substituting this equation into Eq. (7–25a) affords

$$\partial \Delta G = \beta \partial \Delta S - T\partial \Delta S,$$

which is rearranged to give

$$\partial \Delta G = (1 - T/\beta)\partial \Delta S. \tag{9-22}$$

When $\beta = T$, $\partial \Delta G = 0$, and no variation of equilibrium or rate will be expected when substituents or media are changed. If enthalpies and entropies are insensitive to temperature changes or if the change in temperature is small, β will equal T at a real temperature—one at which all the members of a series will react at the same rate. Normally these conditions are not met, however, so β is best considered a mathematical slope rather than a phenomenological temperature [29]. The value of β is called the *isokinetic temperature*.

If a single interaction mechanism is involved in producing $\partial \Delta G$, $\partial \Delta H$, or $\partial \Delta S$, Eq. (9–22) can be expected to apply. In these cases, the isokinetic temperature is an inversion point of relative reactivities or equilibria. The reaction exhibiting the fastest rate or largest equilibrium constant below the isokinetic temperature will be the slowest above it.

At temperatures below β, the reaction rate or equilibrium is controlled mainly by $\partial \Delta H$. In this region the reaction with the lowest activation energy will react fastest and interpretations involving potential-energy surfaces can be made. This is the more familiar case. At temperatures above the isokinetic temperature, however, the controlling factor is $\partial \Delta S$, and interpretations based upon potential-energy surfaces would obviously be in error. The propensity of organic chemists to reason by analogy can lead to difficulties. Generalizations concerning the effects of structure or solvent on reactivity or equilibrium cannot be valid for two reaction series if the generalizations are made from a study of one series below the isokinetic temperature and applied to a second series studied above the isokinetic temperature. However, conclusions drawn from studies of reaction series are normally supported by other types of evidence or, alternatively, the effect of temperature variation can be studied so that the isokinetic temperature is known.

Studies made within a temperature range close to the isokinetic temperature are fairly common. Any generalizations made when this is known to be the case should be accepted with considerable reservations. Of greater importance is the fact that many studies have been made at only one temperature. Interpretation of these data is always questionable, particularly if structure or medium changes are small. It is possible that such a study was inadvertently made near β and that a temperature change of only a few degrees would invert the observed effect. To avoid this problem, any studies made upon a reaction series should include information at more than one temperature. This enables the investigator to calculate $\partial\Delta H$ and $\partial\Delta S$ and to see how these factors contribute to the observations. In general, it is found that electronic effects are contained in the enthalpy factor and that many solvent effects are due to the entropy factor.

In terms of the linear free energy relationships discussed above, it is clear that any reaction series correlated by both a linear free energy equation and the isokinetic relationship will undergo an inversion of the sign of the reaction constant (e.g. ρ) at the isokinetic temperature. Many reaction series that obey a linear free energy relationship do not follow the isokinetic relationship. For these latter series, the free-energy relationship is found to deteriorate as the temperature is changed, unless the value of $\partial\Delta S$ is zero, when

$$\ln k/k_0 = -\partial\Delta G/RT = -\partial\Delta H/RT;$$

but

$$\log k/k_0 = \rho\sigma,$$

so

$$\rho = -\left(\frac{1}{T}\right)(\partial\Delta H/2.3R\sigma),$$

and ρ is an inverse function of absolute temperature if all other terms (ΔH and σ) are temperature-independent. This behavior is common [30]. Reaction series fitting the isokinetic relationship but not a linear free energy relationship are also known.

From the above discussion it becomes obvious that the use of linear free energy equations in reaching theoretical conclusions can be misleading if the reaction is studied at only one temperature. Nevertheless, these equations are valuable tools to the mechanistic chemist when used as supporting evidence along with other types of information. No mechanism can be considered established on evidence of only one type, and it is hoped that the above discussion emphasizes the importance of a varied attack upon mechanistic problems.

PROBLEMS

1. The decomposition of benzenediazonium chloride in dilute aqueous HCl (pH, 1.7) at 25°C is first-order. Although the rate is nearly independent of Cl^- ion concentration the product composition is not. Chlorobenzene is the major product at high Cl^- concentration and phenol predominates at low Cl^- concentrations. Substituent effects are:

Substituent	$k \times 10^7$ (sec^{-1})
m-CH$_3$	3400
H	740
m-Cl	31
m-NO$_2$	0.69

a) Make a Hammett plot of these data.
b) Compute k for p-CH$_3$O. The observed value is 0.11×10^{-7} sec^{-1}. Explain the deviation.

2. Calculate Y values for each solvent system from the rate constants for solvolysis at 25°C of *tert*-butyl bromide and chloride.

Solvent	80% EtOH	100% EtOH	40% EtOH	MeOH	HOAc	80% Acetone
$k_{BuCl} \times 10^6$	9.2	0.097	1300	98	0.21	2.0
$k_{BuBr} \times 10^4$	3.4	0.057	0.34	31	0.10	1.1

3. a) Calculate the ρ-value for the Okamoto-Brown equation using the data for the solvolysis of substituted benzyl chlorides in 50% EtOH at 60°C. Use the method of least squares.

Substituent	$k \times 10^5$ (sec^{-1})
p-CH$_3$	27.3
p-F	4.48
H	3.02
p-Cl	1.69

b) What is the standard deviation of the log k values?
c) Calculate the standard error of ρ.
d) Calculate k for the solvolysis of p-nitrobenzyl chloride. The observed value is 0.198×10^{-5} sec^{-1}.

4. From kinetic data on reactions of trimethylphosphate with a series of nucleophiles, α in the oxibase scale has been calculated to be 1.77. Estimate E_n for $(CH_3O)_2PO_2^-$.

5. The relationship $\log k/k_0 = \gamma L$ has been proposed. For the reaction

$$CH_3O^- + CH_3X \xrightarrow[25°C]{MeOH} CH_3OCH_3 + X^-$$

γ is defined as 1.0 and L as 0.0 for $X = $ Br.
a) Suggest what γ and L measure.
b) Evaluate $\log k$ for methyl chloride, using L for Cl $= -1.61$, for the reaction

$$CH_3X + H_2O \rightarrow CH_3OH + HX.$$

For this reaction γ is 1.082 and k for methyl bromide is 3.31×10^{-7} sec^{-1}.

6. a) It has been stated that a change in mechanism always causes a Hammett plot to be concave upward. Explain why this statement is reasonable.
b) An abrupt break in a Hammett plot can occur without a change in mechanism. This occurs when the rate-determining step changes. Will such a change cause the plot to be concave upward or downward? Explain.

REFERENCES

1. L. P. HAMMETT, *Physical Organic Chemistry*, McGraw-Hill Book Co., New York (1940), pp. 184 ff.
2. H. H. JAFFE, *Chem. Revs.*, **53**, 191 (1953).
3. D. H. McDANIEL and H. C. BROWN, *J. Org. Chem.*, **23**, 420 (1958).
4. W. L. BRIGHT AND H. T. BRISCOE, *J. Phys. Chem.*, **37**, 787 (1933).
5. J. G. KIRKWOOD and F. H. WESTHEIMER, *J. Chem. Phys.*, **6**, 506 and 513 (1938).
6. Y. OKAMOTO and H. C. BROWN, *J. Org. Chem.*, **22**, 487 (1957).
7. H. C. BROWN and Y. OKAMOTO, *J. Am. Chem. Soc.*, **80**, 4979 (1958).
8. S. PATAI and Y. ISRAELI, *J. Chem. Soc.*, 2020 (1960).
9. H. VAN BEKKUM, P. E. VERKADE, and B. M. WEPSTER, *Rec. Trav. Chim.*, **78**, 815 (1959).
10. R. W. TAFT, *J. Phys. Chem.*, **64**, 1805 (1960).
11. R. O. C. NORMAN, G. K. RADDA, D. A. BRIMACOMBE, P. D. RALPH, and E. M. SMITH, *J. Chem. Soc.*, 3247 (1961).
12. Y. YUKAWA and Y. TSUNO, *Bull. Chem. Soc. Japan*, **32**, 965 and 971 (1959).
13. J. E. LEFFLER and E. GRUNWALD, *Rates and Equilibria of Organic Reactions*, John Wiley & Sons, New York (1963), p. 212.
14. M. YOSIOTO, K. HAMAMOTO, and T. KUBOTA, *Bull. Chem. Soc. Japan*, **35**, 1723 (1962).
15. C. K. INGOLD, *J. Chem. Soc.*, 1032 (1932).
16. R. W. TAFT, *J. Am. Chem. Soc.*, **74**, 3120 (1952) and **75**, 4231 (1953).
17. R. W. TAFT, in *Steric Effects in Organic Chemistry* (Ed. M. Newman), John Wiley & Sons, New York (1956), pp. 556 ff.
18. J. D. ROBERTS and W. T. MORELAND, *J. Am. Chem. Soc.*, **75**, 2167 (1953).
19. R. W. TAFT, E. PRICE, I. R. FOX, I. C. LEWIS, K. K. ANDERSON, and G. T. DAVIS, *J. Am. Chem. Soc.*, **85**, 709 (1963).
20. F. H. WESTHEIMER and R. P. METCALF, *J. Am. Chem. Soc.*, **63**, 1339 (1941).
21. C. G. SWAIN and C. B. SCOTT, *J. Am. Chem. Soc.*, **75**, 141 (1953).
22. P. R. WELLS, *Chem. Revs.*, **63**, 171 (1963).
23. J. O. EDWARDS, *J. Am. Chem. Soc.*, **76**, 1540 (1954) and **78**, 1819 (1956).
24. R. E. DAVIS, *J. Am. Chem. Soc.*, **87**, 3010 (1965).
25. R. E. DAVIS and A. COHEN, *J. Am. Chem. Soc.*, **86**, 440 (1964).
26. E. GRUNWALD and S. WINSTEIN, *J. Am. Chem. Soc.*, **70**, 846 (1948).
27. A. STREITWIESER, *Chem. Revs.*, **56**, 571 (1956).
28. J. E. LEFFLER, *J. Org. Chem.*, **20**, 1202 (1955).
29. J. E. LEFFLER, *J. Org. Chem.*, **31**, 533 (1966).
30. C. D. RITCHIE and W. F. SAGER, in *Progress in Physical Organic Chemistry*, Vol. 2, (Eds. S. G. Cohen, A. Streitwieser, and R. W. Taft), Interscience Publishers, New York (1964), p. 323.

CHAPTER 10

ACIDS, BASES, AND SOLUTIONS

If we consider only those reactions occurring in water, the *Arrhenius definitions* of acids as compounds that ionize to produce hydrogen ions and of bases as compounds that ionize to produce hydroxyl ions are adequate. With the recognition that reactions in other media may be understood on similar principles, the definitions of acids and bases have been extended. We shall find most useful the definition of acids as proton donors and bases as proton acceptors given by Lowry and Brønsted. We thereby avoid the limitation of working with only aqueous solutions. This definition also points out the similarities of the two following reactions:

$$HBr + H_2O = H_3O^+ + Br^-,$$
$$HBr + NH_3 = NH_4^+ + Br^-.$$

In this system, the acid yielding a proton forms a second species, known as the *conjugate base* of the acid. Similarly, when a base accepts the proton, the product is called a *conjugate acid*. In the Lowry-Brønsted system of acids and bases, every acid-base reaction produces a new acid and a new base. Thus, the reaction of the acid HBr with the base NH_3 produces a conjugate acid NH_4^+ and a conjugate base Br^-. The importance of this concept is illustrated in the reaction

$$HO_2CCH_3 + H_2O = H_3O^+ + {}^-O_2CCH_3,$$

where acetic acid is converted to its conjugate base, acetate ion, by the base, water. A similar reaction is

$$H_2O + {}^-O_2CCH_3 \rightleftharpoons HO_2CCH_3 + OH^-,$$

where the conjugate base formed in the ionization of acetic acid serves as a base that is converted to its conjugate acid, acetic acid, by the acid, water. Here we note that water can serve as both an acid and a base: many protonated solvents exhibit this amphiprotic behavior.

Water and other amphiprotic solvents undergo a reaction known as self-ionization or *autoprotolysis*, in which equal amounts of the conjugate acid (lyonium ion) and the conjugate base (lyate ion) of the solvent are formed. For water, liquid ammonia, and anhydrous sulfuric acid these reactions are:

$$2H_2O = H_3O^+ + OH^-$$
$$2NH_3 = NH_4^+ + NH_2^-$$
$$2H_2SO_4 = H_3SO_4^+ + HSO_4^-$$

172

The autoprotolysis reaction places an important restriction on the study of acids and bases in solution. The ionization constant of water (assuming unit activity coefficients) is given by

$$k_w = [H_3O^+][HO^-] = 10^{-14}. \tag{10-1}$$

The constant k_w determines the values of acidity possible in the solvent. If we limit the concentration of species to 0.1 M, so that the assumption of unit activity coefficients is reasonable, the most acidic solution possible in water has $[H_3O^+]$ of 0.1 M, and the most basic solution will have $[OH^-]$ equal to 0.1 M. The strength of an acid HA in a given solvent S is measured by the equilibrium constant for the reaction

$$HA + S = HS^+ + A^-. \tag{10-2}$$

If the equilibrium constants for two acids are 100 and 10,000, the second acid is much stronger than the first. Nevertheless, an 0.1 M solution of the first acid in water will react so completely that [HA] is only 10^{-4} M, and since this is such a small value the ionization will seem as complete as that of the second acid where [HA] is 10^{-8} M. In both cases, the $[H_3O^+]$ is so close to 0.1 M that the two solutions appear to have the same acid strength—because water is a relatively "strong" base and any "strong" acid is "completely" ionized to the hydronium ion. The relative strengths of acids cannot be measured if the basicity of a solvent is too great. To make such a measurement we must determine the extent of reaction of the acid in question with the basic solvent; if the acid is stronger than the hydronium ion, the conjugate acid of water, it will be converted completely to the H_3O^+ ion. All such solutions thus appear to have equal acidities, which is known as the *leveling effect*. If two acids are too strong for a comparison in water, a less basic medium must be used.

Similarly, the leveling effect makes two strong bases appear to have equal basicities. In water, any base stronger than hydroxyl ion will be converted to the conjugate acid and the hydroxyl ion is produced:

$$B + H_2O = BH^+ + OH^-.$$

Water, as we have seen, is a rather limited solvent for comparing the strengths of acids and bases. To distinguish between strong acids, a weakly basic solvent is used. For example, hydrochloric acid and sulfuric acid (first ionization) are both completely ionized in water, but in formic acid solution the ionization of hydrochloric acid is incomplete while that of sulfuric acid is still complete. In this manner the order of strength of some common acids is found to be $HNO_3 < HCl < H_2SO_4 < HClO_4$. Similarly, very weak acids are studied in strongly basic solutions, e.g. KNH_2 in liquid ammonia, and very weak bases in a strongly acidic medium such as liquid hydrogen fluoride or sulfuric acid, containing enough water to suppress the reactions

$$2H_2SO_4 = H_3SO_4^+ + HSO_4^-,$$
$$2H_2SO_4 = H_3O^+ + HS_2O_7^-$$
$$H_3SO_4^+ + HS_2O_7^- = H_2SO_4 + H_2S_2O_7.$$

Sulfuric acid is particularly convenient because it may be studied cryoscopically to determine the number of particles formed per mole of added material. Thus, adding benzoic acid results in a freezing-point depression consistent with the presence of two moles of foreign particles, which is taken as evidence for a basic reaction of benzoic acid:

$$HBz + H_2SO_4 = H_2Bz^+ + HSO_4^-.$$

It is important to note that when a series of acids are compared in the same solvent, the most acidic solution is that of the most ionized acid. An aqueous solution of hydrochloric acid is completely ionized and is generally recognized to be more acidic than a solution of acetic acid. However, when the *same* acid is examined in different solutions, the most acidic solution is that in which the acid is the least ionized. We might ask which is the more acidic, a benzene solution of hydrochloric acid or an aqueous one. In the benzene solution, the hydrochloric acid is un-ionized and an added base does not compete with any other materials for the proton. In the aqueous solution, the same base must compete with the basic solvent, water, for control of the proton. Because of this competition, the added base is less protonated in an aqueous solution and we must conclude that the less-ionized benzene solution is the more acidic.

The suitability of various solvents for studying acid-base equilibria is shown in Fig. 10–1. The shaded areas indicate the pK_a range (in water) for which the solvent is useful. The pK_a is the negative logarithm of the equilibrium constant K_a for the reaction indicated in Eq. (10–2).

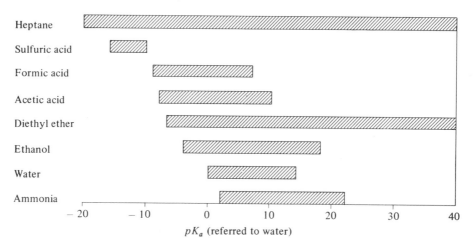

Fig. 10–1. Range of measurable pK_a values in different solvents.

The only definition of acids and bases in serious competition with the Lowry-Brønsted definition is that of Lewis, who defines acids as electron-pair acceptors and bases as electron-pair donors. His definition has little effect upon the list of bases but it admits many new acids, e.g. BF_3 and $AlCl_3$. His concept of acids is fundamentally different from that of the proton and is much less amenable to quantitative description. For this reason, we shall limit ourselves to protonic acids in this chapter.

ACID-BASE CATALYSIS

The addition or loss of a proton by an organic molecule often leads to further molecular changes. The reactions thus started may take several courses, among which are rearrangement, decomposition, or interaction with another molecule. The role of a catalyst in these reactions is to donate or accept a proton and in so doing to activate the reacting molecule.

Acid-base catalysis has been widely studied and several kinetic situations have been recognized. The more common cases will be discussed in general terms, using the symbols S or SH to represent a reacting substrate and HA and B to represent general acids and bases. Of course, A^- is the conjugate base of HA and BH^+ is the conjugate acid of B, so that BH^+ and HA as well as B and A^- may sometimes be the same. Finally, R will be used for a reactant that is not serving as an acid or base and P to represent one or more products. The proton will be represented by H^+, although it is recognized by the reader that this symbol is also used to represent the lyonium ion. Thus, in the aqueous solutions where most studies have been carried out, H^+ represents the hydrated proton.

Specific Acid Catalysis

Reactions that are catalyzed only by the lyonium ion are said to be subject to specific acid catalysis. Mechanistically, this case is observed for the scheme

$$S + H^+ \underset{k_{-1}}{\overset{k_1}{\rightleftharpoons}} SH^+,$$

$$SH^+ + R \xrightarrow[k_2]{slow} P.$$

The rate of this reaction sequence is given by

$$\text{rate} = k_2[SH^+][R]. \tag{10-3}$$

Since the first step is an equilibrium, we can obtain an expression for $[SH^+]$:

$$[SH^+] = (k_1/k_{-1})[S][H^+].$$

Substitution of this into Eq. (10–3) shows that the rate is dependent upon the lyonium ion concentration:

$$\text{rate} = (k_1 k_2/k_{-1})[S][R][H^+]. \tag{10-4}$$

The actual kinetic expression observed depends upon the ratio of k_1/k_{-1} and the relative concentrations of H^+ and S. If k_1/k_{-1} is large, either S or H^+ will be completely consumed to give SH^+ and Eq. (10–3) will be the observed kinetic expression. Most frequently, however, k_1/k_{-1} is small and Eq. (10–4) represents the observed kinetic expression. Pseudo-order rate constants are frequently obtained because the concentration of H^+ is constant if it is regenerated in the second step. The pseudo-order constants will depend upon the concentration of H^+ and kinetic determinations at several concentrations will establish this dependence. The hydrolyses of esters, acetals, and ethers are among the reactions exhibiting specific acid catalysis.

General Acid Catalysis

For a large number of reactions the rate depends not only upon $[H^+]$ but also upon the concentrations of un-ionized acids. Reactions exhibiting this behavior are said to be subject to general acid catalysis.

There are several mechanistic schemes that correspond to this situation. Let us first consider a scheme of similar form to the above but with a different slow step. If the slow step is transfer of a proton from an acid to the substrate, we have the following mechanism:

$$S + HA \xrightarrow[k]{slow} SH^+ + A^- \text{ (or P)},$$

$$SH^+ \xrightarrow{fast} P.$$

The rate is determined by the concentration of HA,

$$rate = k[S][HA],$$

or by the sum of concentrations if more than one acid is present, each acid having a related rate constant:

$$rate = k_a[S][HA_a] + k_b[S][HA_b) + \cdots \tag{10-5}$$

The detection of such a mechanism depends upon isolating a kinetic term for each acidic species. Such behavior is found for the decomposition of the diazoacetate and azodicarbonate ions.

A second mechanism leading to a similar kinetic analysis involves an equilibrium between substrate and lyonium ion followed by a rate-determining proton transfer to base:

$$S + H^+ \underset{k_{-1}}{\overset{k_1}{\rightleftharpoons}} SH^+,$$

$$SH^+ + B \xrightarrow[k_2]{slow} P + BH^+.$$

The rate expression is given by

$$rate = k_2[SH^+][B]. \tag{10-6}$$

Since the concentration of SH^+ is determined by the prior equilibrium, Eq. (10-6) may be converted to

$$K = k_1/k_{-1} = [SH^+]/[S][H^+], \tag{10-7a}$$

$$rate = Kk_2[S][B][H^+]. \tag{10-7b}$$

The rate is thus proportional to the product $[B][H^+]$, which is itself proportional to the concentration of the conjugate acid BH^+, as expressed by the equilibrium

$$BH^+ = B + H^+; \quad K_a = [B][H^+]/[BH^+].$$

Substitution of this equilibrium expression into Eq. (10–7b) shows that the rate is dependent upon $[BH^+]$, the condition of general acid catalysis:

$$\text{rate} = K_a K k_2 [S][BH^+]. \tag{10–8}$$

Again, if more than one acid is present, the rate is determined by a summation of terms for each acid such as is given in Eq. (10–5). An example of this kinetic behavior is the acid-catalyzed mutarotation of glucose.

Finally, general acid catalysis is observed for a reaction series involving formation of a hydrogen-bonded complex between acid and substrate followed by a rate-determining decomposition of the complex:

$$S + HA \underset{k_{-1}}{\overset{k_1}{\rightleftharpoons}} S \cdot HA,$$

$$S \cdot HA \xrightarrow[k_2]{\text{slow}} P.$$

Here the rate expression is

$$\text{rate} = k_2 [S \cdot HA],$$

but

$$[S \cdot HA] = (k_1/k_{-1})[S][HA],$$

so that

$$\text{rate} = (k_1 k_2/k_{-1})[S][HA].$$

This is the general acid-catalyzed condition. In this mechanism, proton transfer may or may not occur in the slow step. If it does not, the mechanism falls outside our rigid definition of acid-base-catalyzed reactions. Nevertheless, as we have seen, the kinetic result is an expected catalytic action of any substance capable of hydrogen bond formation; molecular acids certainly fall within this group.

Specific Base Catalysis

Reactions catalyzed only by the lyate ion show specific base catalysis. In water solution the lyate ion is the hydroxide ion while in ethanol it is the ethoxide ion. The mechanistic scheme that predicts specific base catalysis closely resembles that predicting specific acid catalysis: there is a rapidly established equilibrium involving a proton transfer followed by a slow step not involving proton transfer:

$$SH + B \underset{k_{-1}}{\overset{k_1}{\rightleftharpoons}} S^- + BH^+,$$

$$S^- + R \xrightarrow[k_2]{\text{slow}} P.$$

We can easily arrive at the kinetic expression if we recognize that BH^+ is solvent and therefore would not appear in the rate expression:

$$\text{rate} = k_2[S^-][R] = (k_1 k_2 / k_{-1})[SH][R][B].$$

Many base-catalyzed condensation reactions such as the aldol, Claisen, and Perkin condensations are specific base-catalyzed.

General Base Catalysis

By methods analogous to those used in demonstrating general acid catalysis, it can be shown that general base catalysis is to be expected. For the mechanism

$$HS + B \xrightarrow[k_1']{\text{slow}} S^- + BH^+,$$

$$S^- + R \xrightarrow{\text{fast}} P$$

the expected rate equation is

$$\text{rate} = k_1[HS][B].$$

There will be a similar term for each base present in the system and the rate is the sum of such terms. Such kinetics are observed for the halogenation, isomerization, and racemization of many organic compounds containing an acidic hydrogen.

    A second mechanism predicting general base catalysis involves addition of base to the substrate in a rapidly reached equilibrium followed by a slow reaction of the complex that may, but need not, involve another reactant:

$$HS + B \underset{k_{-1}}{\overset{k_1}{\rightleftharpoons}} HS \cdot B,$$

$$HS \cdot B \xrightarrow[k_2]{\text{slow}} P,$$

$$\text{rate} = k_2[HS \cdot B] = (k_1 k_2 / k_{-1})[HS][B].$$

When this mechanism is operative, considerable specificity for the base may be observed, owing to the fact that the base commonly serves as a nucleophile adding to a carbonyl group with ultimate elimination of another base, such as is observed in the base-catalyzed ester hydrolysis.

General Acid-Base Catalysis

At least one mechanism leads to the prediction that both acids and bases serve as catalysts:

$$HS + HA \underset{k_{-1}}{\overset{k_1}{\rightleftharpoons}} HS \cdot AH,$$

$$HS \cdot AH + B \xrightarrow[k_2]{\text{slow}} P,$$

$$\text{rate} = k_2[HS \cdot AH][B] = (k_1 k_2 / k_{-1})[HS][HA][B]. \qquad (10-9)$$

The same kinetics would also be observed for the scheme

$$B + HS \rightleftharpoons B \cdot HS,$$

$$B \cdot HS + HA \xrightarrow{\text{slow}} P.$$

The kinetic expression (Eq. 10–9) for such mechanisms will be a sum of terms, each of which involves an acid-base pair if more than one pair is present. In an inert solvent, both an acid and a base must be present, but more normally a hydroxylic solvent is employed and the solvent can serve as both an acid and a base. This reduces the kinetic expression to the form

$$\text{rate} = k_{\text{obs}}[S] = k_0[S] + k_{H^+}[H^+][S] + k_{OH^-}[OH^-][S]$$
$$+ k_{HA}[HA][S] + k_{A^-}[A^-][S]. \quad (10\text{–}10)$$

The first term represents the reaction in the absence of catalyst, the second and third terms the contributions of H^+ and OH^-, and the last two terms the reaction catalyzed by the acid HA and its conjugate base A^-.

To evaluate experimentally the catalytic constants in Eq. (10–10), rate measurements must be made with buffer solutions of varying ratios and concentrations. The same approach is used for distinguishing specific and general catalysis, both acid and base, and in this simpler case it is somewhat easier to see how the method works. If a reaction is known to be acid-catalyzed, we can distinguish between specific and general acid catalysis by measuring the rate in two or more solutions containing buffers. For example, if both solutions have the same hydrogen ion concentration but considerably different concentrations of another acid HA, specific acid-catalyzed reactions will proceed at the same rate in both solutions but general acid-catalyzed reactions will proceed faster in the solution with the greater HA concentration. Returning to Eq. (10–10), rate determinations are made, keeping the concentrations of all but one of the reactants constant. A plot of the varying concentration against the observed rate constant will give a line whose slope is equal to the catalytic constant for the reagent of varying concentration. The intercept of each such plot, i.e. $[H^+] = 0$, $[OH^-] = 0$, etc., is the rate constant for the uncatalyzed reaction, k_0 (Fig. 10–2). If there is a range of H^+ and OH^- concentrations in which catalysis by these species is negligible, constants for HA and A^- can be evaluated within the range. If no such pH range exists, a correction must be made for catalysis by H^+ and

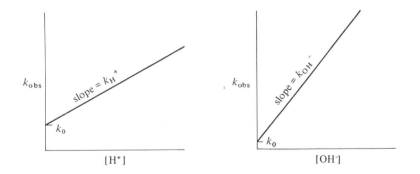

Fig. 10–2. Variation of observed rate constant with catalyst concentration at constant ionic strength.

OH^- ions. Since the ionic strength of the medium can cause rate changes, this variable must be held constant throughout these determinations.

Examination of the mechanisms just discussed will reveal that specific acid catalysis is observed when a proton is transferred to the substrate during an equilibrium step preceding a slow step of the conjugate acid of the substrate. General acid catalysis, on the other hand, is observed when the entire acid is present in the transition state of the slow step, which may occur either by slow proton transfer from the acid, by slow proton transfer to the conjugate base of the acid, or by molecular complex formation. In a similar fashion, specific base catalysis results when a proton is reversibly removed from the substrate by a base during an equilibrium step followed by a slow reaction of the conjugate base of the substrate, and general base catalysis is observed when the base is present in the transition state of the slow step. Finally, when both the entire acid and the base are present in the rate-determining transition state, general acid-base catalysis is observed.

This does not mean that in specific acid catalysis the lyonium ion is the only effective catalyst. Another acid can donate a proton to the substrate. We can show, however, that it is mathematically sufficient to represent the protonation of the substrate by lyonium ion alone. In any acid solution (here aqueous), there are several equilibria to be considered:

$$H_3O^+ + S = HS^+ + H_2O, \tag{10–11}$$

$$HA + S = HS^+ + A^-, \tag{10–12}$$

$$A^- + H_3O^+ = HA + H_2O. \tag{10–13}$$

The sum of Eqs. (10–12) and (10–13) is Eq. (10–11). Thus only Eq. (10–11) need be considered in the mathematical formulation of the protonation of the substrate. Similarly, bases other than the lyate ion may be involved in specific base catalysis but we need not consider them in our analysis of the system:

$$OH^- + SH = S^- + H_2O,$$

$$B + SH = BH^+ + S^-,$$

$$BH^+ + OH^- = B + H_2O.$$

BRØNSTED CATALYSIS LAW

The rate expressions for general acid-catalyzed reactions, e.g. Eq. (10–10), contain terms involving the concentrations of the acid and the catalytic constant k_a for that acid. Brønsted and Pedersen [1] have demonstrated that the effectiveness of acids as catalysts is related to the ionization constants of the acids by the following equations:

$$k_a = G_a K_a^\alpha, \tag{10–14}$$

$$\log k_a = \alpha \log K_a + \log G_a, \tag{10–15}$$

where k_a is the catalytic constant and K_a the ionization constant for the acid, and G_a and α are parameters that depend upon the reaction series and conditions.

Equation (10–15) bears a striking resemblance to the Hammett equation (Eq. 9–6), and it is a simple matter to arrive at Eq. (9–4) by appropriate substitutions into Eq. (10–15). In fact, the Brønsted equation is the first known general linear free energy relationship.

Equation (10–14) may be applied to acids with more than one ionizable proton or to their conjugate bases with more than one equivalent position capable of accepting a proton, if it is slightly modified to an expression (Eq. 10–16) which makes corrections for the statistical factors involved in these cases:

$$k_a/p = G_a(qK_a/p)^\alpha, \tag{10–16}$$

where p is the number of equivalent dissociable protons in the acid and q is the number of positions in the conjugate base to which a proton may be attached. Frequently, the statistical correction is found to be a minor factor, because of the range of k_a or K_a covered, and is therefore omitted.

The Brønsted relationship has been successful in correlating a large number of acid-catalyzed reactions but it breaks down when the structures of the acids are changed drastically. Nevertheless, Eq. (10–15) is satisfactory for correlation of data using acids of the same type, and very good results can be obtained. For example, the acid-catalyzed dehydration of 1,1-ethanediol,

$$CH_3CH(OH)_2 \xrightarrow[\text{acetone}]{92.5\%} CH_3CHO + H_2O,$$

has been extensively studied by Bell and Higginson [2]. The reaction is successfully correlated for a large number of carboxylic acids and phenols acting as catalysts with $\alpha = 0.54$, the mean deviation being 0.15 log unit. This remarkable application covers a range of K_a of 10^{10}. Even better agreements can be noted, if acids of similar structure only are employed. Thus, both the phenols and the aliphatic carboxylic acid catalysts give an excellent correlation, and the benzoic acids give two good lines, one for *meta*, *para* substituents and one for *ortho* substituents. However, much larger deviations were noted for acids whose structures differ even more; nitroalkanes, for example, deviate from the general Brønsted relation by as much as -1.9 log units and diethyl ketoxime deviates by $+2.1$ log units. This dependence upon structure should not surprise the reader in view of the discussion of linear free energy relationships in the preceding chapter.

The Brønsted relationship is also applicable to reactions exhibiting general base catalysis. In one form of the equation, used to correlate the catalytic coefficients of these reactions, K_a is the ionization constant of the conjugate acid of the catalyzing base B and β has the same significance as α in Eq. (10–15):

$$\log k_b = \log G_b - \beta \log K_a. \tag{10–17}$$

To correct for statistical factors the equation is used in the form

$$k_b/q = G_b(p/qK_a)^\beta \tag{10–18}$$

but again this frequently need not be employed. The remarks made previously in relation to Eq. (10–15) apply equally to Eq. (10–17) and this latter form of the Brønsted relationship will not be discussed further.

The Brønsted relationship is sometimes of value in determining reaction mechanisms. In reactions where general acid catalysis results from a mechanism involving only one proton transfer, the value of α may be interpreted as a measure of the degree of proton transfer in the transition state. The reader will recall from Chapter 9 that a rate-equilibrium relationship implies a proportionality between the activation energy of the kinetic reaction and the free energy change for the model equilibrium reaction. Complete transfer of a proton would correspond to ionization giving a proportionality constant (the Brønsted α) of one; at the other extreme, no transfer at all, α would be zero. All Brønsted relationships give values between these two limits for reactions involving proton transfer. Similar limits are placed upon β, with the transfer proceeding from the substrate to the basic catalyst. If the magnitude of α for a reaction differs significantly from that suggested by some particular mechanism, that mechanism may be excluded from consideration.

There are two limitations to the above generalization. First, when K_a is obtained in one solvent (usually water) and k_a in another, we cannot interpret the value of α in such a simple fashion, because there is no simple way of assigning a fraction of the effect of a medium change on log k to the change in the value of log K. (Of course, both rate constants and equilibria should be measured in the same solvent but they seldom are.) Secondly, the slope of the line obtained by plotting log k_a against log K_a may not correspond to the value of α, since this correspondence depends upon the details of the mechanism. The mechanism involving a prior equilibrium followed by slow proton transfer to base is such an example:

$$S + H^+ \underset{k_{-1}}{\overset{k_1}{\rightleftharpoons}} SH^+,$$

$$SH^+ + B \overset{\text{slow}}{\underset{k_2}{\longrightarrow}} P + BH^+.$$

We have seen that the rate of this reaction is given by Eq. (10–8), so that the observed rate constant is given by

$$k_{\text{obs}} = K_a K k_2. \tag{10–19}$$

From the Brønsted relationship, the rate constant for the slow step is given by

$$\log k_2 = \beta \log K_b + \log G, \tag{10–20}$$

where K_b is the equilibrium constant for the reaction

$$B + H_2O = BH^+ + OH^-.$$

Since

$$K_b = \frac{[BH^+][OH^-]}{[B]} = K_{H_2O}/K_a = 10^{-14}/K_a,$$

we can rewrite Eq. (10–20) as

$$\log k_2 = \beta \log 10^{-14}/K_a + \log G$$
$$= -14\beta - \beta \log K_a + \log G. \tag{10–21}$$

We may put Eq. (10–19) in logarithmic form

$$\log k_{obs} = \log K_a + \log K + \log k_2,$$

solve for $\log k_2$,

$$\log k_2 = \log k_{obs} - \log K_a - \log K,$$

and substitute the result into Eq. (10–21):

$$\log k_{obs} = \log K_a - \beta \log K_a + \log K - 14\beta + \log G. \qquad (10\text{–}22)$$

Since $K = [SH^+]/[S][H^+]$ (Eq. 10–7a) and does not depend upon the identity of the acid catalyst and since the last two terms in this equation are also constants, all these terms can be combined to give

$$\log k_{obs} = (1 - \beta) \log K_a + \log G'. \qquad (10\text{–}23)$$

We see that, for this one case of general acid catalysis, a plot of $\log k$ against $\log K_a$ will not give a direct measure of proton transfer. The slope of the line obtained in this manner is actually $(1 - \beta)$, β being the Brønsted parameter for the slow base-catalyzed step. A low observed value of α does not correspond to a low degree of proton transfer in the transition state; on the contrary, it stems from a high value of β in the rate-determining step. A similar situation exists in the analogous general base-catalyzed reaction.

NON-IDEAL SOLUTIONS

In the above discussion, all solutions were considered to be ideal. Similarly, in the discussions of chemical kinetics in previous chapters, the treatment has been applicable only to the gas phase or to ideal solutions. Reactions occurring in solution can be treated in the manner we have used only when the solution is both very dilute (so there is no interaction between the various solute species) and completely inert.

In some reactions, even the presence of a totally inert solvent may alter the kinetic picture. The rates of reactions that occur with an activation energy less than about 5 kcal/mole depend upon the rate at which the molecules move together through the solution. The movement of a molecule through a solvent itself has an activation energy of about 5 kcal/mole and so this movement becomes the "slow" step for a few reactions. Recombinations of ions and of free radicals frequently exhibit diffusion-controlled rates. When a pair of free radicals is generated from a single molecule, as in the decomposition of axo-*bis*-isobutyronitrile (AIBN), the solvent may cause another effect. The radicals must diffuse to become statistically distributed in the solvent but, because of the activation energy of diffusion, they collide many times before they separate and recombination may occur during these collisions. This *cage effect* accounts for the fact that not all the radicals produced from the decomposition of AIBN are effective in initiating radical polymerizations— about four-tenths of them recombine to give dimer while still in the solvent "cage."

Most reactions are not as fast as those considered above and it is with these slower reactions that we will now be concerned. No satisfactory theory has been developed for the effect of solvent upon the rate of chemical reaction, but we can make some general qualitative observations about it.

When reaction occurs between nonpolar molecules the transition state may also be nonpolar. We might expect that any solvent effect which stabilizes the transition state would also stabilize the reactants, the net effect being little or no rate change with changing solvent. This is shown in Table 10–1 for the dimerization of cyclopentadiene and in Table 10–2 for the decomposition of acetyl peroxide.

Table 10–1. Solvent Effect upon the Rate of
Dimerization of Cyclopentadiene

Medium	Relative rate (20°C)
Gas	1.0
Pure liquid	1.1
CS_2	0.9
C_6H_6	1.7
Paraffin	3.0
CCl_4	2.0

Table 10–2. Solvent Effect upon the Rate of
Acetyl Peroxide Decomposition

Medium	Relative rate (85°C)
Gas	1.0
Cyclohexane	0.57
Isooctane	0.67
Benzene	0.72
Acetic acid	0.58
Propionic acid	0.74
Carbon tetrachloride	0.54

Rates of reactions between nonpolar molecules that generate a polar transition state are more solvent-dependent. In this case, the transition state can be stabilized by an increase in the dielectric constant of the solvent, which has the effect of a decreased energy of activation and hence increases the reaction rate. Data for the Menschutkin reaction (Table 10–3) suggest that this effect is qualitatively observed, as does the earlier discussion of the Grunwald-Winstein equation.

We might now expect reactions proceeding from polar reactants to less-polar transition states to show a *decrease* in rate when the dielectric constant of the solvent is increased. In these cases the reactants are stabilized by solvent and this stabilization is lost upon going to the transition state (see Chapter 13).

Table 10–3. Solvent Effect upon the Rate of Reaction of
Triethylamine and Ethyl Iodide

Medium	Dielectric constant (25°C)	Relative rate (100°C)
Hexane	1.9	1
Benzene	2.3	81
Diphenyl ether	3.7	230
Bromobenzene	5.4	320
Acetone	20.5	840
Benzonitrile	25.2	2200
Nitrobenzene	34.6	2800

These qualitative observations have been summarized by Hughes and Ingold [3] from their studies of aliphatic substitution and elimination reactions. According to these authors, the rate of a reaction will increase with the polarity of the medium, if ionic charges arise or are compressed in the transition state. If ionic charges disappear or are spread out in the transition state, the rate of reaction will decrease with increasing polarity of the medium. The reason for this acceleration and retardation has already been mentioned; it is based upon the relative stabilization of reactants and of the transition state by solvation. The situation is graphically represented in Fig. 10–3.

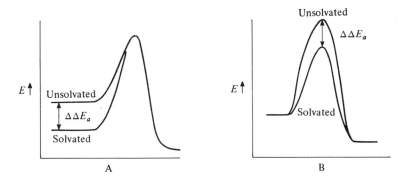

Fig. 10–3. The change in activation energy when reactants (A) and transition state (B) are specifically solvated.

Salt Effects

It has been noted many times that reaction rates can be altered by the presence of ionic species in the reaction medium even when the added ions are not themselves reactants. This effect is especially great for reactions between ions, where deviations from ideal behavior become apparent at low concentrations. For solutions that do not behave ideally, we must define equilibrium constants as belonging to some particular standard state. We shall therefore relate an equilibrium constant to the standard state of an infinitely dilute solution, which can be related to other standard states, such as that of a dilute gas, if the need should arise. Having chosen a standard state, we then define the activity a_i of a molecule A_i so that in the limit, as the concentration C_i of A_i approaches zero, the value of the activity approaches that of the concentration. To do this we introduce an activity coefficient γ_i so that the activity is given by

$$a_i = \gamma_i C_i. \tag{10-24}$$

Turning now to the transition state theory, it will be recalled that the rate of reaction is given by

$$\text{rate} = \nu[AB^\ddagger]. \tag{10-25}$$

Since we are no longer dealing with ideal conditions, we must express $K^\ddagger$ in terms of activities rather than in the concentration terms used in Eq. (7-18):

$$K^\ddagger = a_{AB}^\ddagger/a_A a_B = \gamma_{AB^\ddagger}[AB^\ddagger]/\gamma_A[A]\gamma_B[B]. \tag{10-26}$$

Solving this for the concentration of the activated complex $[AB^\ddagger]$ and substituting it into the rate equation, we get the Brønsted relationships:

$$\text{rate} = k[A][B] = (kT/h)K^\ddagger \frac{\gamma_A \gamma_B}{\gamma_{AB^\ddagger}}[A][B], \tag{10-27}$$

$$k = (kT/h)K^\ddagger \gamma_A \gamma_B/\gamma_{AB^\ddagger}. \tag{10-28}$$

For reactions in dilute aqueous solution the activity coefficients of ions can be obtained by the Debye-Hückel limiting law:

$$\log \gamma_i = -\left[\frac{(2\pi N_0)^{1/2}}{2.303}(e^2/10\epsilon kT)^{3/2}\right]Z_i^2 \mu^{1/2}$$

$$= -AZ_i^2 \mu^{1/2}. \tag{10-29}$$

In this equation A is a term containing universal constants—the dielectric constant ϵ of the solvent and the temperature. (In water at 25°C, A = 0.509.) The symbol Z_i is the charge of the ion, and μ is the ionic strength in the solution, defined as

$$\mu = \tfrac{1}{2} \sum C_i Z_i^2, \tag{10-30}$$

taken over all of the different kinds of ions present.

Writing Eq. (10-28) in logarithmic form yields

$$\log k = \log (kT/h)K^\ddagger + \log \gamma_A + \log \gamma_B - \log \gamma_{AB^\ddagger}, \tag{10-31}$$

into which we can introduce Eq. (10-29) and $Z_A + Z_B$ for $Z_{AB^\ddagger}$ since the charge of the transition state must equal the sum of the charges of the reactants:

$$\log k = \log (kT/h)K^\ddagger - A\mu^{1/2}[Z_A^2 + Z_B^2 - (Z_A + Z_B)^2].$$

This may be reduced to

$$\log k = \log (kT/h)K^\ddagger + 2AZ_A Z_B \mu^{1/2}. \tag{10-32}$$

The first term on the right-hand side of this equation is the expression for the logarithm of the rate constant k_0 in the standard state (*cf.* Eq. 7–20). Therefore, we may write

$$\log k/k_0 = 2AZ_AZ_B\mu^{1/2}. \tag{10–33}$$

The Brønsted-Debye limiting rate equation (10–33) predicts that a plot of $\log k$ against the square root of the ionic strength should be a straight line of slope $2AZ_AZ_B$. For water solutions at 25°C where $A = 0.509$, the slope is Z_AZ_B. This equation has been tested many times and has been found to hold with very good accuracy. Naturally, we should only expect it to work in dilute solutions, because Eq. 10–29 is only applicable for these solutions. Figure 10–4 shows a plot of typical results.

These effects of added salts are known as *primary salt effects*. They are especially important for two reasons. First, because the effects can be correctly predicted from

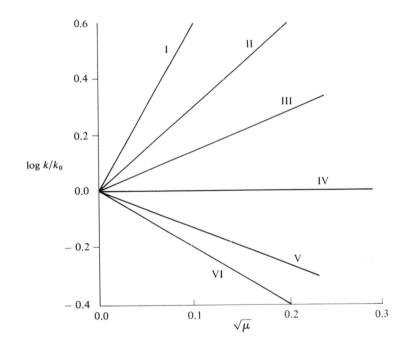

Fig. 10–4. Primary salt effect. (Taken from G. W. Castellan, *Physical Chemistry*, Addison-Wesley Co., Reading, Mass. (1964), p. 647.)

I	$Co(NH_3)_5Br^{+2} + Hg^{+2}$	$Z_AZ_B = 4$
II	$S_2O_8^{-2} + I^-$	2
III	$NO_2NCO_2C_2H_5^- + I^-$	1
IV	Glucose + OH^-	0
V	$H_2O_2 + H^+ + Br^-$	-1
VI	$Co(NH_3)_5Br^{+2} + OH^-$	-2

the transition state theory, they serve as a verification of the theory. Secondly, since rates of reactions involving ions are sensitive to the ionic strength of the medium, kinetic experiments must obviously be planned with care. If pure water is used, any change in ionic strength during the reaction may give erratic rate constants. To overcome this problem, rates of ionic reactions are frequently followed in a solution to which a large excess of an inert salt has been added, so that the ionic strength is effectively kept constant throughout the reaction.

The primary salt effect fits into the Hughes-Ingold qualitative theory dealing with medium polarity and reaction rates discussed above. The addition of an ionic substance to a reaction medium increases the polarity of the medium. We would thus qualitatively predict a large positive salt effect (rate increase) for a reaction between two similarly charged ions and a large negative salt effect (rate decrease) when the reacting ions are oppositely charged. Equation 10–33 predicts a negligible effect for reactions between uncharged species or between an uncharged moiety and an ion. Actually, if two uncharged species form a highly ionic transition state, a rather large positive salt effect is observed and the Hughes-Ingold approach suggests why: charge is greater in the transition state than in the reactants. Reaction between an electrically neutral molecule and an ion generally results in dispersal or spreading out of the charge in the transition state. Although the total charge remains the same, this dispersal suggests that a negative salt effect should be expected, which is usually found even if it is small.

In studying the acid-base-catalyzed reactions discussed above, the careful experimenter will investigate the possibility of primary salt effects. The substrate is normally uncharged in an acid-base-catalyzed reaction and Eq. 10–33 predicts the primary salt effect to be zero. A salt effect can be eliminated by extrapolation to zero ionic strength or by swamping the effect with added salt. Of perhaps greater significance to these reactions is an effect that is not of a kinetic nature at all, the *secondary salt effect*.

This effect may be observed for reactions involving equilibrium steps prior to the rate-determining step. It has to do with the role of ionic strength in determining the extent of dissociation in an equilibrium reaction. For a specific acid-catalyzed reaction where the rate of reaction depends upon hydronium ion concentration, it is apparent that the rate of reaction will be changed by a change in ionic strength if this also changes $[H_3O^+]$.

The Debye-Hückel limiting equation (10–29) may be used to assess the influence of ionic strength. In real solutions, i.e. $\gamma \neq 1$, the equilibrium constant for the dissociation of a weak acid,

$$HA + H_2O = H_3O^+ + A^-,$$

is given by

$$K_a = a_{H_3O^+} a_{A^-} / a_{HA} = \frac{[H_3O^+][A^-]}{[HA]} \times \frac{\gamma_{H_3O^+} \gamma_{A^-}}{\gamma_{HA}}. \tag{10–34}$$

The hydronium ion concentration is given by

$$[H_3O^+] = (K_a[HA]/[A^-])(\gamma_{HA}/\gamma_{H_3O^+}\gamma_{A^-}),$$

which may be placed in logarithmic form and the Debye-Hückel equation (10–29) directly substituted:

$$\log [H_3O^+] = \log K_A + \log [HA]/[A^-] + \log \gamma_{HA} - \log \gamma_{H_3O^+} - \log \gamma_{A^-},$$
$$\log \gamma_{HA} = -AZ_{HA}^2\mu^{1/2} = 0,$$
$$-\log \gamma_{H_3O^+} = AZ_{H_3O^+}^2\mu^{1/2} = A\mu^{1/2},$$
$$-\log \gamma_{A^-} = AZ_{A^-}^2\mu^{1/2} = A\mu^{1/2},$$
$$\log [H_3O^+] = \log K_A + \log [HA]/[A^-] + 2A\mu^{1/2}.$$

The effect of increasing the ionic strength is to increase the hydronium ion concentration.

The ionic strength must be kept constant (when a reaction is examined for general acid catalysis) by changes in buffer concentration. Unless this is done, the increasing ionic strength of the medium as the buffer concentration is increased will lead to a rate increase that may be mistaken for general acid catalysis. It is of course important to use an inert salt to maintain a large, constant ionic strength, as has been mentioned above. This swamping method gives rate constants whose values are often different from those obtained in very dilute solutions but the technique is useful in determining the reaction order. To obtain values of rate constants free of any salt effect, a series of determinations is made at varying ionic strengths and the results are extrapolated to zero ionic concentration. Sometimes the ionic strength can be kept sufficiently low for the effects to be small. In any kinetic study of an ionic reaction the wise investigator will add varying small amounts of ionic materials to discover the effect of ionic strength upon the reaction rate.

Acidity Functions and Acidity Strength

Comparison of the proton-donating abilities of acids in a *single* solvent presents little difficulty: a pH meter gives a logarithmic measure of the activity of the hydrogen ion. In very dilute solutions concentrations can be calculated from these activities; in concentrated acid solutions, however, this cannot be done and some other parameter must be used to measure acidity. Also, the value of the concentration of the solvated proton is useless in comparing the ability of *different* solvent systems to donate a proton to a base, i.e. the acidity of an acid in different solvents.

Therefore, it is more practical to use other functions as measures of acid strength. Consider the reaction

$$HA \overset{K_a}{\rightleftharpoons} H^+ + A^-,$$

where H^+ represents hydrogen ions in whatever form they take in a particular solvent. To prevent the ionization constant changing as salts are added, we define it in terms of activities:

$$K_a = a_{H^+}a_{A^-}/a_{HA} = \frac{\gamma_{H^+}\gamma_{A^-}}{\gamma_{HA}}\frac{[H^+][A^-]}{[HA]}. \tag{10–35}$$

If we use a dilute aqueous solution as a standard, so that the activity coefficients approach 1.0 at infinitely dilute concentrations, the value of K_a may be expressed by concentrations only in dilute solution:

$$K_a = [H^+][A^-]/[HA] = K_{A,w}.$$

Now, if the activity coefficients in some other solvent S are also referred to the dilute aqueous solution, we obtain

$$K_a = K_{A,s}\gamma_{H^+}\gamma_{A^-}/\gamma_{HA} = K_{A,w}. \tag{10–36}$$

For some other acid HB we can write an analogous equation

$$K_a' = K_{A,s}'\gamma_{H^+}\gamma_{B^-}/\gamma_{HB} = K_{A,w}'. \tag{10–37}$$

Dividing (10–36) by (10–37) we obtain

$$K_{A,w}/K_{A,w}' = K_{A,s}\gamma_{A^-}\gamma_{HB}/K_{A,s}'\gamma_{B^-}\gamma_{HA}$$

or

$$K_{A,s} = K_{A,s}'(K_{A,w}/K_{A,w}')(\gamma_{B^-}\gamma_{HA})/(\gamma_{A^-}\gamma_{HB}), \tag{10–38}$$

which shows that the acidity constant of HA in a solvent S may be calculated if we know: (1) the acidity constant of the acid HA in water; (2) the acidity constant of a second acid HB in water; (3) the acidity constant of HB in the solvent S; and (4) the activity coefficient ratio $\gamma_{B^-}\gamma_{HA}/\gamma_{A^-}\gamma_{HB}$. The activity coefficients γ_{HA} and γ_{HB} can be obtained by standard methods, e.g. solubilities, partial pressures. Although the activity coefficients of the anions cannot be obtained directly, the ratio $\gamma_{B^-}/\gamma_{A^-}$ is available from the solubilities of salts.

If we wish to study a series of weak bases we must study them in solutions of varying acidity so that each base will be partially protonated. We then need a measure of the proton-donating ability of the acidic media.

Hammett and Deyrup [4] have suggested that the use of a series of indicators will permit the acidities of strongly acidic media to be referred to the standard state in water by an overlapping technique. Since the indicators are bases and are protonated in the acidic media, in effect we are studying the acidities of the protonated base, A:

$$HA^+ = H^+ + A; \quad K_a = a_{H^+}a_A/a_{HA^+}; \quad pK_a = -\log a_{H^+}a_A/a_{HA^+}.$$

We can rearrange the equation for pK_a to a more convenient form

$$pK_a = \log a_{AH^+}/a_A - \log a_{H^+}. \tag{10–39}$$

In dilute aqueous solutions where activities equal concentrations, Eq. (10–39) reduces to

$$pK_a = \log [HA^+]/[A] + pH \text{ (dilute } H_2O).$$

We determine pK_a by measuring the ratio of $[HA^+]/[A]$ in an aqueous solution of known pH, using a spectrophotometric technique.

If we now consider a second base (indicator) in the same solution,

$$BH^+ \xrightleftharpoons{K'_a} H^+ + B,$$

we can write

$$pK'_a = \log a_{BH^+}/a_B - \log a_{H^+}. \tag{10–40}$$

Subtracting this from Eq. (10–39):

$$pK_a - pK'_a = \log a_{HA^+}/a_A - \log a_{BH^+}/a_B,$$

and rewriting in terms of concentrations we obtain

$$pK_a - pK'_a = \log [AH^+]/[A] - \log [BH^+]/[B] + \log \frac{\gamma_{AH^+}\gamma_B}{\gamma_A\gamma_{BH^+}}. \tag{10–41}$$

Experimentally, it has been found that the ratio of activity coefficients for the conjugate acid of a base and the free base is equal to the ratio for the conjugate acid of a second base and its free base, if the bases are of similar electrical charge and of similar structure (again the reaction series postulate appears):

$$\gamma_{AH^+}/\gamma_A = \gamma_{BH^+}/\gamma_B. \tag{10–42}$$

When this equality is observed, Eq. (10–41) reduces to

$$pK_a - pK'_a = \log [AH^+]/[A] - \log [BH^+]/[B]. \tag{10–43}$$

All of the terms on the right-hand side of this equation are experimentally accessible.

The use of Eq. (10–43) to determine an acidity scale can be illustrated with an actual example.

First, we select an indicator of known pK_a that is basic enough to be partially protonated by dilute aqueous acid, for example, p-aminoazobenzene with pK_a of 2.77. (A dilute aqueous acidic solution where all activity coefficients are 1.0 can be used to determine this pK_a if it is not known.) A slightly weaker second base is selected, which will be partially protonated in a solution not acidic enough for the azo compound to be completely protonated. We then measure the concentrations of the free bases A and B and of their conjugate acids HA^+ and HB^+, and from these values we calculate the pK'_a of the second base. For example, a mixture of p-aminoazobenzene and p-nitroaniline can be used in aqueous HCl to give a pK_a value of 0.99 for the second base. A mixture of p-nitroaniline and a third, even weaker base is then placed in a more acidic medium and the pK'_a is evaluated. When the third base is o-nitroaniline, pK_a is found to be -0.29 in hydrochloric acid, -0.32 in nitric acid, -0.31 in perchloric acid, -0.22 in phosphoric acid, -0.27 in hydrofluoric acid, -0.36 in aqueous trichloroacetic acid, and -0.25 in aqueous trifluoroacetic acid. This leads to a "best" value for the pK_a of the conjugate acid of o-nitroaniline of -0.29, with an average deviation of 0.03 logarithmic units. The pK_a values of many bases have been determined in this way (Table 10–4).

Table 10–4. pK_a Values of Conjugate Acids of Several
Weak Bases*

Base	pK_a
p-Aminoazobenzene	2.77
m-Nitroaniline	2.50
2,4-Dichloroaniline	2.00
Benzeneazodiphenylamine	1.42
p-Nitroaniline	0.99
Diphenylamine	0.78
2,4-Dinitro-N,N-diethylaniline	0.18
2,6-Dichloro-4-nitro-N,N-dimethylaniline	−0.23
o-Nitroaniline	−0.29
4-Chloro-2-nitroaniline	−1.03
4-Chloro-2-nitro-N-methylaniline	−1.49
p-Nitrodiphenylamine	−2.48
2,4-Dichloro-6-nitroaniline	−3.32
p-Nitroazobenzene	−3.47
2,4-Dinitroaniline	−4.53
β-Benzoylnaphthalene	−6.04
6-Bromo-2,4-dinitroaniline	−6.71
Anthraquinone	−8.27
2,4,6-Trinitroaniline	−9.41
p-Nitrotoluene	−10.46
Nitrobenzene	−11.38
2,4-Dinitrotoluene	−12.78

* Selected values taken from Foot and Long [5].

Using this technique we construct a scale for the measurement of the proton-donating ability of various media much broader than the familiar pH scale. The bases that satisfy Eq. (10–42) are called *Hammett bases* or *Hammett indicators*. They work well for aqueous solutions of strong acids up through concentrated H_2SO_4.

To understand the scale we have developed, we change the form of Eq. (10–39) to

$$pK_a = \log[AH^+]/[A] - \log a_H + \gamma_A/\gamma_{AH^+}. \qquad (10\text{–}44)$$

For any solvent, a_{H^+} is independent of the nature of the Hammett base, as is the ratio of γ_A/γ_{AH^+} (*cf.* Eq. 10–42), at least for a large number of bases. Thus, the last term of Eq. (10–44) has a definite value for any solvent system and, since it can be used to obtain the amount of base present in the system as conjugate acid (if pK_a of the base is known), it is a measure of the proton-donating ability of the medium. When the base used is uncharged, this term is called the *Hammett acidity function*, H_0:

$$H_0 = -\log a_{H^+} \gamma_A/\gamma_{AH^+}. \qquad (10\text{–}45)$$

A formally equivalent equation is obtained by substituting Eq. (10–45) into (10–44) and rearranging terms:

$$H_0 = pK_a + \log [A]/[AH^+]. \tag{10–46}$$

In dilute aqueous solutions activity coefficients become equal to 1.0 and H_0 reduces to pH:

$$H_0 = \log a_{H^+} \gamma_A/\gamma_{AH^+}$$
$$= -\log [H^+] = pH \text{ (dilute water)}.$$

For the acidity function to be valid, Eq. (10–42) must be followed. In solutions of low dielectric constant this fundamental postulate may no longer hold, but Eq. (10–42) is known to apply in aqueous solutions of strong acids. No better function for comparing the acidities of different media is available and H_0 is superior to simple stoichiometric acid concentration. Values for several acids are given in Table 10–5.

Table 10–5. H_0 Values for Aqueous Acid Solutions at 25°C*

Acid concentration, moles/liter	HNO$_3$	HCl	HClO$_4$	H$_2$SO$_4$	HF	HBr
0.1	0.98	0.98		0.83		0.98
0.5	0.21	0.20		0.13		0.20
1.0	−0.18	−0.20	−0.22	−0.26	1.20	−0.20
2.0	−0.67	−0.69	−0.78	−0.84	0.91	−0.71
3.0	−1.02	−1.05	−1.23	−1.38	0.60	−1.11
4.0	−1.32	−1.40	−1.72	−1.85	0.40	−1.50
5.0	−1.57	−1.76	−2.23	−2.28	0.28	−1.93
6.0	−1.79	−2.12	−2.84	−2.76	0.15	−2.38
7.0	−1.99	−2.56	−3.61	−3.32	0.02	−2.85
8.0		−3.00	−4.33	−3.87	0.11	−3.34
9.0		−3.39	−5.05	−4.40	−0.24	−3.84
10.0		−3.68	−5.79	−4.89	−0.36	−4.44

* Selected from Foot and Long [5].

Although the indicator-overlap method could be subject to cumulative errors, in a recent test of the reliability of the pK's of many indicator bases, Arnett and Burke [6] found that the pK_a's of a series of conjugated acids of primary amines in water correlated with the heats of protonation of the same amines in concentrated sulfuric acid. Since the pK_a values covered a range of 16 logarithmic units and could only be estimated by the Hammett technique, this correlation increases our confidence in the reliability of the overlap method.

The acidity function H_0 is limited to bases that are uncharged, i.e. the equilibrium

$$HA^+ = H^+ + A.$$

An analogous acidity scale has been established for the equilibrium

$$HA = H^+ + A^-,$$

where the acidity function, designated by H_-, is defined by the following equations:

$$H_- = -\log a_{H^+} \gamma_{A^-}/\gamma_{HA}, \tag{10–47}$$

$$H_- = pK_a + \log [A^-]/[HA]. \tag{10–48}$$

This function has recently been reviewed [7] and appears to be well-established for strongly basic solutions using aromatic amines as indicators. It is a measure of the ability of a solution to remove a proton from an acid. It will be noted that, if the standard state is dilute water, the H_--function becomes identical with pH in dilute aqueous solutions.

Another similar acidity function, based upon the ionization

$$R^+ + H_2O = ROH + H^+,$$

is now written as H_R but was written as C_0 and J_0 in the past. Di- and triaryl carbinols have been used to establish values of H_R, which is defined as

$$H_R = -\log a_{H^+} \gamma_{ROH}/a_{H_2O}\gamma_{R^+}, \tag{10–49}$$

$$H_R = pK_{R^+} + \log [ROH]/[R^+]. \tag{10–50}$$

Again, we note that the acidity function in dilute water solution becomes equal to pH if this medium is used as the reference for the activity coefficients at the point where the a_{H_2O} becomes 1.0. The value of H_R is more sensitive than H_0 to the effective concentration of water. The two functions are compared in Table 10–6 and Fig. 10–5.

Table 10–6. Comparison of H_0 and H_R in
Aqueous Sulfuric Acid at 25°C*

Acid, wt %	H_0	H_R
5	0.1	−0.07
10	−0.31	−0.72
20	−1.01	−1.92
30	−1.72	−3.22
40	−2.41	−4.80
50	−3.38	−6.60
60	−4.46	−8.92
70	−5.65	−11.52
80	−6.97	−14.12
90	−8.27	−16.72
95	−8.86	−18.08
98	−9.36	−19.64

* From Foot and Long [5].

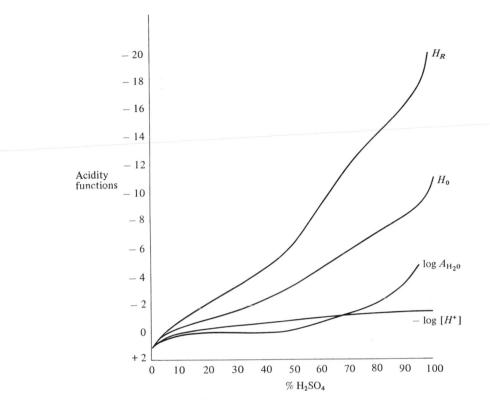

Fig. 10–5. Acidity functions in aqueous sulfuric acid.

Acidity Functions and Kinetics

Many acid-catalyzed reactions are carried out in solutions where hydrogen ion concentration is not a useful measure of acidity. As we have seen, various acidity functions are useful measures of the proton-donating ability of a medium and we might expect to find a relationship between acidity functions and acid catalysis. This relationship would be of special interest if used to solve problems of reaction mechanism.

If we consider the specific acid-catalyzed reaction

$$S + H^+ \underset{K}{\rightleftharpoons} SH^+,$$

$$SH^+ \xrightarrow[k]{\text{slow}} P,$$

the rate equation may be obtained as follows, in the same way that we obtained the Brønsted relationships (Eq. 10–29):

$$\text{rate} = k[SH^+] = kK[S][H^+]\gamma_S\gamma_{H^+}/\gamma_\ddagger$$
$$= kK[S]a_{H^+}\,\gamma_S/\gamma_\ddagger, \tag{10–51}$$

where $\gamma_\ddagger$ is the activity coefficient of the transition state.

The Hammett acidity function was defined as

$$H_0 = -\log a_{H^+} \gamma_A / \gamma_{AH^+},$$

or, if we wish to use the symbol h_0, as

$$h_0 = a_{H^+} \gamma_A / \gamma_{AH^+}.$$

Substituting this into the rate expression (10–51), we get

$$\text{rate} = kK[S]h_0 \gamma_S \gamma_{AH^+} / \gamma_{\ddagger} \gamma_A. \tag{10–52}$$

The activity coefficient term of this equation involves the transition state, which might be expected to have a structure similar to SH^+. If it does and if S resembles the bases used in establishing the H_0 function, Eq. (10–42) might be valid, i.e.,

$$\gamma_S / \gamma_{SH^+} = \gamma_A / \gamma_{AH^+}.$$

In this case, Eq. (10–52) reduces to the expression

$$\text{rate} = kK[S]h_0 = k_{obs}[S]h_0,$$

so that a plot of log k_{obs} against $-H_0$ is expected to give a line of slope equal to 1.0:

$$\log k_{obs} = -H_0.$$

It is not too surprising that slopes frequently fall between 0.85 and 1.15.

An alternative mechanism for acid catalysis is the general acid mechanism

$$S + H^+ \underset{}{\overset{K}{\rightleftharpoons}} SH^+$$

$$SH^+ + B \xrightarrow[k]{\text{slow}} P.$$

The rate expression for this mechanism is

$$\begin{aligned}
\text{rate} &= Kk[S][H^+][B]\gamma_S \gamma_{H^+} \gamma_B / \gamma_{\ddagger} \\
&= Kk[S][H^+]a_B \gamma_S \gamma_{H^+} / \gamma_{\ddagger} \\
&= k_{obs}[S][H^+]a_B \gamma_S \gamma_{H^+} / \gamma_{\ddagger}.
\end{aligned}$$

Since the transition state contains not only SH^+ but also B, we should not expect a linear correlation with the acidity function H_0. If the term

$$a_B \gamma_S \gamma_{H^+} / \gamma_{\ddagger}$$

is constant over an acidity range we should expect the rates of reactions proceeding by this mechanism to be proportional to the hydrogen ion concentration. Because B is most frequently a water molecule, we might interpret a rate dependence upon $[H^+]$ as suggesting an additional water molecule in the transition state. Reactions that show this rate dependence do contain a water molecule in the slow step. Unfortunately, not all reactions that contain a water molecule in the transition state show a rate dependence upon $[H^+]$. This is not surprising in view of the restriction that $a_{H_2O} \gamma_S \gamma_{H^+} / \gamma_{\ddagger}$ must be a constant. However, there is no reason that this should be so (recall that the transition state structure contains a water molecule) and, in fact, reactions known to proceed by this mechanism may show a rate dependence intermediate between $[H^+]$ and h_0 or even a dependence upon h_0 itself when h_0 varies in the same way as $[H^+]$. This mechanistic criterion is known as the *Hammett-Zucker hypothesis.*

The indicators used to obtain the H_R function are quite different from those used to obtain H_0. Reactions proceeding by a mechanism

$$ROH + H^+ \overset{K}{\rightleftharpoons} R^+ + H_2O$$

$$R^+ \xrightarrow[k]{\text{slow}} P,$$

where H_2O is lost in an equilibrium step prior to the rate-determining step with the result that the transition state consists of a molecule of substrate plus a proton minus water, might be expected to show H_R dependence. The reader should compare the transition state structure for this mechanism with the H_R defining equilibrium. The rate expression for this mechanism may be obtained as

$$\text{rate} = kK[ROH]a_{H^+}\gamma_{ROH}/a_{H_2O}\gamma_{\ddagger}$$
$$= k_{obs}[ROH]a_{H^+}\gamma_{ROH}/a_{H_2O}\gamma_{\ddagger},$$

which may be reduced to

$$\text{rate} = k_{obs}[ROH]h_R,$$

A plot of $\log k_{obs}$ against $-H_R$ should then give a line of slope about 1.0. Such behavior has been observed.

The use of acidity functions in determining reaction mechanisms may be summarized thus: a good correlation of H_0 with $\log k$ is suggestive, but not conclusive, evidence that the transition state of the reaction contains a proton along with a molecule of substrate, with no other species present; the dependence of $\log k$ on pH change suggests that a molecule of substrate in the transition state also contains an additional molecule of water and a proton; finally, if $\log k$ is linearly correlated with H_R, the substrate molecule has gained a proton but lost a water molecule in the transition state. We should be especially careful in assigning a mechanism when H_0 dependence is observed, even though the prediction of this dependence from the specific mechanism rests upon fairly safe assumptions. Prediction of pH dependence is highly suspect because of the extreme restriction imposed upon the activity coefficient ratio. Regrettably, these guides to the formulation of a mechanism are at best tentative and additional evidence is required.

Bunnett Relationships

An empirical relationship for the treatment of rate dependence upon acidity function was discovered by Bunnett [8]. He observed that the logarithm of the pseudo-first-order rate constant ($\log k_\psi$) plus H_0 could be plotted against $\log a_{H_2O}$ to give linear plots of slope W (the Bunnett equation):

$$\log k_\psi + H_0 = W \log a_{H_2O}. \tag{10-53}$$

Empirically, Bunnett found that the value of W is determined by the reaction mechanism. For a reaction mechanism in which water does not participate in the rate-determining step, W is found to be between -2.5 and 0.0. Such reactions include the acid-catalyzed hydrolyses of simple acetals, *tert*-butyl acetate and methyl mesitoate. Reactions in which water acts as a nucleophile in the rate-determining step, either by adding to the protonated substrate or by actual substitution, exhibit W-values of 1.2 to 3.3. Evidence for this was obtained from the hydrolyses of ethylenimine, diethyl ether, and amides of carboxylic acids as well as the isomerization of *cis*- and *trans*-benzalacetophenone. Finally, W-values greater than 3.3 were observed for reactions where water serves as a proton transfer agent in the rate-determining step, if the substrate was protonated on nitrogen or oxygen (and presumably other electronegative atoms); if, however, the substrate was protonated on a carbon atom (as in the hydration of olefins and the protodetritiation of $1,3,5$-trimethoxybenzene-2-t) the W-values were close to zero. Examples used for establishing the former criterion were the enolization of ketones, isotopic exchange with solvent of NH_3D^+, $NMeH_2D^+$ and NMe_3D^+, and the cleavage of methylmercuric iodide where the mercuri- group is displaced by a proton furnished by some acid such as hydronium ion.

These observations presumably can be applied to reactions of unknown mechanism in order to classify them in one of the mechanistic schemes. Bunnett suggests that the use of W-plots should supplant the Hammett-Zucker hypothesis described above. Although his approach appears to be superior, mechanistic conclusions drawn from a W-plot should be supported by other evidence. The mechanistic suggestions based upon W-values are summarized in Table 10–7.

Table 10–7. Mechanistic Interpretation of W-Values

W-values	Role of water in transition state
Substrates protonated on O or N	
-2.5–0.0	Not involved
0.0–3.3	Nucleophile
> 3.3	Proton transfer agent
Substrates protonated on C	
ca. 0.0	Proton transfer agent

Equation 10–53 may be considered as a refinement of the Hammett-Zucker equation

$$\log k = -H_0.$$

The value of W may be taken as a parameter characteristic of the differences in substrate and transition state structures whereas the activity of water is a parameter characteristic of the medium. Bunnett has suggested that the W-value is a measure of the difference in hydration between the activated complex and the substrate. We might infer from this suggestion that the *only* mechanistically important feature determining W is the change in hydration, but, although the number of water molecules involved in the reaction is almost certainly an important factor in determining W, it cannot be the sole factor. If it were, no dependence of W upon the specific acid used would be expected, but this dependence does exist; for example, the hydrolysis of methylal, $(CH_3O)_2CH_2$, gives a W-value of -5.26 in aqueous hydrochloric acid, of -2.04 in aqueous sulfuric acid, and of -0.09 in aqueous perchloric acid. Similarly, the W-value for the iodination of acetophenone in perchloric acid-water mixtures is 6.35, while in sulfuric acid-water mixtures it is 3.63.

All of the above discussion applies only to relatively dilute aqueous acid media. At high acid concentrations, deviations are frequently noted. This is not surprising, since the mole fraction of water in 87% H_2SO_4 is less than 0.5. Also, as the acidity is increased, all of the substrate will exist as the conjugate acid at some point and one would expect the reaction rate to become independent of acidity.

SOLVENT ISOTOPE EFFECTS

The criteria developed above have proved very useful in studying the mechanisms of acid-catalyzed reactions. Another tool, the solvent isotope effect, has also been valuable in these studies. Since the autoprotolysis reactions for H_2O and D_2O,

$$2H_2O \xrightarrow{K_H} H_3O^+ + HO^-,$$

$$2D_2O \xrightarrow{K_D} D_3O^+ + DO^-,$$

exhibit an isotope effect K_H/K_D of 6.5, it is believed that D_3O^+ is a stronger acid than H_3O^+ (or alternatively that D_2O is a weaker base than H_2O). This is verified by the data in Table 10–8, which show that weak acids are more highly ionized in H_2O than in D_2O. We may also note that the isotope effect decreases as acid strength increases.

Table 10–8. Isotope Effect for the Equilibria:
$$XH + H_2O = X^- + H_3O^+$$
$$XD + D_2O = X^- + D_3O^+$$

Acid	K_H	K_H/K_D
Chloroacetic acid	1.7×10^{-3}	2.74
Benzoic acid	6.2×10^{-5}	3.13
Acetic acid	1.8×10^{-5}	3.33
p-Nitrophenol	5.7×10^{-8}	3.61
β-Chloroethanol	4.9×10^{-15}	5.0

This change of acid strength will affect the rate of acid-catalyzed reactions when the proton transfer step precedes the rate-determining step. For the specific acid-catalyzed mechanism

$$S + H^+ = SH^+ \xrightarrow{\text{slow}} P,$$

the rate depends upon SH^+ (SD^+) concentration. Since D_3O^+ is a stronger acid than H_3O^+, the concentration of protonated substrate will be greater in D_2O than in H_2O and the reaction will proceed faster in the deuterated solvent if no normal kinetic isotope effect occurs in the second step.

In a similar fashion, the general acid-catalyzed mechanism

$$S + H^+ = SH^+$$

$$SH^+ + B \xrightarrow{\text{slow}} P$$

will give a faster rate in D_2O than in H_2O if the proton removed is different from the one added in the prior step. If the proton removed in the slow step and the proton added in the prior equilibrium are the same we expect a normal kinetic isotope effect, $k_H/k_D > 1$, to offset the solvent isotope effect, $k_H/k_D < 1$. This balance between the two effects normally results in $k_H/k_D > 1$. For the general acid-catalyzed mechanism

$$S + HA = S \cdot HA \xrightarrow{\text{slow}} P$$

we might expect the formation of the equilibrium complex to be insensitive to iso-topic substitution. This mechanism is expected to show a normal kinetic isotope effect if the rate-determining step involves proton transfer from acid to substrate. If no such transfer occurs, the observed isotope effect will be nonexistent, or nearly so.

The solvent isotope effect can also be used in studying base-catalyzed reactions by methods analogous to those above. In basic reactions, DO^- is a stronger base than HO^-. This leads to an expected rate increase in D_2O if an equilibrium is in-volved and no compensating normal kinetic isotope effect occurs later; i.e., there is no subsequent slow proton transfer step. Table 10–9 gives some typical values for the isotope effect observed for acid- and base-catalyzed reactions in light and heavy water.

Table 10–9. Isotope Effects for Acid- and Base-Catalyzed Reactions in H_2O and D_2O*

Reaction	T, °C	Catalyst	k_{H_2O}/k_{D_2O}
Hydrolysis of ethylorthoformate	25	H_3O^+	0.43
Hydrolysis of acetonitrile	105	H_3O^+	0.74
Mutarotation of glucose	25	H_3O^+	1.37
	25	AcOH	2.6
Bromination of acetone	25	H_3O^+	0.48
	25	RCO_2H	0.50
Hydrolysis of acetonitrile	35	OH^-	0.83
Neutralization of nitromethane	5	OH^-	0.74
Bromination of nitromethane	25	AcO^-	1.15
	25	$ClCH_2CO_2^-$	1.31

* Values selected from Wiberg [9].

PROBLEMS

1. What would be a suitable solvent for quantitatively comparing the acidities of each of the following pairs of compounds:
   a) Benzoic acid and m-toluic acid
   b) Aniline and m-toluidine
   c) Sulfuric acid and m-toluenesulfonic acid.

2. The pK_a of o-nitroaniline is -0.29. What is the ratio of concentrations of o-nitroanilinium ion to o-nitroaniline in 0.02 M HCl aqueous solution?

3. Predict the type of catalysis to be expected for the mechanism:

$$B + SH = BH^+ + S^- \xrightarrow{\text{slow}} P + B.$$

4. For the following reactions indicate whether an increase in the ionic strength of the medium would increase the rate, decrease the rate, or have little effect:
   a) Acetate ion + isopropyl bromide
   b) Et_2CClCH_3 in methanol
   c) Conversion of $ClCH_2CH_2NMe_2$ to the corresponding alcohol in aqueous ethanol
   d) Methyl bromide + iodide ion
   e) $Me_3EtN^+ + HO^- \rightarrow Me_3N + CH_2{=}CH_2 + H_2O$

5. Show that the mechanism

$$S + H^+ \xrightarrow{\text{slow}} P$$

   is expected to show a rate dependence upon h_0. How might this mechanism be distinguished from the one used to develop Eq. (10–52)?

6. In 1–6 M sulfuric acid, the rate of dehydration of $tert$-butyl alcohol to isobutene is proportional to h_0 rather than to h_r, in spite of the evidence that a fast prior equilibrium to give a carbonium ion is involved. Interpret this result.

7. The bromination of acetone is general acid-catalyzed and the rate is independent of bromine concentration. The reaction proceeds faster in D_2O than in H_2O (see Table 10–8). Acetone reacts seven times faster than the hexadeutero material. Suggest a mechanism to account for all of these observations.

8. γ-Butyrolactone is not detectably hydrolyzed in neutral solution but is hydrolyzed in acid or basic solution with acyl cleavage. With 1–4 M perchloric acid or hydrochloric acid, the rate of hydrolysis is proportional to the stoichiometric acid concentration (H^+) rather than to the Hammett acidity function (h_0). This reaction is reversible. Predict the dependence of rate on acidity for the reverse reaction (lactonization).

REFERENCES

1. J. N. BRØNSTED and K. J. PEDERSEN, *J. Physik. Chem.*, **108**, 185 (1924).
2. R. P. BELL and W. C. E. HIGGINSON, *Prog. Roy. Soc.*, **A197**, 141 (1949); R. P. BELL, *The Proton in Chemistry*, Cornell University Press, Ithaca, N. Y. (1959).
3. C. K. INGOLD, *Structure and Mechanism in Organic Chemistry*, Cornell University Press, Ithaca, N. Y. (1953), pp. 345–50.

4. L. P. HAMMETT and A. J. DEYRUP, *J. Am. Chem. Soc.*, **54,** 2721 (1932).
5. M. A. PAUL and F. A. LONG, *Chem. Revs.*, **57,** 1 (1957).
6. E. M. ARNETT and J. J. BURKE, *J. Am. Chem. Soc.*, **89,** 4308 (1966).
7. K. BOWDEN, *Chem. Revs.*, **66,** 119 (1966).
8. J. F. BUNNETT, *J. Am. Chem. Soc.*, **83,** 4956, 4968, 4973 and 4978 (1961).
9. K. B. WIBERG, *Chem. Revs.*, **55,** 713 (1955).

CHAPTER 11

DETERMINING REACTION
MECHANISMS

We might now consider what is meant by the term *reaction mechanism*, which has been used several times in the preceding discussions without any precise definition. Ideally, we should like to know everything that occurs as a reactant is transformed into a product—the positions of all the atoms, force constants for all the bonds and the energy content of the system at all times. Such a complete description of the reaction path is generally unattainable: we must be satisfied with less.

The general practice is to attempt to identify and describe certain signposts along the reaction path, namely, the transition state and any species known as reactive intermediates that can be considered "stable." Even this less exact description is beyond the methods presently available to us, since a detailed description of the transition state of a reaction cannot be made from experimental observations and only the simplest reactions can be treated from a theoretical approach. Even then, there is no way to check the theoretical model directly against the actual transition state. Thus, *all* our information about transition states is bound to be indirect. More success has been realized in attempting to identify reactive intermediates by direct experimental methods, and this has been extremely valuable to our understanding of transition states, because, as we shall see, they have a strong structural similarity.

We now face a dilemma. In order to describe a reaction process we must know the structure of any transition state involved in the process, information which is experimentally unavailable. Therefore, we must describe the transition state in terms of evidence that *is* available. However, it is still impossible to *prove* a reaction mechanism. A mechanism can be eliminated from consideration by showing that it is not consistent with observed facts and one may be considered tenable if it is consistent with all the known facts about a reaction, but frequently two or more tenable mechanisms are presented. If they suggest different results for an experiment that has not yet been carried out, the chemist is able to conduct this crucial experiment and eliminate one of the mechanisms. In this manner a mechanism becomes "established"—it accommodates all known facts and is plausible in terms of general chemical considerations. Nevertheless, we are often left with more than one mechanism that fits these criteria, in which case the mechanism considered to be the simplest is generally accepted. Unfortunately, the choice of the simpler of two mechanisms is both intellectually unsatisfying and highly subjective.

The ingenuity of the chemist is the only limitation to establishing a reaction mechanism. Any technique may be used and this chapter will deal with the more important ones, but first we shall look more closely at the importance of reactive intermediates in mechanistic studies.

THE REACTIVE INTERMEDIATE

Most organic reactions proceed in a series of simple steps rather than in one single step corresponding to the stoichiometric equation. The observed reaction, then, is a *composite* of several elementary reactions: the reactants form a product, which in turn reacts under the conditions employed to give another product, and this sequence continues until the observed products are formed. The discussion in Chapter 7 concerning the reaction coordinate is applicable to each step. The reaction coordinate diagram for a complex reaction is formed by combining the diagrams for the elementary steps end to end. The product of one reaction becomes a reactant for the next and is both preceded and followed by a transition state, as is shown in Fig. 11–1. Thus, a reactive intermediate can be defined as a local minimum in a plot of the reaction coordinate, just as a transition state was defined as a local maximum in such a plot.

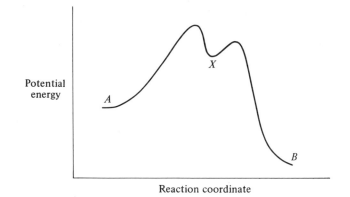

Fig. 11–1. Typical reaction coordinate diagram for a complex reaction involving two steps, $A \rightleftharpoons X \rightarrow B$.

Examination of Fig. 11–1 may suggest several kinetic situations (Fig. 11–2) for the reaction sequence

$$A \underset{k_2}{\overset{k_1}{\rightleftharpoons}} X \xrightarrow{k_3} B.$$

This sequence may be treated by the steady-state approximation:

$$\text{rate} = d[B]/dt = k_3[X],$$
$$d[X]/dt = k_1[A] - k_2[X] - k_3[X] = 0,$$
$$[X] = k_1[A]/(k_2 + k_3),$$
$$d[B]/dt = k_1 k_3[A]/(k_2 + k_3). \tag{11-1}$$

If $k_2 \ll k_3$, Eq. (11–1) may be simplified to give

$$\text{rate} = k_1(A), \tag{11–2}$$

which is the rate of formation of the intermediate. The intermediate, once formed, itself forms products rapidly. If, on the other hand, $k_2 \cong k_3$, the full rate equation (11–1) must be employed. In neither case is an equilibrium established between reactant and intermediate. When this is the situation, the intermediate is known as a *van't Hoff intermediate*. If $k_2 \gg k_3$, an equilibrium is established and the rate expression reduces to

$$\text{rate} = k_1 k_3(A)/k_2 = Kk_3(A). \tag{11–3}$$

In this situation the intermediate is known as an *Arrhenius intermediate*.

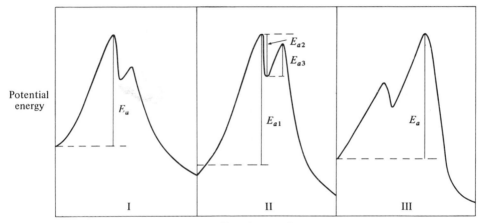

Reaction coordinate

Fig. 11–2. Reaction coordinate diagram for $A \underset{k_2}{\overset{k_1}{\rightleftharpoons}} X \overset{k_3}{\longrightarrow} B$: I, $k_2 \ll k_3$; II, $k_2 \cong k_3$; III, $k_2 \gg k_3$.

When the activation energy is measured for case I in Fig. 11–2, the value is obtained only for the first step; for case III the value is that for the overall reaction, $E_a = E_{a1} + E_{a3} - E_{a2}$. When $k_2 \cong k_3$, the activation energy obtained is for the overall process but it has no physical meaning in terms of elementary reaction, owing to the complex nature of the observed rate constant (see Eq. 11–1). It is sometimes possible to measure the activation energy for the first step and the difference between the third and second steps ($E_{a3} - E_{a2}$). An interesting case in which this has been done is the hydrolysis of benzamide and ethyl benzoate [1].

A classification of reactive intermediates more familiar to organic chemists depends upon structural features. A number of normally stable organic molecules have been recognized as reactive intermediates in certain conditions. Similarly, a number of hypothetical compounds have been proposed as intermediates, whose structure suggests that they would be very reactive or unstable and therefore are unknown as isolable species. In addition, certain others have been proposed with structures containing di- and trivalent carbon, the most common being carbonium ions, carbanions, free radicals, and both singlet and triplet carbenes. Although stable examples of many of these species are known, most of the evidence for their role as reactive intermediates is indirect.

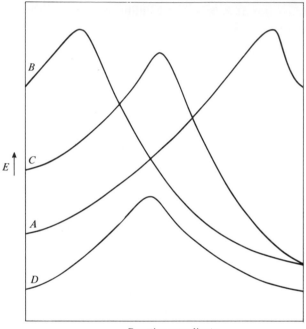

Reaction coordinate

Fig. 11–3. Energy diagram depicting: *A*, endothermic; *B*, fast, exothermic; *C*, slow, exothermic; *D*, thermally balanced reactions.

Interest in reactive intermediates stems from two sources, the role they play in complex reactions and the fact that they serve as models for the experimentally unavailable transition states, to which they are structurally similar. This fact was first clearly stated by Hammond [2], who postulated that, if two states occur consecutively with nearly equal energy contents, their interconversion will involve only a small change in molecular structure. This change in structure must involve both steric and electronic changes but these may occur to differing extents. Four extreme cases are illustrated in Fig. 11–3. Curve *A* represents an endothermic reaction, such as the formation of a highly unstable intermediate, where there is little progress along the reaction coordinate from the transition state to the formation of the product (reactive intermediate). Curve *B* depicts a fast exothermic reaction, where there is little reorganization involved in forming the transition state from the reactant.

(This, of course, corresponds to the destruction of a reactive intermediate.) Curve C represents a slow exothermic process and curve D a thermally balanced reaction. In both these latter cases the transition state has considerably greater energy than either reactant or product and therefore has little similarity to the structure of either.

The validity of these ideas has been experimentally demonstrated many times. All of the linear free energy relationships in which an equilibrium reaction is used as the model, e.g. the Hammett equation, depend upon the structural similarities between transition states and products. Any structural variation that leads to an increase in the free energy of the equilibrium also leads to an increase in the free energy of activation of any reaction whose rate is correlated by the Hammett equation. Here we have extrapolated Hammond's postulate much further than need be. First, we have used free energies even though translational and solvation entropy changes are not expected to follow the postulate—it deals directly with potential energy. Secondly, the use of benzoate ions as transition state models (as done successfully for a Hammett correlation) is less reasonable than using a reactive intermediate formed in a reaction as the model for the transition states preceding and/or following its formation. More direct demonstrations of the validity of the postulate are available. A direct relationship between the rates of reactions believed to proceed *via* carbonium ion intermediates and the stabilities of these ions has been demonstrated for a series of diarylmethyl cations [3], by obtaining pK_{R^+} values from the acidity function H_R and finding a direct parallel between these and the relative rates for alcoholysis of the corresponding diarylchloromethanes. The Okamoto-Brown extension of the Hammett equation is a similar demonstration. A logarithmic relationship between the ionization constants for the formation of carbanions and the rate constants for reactions believed to involve carbanion intermediates has also been found [4]. These demonstrations are equivalent to linear relationships between the free energy of activation and the free energy of the equilibrium. Such a relationship is suggested by Hammond's postulate. The structural similarity between a transition state and an intermediate will be greatest when the energy difference is minimal. Three situations dependent upon this energy difference, which are experimentally resolvable, are illustrated in Fig. 11–4. In some reactions the intermediate is stable enough to be isolated. In others, an intermediate may be formed but it has such a short lifetime that it cannot be isolated. Finally, some reactions proceed without the formation of an intermediate. There are also reactions that exhibit the characteristics both of reactions involving an intermediate and of reactions involving only a transition state. These "borderline mechanisms" suggest that a series of transition states may be operative within a reaction series; that is, some members of the series have structures that lead to an intermediate, others react *via* a transition state alone, and between these two extremes is a continuum of structural variations depending upon a continuum of the relative stabilities of a series of intermediates. An example of this situation is the solvolytic reactions of benzyl halides, in the borderline area between S_N1 and S_N2 reaction mechanisms.

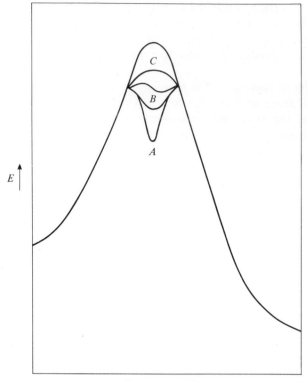

Reaction coordinate

Fig. 11–4. Energy diagram illustrating: *A*, stable, isolable intermediates; *B*, unstable, nonisolable intermediates of differing stabilities; *C*, single transition states of differing stabilities.

Any study of reaction mechanisms must have as one of its goals to demonstrate the formation of any reactive intermediates. The structures both of these intermediates and of all transition states are developed as fully as is consistent with the experimental observations. We shall examine several techniques commonly employed in the study of reaction mechanisms.

KINETIC APPROACH

The most general approach to the study of mechanisms is the kinetic method. Often a knowledge of the reaction order alone provides important mechanistic evidence. Such a case is the first-order halogenation of acetone, to be discussed shortly. More frequently, a proposed mechanism will suggest comparisons of rates under a variety of conditions such as acid-base catalysis (discussed in Chapter 10) or structural changes (Chapter 9).

As we have seen before, the rate equation and the stoichiometric equation need not be related. If the rate equation does not include all of the reactants contained in the stoichiometric equation or if the order of each reactant is not the same as the corresponding stoichiometric coefficient, the reaction is complex. Any complex reaction proceeds in a series of steps or elementary reactions and the mechanism involves reactive intermediates. If the rate and stoichiometric equations *are* related, the reaction may be either simple or complex.

When a complex reaction involves a step that is much slower than any of the other elementary reactions this is called the *rate-determining step*. Kinetics will give information only about the slow step and any steps that precede it. Other methods must be used to learn about subsequent fast steps. When successive steps proceed at about the same rate and there is no one rate-determining step, the rate equation is complex, and no information can be obtained about a single transition state from such a kinetic expression. With a complicated rate equation it is difficult to derive a mechanism from the rate law but the converse is not true, which provides us with an important approach. A proposed mechanism is used to predict a rate law. If the predicted rate law does not agree with experimental results, the mechanism is discarded; if it does agree, the proposed mechanism must then be tested by other approaches. Agreement between a proposed and an observed rate law is not *sufficient* evidence to establish a mechanism but it is *necessary* evidence. Frequently, two sets of intermediates lead to the prediction of the same kinetic equation. Non-kinetic methods must then be used to establish the correct set or, at the very least, the choice is made by analogy with an established reaction pathway.

An elegant use of this approach has recently been reported by Huisgen *et al.* [5]. The reaction of cyclooctatetraene with Diels-Alder dienophiles was proposed to involve an intermediate, bicyclo[4.2.0]octa-2,4,7-triene. For example, compound *C* is formed from the reaction of the cyclooctatetraene, *A*, with maleic anhydride (Eq. 11–4).

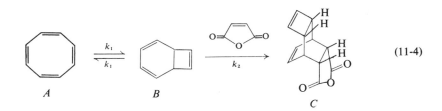

$$A \qquad B \qquad C \qquad (11\text{-}4)$$

The structure of *C* had been established previously [6] and was confirmed by NMR. Analogous structures were found for the products formed with phenyl-cyclooctatetraene and cycloocta-1,3,5-triene and also with the dienophiles tetracyanoethylene, dicyanomaleimide, and fumaroyl chloride. The intermediate *B* was suggested by analogous reasoning with other Diels-Alder reactions: it is generally accepted that, for Diels-Alder addition, the diene must be in a *cis*-planar conformation, which is achieved in B, whereas the tetraene is known to exist in the tub conformation.

Tub conformation of cyclooctatetraene   Conformation of B

The rate of reaction was measured dilatometrically using excess dienophile so that the reaction was pseudo-first-order. This kinetic order was established for all dienophiles at varying excess concentrations and at varying temperatures. In this manner the rate equation

$$dC/dt = k_d[A] \tag{11-5}$$

was established. From the proposed mechanism (Eq. 11–4), a rate equation is derived using the steady-state approximation:

$$dC/dt = k_2[B][D],$$
$$dB/dt = k_1[A] - k_{-1}[B] - k_2[B][D] = 0,$$
$$[B] = k_1[A]/[k_{-1} + k_2[D]],$$
$$dC/dt = k_1k_2[A][D]/[k_{-1} + k_2[D]]. \tag{11-6}$$

If Eq. (11–6), where $[D]$ is the concentration of the dienophile, is compared with the observed rate law equation (11–5), k_d is shown to be complex:

$$k_d = k_1k_2[D]/[k_{-1} + k_2[D]]. \tag{11-7}$$

If the addition is rate-determining ($k_2 \ll k_1, k_{-1}$), k_d is simplified to

$$k_d = k_1k_2[D]/k_{-1}.$$

This predicts that plotting the dienophile concentration against the observed rate constant k_d would give a straight line passing through the origin. Such behavior was found for the addition of the relatively unreactive maleic anhydride to cyclooctatetraene in chlorobenzene at 140°C and to phenylcyclooctatetraene at 70°C in ethyl acetate and in tetrahydrofuran.

If a very reactive dienophile is used, we might expect the formation of the intermediate to become the slow step ($k_2 \gg k_1, k_{-1}$) and the measured rate constant k_d to be equal to k_2. The value of k_d would be independent of diene concentration, which when plotted against k_d would afford a straight line of slope zero. This behavior was observed for the reaction of the very reactive dicyanomaleimide with phenylcyclooctatetraene at 70°C in ethyl acetate and in tetrahydrofuran. This affords a direct measurement of k_1.

From Eq. (11–6) we can see that a plot of $[D]$ against k_d will not afford a straight line if $k_2 \simeq k_1, k_{-1}$. We can rearrange this equation, however, to obtain

$$k_d = k_1 - k_{-1}k_d/k_2[D],$$

and then a plot of $k_d/[D]$ against k_d will give a straight line with slope $-k_{-1}/k_2$. The intercept gives the value of k_1. (Note that the intercept of this plot should be independent of the nature of the dienophile.) This behavior is observed for a number of cases. In this approach, the absolute values of k_{-1} and k_2 are not available when $k_2 \simeq k_1 \simeq k_{-1}$. Huisgen attempted to evaluate them by assuming that k_2 for the bicyclooctatriene is the same as the value of k_2 for the reaction with bicyclooctadiene. This latter value can be measured, as we shall see shortly. Using this estimated value for k_2 he obtained a value for k_{-1}. The equilibrium constant for the first step of Eq. (11–4), $K = k_1/k_{-1}$, was then approximated at 100°C as 0.0001. No physical method is available for the observation of B in such low concentration. The kinetic method could demonstrate the presence of an intermediate, but it alone could not demonstrate that the intermediate had the structure of B.

In an attempt to substantiate Eq. (11–4) as the mechanism for the Diels-Alder addition to cyclooctatetraene, Huisgen [5] studied the same reaction using cyclo-octa-1,3,5-triene. The conversion of this material into bicyclo[4.2.0]octa-2,4-diene had been established earlier [7]. These compounds can be separated via a silver complex of the triene and they are stable below 60°C. With the pure compounds available, the individual rate constants in Eq. (11–8) could be evaluated.

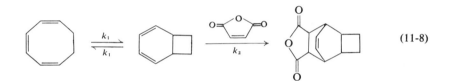

$$(11\text{-}8)$$

Values of k_2 were obtained spectrophotometrically at 15°–30°C, temperatures at which the triene failed to react with maleic anhydride. At higher temperatures, k_1 was measured dilatometrically using tetracyanoethylene as described above for $k_2 \gg k_1, k_{-1}$. Maleic anhydride was used to obtain the ratio k_{-1}/k_2 by plotting $k_d/[D]$ against k_d. From this value and the value of k_2, k_{-1} was available. The value of k_1 obtained with tetracyanoethylene at 95°C was exactly the same as the value obtained when the maleic anhydride data were extrapolated to the intercept. The values of the rate constants were used to calculate the equilibrium constant for the first step. The value obtained agreed with the experimentally observed value.*

The mechanism represented by Eq. (11–8) is fairly well confirmed. The intermediate is a known compound and the chemical evidence supports its presence as a reactive intermediate in the addition of dienophiles to cyclooctatriene. The kinetics observed parallel those for the reaction of cyclooctatetraene. The structures of the proposed intermediates in both reactions are similar. By analogy, the mechanism represented by Eq. (11–4) also seems reasonable.

---

* There is an error in reference 5, in Table 2 on page 14. The entropy of activation reported as −38 eu was calculated by us to be −28 eu.

Another reaction that has been studied by the kinetic approach is the halogenation of acetone [8]. This was one of the earliest examples of the kinetic approach applied to a mechanistic study. Lapworth [9] reported that the rate of halogenation of acetone is proportional to the concentration of acetone and is general acid-base-catalyzed. The concentration of halogen has no effect upon the rate and thus is not involved in the transition state of the rate-determining step. Lapworth suggested that enol formation was the rate-controlling reaction.

Two mechanisms for the enolization reaction have been proposed. Lowry and Faulkner [10] suggested that all general acid-base-catalyzed reactions involve a proton donor and a proton acceptor acting simultaneously:

$$\text{B}^- + \text{H}—\text{CH}_2\text{COCH}_3 + \text{HA} \xrightarrow[k]{\text{slow}} \text{BH} + \text{CH}_2 = \text{C(OH)CH}_3 + \text{A}^-.$$

The kinetic expression predicted for this proposed mechanism is

$$\text{rate} = k[\text{HA}][\text{acetone}][\text{B}^-]. \tag{11–9}$$

A second mechanism has been proposed by Pedersen [11]:

$$(\text{H}_3\text{C})_2\text{C}=\text{O} + \text{HA} \underset{k_{-1}}{\overset{k_1}{\rightleftharpoons}} (\text{H}_3\text{C})_2\text{C}=\text{OH}^+ + \text{A}^-,$$

$$(\text{H}_3\text{C})_2\text{C}=\text{OH}^+ + \text{B}^- \xrightarrow[k_2]{\text{slow}} \text{H}_2\text{C}=\text{C(OH)CH}_3 + \text{HB}.$$

For this step-by-step mechanism, the predicted rate is given by

$$\text{rate} = k_2[\text{H}_3\text{CC}=\text{OH}^+\text{CH}_3][\text{B}^-]. \tag{11–10}$$

The concentration of the proposed intermediate can be obtained from the prior equilibrium

$$k_1/k_{-1} = [\text{H}_3\text{CC}=\text{OH}^+\text{CH}_3][\text{A}^-]/[(\text{CH}_3)_2\text{C}=\text{O}][\text{HA}],$$

$$[\text{H}_3\text{CC}=\text{O}^+\text{HCH}_3] = k_1/k_{-1}[\text{CH}_3\text{COCH}_3][\text{HA}]/[\text{A}^-].$$

We can also include the ionization constant for HA so that

$$[\text{H}_3\text{CC}=\text{O}^+\text{HCH}_3] = (k_1/k_{-1})[\text{CH}_3\text{COCH}_3][\text{HA}^+]/K_{\text{HA}}.$$

Substitution of this into Eq. (11–10) affords

$$\text{rate} = (k_1k_2/k_{-1}K_{\text{HA}})[\text{H}^+][\text{B}^-][\text{CH}_3\text{COCH}_3].$$

The product $[\text{H}^+][\text{B}^-]$ can be replaced by $K_{\text{HB}}[\text{HB}]$. Then the rate equation becomes

$$\text{rate} = (k_1k_2K_{\text{HB}}/k_{-1}K_{\text{HA}})[\text{HB}][\text{CH}_3\text{COCH}_3]. \tag{11–11}$$

Comparison of this equation with Eq. (11–9) shows that the two mechanisms are kinetically distinguishable. The Lowry mechanism predicts a kinetic expression that includes a term involving the product of the concentrations of acid and conjugate base; the Pedersen mechanism predicts a rate expression with no such product. The observed rate constant for the iodination of acetone in an acetate-buffered aqueous solution has been reported [8]. It is

$$k = 5 \times 10^{-10}[H_2O] + 1.6 \times 10^{-3}[H_3O^+] + 15[OH^-] + 5.0 \times 10^{-6}[HOAc]$$
$$+ 1.5 \times 10^{-5}[AcO^-] + 2.0 \times 10^{-5}[HOAc][AcO^-]. \qquad (11-12)$$

This finding suggests that the last term is due to a concerted mechanism. The remaining terms may also be due to the Lowry mechanism, involving a water molecule as the third moiety. Alternatively, the other terms could arise from other equilibria. The term containing $[AcO^-]$ in Eq. (11–12) can be due to the product $[HOAc][HO^-]$, following from the hydrolysis equilibrium

$$K = [HOAc][HO^-]/[AcO^-][H_2O].$$

Anything proportional to $[AcO^-][H_2O]$ is also proportional to $[HOAc][HO^-]$. The other terms can be similarly interpreted. In either event the Lowry mechanism seems to be supported.

There is another possibility—that the reaction proceeds by both mechanisms. The Lowry mechanism could account for the last term in Eq. (11–12), the other terms being due principally to the Pedersen mechanism. This possibility cannot be confirmed or rejected unambiguously by a direct kinetic approach.

Swain [12] has suggested a method of distinguishing between the two mechanisms in a less-direct kinetic approach. In the Lowry mechanism a proton is transferred from an acid in the rate-determining step, but this does not occur in the Pedersen mechanism. The one-step mechanism would be expected to exhibit a substantial kinetic isotope effect when D_2O is employed as solvent, whereas the two-step mechanism would be expected to afford a normal solvent isotope effect. The k_{H_2O}/k_{D_2O} value of about 0.5 [13] indicates that a large portion of the reaction proceeds by the Pedersen mechanism. The kinetic isotope effect of 7.6 [13] observed for the bromination of deutero acetone is no help in distinguishing between the two mechanisms.

Currently, the enolization of ketones in aqueous solution is believed to involve a two-step mechanism [8]. The kinetic approach to this problem did not provide a unique answer, although it did show that the halogenation of ketones is a complex reaction and that the halogen is not involved in the slow step. In this manner, a number of possible mechanisms could be excluded. Further evidence for the importance of the keto-enol equilibrium step has been obtained. The rate of racemization of optically active ketones has been shown to proceed at the same rate as halogenation [14]. Deuterium exchange with deuterated solvent also proceeds at the same rate as halogenation, as do certain base-catalyzed aldol condensations [15].

Another less direct application of the kinetic approach to reaction mechanisms is the use of linear free energy relationships to choose between models for possible transition state structures. An example of this technique involves the abstraction of benzylic hydrogen by free radicals. Because the solvolysis of cumyl chlorides certainly involves generation of positive charge, it was somewhat surprising to find that many free radical abstraction reactions of benzylic hydrogen also fit the Okamoto-Brown equation, Eq. (9–7). The correlation is frequently even better than that obtained with the Hammett equation, Eq. (9–6); this is shown in Table 11–1, which is taken in part from a report by Howard and Ingold [16]. An interpretation of this correlation has been offered [20], in which the reaction is said to involve a transition state with polar character, so that an electron-deficient benzylic carbon atom is involved:

$$ArCH_3 + X\cdot \rightarrow [ArCH_2H\cdot X \leftrightarrow ArCH_2^+ \overset{\cdot}{H} X^- \leftrightarrow Ar\overset{\cdot}{C}H_2H\text{---}X] \rightarrow ArCH_2^\cdot + HX.$$

This interpretation is undoubtedly justified, although there is some controversy whether the small positive charge developed in the transition state should yield a better correlation with σ or with σ^+ [18, 19]. It is possible that the correlation with σ^+ is due to resonance stabilization by the radical canonical structure of the transition state as well as the polar form, and this conclusion is supported by the observation of an appreciable deviation for the *p*-phenyl substituent. In any event, the presence of a polar effect and the necessity of considering a polar transition state in these reactions was discovered by the use of Eqs. (9–6) and (9–7).

Table 11–1. Comparison of σ and σ^+ Correlations for Benzylic Hydrogen Abstraction Reactions*

			σ		σ^+	
Reaction	T, °C	Solvent	ρ	Standard deviation	ρ	Standard deviation
Cl$_3$C + toluene	50	Chloro-benzene			−1.46	0.01
Br + toluene	80	Benzene			−1.39	0.03
Cl + toluene	40	Benzene + CCl$_4$	−0.76	0.06	−0.66	0.02
(CH$_3$)$_3$CO + toluene	40†	Reactants	−0.82	0.01	−0.70	0.02
	40‡	Benzene	−0.75	0.05	−0.60	0.09
	40§	CCl$_4$	−0.86	0.26	−0.68	0.01
RO$_2$ + cumene	60	Chloro-benzene	−0.54	0.06	−0.38	0.02

* From Howard and Ingold [16].
† From Walling and Jacknow [17].
‡ From Gilliom and Ward [18].
§ From Kennedy and Ingold [19].

Because the direct kinetic approach seldom gives unequivocal evidence for a particular reaction mechanism, other types of experimentation must also be employed. These provide supplementary information toward the final deduction of a mechanism. In other words, the best approach to a mechanistic study is a diverse one. The use of other kinds of information will now be illustrated.

NONKINETIC APPROACH

Certainly no mechanism can be proposed, nor is a kinetic study justified, if the identity and yields of the products are unknown. It is not uncommon, however, to find statements in the literature explaining the formation of products on the basis of some postulated mechanism and with no evidence other than the product analysis. This is a very poor policy, even though such proposals usually involve the formation of a specific intermediate whose chemistry may be known or can be predicted by our knowledge of related species. The product criterion for a mechanism is an essential piece of information but is seldom sufficient to exclude all other proposals.

An example of the use of a *product study* in the development of a mechanism can be taken from the work of Skell [21]. Methylene (carbene) chemistry has been widely studied during the past few years. These divalent reactive intermediates are known to add to alkenes to form cyclopropanes but the product mixture is dependent upon the method of generation of the intermediate. Methylene formed from the photolysis of diazomethane adds stereospecifically to *cis*- and *trans*-2-butene [22, 23]:

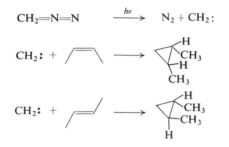

When this reaction is carried out using benzophenone as a photosensitizer [24] or when a great deal of an inert gas is added [23], the addition is nonstereospecific. From the differing product compositions it is apparent that either there is more than one form of methylene or the addition can occur by different paths. The generally accepted explanation [25] is that the direct photochemical decomposition of diazomethane gives singlet methylene that adds in a single step [21]. When an inert gas is present the singlet methylene decays to the more stable triplet form; this must add by steps.

The addition of singlet methylene can, but need not, occur in one step because electrons of opposite spin can pair, but for triplet methylene the addition must lead to a diradical which has to be converted to a singlet species before ring closure can take place. This conversion allows time for σ-bond rotation and leads to the product

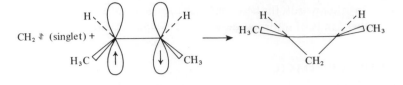

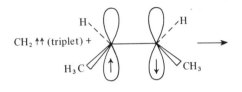

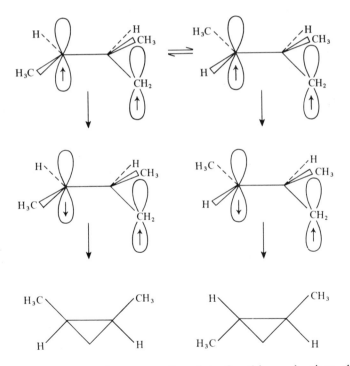

mixture. Although there are other supporting data for this mechanism, the role of product analysis in this mechanistic study is apparent.

A commonly used technique for demonstrating the existence of a reactive intermediate is *trapping*. This involves adding a reagent that reacts with the intermediate in a diagnostic manner with no marked effect upon the rate. The use of a trap is only beneficial if the reaction path is intercepted *after* the formation of the intermediate, for which the best evidence is absence of kinetic change.

An example of effective use of the trapping technique is the study of the decomposition of benzoyl peroxide. The products of this decomposition are those expected from the reaction of both benzoyloxy and phenyl radicals. Hammond and Soffer [26] demonstrated that the initial cleavage afforded benzoyloxy radicals and that phenyl radicals were formed from these:

$$C_6H_5COOCC_6H_5 \rightarrow 2C_6H_5CO_2^{\boldsymbol{\cdot}},$$
$$\underset{O\quad O}{\overset{\parallel\quad\parallel}{}}$$

$$C_6H_5CO_2^{\boldsymbol{\cdot}} \rightarrow C_6H_5^{\boldsymbol{\cdot}} + CO_2.$$

By adding iodine and carrying out the decomposition in moist carbon tetrachloride a quantitative yield of benzoic acid is formed. There is no effect upon the rate of decomposition. Iodine thus serves as a trap for the benzoyloxy radical by forming the rapidly hydrolyzed benzoyl hypoiodite:

$$(C_6H_5CO_2)_2 \rightarrow 2C_6H_5CO_2^{\boldsymbol{\cdot}},$$

$$C_6H_5CO_2^{\boldsymbol{\cdot}} + I_2 \rightarrow C_6H_5CO_2I + I\boldsymbol{\cdot},$$

$$C_6H_5CO_2I + H_2O \rightarrow C_6H_5CO_2H.$$

The presence of exclusive fission of the oxygen—oxygen bond and the formation of the benzoyloxy radical intermediate is elegantly demonstrated by this technique. This approach has been applied to substituted benzoyl peroxides [27], with the expected result that carbon dioxide evolution was eliminated. When applied to diacyl peroxides [28, 29] such as acetyl peroxide, the evolution of carbon dioxide is not eliminated. From this we might assume that diacyl peroxides decompose with carbon dioxide cleavage in the rate-controlling step. However, such a conclusion is not justified without further evidence. Although the conclusion may be correct, there remains a possibility that the trapping agent is not effective enough to capture the acyloxy radical. Interpretation of negative evidence of this kind is very risky, although in the specific case we are examining the supporting evidence [30] suggests that the conclusion is correct.

Occasionally a reaction involves *a rather stable intermediate*. It has proved possible in some cases to isolate such an intermediate, confirm its structure, and demonstrate that the reaction products are formed when the intermediate is submitted to the reaction conditions. The rate at which the products are formed from the intermediate must, of course, be consistent with the kinetics of the overall reaction. For example, the decomposition of benzoyl peroxide in benzene affords biphenyl. Although many mechanisms can be written for this conversion, strong evidence for a two-step addition of phenyl radical to benzene has been obtained by DeTar and Long [31]:

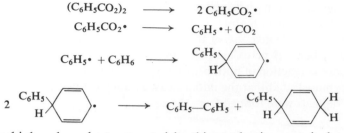

The dihydrobiphenyl product suggested by this mechanism was isolated by these workers when the reaction was carried out under nitrogen and it was shown to be easily oxidized by air under normal reaction conditions. Further evidence for the formation of the phenylcyclohexadienyl intermediate was obtained by isolating tetrahydroquaterphenyls from the reaction medium:

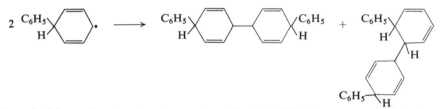

Although this mechanism has been refined further [32], the presence of the intermediate dihydrobiphenyl and coupling products clearly suggests a prior intermediate, the phenylcyclohexadienyl radical. Thus, isolation of one intermediate, dihydrobiphenyl, showed its presence and implicated another intermediate in homolytic aromatic substitution reactions. A closely related approach is to synthesize an intermediate by a route independent of the reaction under study. By subjecting the synthetic material to the reaction conditions, it can be demonstrated whether the correct products are formed at a rate consistent with the overall kinetics. An application of this approach was given above for the Diels-Alder reaction of cyclo-octa-1,3,5-triene *via* the bicyclo[4.2.0]octa-2,4-diene.

Stereochemical changes occurring during a reaction frequently supply important information about the mechanism. If an optically active product is formed from an optically active reactant, any mechanism proposed must account for the retention of the stereoisomeric purity, since in this case no symmetrical intermediate or transition state can occur. Before drawing further mechanistic conclusions it becomes necessary to show whether the configuration of the product is the same as that of the reactant or is inverted, and also whether the product is as optically pure as the starting material. If, on the other hand, a completely racemic product is formed from an optically active reactant, a symmetrical intermediate or transition state is required to explain the racemization. Frequently we find partial racemization but this, too, must be explained on the basis of a symmetrical species.

Stereochemical arguments have been employed to explain the results obtained from studies of photohalogenation reactions [33]. Photochlorination of optically active 1-chloro-2-methylbutane affords a variety of dichloro products [34], among which is optically inactive 1,2-dichloro-2-methylbutane. This result may be explained by postulating a free radical intermediate that either is symmetrical, i.e. planar, or undergoes inversion much more rapidly than chlorination. When the corresponding bromide is photobrominated at a bromine concentration above 0.05 M, only 1,2-dibromo-2-methylbutane is formed and this material is optically active [35]. This reaction, like the first, is known to involve free radicals but the structure of the radical formed in the bromination must be asymmetric to account for the stereochemical result. Skell suggested that the radical formed in the bromination is a bridged radical intermediate that preserves the asymmetry at the active center. The observed kinetic evidence of activation of the hydrogen at C-2 suggests that the C-1 bromine is aiding in the removal of the hydrogen in the transition state leading to this intermediate. Skell thus formulates the mechanism as

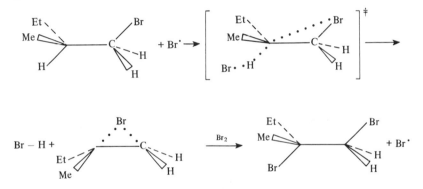

When the bromination is carried out at elevated temperatures (72–80°C) or at low bromine concentrations (<0.05 M), racemization is observed. The degree of racemization is sensitive to the concentration of bromine, suggesting that ring opening to a classical planar or rapidly equilibrating free radical is in competition with the stereospecific bromination step.

Isotopic tracers are frequently used to label the position of an atom and hence to follow the role played by a particular position in a mechanism. This technique has been used in many studies, of which the Claisen rearrangement is typical. Heating allyl ethers of phenols leads to *o*-allylphenols when an *ortho* position is unsubstituted and to the *para* isomer if both *ortho* positions are blocked. By labeling the γ position with C^{14}, the *ortho* product was found to have none of the C^{14} in the terminal position [36]. Thus it was demonstrated that the allyl group became inverted:

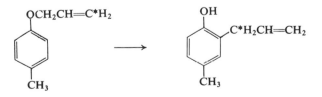

The *para* rearrangement was shown to proceed with retention [37] by the same approach:

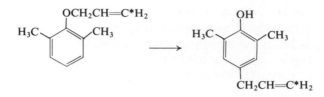

The subtlety of this approach is obvious and it was extended even further. By rearranging a mixture of

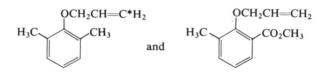

and

—two materials that undergo rearrangement at essentially the same rate—it was shown that the rearrangement was intramolecular. This was done by isolating the product

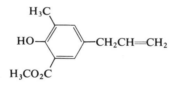

and finding virtually no C^{14}. If the allyl group became statistically distributed, we would expect considerable mixing in the product. Finally, the presence of an intermediate was strongly suggested when the rearrangement

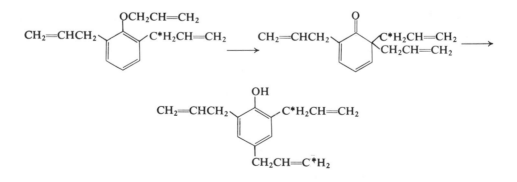

led to the indicated scrambling in the rearranged product [38]. Some of the above information can also be obtained by nonisotopic methods, e.g. the intramolecularity of the reaction has been demonstrated by judicious choice of reactants in a crossover experiment. The products obtained from the mixture

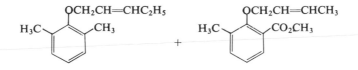

contained no detectable crossed products [39].

Another reaction studied by the isotopic tracer technique is the aminolysis of chlorobenzene with KNH_2 [40]. Starting with chlorobenzene labeled with C^{14} at position 1, aniline is obtained with the C^{14} distributed almost evenly between positions 1 and 2. This is strong evidence in support of a symmetrical intermediate. The postulated mechanism supported by much other evidence involves a benzyne intermediate

The existence of this intermediate in other reactions has now been demonstrated by physical methods. In the flash-photolysis of benzene-diazonium-2-carboxylate benzyne is a primary product that dimerizes to biphenylene [41], as shown by the agreement between the time of decay of the U.V. absorption spectrum of benzyne and the time of decay of its mass spectral peak m/e, 76. These were the same as the rate of appearance of the U.V. spectrum and the m/e peak of 152 for biphenylene [41].

In favorable cases physical methods may be used to follow the appearance and disappearance of intermediates and to determine whether the rates observed fit the rate equations for the consecutive reactions. The recent appearance of extremely sensitive and rapid instruments for measuring physical properties has led to rapid development of techniques for observing intermediates. This approach will no doubt continue to grow as a tool in mechanistic studies. Several methods for following fast reactions are already in use; they include temperature jump, flash-photolysis, phosphorimetry, shock-wave techniques, and spectral line widening of the nuclear magnetic and electron spin spectra [42].

As we have seen, no single approach is sufficient to establish a reaction mechanism. The mechanistic organic chemist must have a variety of approaches at his command and a fertile imagination to utilize the most fruitful ones as he faces different problems. The following chapters will illustrate how the above techniques have been utilized in developing specific mechanisms.

PROBLEMS

1. Suggest a method to distinguish between the following pairs of mechanisms:

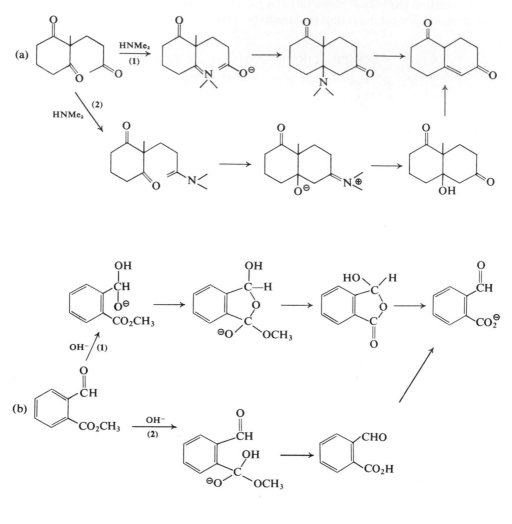

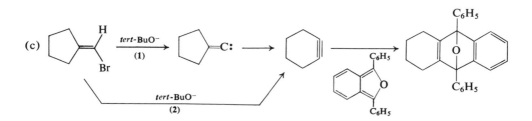

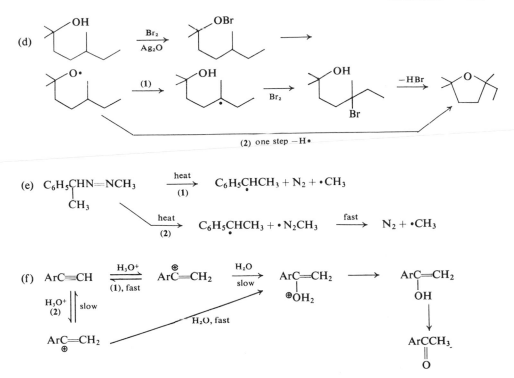

(d)

(e) $C_6H_5CHN=NCH_3$ $\xrightarrow[(1)]{heat}$ $C_6H_5CHCH_3 + N_2 + \cdot CH_3$

with CH_3

$\xrightarrow[(2)]{heat}$ $C_6H_5CHCH_3 + \cdot N_2CH_3$ $\xrightarrow{fast}$ $N_2 + \cdot CH_3$

(f) $ArC\equiv CH$ $\underset{(1), fast}{\overset{H_3O^+}{\rightleftharpoons}}$ $ArC=CH_2$ $\xrightarrow[slow]{H_2O}$ $ArC=CH_2$ $\longrightarrow$ $ArC=CH_2$

H_3O^+ (2) slow

$ArC=CH_2$

2. a) The acid-catalyzed hydrolysis of 2-ethoxy-1-cyclopentenc-1-carboxylic acid gives cyclopentanone:

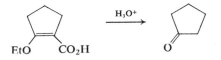

The reaction is general acid-catalyzed and k_{H_2O}/k_{D_2O} values are in the range of 4 ($H_2PO_4^-$ catalysis) to 5 (formic acid catalysis). At low pH where specific hydronium ion catalysis occurs, k_{H_2O}/k_{D_2O} is 2.9. Write as much as possible of a reaction scheme consistent with these results.

b) If this reaction is carried out in EtOH-water solution with sulfuric acid as the catalyst at $-10°C$, the enol form of 2-oxocyclopentanecarboxylic acid is the product. This decarboxylates rapidly on warming. Complete the mechanistic scheme.

c) The hydrolysis of the carboxylate anion proceeds 209 times faster than the unionized acid and is also general acid-catalyzed. Suggest an explanation for this rate enhancement.

3. The Westphalen rearrangement of $3\beta,6\beta$-diacctoxycholenestan-5α-ol occurs with acetic anhydride containing H_2SO_4 or $KHSO_4$:

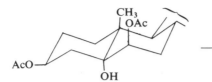 $\longrightarrow$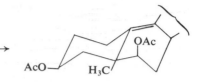

whereas only the 5α-acetate

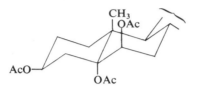

is obtained when other acids, e.g., $HClO_4$ or HCl, are used. This acetate fails to undergo rearrangement when H_2SO_4 is added.

The 5-methoxy compound fails to react in the presence of H_2SO_4.

Under the reaction conditions cholesterol forms cholesteryl hydrogen sulfate very rapidly.

The rate of reaction is first-order in H_2SO_4 and independent of steroid when steroid is in excess and first-order in steroid and nearly independent of acid when H_2SO_4 is in excess at fixed excess acetic anhydride concentration.

a) What would the rate dependence be if an intermediate were formed from one molecule each of steroid and H_2SO_4 in a slow step? In a fast equilibrium step with a low value of the equilibrium constant?

By following the optical rotation it was found that when H_2SO_4 was in excess, initial rotation values obtained by extrapolation to time zero were all the same, specific rotation of $-64°$. When steroid was in excess, the values tended toward that of pure steroid, $-52°$.

b) What is implied by this result?

The rate was also dependent upon acetic anhydride concentration (in acetic acid).

c) What does this result tell us?

Using 6-β-substituted steroids, a Taft equation correlation with ρ-value of -4.8 was observed.

d) Write a mechanism consistent with all the above facts.

4. Treatment of N-chloroacetanilide with HCl affords a mixture of o- and p-chloro-acetanilide that is virtually identical with the mixture obtained by direct chlorination of acetanilide. The rate of disappearance of N-chloroacetanilide is third-order, first-order each in H^+, Cl^-, and N-chloroacetanilide. Addition of anisole to the reaction mixture leads to the formation of chloroanisole. Finally, molecular chlorine can be obtained from a mixture of N-chloroaniline and HCl and the use of radioactive chloride shows that the formation of molecular chloride is reversible. Give a mechanism consistent with all of these facts.

REFERENCES

1. M. L. Bender, R. D. Ginger, and J. P. Unik, *J. Am. Chem. Soc.*, **80**, 1044 (1958).
2. G. S. Hammond, *J. Am. Chem. Soc.*, **77**, 334 (1955).
3. N. C. Deno and A. Schriesheim, *J. Am. Chem. Soc.*, **77**, 3051 (1955).
4. R. G. Pearson and R. L. Dillon, *J. Am. Chem. Soc.*, **75**, 2439 (1953).
5. R. Huisgen, F. Mietzsch, G. Boche, and H. Seidl, *Organic Reaction Mechanisms*, Special Publication No. 19, The Chemical Society, London (1965), pp. 3–20.
6. W. Reppe, O. Schlichting, K. Klager, and T. Toepel, *Annalen*, **560**, 1 and 11 (1948).
7. A. C. Cope, A. C. Haven, F. L. Ramp, and E. R. Trumbull, *J. Am. Chem. Soc.*, **74**, 4867 (1952).
8. R. P. Bell, *The Proton in Chemistry*, Cornell University Press, Ithaca, N. Y. (1959), pp. 147–152 (for more complete discussion).
9. A. Lapworth, *J. Chem. Soc.*, **85**, 30 (1904).
10. T. M. Lowry and I. J. Faulkner, *J. Chem. Soc.*, **127**, 2883 (1925).
11. K. J. Pedersen, *J. Phys. Chem.*, **38**, 581 (1934).
12. C. G. Swain, A. J. DeMilo, and J. P. Cordner, *J. Am. Chem. Soc.*, **80**, 5983 (1958).
13. K. B. Wiberg, *Chem. Revs.*, **55**, 713 (1955).
14. C. K. Ingold and C. L. Wilson, *J. Chem. Soc.*, 773 (1934).
15. K. F. Bonhoeffer and W. D. Walters, *Z. Physik. Chem.*, **A181**, 441 (1938).
16. J. A. Howard and K. U. Ingold, *Can. J. Chem.*, **41**, 1744 (1963).
17. C. Walling and B. B. Jacknow, *J. Am. Chem. Soc.*, **82**, 6113 (1960).
18. R. D. Gilliom and B. F. Ward, *J. Am. Chem. Soc.*, **87**, 3944 (1965).
19. B. R. Kennedy and K. U. Ingold, *Can. J. Chem.*, **44**, 2381 (1966).
20. G. A. Russell, *J. Org. Chem.*, **23**, 1407 (1958).
21. P. S. Skell and A. Y. Garner, *J. Am. Chem. Soc.*, **78**, 5430 (1956).
22. R. C. Woodworth and P. S. Skell, *J. Am. Chem. Soc.*, **81**, 3383 (1959); W. von E. Doering and P. M. LaFlamme, *J. Am. Chem. Soc.*, **78**, 5447 (1956).
23. F. A. L. Anet, R. F. W. Bader, and A. M. Van der Auwera, *J. Am. Chem. Soc.*, **82**, 3217 (1960).
24. K. R. Kopecky, G. S. Hammond, and P. A. Leermakers, *J. Am. Chem. Soc.*, **84**, 1015 (1962).
25. W. Kirmse, *Carbene Chemistry*, Academic Press, New York (1964).
26. G. S. Hammond and L. M. Soffer, *J. Am. Chem. Soc.*, **72**, 4711 (1950).
27. F. D. Greene, G. R. Van Norman, J. C. Cantrill, and R. D. Gilliom, *J. Org. Chem.*, **25**, 1790 (1960).
28. D. F. DeTar and R. C. Lamb, *J. Am. Chem. Soc.*, **72**, 4711 (1950).
29. H. J. Shine, J. A. Waters, and D. M. Hoffman, *J. Am. Chem. Soc.*, **85**, 3613 (1963).
30. W. A. Pryor, *Free Radicals*, McGraw-Hill Book Co., New York (1966), p. 99.
31. D. F. DeTar and R. A. J. Long, *J. Am. Chem. Soc.*, **80**, 4742 (1958).
32. D. H. Hey, M. J. Perkins, and G. H. Williams, *J. Chem. Soc.*, 3412 (1964).
33. P. S. Skell, *Organic Reaction Mechanisms*, Special Publication No. 19, The Chemical Society, London (1965), p. 131.
34. H. C. Brown, M. S. Kharasch, and T. H. Chao, *J. Am. Chem. Soc.*, **62**, 3435 (1940).
35. P. S. Skell, D. L. Tuleen, and P. D. Readio, *J. Am. Chem. Soc.*, **85**, 2849 and 2850 (1963).

36. J. P. Ryan and P. R. O'Conner, *J. Am. Chem. Soc.*, **74,** 5866 (1952); H. Schmid and K. Schmid, *Helv. Chim. Acta,* **35,** 1879 (1952).
37. H. Schmid and K. Schmid, *Helv. Chim. Acta,* **36,** 489 (1953).
38. K. Schmid, W. Haegele, and H. Schmid, *Helv. Chim. Acta,* **37,** 1080 (1954).
39. S. J. Rhoads and R. L. Crecelius, *J. Am. Chem. Soc.*, **77,** 5060 (1955).
40. J. D. Roberts, D. A. Semenow, H. E. Simmons, and L. A. Carlsmith, *J. Am. Chem. Soc.*, **78,** 601 (1956).
41. M. E. Schafer and R. S. Berry, *J. Am. Chem. Soc.*, **87,** 4497 (1965) and references therein.
42. J. E. Leffler and E. Grunwald, *Rates and Equilibria of Organic Reactions*, John Wiley & Sons (New York), 1963.

CHAPTER 12

ELECTROPHILIC AROMATIC
SUBSTITUTION

The electrophilic aromatic substitution reaction has been studied extensively, and many of the questions that we might ask about it have been more or less satisfactorily answered. For example, we can now predict fairly accurately where substitution will occur on a ring or a polynuclear compound or which of two aromatic compounds will be the more reactive. We also know that more than one step is involved in the substitution process. There are other questions to which less complete answers are available: What is the role of solvent? Is there an order of electrophilicity for the attacking species? What, in fact, is the substituting species? Can orientation be altered by catalyst changes? Work on all of these questions continues at a dizzying pace.

The mechanism commonly given in introductory organic chemistry texts involves the attack of an electrophile upon the aromatic compound. This attack forms an intermediate cyclohexadienyl carbonium ion. These species are frequently called σ complexes [1] or, as suggested by Doering [2], benzenonium ions. The intermediate then decomposes to product by loss of a proton and rearomatization of the π system. This mechanism is formalized as

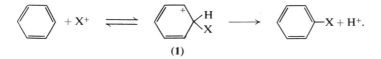

(1)

THE MECHANISM OF ELECTROPHILIC AROMATIC SUBSTITUTION

σ Complexes

There is considerable evidence that species such as (1) do exist. For example, although toluene fails to react with aluminum chloride at $-78°C$, addition of hydrogen chloride causes the aluminum chloride to dissolve. The green color of the resulting solution is believed to be due to the formation of a complex $Ar_n \cdot HCl \cdot AlCl_3$ [3]. Again, aluminum bromide and toluene form an unstable, colorless complex but the addition of hydrogen bromide produces a red solution. Here, the complex involved is believed to be $Ar_n \cdot HBr \cdot AlBr_3$ [4]. Since both the above-mentioned complexes are good conductors of electricity, they are ionic [1]. When deuterium chloride is used, a rapid exchange of ring hydrogens is observed [5]. All these results are consistent with the structure

Similarly, methylated benzenes give colored solutions that are electrical conductors in liquid hydrogen fluoride [6]. The concentration of the complex was increased by adding boron trifluoride [7]. After one mole of this had been added, any further addition had little effect. The stoichiometry of these complexes was thus suggested and later shown to be $1Ar:1HF:1BF_3$ [8]. The presence of complexes in solution, such as the above, has been demonstrated by conductivity measurements [7], vapor pressure determinations [3, 4, 6], and solvent partition experiments [6, 9]. Many complexes have actually been isolated as solid salts and some of them are remarkably stable. Table 12–1, taken from the work of Olah and Kuhn, gives the decomposition points of several species believed to be σ complexes. The $Ar \cdot HF \cdot BF_3$ complexes conduct electricity in the molten state and decompose to boron trifluoride, hydrogen fluoride, and alkylbenzene when heated [8]. Doering has succeeded in isolating heptamethylbenzenonium tetrachloroaluminate as a crystalline compound [2]. Thus, not only protons but also other groups may be added to the aromatic ring to give isolable σ complexes. Olah and Kuhn have similarly isolated stable complexes with the addition of other reagents, e.g. ethyl and propyl fluorides, formyl fluoride, propionyl fluoride, and nitryl fluoride [8]. These complexes decompose upon heating to give substituted aromatics. Some examples of these reactions follow.

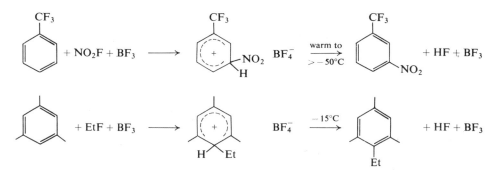

The isolation of extremely stable hexafluoroantimonate complexes allowed Olah to study their chemical properties. He found that the $C_6H_6 \cdot HF \cdot SbF_5$ complex reacted with maleic anhydride in liquid hydrogen fluoride and sulfur dioxide solutions to give low yields of Diels-Alder adduct [10]. Thus it appears that the conjugated π system shows normal π bond reactivity.

Further evidence for the existence of σ complexes comes from spectral studies. Gold and Tye observed the electronic spectrum of protonated anthracene in concentrated sulfuric acid [11]. The spectrum did not resemble that of anthracene obtained in inert solvents but was very similar to that of diphenylethylene in sulfuric

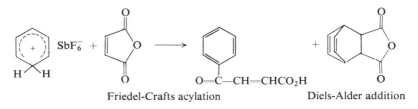

Friedel-Crafts acylation   Diels-Alder addition

acid. This similarity was interpreted as arising from the diphenylmethyl carbonium ion common to both species [11].

Reid [12] has found that the spectrum of the anthracene–hydrogen fluoride–boron trifluoride complex is very similar to that obtained by Gold and Tye. Presumably the same cationic moiety is formed in both media.

Unambiguous evidence for the structure of the benzenonium complexes has been obtained from nuclear magnetic resonance (NMR) spectra [2, 9, 10, 13–15]. A number of systems have been examined by NMR techniques and all clearly show the —CH_2— or —$CHCH_3$— group. Low temperatures must be employed to obtain good resolution. At higher temperatures (above $-60°C$), rapid proton exchange reactions cause line broadening. Examples of NMR spectra given by Olah [10], together with assignments of the protons, are shown in Figs. 12–1 and 12–2.

There is no longer any doubt whether σ complexes exist or what their structures are. Their existence, however, does not prove that they are involved in the substitution reaction. We must look at other evidence to determine their importance as reaction intermediates.

Table 12–1. Decomposition Temperatures of σ Complex Salts in Degrees Centigrade

Ar	$Ar \cdot HF \cdot BF_3$*	$Ar \cdot HF \cdot PF_5$†	$Ar \cdot HF \cdot SbF_5$†
$1,3\text{-}(CH_3)_2C_6H_4$	-55	-24	37
$1,3,5\text{-}(CH_3)_3C_6H_3$	-15	8	51
$1,2,4,5\text{-}(CH_3)_4C_6H_2$			62
$1,2,3,5\text{-}(CH_3)_4C_6H_2$	-10		
$(CH_3)_5C_6H$		10	57
$(CH_3)_6C_6$		13	95

* From Olah *et al.* [8].
† From Olah [10].

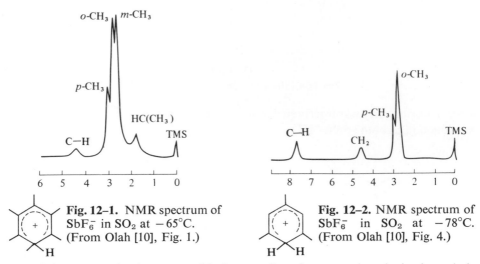

Fig. 12–1. NMR spectrum of SbF₆⁻ in SO₂ at −65°C. (From Olah [10], Fig. 1.)

Fig. 12–2. NMR spectrum of SbF₆⁻ in SO₂ at −78°C. (From Olah [10], Fig. 4.)

If the σ complex is an unstable intermediate in aromatic substitutions, it is reasonable to assume that the transition state leading to this intermediate will closely resemble it [16]. Hence, we might expect to find a correlation between rates of substitution and stabilities of σ complexes. Figure 12–3 shows an excellent correlation of the relative rates of bromination [17] with the relative stabilities for protonated aromatics in liquid hydrogen fluoride. Thus, the expected correlation has been found, but it is still not conclusive proof that a σ complex is an intermediate—such a correlation will always be found if the transition state resembles the σ complex, even if the latter is *not* an intermediate.

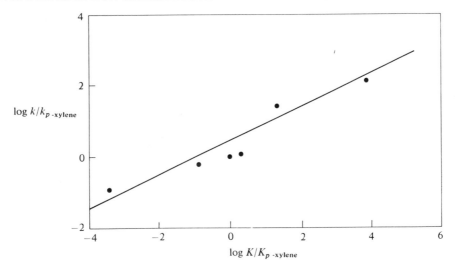

Fig. 12–3. Relative rates of bromination *versus* relative stabilities of ArH⁺F⁻.

Furthermore, if σ complexes are intermediates in the aromatic substitution reaction, they must decompose to give the correct product. It has already been mentioned that stable complexes do this, but this does not prove that σ complexes play a role in the reaction any more than does the correlation of rates with stabilities, although again this condition must be met if they *do* play a role. Unfortunately, the conditions used to prepare, isolate, and decompose the σ complexes of Olah and Kuhn [8] were not typical of the conditions of aromatic substitution reactions. Ideally, we should like to detect a σ complex during an actual substitution reaction. We must also show that the formation and decomposition of the complex occur in agreement with the kinetics of the overall reaction. To do this, it is necessary to find a reaction in which the formation of the intermediate is more rapid than its decomposition; such a reaction would not fit the steady-state approximation. The bromination of the disodium salt of 2-naphthol-6,8-disulfonic acid fits this requirement [18, 19]:

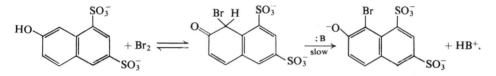

When the reactants are mixed, the bromine color rapidly disappears. The product is not formed immediately, however, because the bromine may be titrated even after its color has gone and titratable bromine is found to disappear only slowly. The σ complex can be observed by its NMR spectrum immediately after the reactants are mixed. Decomposition of the intermediate is linearly dependent upon the concentration of base, because it is decomposing to the substitution product. Bromination with hypobromous acid was also studied. The rate of bromination is nearly the same for both reagents. Again, this must be so if the decomposition of the intermediate is the rate-controlling step. It was also observed that the rate of formation of product did not depend upon either bromide ion in the bromine reaction or the pH in the HOBr reaction. Thus, the kinetics of the overall reaction fitted the observations and the σ complex was actually observed. Similar results have been obtained by other workers using other phenols [20–23]. The special stability of the intermediates in substitutions of phenols is probably due to the formation of a neutral quinoid structure by loss of the phenolic proton.

The first, and perhaps still the most convincing, evidence for an intermediate in aromatic substitution was obtained by Melander [24, 25], who studied the nitration of several tritiated aromatics and found no primary isotope effect. Examining the mechanism that we have been considering, we find that no isotope effect would be expected if $k_2 \gg k_{-1}$:

$$Ar + NO_2^+ \underset{k_{-1}}{\overset{k_1}{\rightleftharpoons}} (ArNO_2)^+ \overset{k_2}{\longrightarrow} ArNO_2 + H^+.$$

When k_2 is much greater than k_{-1} no C—H bond is broken in the rate-determining step k_1. Perhaps this is more easily seen by making the steady-state assumption. We can write

$$d(\text{ArNO}_2)/dt = k_{obs}(\text{Ar})(\text{NO}_2^+) = k_2(\text{ArNO}_2^+). \tag{12–1}$$

The steady-state treatment gives

$$k_1(\text{Ar})(\text{NO}_2^+) = k_{-1}(\text{ArNO}_2^+) + k_2(\text{ArNO}_2^+), \tag{12–2}$$

which can be rearranged to give

$$(\text{ArNO}_2^+) = k_1(\text{Ar})(\text{NO}_2^+)/(k_{-1} + k_2). \tag{12–3}$$

Substitution of this into Eq. (12–1) and elimination of like terms affords

$$k_{obs} = \frac{k_1 k_2}{k_{-1} + k_2}. \tag{12–4}$$

From Eq. (12–4) we can see that, when $k_2 \gg k_{-1}$, the term $(k_{-1} + k_2) \cong k_2$ and $k_{obs} \cong k_1$, which is in agreement with Melander's results. Still, this does not prove the existence of an intermediate, only that there is very little C—H stretching in the transition state of the nitration reaction. If we do not accept the presence of an intermediate, however, we are forced into a difficult position. Imagine the reverse process and recall the principle of microscopic reversibility (Chapter 7). If an intermediate is not involved, the transition state for the reverse reaction, albeit this is an imaginary reaction, is not reached until the C—H bond is formed. This requirement is difficult to visualize, particularly since the necessary result, a σ complex, is known to be stable in other cases (*vide supra*).

It would be unfair to proceed without pointing out some other results of Melander's work. What is expected when k_{-1} is much larger than k_2? Returning to Eq. (12–4), the term $(k_{-1} + k_2)$ becomes nearly equal to k_{-1} and k_{obs} becomes $k_1 k_2/k_{-1}$. When this occurs, a primary isotope effect would be expected, since the observed rate is dependent upon a step involving C—H bond breaking. This is the situation described above for the bromination of 2-naphthol-6,8-disulfonic acid and a primary deuterium kinetic isotope effect has been observed for this reaction [26]. A number of other substitution reactions are now known that exhibit isotope effects, both large and small [27]. One very attractive mechanism is ruled out by Melander's results. A concerted mechanism would allow the aromatic π electron system to remain nearly undisturbed, permitting the aromatic resonance energy to be maintained throughout the reaction. Of course, since the displacement of the hydrogen would lead to an isotope effect, this mechanism must be discarded.

The evidence presented above has led chemists to accept the σ complex, or benzenonium ion, as an intermediate in the electrophilic aromatic substitution reaction. Another type of aromatic complex, the π complex, is also known. Is it possible that both types of complex are important in the substitution reaction?

π Complexes

A number of electrophiles react with electron donors to give species in which no new covalent bond has been formed [28, 29]. Electrophiles showing this behavior include picric acid, the halogens, hydrogen halides, copper and silver ions, oxygen, and tetracyanoethylene. The electron donors may be aromatics, alkenes, alkynes, amines, etc. These two groups form π complexes or *charge-transfer complexes*. Except for the picrates, which are solids, most are found only in solution. To study complex formation in solution, deviations of the properties of the solution from those of an ideal solution are measured. Among the properties that have been employed are spectra, vapor pressure, viscosity, melting points, refractive index, conductivity, dielectric constants, surface tension, and dipole moment changes [30].

The structure of the π complex formed when a solution of equimolar amounts of bromine in benzene is frozen has been determined [31]. The bromine lies along the axis perpendicular to the benzene ring, the bromine-bromine bond length is unchanged, and the distance from one bromine atom to the plane of the nearest benzene ring is 3.36 Å, too long for a typical covalent bond:

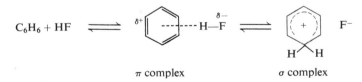

Not all π complexes are so symmetrical. In the complex formed between silver ion (perchlorate) and benzene, the silver ion lies above one of the carbon atoms and the C—C bond lengths of benzene are altered, as are the bond angles within the ring [32]. Thus, it appears that there is no sharp dividing line between σ and π complexes. An equilibrium, however, can exist between an aromatic and the two types of complex [33, 34]:

$$C_6H_6 + HF \;\rightleftharpoons\; \underset{\pi\ \text{complex}}{\delta^+ \bigcirc \text{----}\ H\!-\!\overset{\delta^-}{F}} \;\rightleftharpoons\; \underset{\sigma\ \text{complex}}{\left(\bigcirc^+\right)\underset{H\ \ H}{}}\ F^-$$

The properties of σ and π complexes are compared in Table 12–2.

To demonstrate the role of π complexes in the aromatic substitution process, we might apply a correlation of rates against π complex stabilities. Olah *et al.* have succeeded in making such correlations for benzylation [35], nitration [36, 37], bromination [38, 39], isopropylation [40, 41], and (with somewhat less success) for chlorination [42] and *tert*-butylation [43]. These workers used solvents such as nitromethane, tetramethylene sulfone, sulfur dioxide, and carbon disulfide, all of which gave homogeneous solutions. The stabilities of several π and σ complexes are

Table 12–2. Differences in Properties of σ and π Complexes

Reference	σ Complex	π Complex
4	Orange to black color	Colorless to yellow
1	H isotope exchange occurs	No H exchange
1	Electrical conductivity	No conductivity
Table 12–3	Large substituent effects upon stability	Small substituent effects

given in Table 12–3. The relative rates of some reactions presumed to involve rate-controlling formation of σ complexes are given in Table 12–4, and Table 12–5 shows the same data for reactions involving π complexes.

Table 12–3. Relative Stabilities of Some Complexes

Ar	π Complexes*				σ Complexes†
	I_2	Br_2	Ag^+	HCl	HF—BF_3
Benzene	1.0	1.0	1.0	1.0	
Toluene	1.1	1.4	1.2	1.5	1
o-Xylene	1.8	2.2	1.3	1.9	200
m-Xylene	2.1	2.1	1.3	2.1	2,000
p-Xylene	2.1	2.2	1.1	1.6	100
Mesitylene	5.5		0.8	2.6	280,000

* The data for I_2 and Ag^+ are taken from Andrews and Keefer [44], those for Br_2 from Keefer and Andrews [45], and those for HCl from Brown and Brady [1].
† From McCaulay and Lien [6].

Table 12–4. Relative Rates of σ Complex-Controlled Reactions

Ar	Br_2, 85% HOAc, 25°C	Cl_2, HOAc, 25°C*	Cl_2, CH_3NO_2, 25°C†
Benzene	1	1	1
Toluene	605	344	2,445
o-Xylene	5,320	2,100	
m-Xylene	51,400	18,500	247,000
p-Xylene	2,520	2,080	14,200
Mesitylene	18,900,000		5,000,000

* From Brown and Stock [17].
† From Olah et al. [42] and Stock and Himoe [46].

It can be seen that the substrate selectivities are very low for the reactions in Table 12–5. We might expect these reactions to show low positional selectivity as well: that is, the $o:m:p$ ratio of products from substituted benzenes would approach the statistical value of $2:2:1$. This is not the case, however. The same high positional selectivity that is observed for σ-controlled reactions is also observed in π complex-controlled substitutions (Table 12–6).

Table 12–5. Relative Rates of Reactions Suggested to Be Controlled by π Complexes*

Ar	I Br_2, $FeCl_3$, CH_3NO_2	II i-PrBr, $AlCl_3$, CH_3NO_2	III NO_2BF_4, TMS†	IV Cl_2, $FeCl_3$, CH_3NO_2
Benzene	1.0	1.00	1.00	1.0
Toluene	3.6	2.03	1.67	13.5
o-Xylene	3.9	2.21	1.75	38.0
m-Xylene	5.6	2.80	1.65	110
p-Xylene	4.3	2.70	1.96	43.9
Mesitylene	15.9	0.35	2.71	

* The data for solution I are taken from Olah *et al.* [38], those for solution II from Olah *et al.* [40] and Olah and Overchuk [41], those for solution III from Olah and Overchuk [37], and those for solution IV from Olah *et al.* [42]. All experiments were carried out at 25°C.

† TMS = tetramethylene sulfone.

Table 12–6. Substrate Selectivities and Isomer Distributions of Reactions of Toluene

Reactant	Solvent and catalyst	T, °C	k_t/k_B*	o	m	p	Reference
			Bromination				
Br_2	85% HOAc	25	605	32.9	0.3	66.8	17
HOBr	50% Aq. dioxane	25	36.2	70.3	2.3	27.4	47
Br_2	$CH_3NO_2 \cdot FeCl_3$	25	3.6	68.7	1.8	29.5	38
			Chlorination				
Cl_2	HOAc	25	344	59.8	0.5	39.7	17
HOCl	Aq. $HClO_4$	25	60	74.6	2.2	23.2	48
Cl_2	Aromatic solv. $CH_3NO_2 \cdot AlCl_3$	25	18.3	63.2	2.0	34.8	42
			Nitration				
HNO_3	Acetic anhyd.	30	23	58.4	4.4	37.2	49
HNO_3	90% HOAc	45	24	56.5	3.5	40.0	50
NO_2BF_4	Tetramethylene sulfone	25	1.7	65.4	2.8	31.8	36

* k_t/k_B = rate of toluene substitution/rate of benzene.

Olah *et al.* [37, 40, 41] have interpreted their results as follows. To account for the low substrate selectivity and the correlation of this selectivity with π complex rather than σ complex stabilities, they suggest that the rate-determining step involves a transition state similar to a π complex. The high selectivity exhibited by isomer distribution is believed to be determined by a second transition state. The similarity between isomer distributions of Olah's reactions and those reactions controlled by a σ complex suggests that the transition state determining isomer distributions resembles a σ complex.

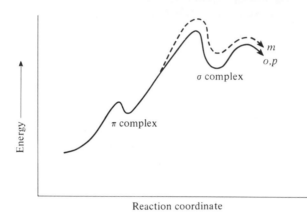

Fig. 12–4. Energy diagram of σ complex-controlled reactions.

The view that strong electrophiles are capable of forming π complexes seems reasonable. It is not obvious, however, why the rate-determining step should involve the π complex in Olah's cases, but this may be explained by the fact that NO_2BF_4 in tetramethylene sulfone solution has been shown to exist as clusters of ions rather than as free ions. Cryoscopic measurements suggest that the clusters are ion pairs and conductivity results suggest ion triplets [51]. For the π complex to form, the electrophile must move away from its oppositely charged partner—a high-energy process. When this separation of oppositely charged ions is not required, e.g. for free NO_2^+, the π complex can form easily and the formation of the σ complex requires the greater amount of energy. A reasonable energy diagram for σ complex-controlled substitution is given in Fig. 12–4. The π complex, as well as the transition state leading to it, may be completely by-passed. A similar diagram for reactions controlled by π complex formation is given in Fig. 12–5. The presence of the σ complex shown in Figs. 12–4 and 12–5 is strongly suggested by the arguments presented previously. There is no such compelling evidence that the first complex shown in Fig. 12–5 actually is a π complex. There must be two transition states because substrate and positional selectivities are determined by different steps in the reaction. If there are two transition states, then an intermediate must be formed between them. Since the substrate selectivity results suggest that the transition state resembles a π complex and since the existence of π complexes is well known, Olah has assigned the intermediate the structure of a π complex.

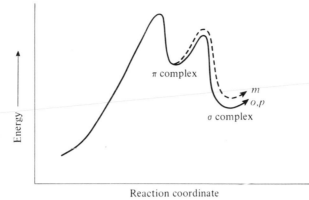

Fig. 12–5. Energy diagram of π complex-controlled reactions.

The nitration results obtained by Olah *et al.* [36, 37] have recently been questioned. Tolgyesi [52] claimed that the substrate selectivity results are dependent upon the rate of mixing and, therefore, that Olah was looking at a diffusion rather than a rate-controlled process. This would be an important limitation to the use of relative rates obtained by competitive techniques. Olah and Overchuk [37] showed that as little as 0.72 gm of water in 1.0 liter of solvent would completely change the nitronium ion salt to a more selective nitrating species. Even more convincing evidence supporting Olah's interpretation has been found. Absolute rate constants were obtained for the benzylation, isopropylation, and *tert*-butylation of benzene and toluene [40, 41]. The relative rates calculated from these absolute values were within experimental agreement with the competitive rate results, which confirms the values for these reactions. Thus, the suggestion that low substrate selectivity results from diffusion-controlled rather than kinetically controlled conditions can be rejected for alkylations, if not for nitration.

Attacking Species in Nitration

Since Olah based his explanation of π complex kinetic control upon separation of NO_2^+ from BF_4^-, the attacking species in most other nitrations must not involve a nitronium ion-anion pair. What then *is* the attacking species? Much effort has been spent upon this problem and it is now fairly well understood.

When freezing-point depressions of dilute solutions of nitric acid in concentrated sulfuric acid were studied [53, 54], it was found that the number of particles formed from a nitric acid molecule is nearly four. This is believed to be due to ionization, according to the equation

$$HNO_3 + 2H_2SO_4 \rightarrow NO_2^+ + H_3O^+ + 2HSO_4^-.$$

The evidence for the existence of the nitronium ion is overwhelming: both its infrared [55] and Raman [56] spectra have been observed, and isolation [57] and X-ray crystallographic studies [58, 59] of nitronium salts have also demonstrated its existence. In concentrated nitric acid, nitronium ion is believed to be formed by the self-dehydration equilibrium

$$2HNO_3 = NO_2^+ + NO_3^- + H_2O.$$

Additions of small amounts of either water or dinitrogen pentoxide cause much less of a freezing-point depression than anticipated [60], as is to be expected if the addition suppresses an equilibrium that already exists. The effect of water on the above equilibrium is obvious and, since dinitrogen pentoxide exists as a mixture of nitronium ions and nitrate ions in nitric acid solution [61], both these ions would repress the equilibrium also. Autoprotolysis,

$$2HNO_3 = H_2NO_3^+ + NO_3^-,$$

might also be important in concentrated nitric acid solutions, but Raman spectra show that this equilibrium is not very important. The relative concentration of nitrate ion to nitronium ion was found to be 1.09 at $-15°C$ [61].

With the above evidence for the existence of nitronium ion in these nitrating media as background, the kinetics of nitration can be examined. The nitration of nitrobenzene in sulfuric acid was the first to be studied by kinetic methods [62]. The kinetics of this reaction, as well as of several others, fit the rate equation

$$rate = k_2[ArH][HNO_3].$$

All the aromatic reactants that have been found to fit this rate equation are strongly deactivated [63]. Active aromatics react so rapidly that the rate of reaction is controlled by the rate of dissolution.

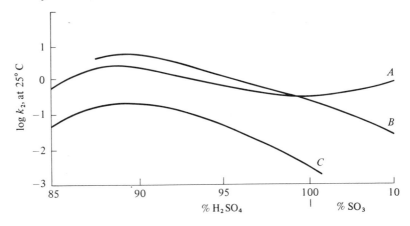

A, trimethylanilinium ion; $k_2(90\%)/k_2(100\%) = 3.8$;
B, nitrobenzene; $k_2(90\%)/k_2(100\%) = 8.7$;
C, anthraquinone: $k_2(90\%)/k_2(100\%) = 48$.

Fig. 12–6. Variation of rate of nitration in sulfuric acid media. (From de la Mare and Ridd [63], Fig. 5.2.)

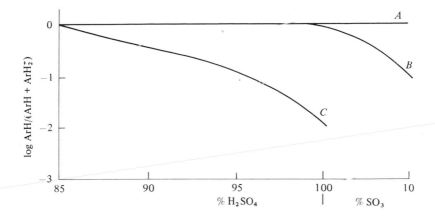

Fig. 12–7. Variation of extent of protonation in sulfuric acid media. See Fig. 12–6 for legend. (From de la Mare and Ridd [63], Fig. 5.3.)

A change of medium from 90% to 100% sulfuric acid causes a marked decrease in rate [64]. This is graphically illustrated in Fig. 12–6, taken from de la Mare and Ridd [63]. Several explanations of this behavior are possible. The explanation that the rate is faster in 90% acid because a base is needed to remove the proton from the σ complex cannot be accepted. Melander's isotope effect results have shown that this is *not* the rate-determining step in nitration [24]. A second explanation might be that protonation of the aromatic substrate in 100% sulfuric acid decreases the concentration of the reactive aromatic moiety. Examination of Fig. 12–7 [63] sheds light on this possibility. Protonation of anthraquinone may be the *main* cause of the rate decrease of this substance but it cannot be the only cause, since this will not explain the decrease of rate for trimethylanilinium ion, which is not protonated in 100% sulfuric acid. Similarly, the extent of protonation of nitrobenzene will not account for its far greater rate decrease. An acceptable explanation of the rate decrease is based on an environmental effect. The rate of nitration should follow the equation [65]

$$\text{rate} = k[NO_2^+][ArH]\gamma_{NO_2^+}\gamma_{ArH}/\gamma_{TS};$$

that is, the rate is dependent upon the ratio $f_{NO_2^+}/f_{TS}$. It is known that there is a difference in the ion-solvation properties of 90% and 100% sulfuric acid. If the ratio of activity coefficients is lower in 100% acid than in 90%, the results can be qualitatively explained [64, 65]. In other words, rates of reactions that proceed from a polar reactant (NO_2^+) to a less-polar transition state are decreased if the dielectric constant of the medium is increased. Pure sulfuric acid is believed to have a higher dielectric constant than acid containing either water or SO_3 [64]. This explanation is consistent with a rate-determining attack of nitronium ion on the aromatic species

$$NO_2^+ + ArH \rightarrow ArHNO_2^+.$$

Further tests of this mechanism are available.

The nitration of deactivated aromatics in concentrated nitric acid is pseudo-first-order:

$$\text{rate} = k_1[\text{ArH}].$$

To test the importance of the nitronium ion formed *via* self-dehydration, nitrate ions or sulfuric acid can be added [66]. Small amounts of nitrate ion are found to slow the reaction drastically. This is to be expected if shifting the self-dehydration equilibrium to the left lowers the concentration of the reactive species, e.g. NO_2^+. Added sulfuric acid increases the rate of nitration and alters the concentration of nitrate ion by protonating it:

$$NO_3^- + H_2SO_4 = HNO_3 + HSO_4^-.$$

Thus, the nitronium ion concentration is increased by shifting the self-dehydration equilibrium to the right.

Another test of the role of nitronium ion in nitration has been conducted in dilute nitric acid [67]. Using reactive aromatic compounds the rate equation can be reduced to zero-order kinetics. For this to occur,

$$k_3[NO_2^+][\text{ArH}] \gg k_2[NO_2^+][H_2O]:$$

$$HNO_3 + H^+ \underset{k_2}{\overset{k_1}{\rightleftharpoons}} NO_2^+ + H_2O,$$

$$NO_2^+ + \text{ArH} \xrightarrow{k_3} \text{ArHNO}_2^+.$$

This condition appears to be satisfied for the compounds

when they are in relatively high concentration. As the reactants are used up, $k_2[NO_2^+][H_2O]$ becomes important and first-order kinetics are observed. Using O^{18}-labeled water, it was found that the rate of O^{18} exchange between nitric acid and water is about the same as the rate of nitration. This must mean that both reactions have the same rate-controlling step. Formation of the nitronium ion is the most reasonable step common to both processes.

As mentioned above, kinetic studies of reactive aromatics cannot be carried out satisfactorily in mineral acid solutions. This problem has been overcome by using nitromethane as solvent for nitration studies. Using excess nitric acid, a constant reaction rate was obtained throughout the mono-nitration reaction [68], so that the aromatic substrate plays no part in the rate-determining step in this medium. Addition of nitrate ion caused a rate decrease but no change in kinetic order. If self-dehydration is a one-step process, as written above, we would expect a decrease in rate with added nitrate ion, caused by competition of the nitrate ion and the aromatic species for the nitronium ion. We might also expect that this competition would lead to a change in kinetic order. That is, the more aromatic the species present, the better it would compete with nitrate ion. Since this does not occur, the added nitrate ion must be acting upon an equilibrium preceding the formation of the nitronium ion. The generally accepted mechanism [63] of formation of nitronium ion is

$$2HNO_3 \; \underset{}{\overset{fast}{\rightleftharpoons}} \; H_2NO_3^+ + NO_3^-,$$

$$H_2NO_3^+ \; \overset{slow}{\longrightarrow} \; NO_2^+ + H_2O.$$

The effect of added nitrate ion is to suppress the formation of the nitric acidium ion in the first step. A proton donor stronger than nitric acid should have a catalytic effect by increasing the concentration of nitric acidium ion. Sulfuric acid is a strong catalyst. Added water has little effect upon the rate; therefore, its reaction with nitronium ion must be much slower than the reaction of activated aromatics with this ion. Were this not so, zero-order kinetics would not be observed. Also, since water is not protonated under the reaction conditions, it has no indirect effect *via* the formation of nitrate ions.

The above is consistent with a mechanism of nitration involving several steps. We have examined how these various steps have been studied. The idea is simply to isolate each step by making it the kinetic controlling step. To use this simple approach, however, requires a great deal of ingenuity and skill.

QUANTITATIVE REACTIVITY CORRELATIONS

Although it is frequently impossible to measure the rates of aromatic substitutions directly, the method of relative rates can be employed (see Chapter 6). For example, although toluene is nitrated very rapidly by nitric acid in acetic acid at 45°C, nitration of a mixture of toluene and benzene reveals that toluene is nitrated 24 times faster than benzene [69]. By using other substituted benzenes, a list of reactivities such as that given in Table 12–7 is obtained. Frequently, from the same experiment

Table 12–7. Relative Rates of Nitration

Compound	Relative Rate
C_6H_6	1 (assumed)
C_6H_5Cl	0.033*
$C_6H_5C(CH_3)_3$	15.7†
$C_6H_5CH_3$	24†

* Nitration with acetyl nitrate in acetic anhydride at 18°C. (From Bird and Ingold [70].)
† Nitration in 90% acetic acid at 45°C. (From Cohn *et al.* [69].)

that gives us the relative rates, we can obtain the amount of substitution occurring at the *ortho, meta,* and *para* positions of the substituted benzene. Thus, from one experiment, we may learn not only relative substrate reactivities but also relative reactivities of each position within one (or both) of the reactants. This type of data is of the form

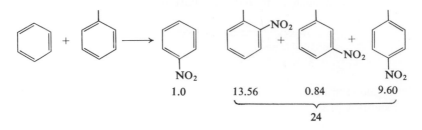

$$\underset{1.0}{} \qquad \underset{13.56}{} \qquad \underset{0.84}{} \qquad \underset{9.60}{}$$

$$24$$

   The rate constant of substitution of toluene must be $k_p + 2k_m + 2k_o$, where k_o is the rate constant of one of the *ortho* positions, k_m that of one of the *meta* positions and k_p that of the *para* position. The rate constant of one of the positions of benzene can be written as k_b if the total rate constant of benzene, k_B, is taken as $6k_b$. From this we can write

$$k_{\text{toluene}}/k_B = (2k_o + 2k_m + k_p)/6k_b = 24(\text{nitration}).$$

We can also write an expression giving the fraction of each isomer, that is, the rate at the *ortho* positions relative to the total rate of the substituted benzene:

   Fraction o product $= 2k_o/(2k_o + 2k_m + k_p) = 13.56/24 = 0.565(\text{nitration}).$

From these two expressions, we can compare the rate of nitration of a single position in toluene with that of a single position in benzene:

$$2k_o + 2k_m + k_p = 144k_b$$

and

$$2k_o + 2k_m + k_p = 2k_o/0.565.$$

Therefore,

$$144k_b = 2k_o/0.565$$

and

$$k_o/k_b = 41.$$

This value, k_o/k_b, is called the *partial rate factor* and is given the symbol O_f^{methyl}. Similarly we can obtain the partial rate factors for the other positions in toluene:

$$M_f^{\text{methyl}} = k_m/k_b = 2.5,$$
$$P_f^{\text{methyl}} = k_p/k_b = 58.$$

Excellent correlations for a number of substitution reactions are obtained for the partial rate factors for the *meta* and *para* positions with σ^+ (see Chapter 9). Figure 12–8 shows such a correlation for nitration [71].

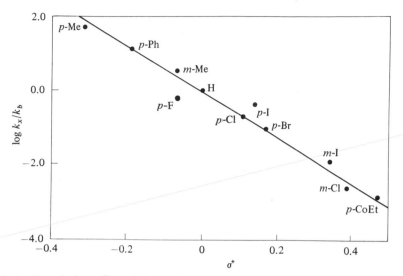

Fig. 12–8. Correlation of partial rate factors with σ^+ for nitration. (From Brown and Okamoto [71], Fig. 4.)

Partial rate factors for the *ortho* position do not give a satisfactory correlation, owing to steric factors.

This treatment has led to one recent qualitative success. The σ^+ value of *p*-NMe$_3^+$ is 0.41 and the same group in the *meta* position has a value of 0.36. This suggests that aromatic substitution should occur at the *para* position only slightly more slowly than at the *meta* (ρ is negative, -12.14 for bromination [71] and -6.22 for nitration [71]). Until recently, nitration of the trimethylanilinium ion was believed to give *only meta* substitution [63, 72] and this was explained by two approaches [73]. One suggested that the transition state for *para* substitution was destabilized relative to that for *meta*:

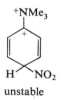

unstable

The second explained the *meta* orientation by claiming greater electron withdrawal from the *para* position in the reactant:

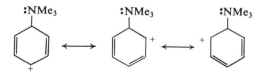

Neither explanation gives a satisfactory reason for the similar values of σ^+, since this is a measure of electron withdrawal. Recently it has been reported that nitration of the trimethylanilinium ion gives 11% *para* substitution [74]. The partial rate factors for this reaction are 1.0×10^{-8} at the *para* and 4.2×10^{-8} at the *meta* positions [74]. The anilinium ion undergoes nitration with partial rate factors of 195×10^{-8} at the *para* position and 162×10^{-8} at the *meta* [74]. The difference is believed to be due to dispersal of the positive charge by hydrogen bonding in the anilinium ion. Although these results are not in quantitative agreement with the $\rho\sigma^+$ relationship, the prediction that the *para* position should undergo substitution has been realized.

Partial rate factors are intermolecular comparisons and can be converted to intramolecular selectivity values:

$$P_f/M_f = (k_p/k_b)/(k_m/k_b) = k_p/k_m.$$

Since $\log P_f = \rho\sigma_p^+$ and $\log M_f = \rho\sigma_m^+$, we can write

$$\log P_f - \log M_f = \log P_f/M_f = \rho(\sigma_p^+ - \sigma_m^+).$$

Brown and his coworkers have found that $\log P_f$ is linearly related to $\log P_f/M_f$ for most substituents [75]. Substitution into this gives

$$\log P_f = C \log P_f/M_f$$

$$(\log P_f)/(\log P_f/M_f) = \sigma_p^+/(\sigma_p^+ - \sigma_m^+) = C,$$

which provides a check on the validity of the equation. For the methyl group

$$\sigma_p^+/(\sigma_p^+ - \sigma_m^+) = -0.31/-0.31 - (-0.07) = 1.3.$$

This is in excellent agreement with the value of 1.325 obtained from 32 reactions by Brown *et al.* [75]. Figure 12–9 gives the correlation for some of their reactions. This relationship works equally well for M_f but it breaks down for O_f, presumably because of steric factors.

The correlation of partial rate factors with σ^+ relates several substituents to a single reactant. The relationship shown in Fig. 12–9 correlates several reactants with a single substituent, albeit *meta* and *para*.

From the above relationships we can learn something useful about reactions. The values of σ^+ are determined for the solvolysis of cumyl chlorides (see Chapter 9), a process involving carbonium ion formation. Reactions that show a linear free energy relationship with σ^+ must be related in some manner. The most reasonable assumption is that aromatic substitution also involves formation of positive charge, which of course agrees with the formation of a σ complex type of transition state. Should π complex formation control the reaction, no correlation with σ^+ would be expected; indeed, none is found in the cases described by Olah *et al.* [37, 38, 41]. Also, the selectivity relationship suggests that a reagent which is highly selective between *meta* and *para* substitution will also be highly selective between benzene and another aromatic species. This can be true only if both selectivities are determined by the same transition state. Thus, we find that for the highly selective reagent bromine P_f/M_f is 440 and P_f is 2420 [17], whereas the more reactive hypobromous acid gives lower values for both, 23.6 and 59 [17, 47]. If the two selectivities are determined in different steps of the reaction, no correlation can be expected nor is any found. For example, the bromination of toluene with ferric chloride, bromine, and nitromethane solvent gives 6.4 for P_f, indicating low substrate selectivity [38]. The value of P_f/M_f of 33.5 indicates even greater positional selectivity than is observed with hypobromous acid bromination. That the selectivity relationship does not hold when π complexes determine substrate selectivity is also clearly indicated by the *meta* partial rate factors. If a reagent were completely nonselective it would react with a single position in benzene as rapidly as it reacted with any one position in toluene. Also, no one position in toluene would be more reactive than any other. This would lead to a minimum value of one for the *meta* partial rate factor of toluene. But the value of M_f for toluene in the above bromination is 0.18 [38]. Since the reagent cannot be less selective than statistical, the relationship cannot hold.

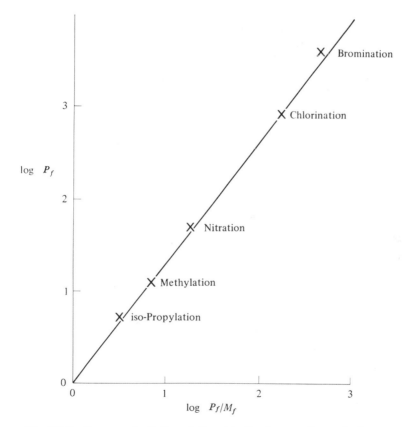

Fig. 12–9. Brown selectivity relationship for the reactions of toluene.

APPLICATION OF MOLECULAR ORBITAL CALCULATIONS

Several approaches may be taken when applying molecular orbital calculations to the reactivity problem. Reactivity may be determined by the reactants in the ground state, if the transition state structure closely resembles that of the reactants; in this case, calculations should be based upon the structure of the reactants alone. Similarly, if the nature of the products determines reactivity, calculations should be based upon each product's molecular structure. Equilibrium reactions might be investigated by calculating the differences in energies of the reactants and products. Finally, if differences between transition states determine reactivities, calculations should be based upon the structures of the transition states. Unfortunately, none of these structures are known very precisely for any but the most simple reactions. If, however, a reactive intermediate is formed, it might serve as a model of the transition state. In most aromatic substitutions, as we have seen, a σ complex is formed which is thought to resemble the transition state controlling both intra- and intermolecular reactivities. The following account will demonstrate how some of the methods have been applied to aromatic substitution problems.

One of the qualitative theories frequently employed to predict the position of substitution on an aromatic species states that substitution will occur at the site of greatest electron density [73]. If this is correct, the calculated electron density q_r (see Chapter 4) should give a good correlation with experimental results. An electrophilic species would be expected to attack at a site of high electron density [76]. In using q_r as an index to reactivity, we are assuming that the transition state resembles the reactants or that reactivity is determined by Coulombic attractions between the reactive species. The latter idea, discussed above, leads to inconsistencies in the case of the halobenzenes. Also, alternant hydrocarbons, e.g. naphthalene, have all q values equal to one. Thus, this approach is unsatisfactory because it is based upon two incorrect assumptions—that transition states do not determine reactivity and that a large number of hydrocarbons do not give usable values of q_r. This latter difficulty may be avoided by using the "frontier electron" approach of Fukui et al. [77], who suggested that the attacking electrophile would react with the electrons in the highest occupied orbital and at the position of greatest electron density within this orbital. Hence, the largest value of c_r^2 (actually Nc_r^2) for the highest occupied orbital will be the most reactive site. This approach is somewhat more successful than that employing q_r.

A second approach is to consider the σ complex as a model for the transition state. In the σ complex the original aromatic system has been destroyed and a new cationic species formed. Wheland suggested that the difference in π electron energies of the two (the localization energy, L_r^+) would control the reactivity [78]. Calculating the π energy for each of the possible localized positions of a large molecule can become rather tedious although the results obtained are good. Dewar [79] has developed a speedier method that gives equally satisfactory results, employing the coefficients of the nonbonding molecular orbital of the σ complex. However, the method works only for odd-alternant cations (and anions).

To obtain the coefficients of the nonbonding molecular orbital, we simply star alternate atoms so that no two stars are on adjacent atoms and so that there are more starred atoms than unstarred ones, if this is possible. Next we number the stars so that the sum of the starred atoms adjacent to any unstarred one is zero. To obtain the coefficients of the nonbonding orbital, we then sum the square of the stars and solve for the star, using the normalization requirement. This method is illustrated for the benzyl cation.

Benzyl cation   Starred   Numbered

It can be seen that at position a, the sum of the adjacent stars $(+2, -1, -1)$ is zero. To obtain the coefficients we calculate

$$(2\star)^2 + \star^2 + (-\star)^2 + (-\star)^2 = 7\star^2 = 1 \text{ (the normalization requirement)},$$

from which we get the value of the star: $\star = 1/\sqrt{7}$. The coefficients, c_r, are therefore

$$-c_b = c_d = -c_f = 1/\sqrt{7} \text{ and } c_g = 2/\sqrt{7}.$$

To apply this method to the σ complex obtained in aromatic substitution, we isolate a site where reaction can occur in the aromatic species. The reader might attempt to evaluate the coefficients of the remaining cation by the above method. Using the absolute values of the coefficients of the positions adjacent to the isolated atom, c_q and c_s, the Dewar number, N_r, is calculated by means of the equation

$$N_r = 2(c_q + c_s)\beta.$$

This gives a value for the localization energy and the lowest value of N_r is the most reactive position. For example, consider naphthalene:

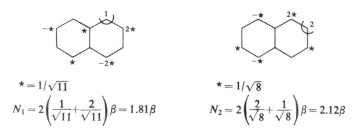

$$\star = 1/\sqrt{11}$$
$$N_1 = 2\left(\frac{1}{\sqrt{11}} + \frac{2}{\sqrt{11}}\right)\beta = 1.81\beta$$

$$\star = 1/\sqrt{8}$$
$$N_2 = 2\left(\frac{2}{\sqrt{8}} + \frac{1}{\sqrt{8}}\right)\beta = 2.12\beta$$

We predict from this that the 1 position in naphthalene is easier to isolate than the 2 position, which agrees with the greater reactivity of naphthalene in the 1 position. The Dewar method was developed as a perturbation of the σ complex and the values of N_r are smaller than L_r^+ [80].

In general, results are slightly better when the σ complex is used as a model than when reactants are used; i.e., a better correlation is obtained by using N_r or L_r^+ than by using q_r or the frontier electron approach. Several values for N_r, L_r^+, and partial rate factors for nitration are given in Table 12–8. It can be seen that experimental agreement is good with both reactivity indices. An obvious exception is the 4 position of phenanthrene, probably owing to steric factors caused by the *peri*-hydrogens. Because steric effects are not considered in these calculations, the student must use his intuition and experience when predicting relative reactivities.

Table 12–8. Relative Reactivities (L_r^+ and N_r) for Nitration.

Ar	r	f_r^*	L_r^+	N_r
(benzene)	1	1	2.54	2.31
(naphthalene)	1	470	2.30	1.81
	2	50	2.48	2.12
(phenanthrene)	1	360	2.32	1.86
	2	92	2.50	2.18
	3	300	2.45	2.04
	4	79	2.37	1.96
	9	490	2.30	1.80
(biphenyl)	2	30	2.40	2.07
	4	18	2.45	2.07

*From Dewar *et al.* [81].

Several other molecular orbital indices of reactivity in electrophilic aromatic substitutions have been suggested. These have recently been reviewed [80].

PROBLEMS

1. In the diazo coupling reaction of I shown below the position of attack is dependent upon the acidity of the medium, as indicated by the arrows. Explain this phenomenon.

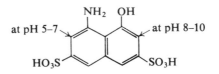

2. The reaction rate for nitration of reactive aromatics in nitromethane solution using excess nitric acid is found to be independent of the concentration of the aromatic species and also of the identity of the aromatic. Added salts normally increase the reaction rate, with the exception of nitrates which cause strong rate retardation. Addition of small amounts of water has little effect upon the reaction rate.
   a) Suggest a mechanism consistent with *all* of the above facts.
   b) Explain the catalytic effect of small amounts of sulfuric acid within your mechanistic scheme.

3. The reaction of mercuric trifluoroacetate with benzene and toluene in trifluoroacetic acid yielded rate constants at 25°C of 2.85×10^{-2} and 2.82×10^{-1} liter/mole-sec., respectively, and an isomer distribution of 12.2% *o*-, 8.6% *m*-, and 79.2% *p*-tolyl-mercuric trifluoroacetate. What are the partial rate factors for this reaction?

4. The bromination reaction gives a *p*-value (using σ^+) of -12.1 when carried out in aqueous acetic acid at 25°C using Br_2 but only -5.8 when bromination results from the reaction with HOBr, $HClO_4$, and 50% dioxane at 25°C. The partial rate factors for the first conditions are 600 for *ortho*, 5.5 for *meta*, and 2420 for *para* for the reaction with toluene. The analogous values are 76, 2.5, and 59 for the second conditions. Account for these differences.

5. Nitration has been studied under a variety of conditions. Below are data for two examples. Give a satisfactory explanation for the observed similarity in isomer distribution and the difference in k_t/k_b ($k_{toluene}/k_{benzene}$).

Nitrating agent	Conditions	k_t/k_b	\multicolumn{3}{c}{Isomer distribution}
			o	*m*	*p*
HNO_3	HOAc, 25°C	28.8	56.9%	2.8%	40.3%
NO_2AsF_6	CH_3NO_2, 25°C	0.97	66.6%	2.1%	31.3%

6. Acetic anhydride reacts with concentrated nitric acid to give the rather unstable acetyl nitrate, $CH_3CO_2NO_2$, a useful nitrating agent. With mixtures of benzene and toluene, acetyl nitrate produces a mixture of nitrobenzene and *o,p*-nitrotoluenes. When nitrated together, toluene is 25 times more reactive than benzene, although both proceed at the same rate when reacted separately. Give a mechanism consistent with these rate results.

7. The relative rate of *tert*-butylbenzene (compared to benzene) is 15.7 in the nitration reaction. The isomer distribution of the nitro product is 79.5% *p*-, 8.7% *m*-, and 11.8% *o*-. Calculate the partial rate factors for the nitration of *tert*-butylbenzene.

8. The following reactions are all carried out at 25°C in aqueous hypochlorous acid (HOCl) containing perchloric acid (H^+) and silver perchlorate (Ag^+) sufficiently concentrated that the concentrations of chlorine (Cl_2) and chloride ion (Cl^-) are extremely low and the rates are unaffected by further increases of the Ag^+ ion concentration. Considering *all* of the facts below concerning the four reactions, give a possible rate-determining step for each.
   a) The chlorination of benzoic acid to give *m*-chlorobenzoic acid is third-order ($k_3[C_6H_5CO_2H][HOCl][H^+]$). The concentrations of benzoic acid used were low.
   b) The chlorination of phenol at very low phenol concentration is second-order ($k_2[HOCl][H^+]$).

c) At high phenol concentration (above 0.01 M) the chlorination is third-order ($k_3'[C_6H_5OH][HOCl][H^+]$). Anisole behaves similarly to phenol but k_3' is not so large. In D_2O, k_3' is twice as large as in H_2O.

d) Chlorination of *tert*-butanol to give *tert*-butyl hypochlorite is second-order ($k_2'[HOCl][H^+]$). The value of k_2' is about 10^4 times larger than k_2 in (b) above.

9. Using Dewar numbers, estimate the position where free radical substitution is most apt to occur in phenanthrene.

10. The Dewar method for obtaining localization energies can also be used to obtain electron densities for odd-alternant ions. Explain, and apply the method to the benzyl cation.

11. The chlorine in 9-chlorophenanthrene may be displaced by hydroxide ion. Consider the corresponding rates of displacement of the compounds having each of the other carbon atoms successively replaced by CH_3N^+. Which of these nine substitutions would you expect to increase the rate most?

REFERENCES

1. H. C. Brown and J. D. Brady, *J. Am. Chem. Soc.*, **74**, 3570 (1952).

2. W. von E. Doering, M. Saunders, H. G. Boyton, H. W. Earhart, E. F. Wadley, W. R. Edwards, and G. Laber, *Tetrahedron*, **4**, 178 (1958).

3. H. C. Brown and H. W. Pearsall, *J. Am. Chem. Soc.*, **74**, 191 (1952).

4. H. C. Brown and W. J. Wallace, *J. Am. Chem. Soc.*, **75**, 6265 and 6268 (1953).

5. A. Klit and A. Langseth, *Z. Physik. Chem.*, **176**, 65 (1936).

6. D. A. McCaulay and A. P. Lien, *J. Am. Chem. Soc.*, **73**, 2013 (1951); *Tetrahedron*, **5**, 186 (1959).

7. M. Kilpatrick and F. E. Luborsky, *J. Am. Chem. Soc.*, **75**, 577 (1953).

8. G. A. Olah, S. J. Kuhn, and A. Pavlath, *J. Am. Chem. Soc.*, **80**, 6535 and 6541 (1958); *Nature*, **178**, 693 (1956).

9. E. L. Mackor, A. Hofstra, and J. H. van der Waals, *Trans. Faraday Soc.*, **54**, 66 and 187 (1958).

10. G. A. Olah, *J. Am. Chem. Soc.*, **87**, 1103 (1965).

11. V. Gold and F. L. Tye, *J. Chem. Soc.*, 2172 (1952).

12. C. Reid, *J. Am. Chem. Soc.*, **76**, 3264 (1954).

13. G. Dallinga, E. L. Mackor, A. Hofstra, and A. A. Verrijn Stuart, *J. Mol. Phys.*, **1**, 123 (1958).

14. C. MacLean and E. L. Mackor, *J. Mol. Phys.*, **4**, 241 (1961); *Disc. Faraday Soc.*, **34**, 165 (1962).

15. T. Birchall and R. J. Gillespie, *Can. J. Chem.*, **42**, 502 (1964).

16. G. S. Hammond, *J. Am. Chem. Soc.*, **77**, 334 (1955).

17. H. C. Brown and L. M. Stock, *J. Am. Chem. Soc.* **79**, 1421 and 5175 (1957).

18. M. Christen and H. Zollinger, *Helv. Chim. Acta*, **45**, 2057 and 2066 (1962).

19. M. Christen, W. Koch, W. Simon, and H. Zollinger, *Helv. Chim. Acta*, **45**, 2077 (1962).

20. L. G. Cannell, *J. Am. Chem. Soc.*, **79**, 2927 and 2932 (1957).

21. P. B. D. de la Mare, O. M. H. el Dusouqui, J. G. Tillett, and M. Zeltner, *J. Chem. Soc.*, 5306 (1964).

22. A. A. VOLODKIN and V. V. ERSHOV, *Izv. Akad. Nauk SSSR, Otd. Khim. Nauk*, 2022 (1962); *Chem. Abstr.*, **58**, 11251 (1963).

23. E. S. LEWIS and M. C. R. SYMONS, *Quart. Rev.*, **12**, 230 (1958).

24. L. MELANDER, *Nature*, **163**, 599 (1949); *Acta Chem. Scand.*, **3**, 95 (1949); *Arkiv Kemi*, **2**, 211 (1950).

25. U. BERGLUND-LARSSON and L. MELANDER, *Arkiv Kemi*, **6**, 219 (1953).

26. H. ZOLLINGER, *Experientia*, **12**, 165 (1956).

27. E. BERLINER, in *Progress in Physical Organic Chemistry*, Vol. II (Eds. S. G. Cohen, A. Streitwieser, and R. W. Taft), Interscience Publishers, New York (1964).

28. L. J. ANDREWS, *Chem. Revs.*, **54**, 713 (1954).

29. L. J. ANDREWS and R. M. KEEFER, in *Advances in Inorganic Chemistry and Radiochemistry*, Vol. III (Eds. H. J. Emeleus and A. G. Sharpe), Academic Press, New York (1961), pp. 91–131.

30. L. N. FERGUSON, *The Modern Structural Theory of Organic Chemistry*, Prentice-Hall, Englewood Cliffs, N. J. (1963), pp. 103–125.

31. O. HASSEL, *J. Mol. Phys.*, **1**, 241 (1958); O. HASSEL and C. ROMMING, *Quart. Revs.*, **16**, 1 (1962).

32. H. G. SMITH and R. E. RUNDLE, *J. Am. Chem. Soc.*, **80**, 5075 (1958).

33. R. A. ZINGARO and W. E. TOLBERG, *J. Am. Chem. Soc.*, **81**, 1353 (1959).

34. H. TSUBOMURA, *J. Am. Chem. Soc.*, **82**, 40 (1960).

35. G. A. OLAH, S. J. KUHN, and S. H. FLOOD, *J. Am. Chem. Soc.*, **84**, 1688 (1962).

36. G. A. OLAH, S. J. KUHN, and S. H. FLOOD, *J. Am. Chem. Soc.*, **83**, 4571 (1961).

37. G. A. OLAH and N. A. OVERCHUK, *Can. J. Chem.*, **43**, 3279 (1965).

38. G. A. OLAH, S. J. KUHN, S. H. FLOOD, and B. A. HARDIE, *J. Am. Chem. Soc.*, **86**, 1039 (1964).

39. G. A. OLAH, S. J. KUHN, S. H. FLOOD, and B. A. HARDIE, *J. Am. Chem. Soc.*, **86**, 1044 (1964).

40. G. A. OLAH, S. H. FLOOD, S. J. KUHN, M. E. MOFFATT, and N. A. OVERCHUK, *J. Am. Chem. Soc.*, **86**, 1046 (1964).

41. G. A. OLAH and N. A. OVERCHUK, *J. Am. Chem. Soc.*, **87**, 5786 (1965).

42. G. A. OLAH, S. J. KUHN, and B. A. HARDIE, *J. Am. Chem. Soc.*, **86**, 1055 (1964).

43. G. A. OLAH, S. H. FLOOD, and M. E. MOFFATT, *J. Am. Chem. Soc.*, **86**, 1060 (1964).

44. L. J. ANDREWS and R. M. KEEFER, *J. Am. Chem. Soc.*, **74**, 4500 (1952).

45. R. M. KEEFER and L. J. ANDREWS, *J. Am. Chem. Soc.*, **72**, 4677 (1950).

46. L. M. STOCK and A. HIMOE, *J. Am. Chem. Soc.*, **83**, 1937 and 4605 (1961).

47. P. B. D. DE LA MARE, and J. T. HARVEY, *J. Chem. Soc.*, **36** (1956).

48. P. B. D. DE LA MARE, J. T. HARVEY, M. HASSON, and S. VARMA, *J. Chem. Soc.*, 2756 (1958).

49. C. K. INGOLD, A. LAPWORTH, E. ROTHSTEIN, and D. WARD, *J. Chem. Soc.*, 1959 (1931).

50. H. COHN, E. D. HUGHES, M. H. JONES, and M. G. PEELING, *Nature*, **169**, 291 (1952).

51. G. A. OLAH, S. J. KUHN, S. H. FLOOD, and J. C. EVANS, *J. Am. Chem. Soc.*, **84**, 3687 (1962).

52. W. S. TOLGYESI, *Can. J. Chem.*, **43**, 343 (1965).

53. R. J. GILLESPIE, J. GRAHAM, E. D. HUGHES, C. K. INGOLD, and E. R. A. PEELING, *J. Chem. Soc.*, 2504 (1950).

54. A. HANTZSCH, *Z. Physik. Chem.*, **61**, 257 (1908).
55. R. M. MARCUS and J. M. FRESCO, *J. Chem. Phys.*, **27**, 564 (1957).
56. C. K. INGOLD, D. J. MILLEN, and H. G. POOLE, *J. Chem. Soc.*, 2576 (1950).
57. D. R. GODDARD, E. D. HUGHES, and C. K. INGOLD, *J. Chem. Soc.*, 2559 (1950).
58. E. G. COX, G. A. JEFFREY, and M. R. TRUTER, *Nature*, **162**, 259 (1948).
59. P. E. GRISON, K. ERICKS, and J. L. DE VRIES, *Acta Cryst.*, **3**, 290 (1950).
60. R. J. GILLESPIE, E. D. HUGHES, and C. K. INGOLD, *J. Chem. Soc.*, 2552 (1950).
61. C. K. INGOLD and D. J. MILLEN, *J. Chem. Soc.*, 2600 (1950).
62. H. MARTINSEN, *Z. Physik. Chem.*, **50**, 385 (1904); **59**, 605 (1907).
63. See P. B. D. DE LA MARE and J. H. RIDD, *Aromatic Substitution, Nitration and Halogenation*, Butterworth & Co., London (1959) for other references.
64. R. J. GILLESPIE and D. G. NORTON, *J. Chem. Soc.*, 971 (1953).
65. See Eq. 10–27.
66. E. D. HUGHES, C. K. INGOLD, and R. I. REED, *J. Chem. Soc.*, 2400 (1950).
67. C. A. BUNTON and E. A. HALEVI, *J. Chem. Soc.*, 4917 (1952).
68. G. A. BENFOLD and C. K. INGOLD, *J. Chem. Soc.*, 929 (1938).
69. H. COHN, E. D. HUGHES, M. H. JONES, and M. G. PEELING, *Nature*, **169**, 291 (1952).
70. M. L. BIRD and C. K. INGOLD, *J. Chem. Soc.*, 918 (1938).
71. H. C. BROWN and Y. OKAMOTO, *J. Am. Chem. Soc.*, **80**, 4979 (1958).
72. F. R. GOSS, W. HANHART, and C. K. INGOLD, *J. Chem. Soc.*, 1280 (1928).
73. J. HINE, *Physical Organic Chemistry*, 2nd Ed., McGraw-Hill Book Co., New York (1962), pp. 374–375.
74. M. BRICKMAN, R. FOSTER, and J. H. RIDD, *Proc. J. Chem. Soc.*, 228 (1962); J. H. RIDD and J. H. P. UTLEY, *Proc. J. Chem. Soc.*, 24 (1964); M. BRICKMAN and J. H. RIDD, *J. Chem. Soc.*, 6845 (1965); M. BRICKMAN, J. H. P. UTLEY, and J. H. RIDD, *J. Chem. Soc.*, 6851 (1965).
75. C. W. McGARY, Y. OKAMOTO, and H. C. BROWN, *J. Am. Chem. Soc.*, **77**, 3037 (1955); L. M. STOCK and H. C. BROWN, *J. Am. Chem. Soc.*, **81**, 3323 (1959).
76. G. W. WHELAND and L. PAULING, *J. Am. Chem. Soc.*, **57**, 2086 (1935).
77. K. FUKUI, T. YONEZAWA, and H. SHINGU, *J. Chem. Phys.*, **20**, 722 (1952); K. FUKUI, T. YONEZAWA, C. NAGATA, and H. SHINGU, *J. Chem. Phys.*, **22**, 1433 (1954).
78. G. W. WHELAND, *J. Am. Chem. Soc.*, **64**, 900 (1942).
79. M. J. S. DEWAR, *Rec. Chem. Progr.*, **19**, 1 (1958).
80. A. STREITWIESER, *Molecular Orbital Theory for Organic Chemists*, John Wiley & Sons, New York (1961), Chap. 11.
81. M. J. S. DEWAR, T. MOLE, and E. W. T. WARFORD, *J. Chem. Soc.*, 3581 (1956) and references therein.

CHAPTER 13

NUCLEOPHILIC SUBSTITUTION AND ELIMINATION REACTIONS AT SATURATED CARBON

The multitude of known reactions of organic compounds may be classified into a relatively small number of reaction types. Among these is the *substitution* of one atom or group of atoms at a saturated carbon by another electron-rich atom or group. This nucleophilic reaction is commonly accompanied by *elimination reactions* and by *rearrangements*. Because many of these reactions evolve from a common intermediate, they are valuable tools in learning about the intermediate. In this chapter we shall examine substitution, elimination, and rearrangement reactions with special emphasis on the similarities between them.

NUCLEOPHILIC SUBSTITUTION

The heterolytic reaction of a nucleophile X displacing another group Y at a saturated carbon atom may be generalized as

$$X + R\!-\!Y \rightarrow X\!-\!R + Y.$$

The reagent X and the displaced group Y are Lewis bases. When X is a solvent molecule, the reaction is termed a *solvolytic reaction*; when X is a solute, the term *nonsolvolytic reaction* is used. Examples of known entering and leaving groups are:

$$X = HO^-, RO^-, R_3C^-, CN^-, RS^-, RCO_2^-, S_2O_3^=, \text{halide ions}, H_2O, ROH, R_3N;$$
$$Y = N_2, ROH, \text{halide ion}, R_3N, RCO_2^-.$$

This list, though not exhaustive, gives an idea of the generality of the reaction type.

Mechanism

The *Finkelstein reaction* of iodide ion and methyl bromide in acetone is typical of many displacement reactions:

$$CH_3Br + I^- \xrightarrow{\quad\text{O}\quad} CH_3I + Br^-.$$

This reaction is found to be first-order in both methyl bromide and iodide ion [1]. Reactions exhibiting second-order kinetics are classified as S_N2 [2]. This kinetic behavior tells us that both reacting species are present in the transition state of the rate-determining step. Accordingly, the S_N2 displacement reaction has been reasonably interpreted to proceed by a mechanism such as

$$X + RY \rightarrow X---R---Y \rightarrow X\!-\!R + Y.$$

We might now ask whether the structure X – – – R – – – Y represents a transition state or an intermediate. Early calculations for the reaction of hydrogen atoms with hydrogen molecules suggested that the analogous structure H – – – H – – – H was an intermediate [3] but more recent calculations indicate it is only a transition state [4] and, in fact, no experimental evidence for an intermediate has ever been presented. Although this is not proof of the absence of an intermediate, it does strongly suggest that if an intermediate *is* involved it is of very low stability. According to Hammond's postulate, the structure of the transition states on either side of the intermediate must closely resemble the structure X – – – R – – – Y [5]. We will accept this structure as a reasonable approximation to the transition state structure and, in future discussion, treat the S_N2 mechanism as if only a transition state is involved.

If the S_N2 displacement reaction involves both reactants in the transition state and if the displaced group is leaving, the entering group must attack from the opposite side of the carbon atom. This geometry is reasonable, from two considerations: it provides the least hindered route for the nucleophile and, if the carbon is rehybridized to sp^2 orbitals, the p orbital is available to combine with orbitals of both the entering and the leaving groups in the usual LCAO manner. This combination will lead to three orbitals, two of which, the bonding and the nonbonding, will contain the four electrons. In this picture, carbon is pentavalent and has the configuration of a trigonal bipyramid. A diagram of the atomic orbitals that are combined in the LCAO approach is given in Fig. 13–1.

Fig. 13–1. Atomic orbital representation of the transition state of an S_N2 reaction. (From Streitwieser [5], Fig. 3.)

If this model of the transition state (Fig. 13–1) is correct, there is a stereochemical consequence—the configuration of the reacting carbon atom undergoes a *Walden inversion* upon going to products.

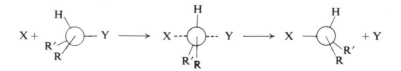

There was early evidence for this inversion. Walden first discovered a number of cases where inversion must have occurred [6a], and then, using an asymmetrically substituted carbon atom, Phillips demonstrated that a series of reactions produced inversion with very little racemization [6b]. He converted dextrorotatory benzyl-methyl carbinol into the levorotatory enantiomer by a series of reactions believed to involve only one displacement reaction at the asymmetric carbon atom.

$$C_6H_5CH(OH)CH_3 \xrightarrow{\text{TsOCl}} C_6H_5CH(OTs)CH_3$$
$$\alpha, +33°$$

$$\downarrow \text{CH}_3\text{CO}_2^-$$

$$C_6H_5CH(OH)CH_3 \xleftarrow{\text{OH}^-} C_6H_5CH(OAc)CH_3$$
$$\alpha, -32$$

The first step, formation of the p-toluenesulfonate (hereafter called tosylate), prob-ably does not involve reaction at the carbon atom at all. The third step, hydrolysis of acetate, normally involves acyl carbon-oxygen cleavage and again the asymmetric carbon atom is probably left unchanged. This leaves only the second step for the inversion. More direct proof that each bimolecular substitution involved inversion was afforded by the demonstration that the rate of inversion of 2-octyl iodide was equal to the rate of exchange of this compound with radioactive iodide ion [7].

As a result of these experiments and several parallel studies with other compounds, we now believe that inversion of configuration is the rule for bimolecular nucleophilic substitution at a saturated carbon atom [8].

Not all nucleophilic substitution reactions show second-order kinetics. There is a group of reactants that under certain conditions react with a rate dependent only upon the RX concentration. An example is the aqueous hydrolysis of tert-butyl iodides [9]:

$$(CH_3)_3CI \xrightarrow[\text{OH}^-]{\text{H}_2\text{O}} (CH_3)_3COH + I^-.$$

Since the nucleophile does not appear in the rate-determining step for this type of reaction, a unimolecular reaction of the substrate must be followed by rapid nucleo-philic reaction. The mechanism proposed, termed an S_N1 mechanism, involves formation of an intermediate carbonium ion that reacts rapidly with available nucleophile:

$$RY \rightarrow R^+ + Y^- \xrightarrow[X]{fast} R-X.$$

If an intermediate carbonium ion is formed in the S_N1 process, we might ask what the effect of this species will be upon the direction of approach of the nucleophile. Nucleophilic attack at a free planar carbonium ion would lead to complete racemization. This behavior (or close to it) is observed for some unimolecular substitutions; for instance, the hydrolysis of 1-phenylethyl chloride in 80% aqueous acetone affords nearly racemic alcohol [10].

It would seem that we have two clear-cut criteria for distinguishing between the S_N1 and S_N2 mechanisms but, unfortunately, this is not the case. Certainly, the evidence for first- or second-order kinetics would appear to provide the basis for a mechanistic assignment. If kinetic order is our criterion, there can be no intermediate mechanism and a nucleophile is either present (S_N2) or absent (S_N1) in the rate-determining transition state [11]. If both transition states are present in solution at the same time, we must say that simultaneous S_N1 and S_N2 processes properly describe the mechanism. We should then expect to observe a complex rate constant k_{obs}, consisting of first-order (k_1) and second-order (k_2) rate constants. Equation (13–1) gives the form of k_{obs}, where [N] is the concentration of the nucleophile:

$$k_{obs} = k_1 + k_2[N]. \tag{13–1}$$

In many substitution reactions the solvent serves as a nucleophile and an S_N2 mechanism affords pseudo-first-order kinetics, so that we cannot use the kinetic criterion as a guide to the operative mechanism. Although it would seem that the stereochemical criterion would still resolve the mechanistic choice, this has led to considerable controversy. The problem has been that a number of reactants believed to react *via* a carbonium ion intermediate have also been shown to involve considerable inversion of configuration. Generally, tertiary alkyl carbonium ions are relatively long-lived and these species exhibit considerable racemization, as in the case of the alcoholysis (with the solvent alcohol serving as the nucleophile) or first-order hydrolysis of 3,7-dimethyl-3-octyl chloride and 3,7-dimethyl-3-octyl acetate, where a 70 to 80% loss of optical activity has been reported [12]. Other stabilized carbonium ions show similar behavior, i.e. considerable racemization. When less stable carbonium ions are believed to be involved in a substitution reaction, the results are less clear-cut. For example, the acetolysis of 2-octyl tosylate proceeds with as much as 98% inversion [13], even though the reaction appears to involve a carbonium ion [13, 14]. The stereochemical criterion of mechanism is not sufficient. A reaction proceeding by an S_N2 mechanism must show inversion of configuration. The S_N1 mechanism may lead to total racemization but this is a limit. To summarize, predominant inversion may occur even though a carbonium ion is formed.

Therefore, the two mechanisms for nucleophilic substitution presented above are generally considered to be limiting mechanisms only. A reaction is clearly demonstrated to proceed by an S_N2 mechanism, if it is bimolecular, and it will involve stereochemical inversion; a reaction proceeding with stereochemical racemization clearly involves an S_N1 mechanism and will be unimolecular. Reactions that appear to proceed with formation of a carbonium ion but also to exhibit predominant inversion of configuration are termed *borderline reactions*. Normally, deviations from S_N1 behavior are in the direction of S_N2 behavior [15]. There are two schools of thought over the explanation of this borderline region of the substitution mechanism.

One approach states that, where the reaction is clearly S_N1 but inversion predominates, the carbonium ion is shielded by the leaving group [2]. Thus, if the entering nucleophile is blocked from one side of the carbonium ion by the departing group, substitution will occur on the opposite side and the product has an inverted configuration. The shielding group is free to move after the heterolysis of the bond. However, if the carbonium ion is stable enough to maintain identity until the departing group has left its vicinity, either side is open to nucleophilic attack and racemization occurs. It is observed that the lifetime of the carbonium ion depends on its stability and on the ability of the solvent to support ionization. Although the process of shielding during S_N1 reactions can be easily visualized, we are forced into accepting such terms as "lifetime of the carbonium ion" that are not easily defined.

A second approach to the problem of S_N1 inversion involves a pentacovalent carbonium ion intermediate [5, 16]. This can be visualized as a carbon atom with three sp^2 hybrid orbital bonds and a p orbital. Both lobes of the p orbital overlap with orbitals of other molecules. If the carbonium ion were free, it would have greater energy than it has when the vacant p orbital is combined linearly with the two orbitals of the two Lewis bases, which may be solvent molecules or the departing group or both. These are weakly bonded to the central carbon atom and are easily replaced. The extreme case is represented in Fig. 13–1, where one of the groups is the entering nucleophile and the other the departing species; as discussed above, we can consider this to be the transition state for an S_N2 reaction. If we vary the structure about the central carbon atom so that the energy of the hypothetical free carbonium ion is decreased by electron supply from the substituents, the structure given in Fig. 13–1 is stabilized and transformed to that of an intermediate. As the hypothetical carbonium ion becomes increasingly stable, the bonds of the intermediate become weaker. Finally, when a very stable carbonium ion is formed, the Lewis bases are weakly held and easily replaced. This rapid exchange of groups leads to replacement of the departing group by a solvent molecule and racemization results. This approach is particularly applicable to solvolytic substitution reactions, as seen in the following scheme:

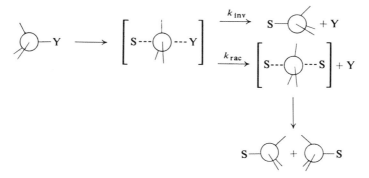

This formulation is especially useful because it replaces the poorly defined terms, shielding and carbonium ion lifetime, with precisely defined specific rates of inversion and racemization. The ratio k_{inv}/k_{rac} is the relative rate of the two modes of consumption of the intermediate.

The similarity between the intermediate proposed for the S_N1 reaction and the transition state for the S_N2 reaction is obvious. The difference between them is one of energy. Referring to Fig. 11–4 we see that when the structure is unstable it represents a transition state (C in Fig. 11–4) and when it is stable it represents an intermediate (A). In explaining the intermediate cases, two views are held, as we have seen above. The Doering-Zeiss intermediate (Fig. 13–1) emphasized covalent bonding in the stabilization of the center of positive charge by solvating groups and it uses terms that apply to precisely defined concepts. The other view emphasized electrostatic solvation but is described in poorly defined terms.

Which view is correct? There is considerable controversy on this question and in fact both viewpoints may be applicable to the actual reaction mechanism [15]. Although the reader should attempt to keep this problem in mind throughout the rest of this chapter, there is one important study that may apply directly to the problem and may perhaps give an answer [17]. Solvolytic substitution reactions at bridgehead carbon atoms are known to proceed slowly. The relative rates of several of these compounds are given in Fig. 13–2. Although many explanations have been offered for this inertness (see references 17 and 18 and references therein), the surprising feature is that the 1-halo adamantanes are only 10^3 times less reactive than tert-butyl halides. Certainly, the back of the adamantyl cation is protected so that no solvent molecule can overlap with the rear lobe of the developing p orbital. It would appear that the electrostatic solvation stabilization theory is supported by the relatively high reactivity of the 1-halo adamantanes. However, the carbonium ion may be stabilized by rear lobe overlap with tertiary C—H bonding orbitals.

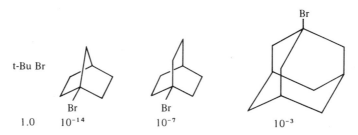

Fig. 13–2. Relative rates of solvolysis of bridgehead bromides, at 25°C. (From Schleyer and Nicholas [17].)

Medium Effects

The effect of medium variations on reaction rates was discussed in Chapter 10. The qualitative theory of Hughes and Ingold is an attempt to relate the relative solvation energies of the reactants and the transition state to the changes in charge distribution as the reactants proceed along the reaction coordinate to the transition state. Table 10–3 gave an example of uncharged reactants proceeding to a charged transition state. That reaction shows bimolecular kinetics and clearly fits into an S_N2 mechanistic description:

$$Et_3NI + CH_3CH_2I \rightarrow \left[\overset{H}{\underset{\underset{CH_3}{H}}{Et_3\overset{\delta+}{N}\text{---}\overset{|}{C}\text{---}\overset{\delta-}{I}}} \right]^{\ddagger} \rightarrow Et_4N^+ + I^-,$$

where noncharged reactants form an activated complex that is polar. If the polar transition state is solvated, it can be stabilized relative to the unsolvated species. Solvents of high dielectric constant can do this and, as seen in Table 10–3, the reaction rate is proportional to solvent dielectric constant. Let us now interpret some other reactions with the qualitative solvent theory as our guide.

If one of the reactants is charged we might expect that the transition state would disperse the charge and that solvation would then stabilize the reactant relative to the less-polar activated complex. Such a reaction is the exchange of iodine between iodide ion and 1-iodobutane, which has been studied by the radioactive iodine technique:

$$n\text{-}BuI + I^{*-} \rightarrow \left[\overset{H}{\underset{\underset{C_3H_7}{H}}{\overset{*}{I}\underset{\delta-}{\text{---}}\overset{|}{C}\underset{\delta-}{\text{---}}I}} \right]^{\ddagger} \rightarrow n\text{-}BuI^* + I^-.$$

The results for this reaction, given in Table 13–1 [19], suggest that our expectation is correct, but within limits. For a closely related series of solvents the rate decreases as the dielectric constant increases. When we move from one solvent series to another, e.g. ROH to CH_3CN, large changes occur, which are perhaps due to specific effects of the solvent. The hydroxylic solvents probably stabilize the charged nucleophile

Table 13–1. Solvent Effect upon the Rate of Iodine Exchange of n-Butyl Iodide at 25°C

Solvent	Dielectric constant	k, liters/mole-hr	Relative rate
Methanol	32.7	0.23	0.20
Ethanol	24.2	1.17	1.00
n-Butanol	17.3	6.0	5.1
n-Hexanol	12.8	6.7	5.7
n-Dodecanol	6.15	8.0	6.8
Acetic acid	6.27	1.7	1.5
Acetonitrile	36.7	10.9	9.3

Table 13–2. Solvent Effect upon the Rate of Reaction of Trimethylsulfonium Ion with Hydroxide Ion at 100°C

Vol. of H_2O in EtOH, %	$k \times 10^4$, liters/mole-sec	Relative rate
0	7240	19600
20	178	482
40	15.1	40.1
100	0.369	1.0

not only by the bulk effect of dielectric constant but also by hydrogen bonding. This latter solvent-nucleophile interaction is not possible with acetonitrile and we observe a substantial change in reactivity in going from one solvent to the other. For bimolecular nucleophilic substitutions this hydrogen bonding is very important and, in general, anionic nucleophiles are more reactive in dipolar aprotic solvents than in the more common hydroxylic solvents. If nucleophile and substrate are oppositely charged the effect of changing the solvent should be even greater. The second-order rate constants for the reaction of trimethylsulfonium ion with hydroxide ion [20] are given in Table 13–2 and, as predicted, the effects observed are large:

$$Me_3S^+ + OH^- \rightarrow \left[\overset{\delta-}{HO} \underset{\underset{H}{|}}{---} \overset{\overset{H \ H}{\backslash /}}{C} \overset{\delta+}{---} SMe_2 \right]^{\ddagger} \rightarrow MeOH + SMe_2.$$

It appears that we can qualitatively predict the effect of solvent change upon the rate of bimolecular substitution reactions. The same is true for unimolecular (S_N1) substitutions. The solvolytic reactions of *p*-methoxyneophyl tosylate [21] present a typical example:

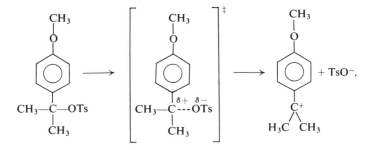

In this ionization, charge is being created in the transition state. This charge would be stabilized by increasing the dielectric constant of the solvent, with a resultant rate increase. Table 13–3 shows the expected trend within a series of similar solvents. Again we note the effect which a change from protic to aprotic solvent superimposes

Table 13-3. Solvent Effect upon the Rate of Solvolytic Reaction of *p*-Methoxy-neophyl Tosylate at 75°C*

Solvent	Dielectric constant	$-\log k$	Relative rate
H_2O	78.54	1.180	39
80% EtOH	67.6	2.505	1.85 (25°C)
HCO_2H	58	0.929	153 (25°C)
$MeNO_2$	36.7	3.921	7.3×10^{-2}
MeCN	36.7	4.221	3.6×10^{-2}
EtOH	24.30	3.204	0.37
Me_2CO	20.7	5.067	5.1×10^{-3}
Et_2O	4.23	7.3	*ca.* 3×10^{-5}
$MeCO_2H$	6.2	2.772	1.00 (25°C)

* Data from Smith *et al.* [21], Table XI (in part).

on the general correlation with dielectric constant. Here, however, the effect is in the opposite direction to that noted in Table 13-1: the leaving group, and hence the transition state, is stabilized by the specific hydrogen bond interaction. We must always consider the possibility of this specific solvation when examining solvent effects upon reaction rates. Certainly, hydrogen bonding is not the only such specific interaction that can occur between solvent and a reacting moiety. The analysis of such effects of medium change has recently been reviewed [22].

The Hughes-Ingold theory of solvent effects is based upon the relative solvent stabilization of reactants and transition states and ΔG^* appears to behave in accord with the ideas presented. As a detailed description, however, it is not adequate. A recent, important paper [23] examined the complexity of ΔH^* and ΔS^*. It has been found that much of the medium effect is due to variations in solvation of the reactants in S_N1 reactions, whereas the Hughes-Ingold theory assigns the chief role to variations in transition states. It is still a useful theory, particularly for qualitatively predicting solvent effects, but should be used with caution when describing reaction mechanisms.

The reaction of benzhydryl chloride with ethanol is accelerated by the addition of small amounts of water [24] and this rate increase is marked. In ethanol the product is benzhydryl ethyl ether, but when water is added benzhydrol is also formed. We might expect that the rate increase is due to the formation of benzhydrol but the amount formed is insufficient to account for the large rate increase. The main effect of water, in fact, is to increase the rate of ether formation. When the rate of reaction and the products are determined in different steps, as in this case, the presence of an intermediate is indicated. This is consistent with an S_N1 mechanism. Thus, we might suggest a rate-product criterion for determining between the S_N1 and S_N2 mechanisms. In the bimolecular substitution reaction, the effect of solvent on rates must be linked to its effect on product composition. As we have seen, this does not happen in the S_N1 route.

We have noted the effect of solvent changes upon rates and product distribution. As discussed in Chapter 10, we can also alter a reaction medium by the addition of salts, which produce a predictable change in reaction rate. As a salt is added, the polarity of the reaction medium changes and we can apply the Hughes-Ingold theory to the prediction of rate effects. The reaction of p,p-dimethylbenzhydryl chloride in 85% aqueous acetone [25] clearly shows the effects of added salts on an S_N1 reaction. The data in Table 13–4 show a normal salt effect for added LiBr, NaN$_3$, and NMe$_4$NO$_3$ but the LiCl result appears to be anomalous.

Table 13–4. Effect of Added 0.05 M Salts upon Solvolysis Rates of $(p\text{-}CH_3C_6H_4)_2CHCl$ in 85% Aqueous Acetone, at 0°C*

Salt	$k \times 10^5$, sec^{-1}	Relative rate
None	47.0	1.00
LiBr	68.5	1.46
NaN$_3$	70.5	1.50
NMe$_4$NO$_3$	72.0	1.53
LiCl	23.0	0.49

* Data from Bateman *et al.* [25].

We shall now examine each result reported in Table 13–4 in somewhat more detail. Lithium bromide slightly increases the reaction rate by the salt effect and the product is 100% alcohol, as when no salt is added. We might ask why the bromide ion does not successfully compete with water as a nucleophile. The relative rate of solvolysis of benzhydryl bromide and chloride in 90% aqueous acetone containing 0.1 M NaN$_3$ is 33.5 at 50°C [2]; thus, any bromide formed reacts rapidly to produce alcohol. When sodium azide is added, a rate increase similar to that caused by lithium bromide addition is observed and the product composition is changed to 40% alcohol and 60% azide [25]. The nucleophilic azide ion successfully competes with water, with no marked change in rate. This suggests the slow formation of an intermediate that is rapidly consumed by the nucleophile. We saw above that a nucleophilic solvent mixture could demonstrate the formation of an intermediate by showing that the rate- and product-determining steps were different. Now we can also demonstrate this by adding a reagent that serves as a trap for the intermediate with only a minor effect on the rate. The rate increase observed is not large enough to account for the high proportion of azide in the product mixture. When tetramethyl ammonium nitrate is added, the usual small rate increase is observed but nitrate ion is too poor a nucleophile to compete for the intermediate and only alcohol is obtained.

The effects of these added salts can be explained on the basis of a unimolecular (S_N1) mechanism:

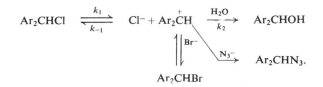

Using this scheme, let us now attempt to explain the result of lithium chloride addition. The rate of appearance of the carbonium ion intermediate is given by

$$d[A]/dt = k_1[RCl] - k_2[A] - k_{-1}[A][Cl^-],\qquad(13\text{--}2)$$

where $[A]$ is the concentration of the intermediate. If we apply the steady-state approximation, $d[A]/dt = 0$, to Eq. (13–2), we obtain an expression for $[A]$:

$$[A] = k_1[RCl]/[k_2 + k_{-1}[Cl^-]].\qquad(13\text{--}3)$$

The observed rate is given by

$$\text{obs. rate} = k_{obs}[RCl] = k_2[A]\qquad(13\text{--}4)$$

and substitution affords

$$k_{obs}[RCl] = k_2\left(\frac{k_1[RCl]}{k_2 + k_{-1}[Cl^-]}\right) = \frac{k_1[RCl]}{1 + (k_{-1}/k_2)[Cl^-]}.\qquad(13\text{--}5)$$

The rate expression (13–5) suggests that chloride ion will decrease the rate of reaction by a mass law effect on the equilibrium between the reactive intermediate and reactants. The importance of this mass law or common ion effect will depend upon the ratio $k_{-1}/k_2[Cl^-]$. If this ratio is large, rate retardation will result; on the other hand, if the intermediate is very reactive so that the ratio is small, no rate retardation will be observed. This lack of rate retardation after addition of a common ion is observed in the hydrolysis of *tert*-butyl bromide in 85% acetone [26] and in other reactions where an unstable carbonium ion is formed. When a common ion effect is observed, it is strong evidence for the formation of an intermediate but the absence of such an effect does not imply the absence of an intermediate.

Further examination of the substitution reactions of benzhydryl compounds shows that there are more subtle salt effects [27, 28]. The solvolytic alkyl-oxygen cleavage of *p*-chlorobenzhydryl *p*-nitrobenzoate in 80% aqueous acetone at 99.6°C reveals these effects very clearly. The data [28] for this reaction are given in Table 13–5. The rate constants in this table are for the following reactions:

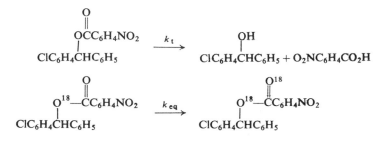

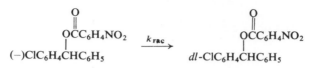

The reactions are all first-order and the last two are intramolecular. All three reactions proceed at different rates.

Table 13–5. Rate Constants for Solvolysis (k_t), Oxygen Equilibration (k_{eq}), and Racemization (k_{rac}) for the Solvolysis of p-Chlorobenz-hydryl p-Nitrobenzoate in 80% Aqueous Acetone at 99.6°C*

	$k \times 10^3$, hr^{-1}		
Salt	k_t	k_{eq}	k_{rac}
None	4.41	6.5	2.76
0.14 M NaN$_3$	ca. 15	5.9	0.0

* Data from Goering and Levy [28], Table I.

Our previous mechanism with a single intermediate does not accommodate these data. One of the most significant observations is that racemization is completely stopped by the presence of azide ion while the equilibration reaction is hardly affected. This clearly shows that racemization occurs *via* an easily capturable intermediate whereas equilibration occurs *via* an intermediate that is difficult to capture. Also, since both of these reactions are exclusively intramolecular, a free carbonium ion cannot be the intermediate involved in either one. This species would lead to exchange of the anion, an intermolecular process that does not occur. In order to explain the results in Table 13–5, at least two different intermediates must be invoked. One intermediate, difficult to capture with a reactive nucleophile but ionic enough to allow the ester oxygens to become equivalent, is called a *tight-ion pair*. The second intermediate can be captured by a reactive nucleophile but in the absence of such a reactive species can collapse back to covalently bonded reactant. Unlike the first intermediate, this one leads to racemization and therefore must be symmetrical, since it leads to loss of optical integrity. It is called a *solvent-separated ion pair*. The mechanism that we must now use to account for these results was developed by Winstein, who discovered similar difficulties in other systems [29]:

$$\text{Ar}_2\text{CHX} \rightleftharpoons \text{Ar}_2\text{CH}^+ \, \text{X}^- \rightleftharpoons \text{Ar}_2\text{CH}^+ \, \| \, \text{X}^- \rightarrow \text{product.}$$

Tight-ion pair   Solvent-separated ion pair

At this point it is tempting to equate the solvent-separated ion pair with a free carbonium ion. The above data suggest that this cannot be done. Return to reactant from the solvent-separated ion pair occurs with considerable retention of configuration (*ca.* 60%), as shown by the value of k_{rac} being lower than k_{eq}. This could not be the case if the intermediate were "free"; it would then lead to total racemization. The possibility of yet another intermediate, a fully dissociated ion, has been presented. Winstein and coworkers [27] studied the reactions of p-chlorobenzhydryl chloride, which has two significant differences from the p-nitrobenzoate system: in the 80% acetone solvolysis of the chloride at 25°C, azide ion does not totally suppress racemization and common ion depression (intermolecular exchange) is also significant. This mass law effect is consistent with the presence of dissociated ions, and so we conclude that in this system the solvent-separated ion pair is not fully capturable and dissociates fully to give free ions. We can write a mechanism for ionization that is now rather complex:

$$RX \rightleftharpoons R^+X^- \rightleftharpoons R^+ \,\|\, X^- \rightleftharpoons R^+ + X^- \rightarrow \text{products.}$$

The importance of each of these intermediates depends upon both the substrate and the reaction conditions. Before we examine this, we shall try another approach to studying this mechanism. Although the systems now to be discussed are those with which the mechanism was originally developed, we shall use the mechanism to explain the results.

We may examine the role of dissociated ions by looking at the mass effect produced by common ions. If no rate depression is observed when a common ion is added, dissociated ions are probably not involved in a particular reaction. The exception occurs when the rate of recombination is much smaller than the rate of subsequent reaction. A rate depression is not conclusive evidence of the presence of dissociated ions, however. When a common ion is added to the solvolytic mixture of threo-1-methyl-2-phenylpropyl tosylate or threo-2-p-methoxyphenyl-1-methylpropyl brosylate in acetic acid no common ion depression is observed, only a shallow linear normal salt effect. On the other hand, addition of tosylate ion to the acetolysis of 2-p-methoxyphenylethyl tosylate produces a depression of the titrimetric rate constant. The depression is small, however, and a minimum is reached at relatively low common ion concentrations, after which a normal linear salt effect is observed. Extrapolation of the linear portion of a plot of k_t against salt concentration gives k_t^d, the fully depressed rate constant corrected for normal salt effects. This represents the rate constant for production of solvolysis product arising from ion pairs only. (The value of k_t includes production of product from both ion pairs and dissociated ions.)

The really interesting result is obtained when a noncommon ion salt is added to substrates such as threo-2-p-methoxyphenyl-1-methylpropyl brosylate in the acetolysis reaction. At low concentrations (ca. 10^{-3} M) of added lithium perchlorate, a steep special-salt effect is observed; at higher concentrations only the normal salt effect is obtained. Extrapolation of the shallow part of the curve to zero salt concentration produces a rate constant value, k_{ext}^0, that includes the special-salt but not the normal salt effect. Perhaps even more startling is that k_{ext}^0 may fall quite short of the value obtained for the polarimetric rate constant k_α in the p-methoxyphenyl-1-methylpropyl system ($k_\alpha/k_t^0 = 4:1$; $k_{ext}^0/k_t^0 = 3:1$). With the β-substituted 2,4-dimethoxyphenylethyl system, k_{ext}^0 and k_α are equal. The interpretation of these results is that the very weakly nucleophilic perchlorate ion traps the solvent-separated ion pair, preventing its return, but the tight-ion pair can still return to reactant, although there is a loss of optical activity [29, 30]. The relationships just discussed are shown in Fig. 13–3. The mechanism presented for the benzhydryl system adequately interprets the results given here, if the role of the noncommon ion salt is to trap the solvent-separated ion pair to a new ion pair containing a new anion. If this anion is not reactive, solvolysis product results; if it is nucleophilic, a new product, e.g. azide, can result. This approach to the study of ion pairs has recently been reviewed [30].

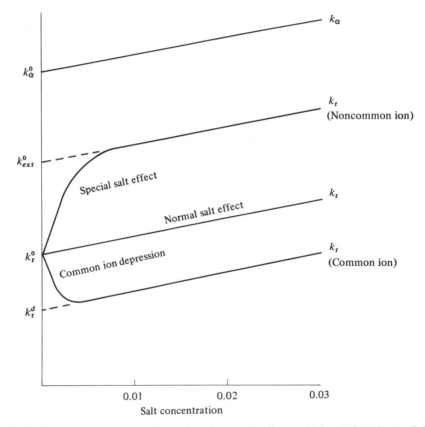

Fig. 13–3. Schematic representation of various salt effects. (After Winstein *et al.* [30], Fig. 1.)

The importance of each ion pair in solvolysis reactions is determined by the substrate and by the solvent medium. In general, the more stable the carbonium ion formed, the further it will proceed toward dissociation before it reacts with the solvent. Similarly, increased ion-dissociating power will tend to produce ions more nearly dissociated. As solvent nucleophilicity is increased, however, the ion pair undergoes more rapid exchange and the formation of dissociated ion pairs is inhibited. For example, in the acetolysis of 2,4-dimethoxyphenylethyl brosylate nearly all ion pairs are solvent-separated and dissociated ions are also present, so that the results obtained for this system can be rationalized without using the tight-ion pair species. With the p-methoxyphenylethyl system, all three ionic species must be employed in a chemical and kinetic description. In the least stable phenylethyl system, dissociated ions are not involved. Table 13–6 suggests the role of solvent in the solvolysis of $threo$-2-p-methoxyphenyl-1-methylpropyl brosylate. The solvents are arranged in order of decreasing k_α, which is a measure of ionizing ability. It can be seen that k_α/k_t generally increases as the solvent is less able to dissociate the ionic species. Effects due to nucleophilicity and other specific solvent effects are superimposed upon this trend.

Table 13–6. k_α/k_t for $threo$-2-p-Methoxyphenyl-1-methylpropyl Brosylate in Various Solvents*

Solvent	k_α/k_t
75% AcOH—HCO$_2$H	1.1
AcOH	4.1
50% AcOH—Ac$_2$O	1.8
EtOH	1.3
10% HCO$_2$H—dioxane	16
n-C$_7$H$_{15}$CO$_2$H	7
Ac$_2$O	4.1
10% AcOH—C$_6$H$_6$	16
Me$_2$CO	8
12.5% AcOH—dioxane	20

* Data from Winstein et $al.$ [30], Table 1.

The S$_N$1 mechanism involves a rather complex series of events. Current observations can be explained within the scheme

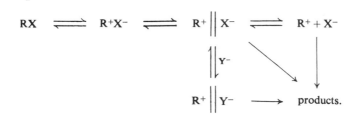

$$RX \rightleftharpoons R^+X^- \rightleftharpoons R^+ \| X^- \rightleftharpoons R^+ + X^-$$

The importance of each of these steps must be determined for each substrate and solvent system.

A quantitative treatment of solvent effects on the kinetics of substitution reactions is the linear free energy relationship of Grunwald and Winstein [31] (Eq. 9–20):

$$\log k/k_0 = mY.$$

In Chapter 9, we noted that substrates reacting by an S_N1 mechanism exhibit values of m near unity while those reacting by an S_N2 mechanism show much lower m-values. The reactants reacting *via* an S_N2 mechanism also show deviations in their correlation with Eq. (9–20) when dissimilar solvents are employed. Thus, when the rate of a solvolysis reaction in a solvent of high nucleophilicity, such as aqueous ethanol, is compared with that in a solvent of low nucleophilicity, such as formic (or acetic) acid, the rates may differ greatly even though both solvent systems have the same Y-value. This is to be expected if the model for Eq. (9–20) does not include nucleophilicity. Results are shown in Table 13–7. The Grunwald-Winstein equation is limited by this perturbation of nucleophilic attack upon the substrate. The deviation observed in this manner permits an assessment of the importance of nucleophilic participation in the reaction relative to that in the reaction of *tert*-butyl chloride and, therefore, provides useful information.

Table 13–7. Effect of Solvent Nucleophilicity upon Solvolysis Rates*

Compound	T, °C	m(aq. EtOH)	k_{EtOH}/k_{HCO_2H}
CH_3Br	50	0.26	200
CH_3OTs	75	0.23†	55
EtBr	55	0.34	80
EtOTs	50	0.26	18
n-PrBr	95	(0.34)‡	68
iso-PrBr	50	0.54	20
tert-BuCl	25	1.00	1
$C_6H_5CH_2Cl$	50	0.43	4
⬡—Br	100	0.88	0.5

* From Streitwieser [5].
† Value for $MeOSO_2C_6H_5$ at 50°C.
‡ Assumed value.

We now have two other criteria for choosing between S_N1 and S_N2 mechanisms. In general, S_N2 reactions exhibit values for $k_{aq.\ EtOH}/k_{HCO_2H}$ of 20 to 200 and for m of 0.25 to 0.35, whereas the corresponding values for S_N1 reactions are both about unity. Clearly, the rate ratio is more sensitive than the m-value in Eq. (9–20).

The Nucleophile

Linear free energy relationships for the correlation of nucleophilic reactivity were discussed in Chapter 9 and several difficulties with these equations were pointed out at that time. The acceptance of a two-parameter equation such as that of Swain and Scott (Eq. 9–12) implies that there is a unique order for nucleophilicity, a notion which is contradicted by the erratic behavior of hydroxide ion. Also, if n is a measure of nucleophilicity, it should work in any nucleophilic reaction, but the nucleophilic aromatic substitution reactions of p-nitrofluorobenzene are cases where not only is n inadequate but even the unique qualitative order of nucleophiles fails [32]. Nevertheless, the Swain-Scott equation appears to be adequate for reactions for which the methyl bromide–water reaction is a model.

Table 13–8. Comparison of Nucleophilicity and Basicity for Several Reagents

Reagent	$n*$	$H\dagger$	Reagent	$n*$	$H\dagger$
NO_3^-	1.0	0.4	$(NH_2)_2CS$	4.1	0.8
$SO_4^=$	2.5	3.7	HO^-	4.2	17.5
Cl^-	2.7	-3.0	SCN^-	4.4	1.0
$CH_3CO_2^-$	2.7	6.5	$C_6H_5NH_2$	4.5	6.3
$C_6H_5O^-$	3.5	11.7	I^-	5.0	-9.0
Br^-	3.5	-6.0	$SO_3^=$	5.1	9.0
C_5H_5N	3.6	7.0	CN^-	5.1	10.9
N_3^-	4.0	6.5	$S_2O_3^=$	6.4	3.6

* From Table 9–11.
† From Table 9–13.

We might expect there to be a relationship between nucleophilic reactivity and basicity [33]. This expectation is valid only if reagents of the same charge type and with the same reacting center are considered. Thus, acetate ion is both less nucleophilic and less basic than phenoxide ion but hydroxide ion is both more reactive and a stronger base. A comparison of nucleophilicity as measured by n with basicity as measured by H is given in Table 13–8. It is readily apparent that no general nucleophilicity-basicity relationship exists, although the trend observed suggests that basicity must play a role in determining nucleophilicity. In addition to basicity, two other factors are recognized as important sources of nucleophilicity [34]. *Polarizability* permits rearrangement of the electrons of the nucleophile to form strong bonds by bonding electron movement toward the substrate and at the same time to reduce repulsions by nonbonding electron movement away from the substrate. The α *effect* occurs when there is an electronegative atom with unshared electrons adjacent to the nucleophilic atom. In the transition state electrons leave the nucleophilic atom for a substrate; delocalization of the electrons on the adjacent atom in the direction of the now electron-poor nucleophilic atom will stabilize the structure and so lead to a faster rate. These three effects are thought to be independent of each other [34]. The α effect is always present but its magnitude is variable. Basicity is expected to be very important when the interaction of a nucleophile with substrate resembles that of the nucleophile with a proton. Substrates with a high concentration of positive charge and a low electron density at the site of attack, such as carbonyl carbon, fulfill these requirements. Polarizability is the dominant factor when the nucleophilic atom is highly electronegative (so that the basicity is decreased) and also has several valence shell electrons. The latter condition is important in making the species polarizable. One other factor, *electrostatic attraction*, has also been discussed in relation to nucleophilicity [35].

In view of the importance of all these different effects in determining nucleophilicity, it is surprising that the simple Swain-Scott equation works at all. The Edwards equation (Eq. 9–19) attempts to assess the importance of only two effects, basicity and polarizability. The α effect and the electrostatic effect are therefore lumped into the parameters representing basicity and polarizability. We might question the value of either parameter to measure a property of fundamental importance. Both the Swain-Scott and Edwards equations throw such further variables as solvent effects into the adjustable parameters and neither equation handles variable steric effects. These equations should not be used to justify fundamental theoretical arguments, although they are both highly successful for correlating data, for predicting rate constants, and for expressing reactivity. The simplicity of the Swain-Scott formulation over that of Edwards recommends it for any of these functions.

A number of nucleophiles have more than one position with nucleophilic activity. These *ambident* [36] or *ambifunctional* [37] nucleophiles include such species as cyanide, nitrite, cyanate, and thiocyanate ions, more complex ions such as enol anions, and molecular nucleophiles such as enols and enamines.

The reaction of silver nitrite with substituted benzyl bromides [36] illustrates some of the effects of an ambident nucleophile (Table 13–9). The effect of the substituent

$$p\text{-}XC_6H_4CH_2Br + AgNO_2 \rightarrow p\text{-}XC_6H_4CH_2NO_2 + p\text{-}XC_6H_4CH_2ONO$$

on the rate for this reaction clearly demonstrates that the reaction proceeds through a transition state with considerable positive charge upon the benzylic carbon atom. The carbonium ion character must increase as the series progresses from *p*-nitro to *p*-methoxy benzyl bromide. The amount of nitrite ester also increases. This observation has been formulated into a rule [36] stating that, as the S_N1 character of a

Table 13–9. Rates and Products of Reaction of Silver Nitrite with Benzyl Bromides at 0°C in Ether*

p-X	Half-life, min	% Nitro	% Nitrite
NO$_2$	180	84	16
H	16	70	30
CH$_3$	1	52	48
OCH$_3$	Very small	39	61

* Data from Kornblum *et al.* [36].

reaction increases, the yield of product resulting from bond formation with the more electronegative atom of the ambient nucleophile increases. Conversely, as the S_N2 character increases, more product will result from bonding at the least electronegative atom. The importance of electrostatic effects upon nucleophilicity helps to explain these results. The atom of the nucleophile bearing the greatest negative charge is electrostatically attracted to the center of positive charge in the substrate. When bond breaking in the substrate is not so important, reaction occurs at the atom of lower electronegativity. This generally leads to the formation of the stronger bond and thus the transition state for this reaction is stabilized by the forming bond. Although it has been claimed that this rule fails for the anions of nitroalkanes [37], it has been demonstrated that C-alkylation of the lithium salt of 2-nitropropane involves a fundamentally different mechanism [38].

It should be possible to control the product obtained with ambient nucleophiles by changing conditions to increase (or decrease) the positive charge on the electrophile. Thus, alkali metal cyanides react with alkyl iodides to produce nitriles (i.e. C-alkylation) but with silver cyanide to produce isocyanides (N-alkylation) [36]. The role of silver is to polarize the C—I bond, by an electrophilic pull on the iodide, thus increasing the carbonium ion character of the transition state. This electrophilic catalytic activity need not lead to free carbonium ions nor are free carbonium ions required for alkylation of the more electronegative atom. The reaction of 2-octyl halides with silver nitrite produces nitrite ester and nitroalkane, both with inversion of configuration [39]; this is consistent with an S_N2 mechanism in the formation of both products. These results, and many others that are similar, have been used to argue that there is a continuous range of mechanisms for nucleophilic substitution, with the S_N1 and S_N2 mechanisms as limiting extremes [39].

Leaving Group Stability

Formation of the transition state in either an S_N1 or S_N2 reaction involves transfer of charge to the departing group. In both reactions we might expect there to be an increase in rate as the stability of the departing group increases. In general, this assumption is correct. Alkyl chlorides are less reactive than the corresponding bromides by a factor of about 50 and iodides are about two to five times more reactive than the bromides [2]. This order is remarkably independent of the reaction mechanism.

If the structure of the departing group is changed considerably so that there is a drastic change in the stability of the departing groups, a change in mechanism can occur. Also, since bond breaking is considerably more important in S_N1 than in S_N2 reactions, rates of the former are more sensitive to the leaving group. Thus, a highly stabilized leaving group may promote an S_N1 mechanism or at least increase the importance of bond breaking in the transition state so that the reaction shows considerable S_N1 character. This sensitivity to leaving group stability has been employed as another criterion for distinguishing between S_N1 and S_N2 mechanisms [40]. Hoffmann observed that, for reactions believed to proceed by an S_N2 mechanism,

Table 13–10. Relative Rates of Solvolysis*

Substrate	T, °C	k_{H_2O}/k_{HCO_2H}	$k_{OTs}/k_{Br}(H_2O)$
neo-pentyl tosylate	50	3.7	4
tert-butyl bromide	25	80	> 4000

* Data from Hoffmann [40], Table 4 (in part).

the relative rates were usually less than one when the tosylate was compared with the bromide, but for S_N1 reactions the ratio was large. For example, the bimolecular reaction of chloride ion with methyl bromide or tosylate in acetone at 25°C gave $k_{OTs}/k_{Br} = 0.42$ while the ethanolysis of α-tosyl ethylbenzene at 0°C proceeded 2270 times faster than the corresponding bromide [40]. Although this criterion is not firmly established, it would appear that intermediate values may provide a measure of the degree of electron transfer at the transition state. Table 13–10 compares two different criteria for distinguishing between the limiting mechanisms for nucleophilic substitution. The rate dependence on the leaving group gives a considerably more sensitive guide than the rate dependence based upon solvent effects. For estimating transition state carbonium ion character in reactions that do not clearly fall into one of the limiting mechanistic classes, k_{OTs}/k_{Br} would appear to be the better measure. Although some limitations to this latter mechanistic criterion have been pointed out [40], it will probably be used increasingly in the future.

Structural Effects

The substitution of alkyl groups on the reaction carbon results in a decrease in the rate of bimolecular substitutions (Table 13–11). The effect of added alkyl groups is to increase electron supply at the reactive center by an inductive effect. The importance of this electron supply in determining rates of reaction depends, of course, upon the electron density of the transition state relative to that of the reactant. If

Table 13–11. Relative Rates of Bimolecular Substitution Reactions in Acetone at 25°C*

Reaction	R						
	Me	Et	n-Pr	iso-Pr	*tert*-Bu	iso-Bu	neo-Pe × 10^5
RCl + Cl⁻	71	1					
RBr + Cl⁻	61	1	0.65	0.013	0.0029	0.15	2.6
RI + Cl⁻	11	1	0.58	0.032		0.038	1.4
RBr + Br⁻	76	1	0.65	0.011	0.0030	0.033	1.5
RBr + I⁻	140	1	0.82	0.0078	0.0051	0.036	1.2

* Data from de la Mare *et al.* [41], Table 20 (in part).

positive charge is developed at the reacting carbon, the substitution of electron-releasing alkyl groups should accelerate the reaction. The development of positive (or negative) charge depends upon the importance of both bond breaking and bond making at the transition state. This can be seen from Table 13–11 by examining the series of alkyl halides reacting with chloride ion. When the leaving group is chloride, a symmetrical transition state should result and bond breaking become increasingly important as the leaving group is changed to bromide and iodide ion. In this series, substitution of a methyl group increases the relative rate 5.5 times more for the iodide than for the chloride. As stronger nucleophiles are used, bond formation should become more important, while alkyl substituents will tend to destabilize the transition state that is undergoing a build-up of electrons. This effect is shown in Table 13–11 for the series of nucleophilic halide ions. An *a priori* prediction of the importance of bond making and bond breaking cannot be made at the present time. Observed electronic effects, however, can be explained within the above approach.

Steric effects are far more important than electronic effects in determining reaction rates of S_N2 reactions. The transition state for the S_N2 mechanism involves considerable crowding because a fifth group must be accommodated about the reacting carbon atom. From Table 13–11 we see that increased substitution about the reacting center causes a rate decrease; Me > Et > iso-Pr > *tert*-Bu. This is due in great part to steric hindrance, as shown by the effect of substitution on a β carbon. The addition of one alkyl group on the β carbon has a small rate-retarding effect (*cf.* Et > n-Pr), because the single substituent can rotate away from the entering group, and this imposes rotational and vibrational restrictions on the transition state if steric interactions are to be avoided. It has been found [41] that the rate retardation observed for the change of ethyl to propyl in the bromide exchange reaction is due to the Arrhenius pre-exponential factor and not to an increased energy of activation (Table 13–12). This result is consistent with rotational and vibrational restrictions within the transition state. The addition of a second β alkyl

Table 13–12. Arrhenius Parameters for Bimolecular Halide Ion Exchange with Alkyl Bromides in Acetone at 25°C*

	Halide	Me	Et	n-Pr	iso-Bu	neo-Pe
$\log A$†	Cl	10.7	10.1	9.8	9.6	8.6
E_a†		15.8	17.5	17.5	18.9	22.0
$\log A$	Br	9.3	8.9	8.6	8.4	7.4
E_a		15.7	17.6	17.8	18.3	21.7
$\log A$	I	11.4	11.0	10.8	10.3	10.2
E_a		16.3	18.9	19.0	19.9	24.2

* Data from de la Mare *et al.* [41], Table 20 (in part).
† Results for A are given in liters/mole-sec and for E_a in kcal/mole.

group does not cause much further restriction of the transition state conformation and steric hindrance becomes the dominant factor in determining the rate. The marked deactivation that occurs when a third methyl is added (neo-pentyl bromide in Table 13–11) is a result of both great steric strain and highly restricted rotation.

Table 13–13. Rates of Solvolysis and Lyate-Ion Displacements*

Substrate	Solvent	T, °C	$k_1 \times 10^5$, sec^{-1}	$k_2 \times 10^5$, liters/mole-sec	k_2/k_1
MeBr	80% EtOH	55	0.349	2,040	5840
EtBr	80% EtOH	55	0.139	171	1230
iso-PrBr	80% EtOH	80	2.9	128	44
tert-BuBr	80% EtOH	25	38.5	*ca.* 0	*ca.* 0
MeOSO$_2$C$_6$H$_5$	EtOH	70	7.05	10,300	1460
EtOSO$_2$C$_6$H$_5$	EtOH	70	3.06	4,010	1310
iso-PrBr	EtOH	70	10.2	700	69

* From Streitwieser [5], Table 17 (in part).

While electronic effects are much less important than steric effects in S_N2 reactions, the roles are reversed in S_N1 reactions. In the unimolecular substitution mechanism, hindrance of the nucleophile cannot occur. The electronic effects of alkyl groups upon reaction rates are in the expected direction for a highly polar transition state. Table 13–13 gives a direct comparison of the effects of substitution on uni- and bimolecular substitution reactions. When reaction is carried out in a hydroxylic solvent containing lyate ion, both S_N1 and S_N2 mechanisms can occur, leading to a kinetic expression of the form

$$\text{rate} = k_1[RX] + k_2[RX][SO^-].$$

The constant k_1 measures the rate of reaction with solvent and is first-order; the second-order rate constant k_2 measures the rate of displacement by lyate ion. If a direct displacement reaction is occurring in pure solvent, the rate should be greatly enhanced by the presence of the much more nucleophilic lyate ion. On the other hand, if reaction proceeds through a slow ionization step, the presence of lyate ion should cause only a small effect upon the rate. A value of k_2/k_1 will suggest the importance of the direct displacement reaction. Table 13–13 shows that, as alkyl groups are added, the importance of the S_N2 process is decreased.

NEIGHBORING GROUP PARTICIPATION

When a substituent is present on an atom β to a carbon atom undergoing a nucleophilic substitution reaction, it frequently interacts with the reacting atom. This process is called neighboring group participation [42].

A classic study of neighboring group participation was carried out by Cram with the 3-phenyl-2-butyl tosylate system [43], studying the acetolysis and formolysis of the optically pure diastereomers. The L-*threo* isomer at 75°C produced a 53% yield of acetates (elimination also occurs, affording alkenes) of which 95% was racemic *threo*, 0.6% was L-*threo*, and 4% was *erythro*. In the more dissociating formic acid solution at 25°C, where the total ester yield was 70%, the respective yields were >99%, <0.02%, and <0.01%.

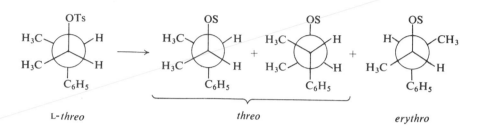

The acetolysis of the D-*erythro* isomer produced a 68% yield of ester, of which 94% was D-*erythro* and 5% was D-*threo*; the formolysis reaction produced a 71% overall yield, of which more than 99% was D-*erythro* and less than 0.5% was D-*threo*.

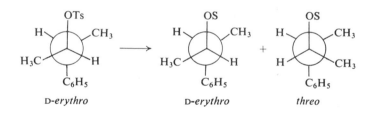

Before discussing the explanation of the high degree of stereospecificity exhibited by these reactions, we might look at some other information. The racemization of the *threo*-tosylate proceeds considerably faster than formation of the toluenesulfonic acid [43], so that intimate ion pairs must be formed. In the acetolysis reaction, about 80% of the product results from reaction of racemic tosylate but in the formolysis reaction only 25% of the product is thus produced. Isotopic labeling reveals phenyl migration—in 50% of the product the phenyl group has moved to the adjacent carbon that was originally bonded to the tosylate [44].

Much heated debate has been generated over the interpretation of these stereochemical results [45–47]. It is now generally agreed that a bridged ion is involved as an intermediate in the reaction [45, 47]. If we assume for the moment that the intermediate is symmetrical [45], the results of stereoselectivity are easily explained in the following schemes:

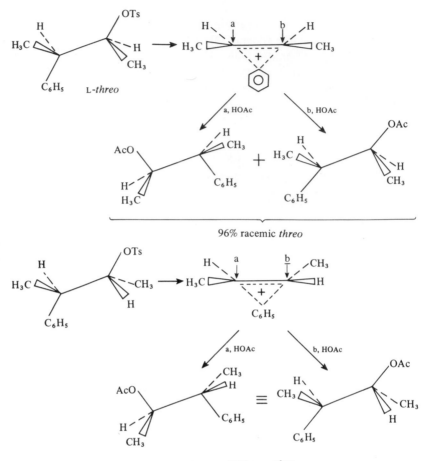

96% racemic *threo*

94% L-*erythro*

The presence of a symmetrical intermediate explains the formation of the major products very elegantly. The small amount of crossover products, e.g. *threo*-acetate from *erythro*-tosylate, could result from competition of the solvent to produce inverted product directly. The observation of greater leakage in acetic acid than in the less-nucleophilic formic acid is consistent with this picture.

Any kinetic effect observed for neighboring group participation will depend upon the transition state structure. Kinetic evidence alone cannot be used to demonstrate the formation of a bridged ion as an intermediate. The acetolysis of *threo*-3-phenyl-2-butyl tosylate is slower ($k = 2.38 \times 10^{-6}$ sec^{-1}) than the acetolysis of 2-butyl tosylate ($k = 4.3 \times 10^{-6}$ sec^{-1}) [48]. Because the 3-phenyl-2-butyl system forms ion pairs, the acetolysis rate is not equal to the rate of ionization. The ionization rate of 2-butyl tosylate is reported to be three times smaller than that of the 3-phenyl system [45]. In addition, if the rate-retarding inductive effect of a phenyl ring is taken into account, the 3-phenyl-2-butyl tosylate is estimated to react 24 times faster than it would without phenyl participation [45]. This rate increase due to phenyl participation can be greatly increased by making structural changes to stabilize the transition state (and also the intermediate), for example, by adding a p-methoxy group. Indeed, this structural change increases the rate by a factor of nearly 80 in acetolysis [49]. A *para*-O⁻ substituent in the β-phenylethyl system leads to an estimated 10^6-fold rate increase over the p-methoxy compound in methanolysis [50]. Furthermore, the intermediate can be observed spectroscopically and has even been isolated [50]:

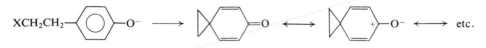

Below pH 8, the stable spirodienone was protonated to the p-hydroxyphenonium ion, which reacts rapidly with solvent [50].

It appears that aromatic neighboring groups can aid in the removal of leaving groups and can also form reactive intermediates. The structure of the intermediate is open to question although the evidence available may provide some clues. The special case of the spirodienone, where a stable neutral species is formed, lends credibility to the view that such species can exist as reactive intermediates. Perhaps of even greater interest is the recent report of the isolation of stable p-anisonium and 2,4,6-trimethylphenonium ion formed by an aryl participation route through ionization of the β-arylethyl chlorides in SbF_5—SO_2 at $-70°C$ [51]. The NMR spectra of both ions are consistent with a symmetrical structure and are very similar to the corresponding benzenonium ions:

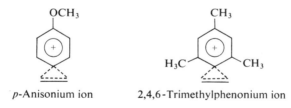

p-Anisonium ion   2,4,6-Trimethylphenonium ion

Of course, these conditions are not at all like those used in the substitution reactions we have been discussing. Treatment of the ions with methanol at $-80°C$ did yield more than 80% of the β-methyl ethers [51]. This evidence favors Cram's assignment of a symmetrical structure to the reactive intermediate in the substitution reactions [45]. Brown, on the other hand, has suggested the existence of two intermediates that are rapidly equilibrating, basing his conclusion on the fact that the formolysis of β-arylethyl tosylates fails to correlate with either σ or σ⁺ constants but has values falling somewhere between the two [47] (Fig. 13–4). He interpreted the positive drift from a σ correlation to mean that participation increases as the aryl group is activated and the negative drift from the σ⁺ correlation to indicate that charge delocalization, and therefore participation, was not great. However, since this observation is not consistent with the fact that many aromatic substitution reactions (see Chapter 12) *are* correlated with σ^+ constants, he suggested that the transition state resembles a π complex rather than a complex in aromatic substitution reactions. From this point on, his reasoning follows that outlined in Chapter 12 in regard to a π complex intermediate in electrophilic aromatic substitution. Two such structures must be proposed and they must be rapidly equilibrating to account for the stereochemical results cited above. Brown [47] pictures them as

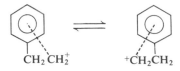

and suggests that the phenonium ion represents a transition state between these two species. To the present author, there appear to be two fallacies in this reasoning. First, it overlooks the fact that aromatic substitutions, believed to be controlled by π complex transition states, are not as selective as the solvolytic reaction; for example, the formolysis reaction of β-p-tolylethyl tosylate is nine times as reactive as the unsubstituted phenylethyl tosylate [47], while toluene is only 1.5 times as reactive as benzene in the π-controlled ethylation reaction [52]. Secondly, and what is perhaps more important, it ignores the charge delocalization into the cyclopropyl ring, which would decrease the charge upon the aromatic ring, so that substituent effects would be smaller than in the absence of such delocalization. The Cram structure for phenonium ions [45] does include this delocalization and the NMR spectra of the salts isolated by Olah [52] also give strong support to it. The evidence cited by Brown *et al.* [47] in favor of the existence of two equilibrating ions can be interpreted just as easily in terms of the single symmetrical ion suggested by Cram.

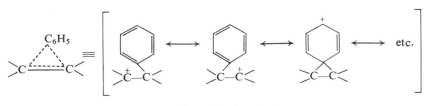

Phenonium ion structure

Brown *et al.* suggested that at least one important reason for rejecting the phenonium ion as an intermediate is that it does not fit classical valence bond theory [46]. Certainly, the resonance structures that must be employed in valence bond terminology are high-energy structures and might be expected to contribute little resonance stabilization to the cation. For this reason the phenonium ion is often called a *nonclassical ion*, although the use of this term varies from author to author.

Brown [46] has suggested that a nonclassical carbonium ion is one in which the position of at least one atom is markedly different from that predicted on the classical structural principles, Bartlett [53] that a nonclassical ion is one that involves delocalized σ bonding electrons. Thus, the phenonium ion is not a nonclassical ion by Bartlett's definition but is by Brown's. Whichever definition is finally accepted, the phenonium ion presents many of the same structural problems that are connected with the nonclassical ions included in Bartlett's definition. Brown categorizes neighboring groups into those with sufficient electrons for all the required bonds and those that are electron-deficient [46]. The latter case is that of Bartlett. Further classification of the normal or electron-sufficient carbonium ions has been proposed [47]. If normally nonbonding electrons are employed in bond formation of the carbonium ion, the ion is of the n type; if π bonding electrons are employed, it is of the π type. Clearly, the arylonium ions we have been discussing are of the π type.

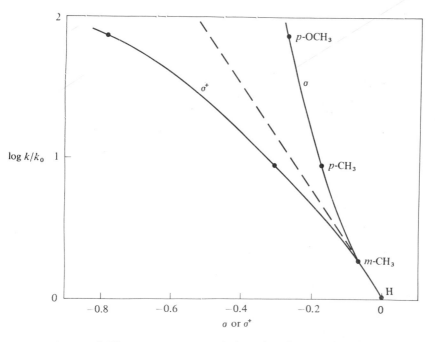

Fig. 13–4. Failure of Hammett-type correlation for formolysis of substituted β-arylethyl tosylates.

Participation of the n type is common [47], and the results obtained with the halogens are typical of this. The reaction of fuming hydrobromic acid and optically active *threo*-3-bromo-2-butanol afforded *dl*-2,3-dibromobutane while the optically active *erythro*-bromohydrin yielded *meso*-dibromide [54]:

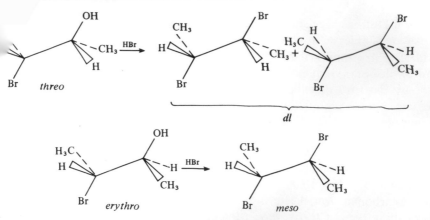

The mechanism of this reaction is most reasonably explained by protonation of the alcohol to give the oxonium ion. If a simple S_N2 step followed, with bromide ion displacing water, the *threo* isomer would form *meso*-dibromide. If water were lost to give a carbonium ion by an S_N1 mechanism, both bromohydrins should give a mixture of *dl*- and *meso*-dibromides. To account for the products observed, a symmetrical bromonium ion was proposed as an intermediate:

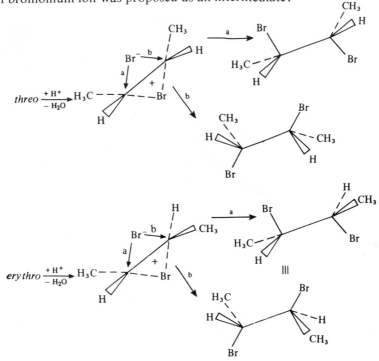

Bromide ion attack opens the ring to give the observed products. In this reaction, nonbonded electrons of the bromine atom are used to displace the water molecule

and form the intermediate bromonium ion. Alternatively, water may depart
assistance from the neighboring bromine but then formation of a cyclic interm
must follow prior to rotation about the carbon-carbon bond in order to accoun
the observed products.

Reactions that proceed with the neighboring group participating significantly
the transition state are said to involve *anchimeric assistance*. This will result in an
increased reaction rate, which is one criterion for participation. Two other criteria
are also commonly employed in investigating these effects: if rearrangement occurs,
the *isolation of rearranged products*, as described above for phenyl participation, or
the *stereochemical result*, which we used in the bromohydrin reactions. These two
criteria can sometimes be used when anchimeric assistance is absent, that is, when
participation occurs after the rate-determining step [5].

The principal difficulty in applying the criterion of rate enhancement is estimating what the rate would be in the absence of assistance. Although we alluded to
this problem during the discussion of phenyl participation, let us now examine one
approach to this problem in greater detail. The difficulty is to estimate the role of the
inductive effect of an adjacent substituent upon the rate of reaction. By using
1,2-substituted cyclohexyl compounds, participation from the side opposite the
leaving group can be excluded in the *cis* isomers while *trans* isomers can assume a
conformation favorable to rearward participation. The assumption that *cis* and
trans isomers react at the same rate in the absence of anchimeric assistance, is supported by the observation that the acetolysis of *cis*- and *trans*-1,2-cyclohexyl
dibrosylate occurs with a rate ratio of only 1.1 [55]. With this assumption, the rate
ratio of *trans*- to *cis*-disubstituted-1,2-cyclohexyl compounds can be taken as a
rough measure of anchimeric assistance. Some values for these compounds are
given in Table 13–14.

From Table 13–14 it is clear that, although the overall rate of a reaction may be
slower than for the parent compound, neighboring group participation can still
provide considerable driving force for the reaction. The 2-acetoxycyclohexyl
brosylates are representative: the participation of the acetoxy group in solvolytic
reactions is amply demonstrated by product studies as well as by the above kinetic
approach. Winstein *et al.* [58] have proposed that an acetoxonium cyclic intermediate
ion is the result of participation:

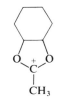

Acetoxonium ion

This intermediate is captured in a number of cases. Optically active *trans*-2-acet-
oxycyclohexyl tosylate is solvolyzed in acetic acid containing acetate ion to give

 trans-diacetate at 100°C. At lower temperatures *cis*-diacetate is also ob-
 ... When moist acetic acid is employed, a mixture of *cis*-mono- and diacetates is
 ...ained. Dry ethanol solvolysis produces isolable orthoester. Protonation of the
 ...ene acetal has also been carried out and this material behaves similarly, a result
 ...which strongly supports a common intermediate, the acetoxonium ion. Furthermore, in glacial acetic acid containing *p*-toluenesulfonic acid, the *trans*-acetoxy
tosylate was formed from the ketene acetal. Here, the existence of a reactive intermediate suggested by kinetic evidence is supported by stereochemical evidence, by
trapping to give isolable products, and by preparation of the intermediate by another
route. The reactions discussed are shown in the following scheme:

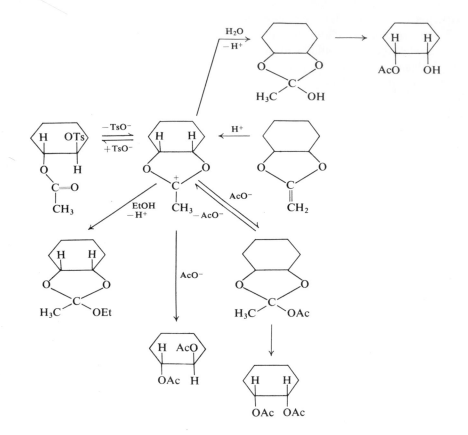

ALLYLIC SUBSTITUTIONS

Before examining σ type participation by neighboring groups, we will consider the
effect of a carbon-carbon double bond adjacent to a carbon atom that is undergoing
a substitution reaction. Allylic compounds may react by an S_N2 process that proceeds faster than for the corresponding saturated compound [59]. For example,

Table 13–14. Relative Acetolysis Rates of Cyclohexyl Compounds at 75

Compound	Relative rate	k_{trans}/k_{cis}	
Cyclohexyl brosylate	1.00		5.
cis-2-chlorocyclohexyl brosylate	1.34×10^{-4}	3.8	56
trans-2-chlorocyclohexyl brosylate	4.80×10^{-4}		56
cis-2-bromocyclohexyl brosylate	1.24×10^{-4}	820	56
trans-2-bromocyclohexyl brosylate	0.101		55
trans-2-iodocyclohexyl tosylate	1170*	27×10^5†	55
cis-2-acetoxycyclohexyl brosylate	3.79×10^{-4}	630	55
trans-2-acetoxycyclohexyl brosylate	0.240		55
cis-2-chlorocyclohexyl phenyl sulfide	0.012‡	4.5×10^5	57
trans-2-chlorocyclohexyl phenyl sulfide	5.4×10^3‡		57

* Relative to tosylate at 24°C.
† Estimated in Streitwieser [5], Table 29 (in part).
‡ In 80% aqueous ethanol, relative to cyclohexyl chloride.

n-propyl chloride reacts with ethanolic sodium ethoxide at 44.6°C at a rate only 0.027 times that of allyl chloride [60]. This reaction process is subject to most of the same effects (nucleophile, leaving group, steric, etc.) that have been discussed for alkyl compounds, and, as with alkyl compounds, bimolecular reactions at the substituted atom are strongly retarded by α alkyl groups. The reaction of 1,1-dimethylallyl chloride with thiophenoxide ion in ethanol produces no normal bimolecular product [61], although bimolecular reaction proceeds at least twice as fast as the same reaction of 1-methylallyl chloride. The product obtained for the dimethyl compound is rearranged but that obtained for the monomethyl chloride is predominantly normal:

$$CH_2{=}CHCMe_2Cl + C_6H_5S^- \xrightarrow{-Cl^-} C_6H_5SCH_2CH{=}CMe_2$$

$$CH_2{=}CHCHMeCl + C_6H_5S^- \begin{cases} \xrightarrow{-Cl^-} CH_2{=}CHCHMeSC_6H_5 \quad \sim 95\% \\ \xrightarrow{-Cl^-} C_6H_5SCH_2CH{=}CHMe. \quad \sim 5\% \end{cases}$$

The rearranged product is formed by a mechanism which involves synchronous bond formation, double bond migration, and bond breaking and is called the S_N2' mechanism:

$$X^- \quad CH_2{=}CH{-}CH_2{-}Y.$$

eochemistry of the S_N2' process is illustrated by the reactions of *trans*-6-clohex-2-en-1-yl 2,6-dichlorobenzoates with piperidine [62]. The nucleophile s the ring system *cis* to the departing group:

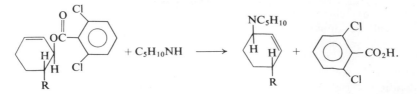

Allyl compounds also undergo substitution by a mechanism analogous to the S_N1 process, called the S_N1' mechanism. We might expect the adjacent double bond to enhance the rate of ionization by conjugative stabilization of the transition state, but this effect is apparently opposed by the inductive effect of the bond [59]. Although allyl chloride undergoes solvolysis in 99.5% formic acid at a rate faster than that of n-propyl chloride, the rate is increased by only a factor of 26 [63].

The presence of substituents that stabilize positive charge accelerates the ionization reaction. This effect is greatest in the 1 position, principally because 1-substituted compounds are thermodynamically less stable than 3-substituted compounds. Substituents in the 2 position have little rate-enhancing effect while those in the 3 position are nearly as effective as those in the 1 position. Table 13–15 illustrates this general trend. The marked effect observed for methyl substitution on either the 1 or 3 position in contrast to that on the 2 position is due to the charge distribution being concentrated on those two atoms. (Recall that the charge of allyl cation calculated in Chapter 4 was equally distributed on the terminal atoms.)

Table 13–15. Relative Rates of Hydrolysis of Allyl Chlorides in 99.5% HCO_2H*

Compound	Relative rate
$CH_3CH_2CH_2Cl$	0.04
CH_2=$CHCH_2Cl$	1.0
CH_2=$CHCHClCH_3$	5670
CH_2=$C(CH_3)CH_2Cl$	0.55
CH_3CH=$CHCH_2Cl$	3550
CH_2=$CHC(CH_3)_2Cl$	8×10^7†
$(CH_3)_2C$=$CHCH_2Cl$	2×10^7†

* Data from Vernon [63], at varying temperatures.
† Estimated from data in 50% ethanol.

If an ionic intermediate is formed in the S_N1' process, the products obtained from 1- and 3-methylallyl compounds should be the same; both would give a common intermediate:

CH$_3$CH=CHCH$_2$X

CH$_3$CHXCH=CH$_2$

$\xrightarrow{}$ CH$_3\overset{\delta+}{CH}$=CH=$\overset{\delta+}{CH}_2$

CH$_3$CH—CHCH$_2$S

CH$_3$CHSCH=CH$_2$.

Table 13–16, taken from the review of DeWolfe and Young [59], shows that the product mixtures obtained from the two isomers are usually not the same. Although one of the isomers may be reacting *via* a carbonium ion it is clear that both isomers are not. However, as the solvent ionizing power increases and/or nucleophilicity decreases, the two isomers give product mixtures more nearly alike. This is to be expected as both isomers approach the limiting solvated-ion mechanism: structural changes that favor carbonium ion formation also tend to increase the similarity of product mixtures.

Table 13–16. Substitution Products of Allylic Halides*

Compound	Conditions	Percentage of primary product	Difference
CH$_3$CH=CHCH$_2$Cl	EtOH + CaCO$_3$,	91	38
CH$_3$CHClCH=CH$_2$	78°C	53	
CH$_3$CH=CHCH$_2$Cl	EtOH + Ag$_2$O,	70	24
CH$_3$CHClCH=CH$_2$	78°C	46	
CH$_3$CH=CHCH$_2$Cl	0.5 N Na$_2$CO$_3$,	55	19
CH$_3$CHClCH=CH$_2$	25°C	36	
CH$_3$CH=CHCH$_2$Cl	H$_2$O + Ag$_2$O,	45	11
CH$_3$CHClCH=CH$_2$	25°C	34	
CH$_3$CH=CHCH$_2$Cl	HOAc + AgOAc,	60	4
CH$_3$CHClCH=CH$_2$	25°C	56	
(CH$_3$)$_2$C=CHCH$_2$Cl	MeONa, MeOH	100	66
(CH$_3$)$_2$CClCH=CH$_2$	25–60°C	33	
(CH$_3$)$_2$C=CHCH$_2$Cl	EtOH + CaCO$_3$,	48	18
(CH$_3$)$_2$CClCH=CH$_2$	25°C	30	
(CH$_3$)$_2$C=CHCH$_2$Cl	10% aq. Na$_2$CO$_3$	15	0
(CH$_3$)$_2$CClCH=CH$_2$	or aq. Ag$_2$O	15	
(CH$_3$)$_2$C=CHCH$_2$Cl	HOAc + AgOAc,	55	0
(CH$_3$)$_2$CClCH=CH$_2$	25°C	55	

* Selected values from De Wolfe and Young [59], Table 9.

We can explain the results in Table 13–16 in two ways. The first explanation would say that unimolecular and bimolecular reactions are competitive and that, as conditions are changed to favor ionization, the unimolecular process increases in importance. This view is no longer generally accepted [5, 59].

The acetolysis of 3-chloro-3-methylbutene proceeds with competitive isomerization to 2-methyl-4-chlorobut-2-ene [64]:

$$Me_2CClCH=CH_2 \xrightarrow{HOAc} Me_2C=CHCH_2Cl.$$

This arrangement is first-order but is not subject to a common ion effect. These facts are consistent with the formation of an ion pair that can collapse to either reactant or rearranged reactant by a process called *internal return* (the second explanation of the results in Table 13–16):

$$Me_2CClCH=CH_2 \rightleftharpoons Me_2C\underset{CH}{\overset{Cl^-}{\diagup}}CH_2 \rightleftharpoons Me_2C=CHCH_2Cl.$$

Internal return has been found to occur during a number of allylic solvolysis reactions. We previously examined ion pair formation when discussing the S_N1 substitution reaction and the data in Table 13–16 are understandable on the basis of that discussion. With conditions highly favorable to ionization, the allylic carbonium ions reach their most stable configuration, probably that of the ion pair. With better nucleophilic solvents the reaction occurs so rapidly after passing over the energy barrier that the leaving group is still very close to the carbon atom to which it had been bonded. The predominant reaction then produces an unrearranged product because the developing charge is partially maintained at the original carbon atom by electrostatic attraction. In this description the activated species is losing energy on its way to a stable ion but is intercepted by a reactive nucleophile.

An interesting application of the results obtained by examining product distributions has been presented by Kochi [65]. The oxidation of olefins by peroxy esters in the presence of copper salts affords allylic esters (see reference 66 for a review of these reactions). This oxidation may involve a ligand transfer from the copper salt directly to an allyl radical formed by prior H-abstraction

$$\overset{\displaystyle \cdot}{\overbrace{C \cdots C \cdots C}} + Cu(II)X_n \rightarrow C=C-CX + Cu(I)X_{n-1}$$

or it may involve an electron transfer to produce an allylic carbonium ion:

$$\overset{\displaystyle \cdot}{\overbrace{C \cdots C \cdots C}} + Cu(II)X_n \rightarrow \overset{+}{\overbrace{C \cdots C \cdots C}} + Cu(I)X_n.$$

When butenes are subjected to the same reaction conditions in acetic acid-acetonitrile solvent, a mixture of butenyl acetates is obtained. The product composition depends upon the nature of the copper salt. For example, simple copper acetate gives a product mixture strongly favoring the terminal olefin; thus, the reaction of either *cis*- or *trans*-2-butene affords an ester product composed of about 90% 1-but-2-enyl acetate and a similar product ratio is obtained from 1-pentene. When the added copper salt is fully coordinated with such ligands as 1,10-phenanthroline, the product distribution is dramatically altered: in this case, the product obtained from both *cis*- and *trans*-2-butene, as well as from 1-butene, is composed of 45% 1-but-2-enyl acetate and 55% 3-but-2-enyl ester. This latter result corresponds closely with the results obtained from both the silver-ion-assisted acetolysis of the butenyl chlorides (Table 13–16) and the deamination of the butenyl amines by nitrous acid [65]. On the basis of the similar composition of the products formed in the copper phenanthroline reaction and in the other carbonium ion reactions, Kochi [65] postulated that the butenyl cation was formed as a common intermediate in all three reactions and that an electron-transfer process led to the formation of the carbonium ion. The different product mixture obtained with simple copper acetate indicates that this reaction must proceed by another route.

When a double bond is α to the reacting carbon in unimolecular substitution reactions, the rate increase is easily explained by electron delocalization in the transition state that precedes the resulting allylic ion:

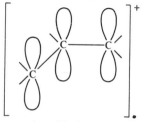

This normal delocalization seems less likely to occur if a methylene group is placed between the reacting center and the carbon-carbon double bond, to form a homo-allylic compound:

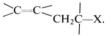

It is therefore surprising to find that homoallylic compounds frequently show rate enhancements when compared with analogous saturated compounds [42]. The ethanolysis of 3-butenyl benzenesulfonate (hereafter called allylcarbinyl benzene-sulfonate) proceeds at only half the rate of n-butyl benzenesulfonate [5]. On the other hand, acetolysis of 4-methyl-pent-3-enyl tosylate proceeds at a rate 1200 times that of ethyl tosylate [66]. This large rate increase is probably due to participation of the double bond forming the homoallylic carbonium ion as a reactive intermediate. The isolation of 2-cyclopropylpropene as well as the expected acetate also implies double bond participation:

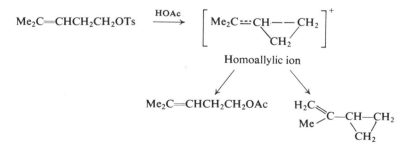

Homoallylic ion

Undoubtedly, the two terminal methyl groups contribute to the stability of the ion, although their presence is not necessary to observe anchimeric assistance, since allylcarbinyl tosylate solvolyzes 3.7 times faster than n-butyl tosylate at 50°C in 98% formic acid and 1.3 times faster in 80% formic acid [67]. This rate ratio change was shown to be almost entirely due to a change in the rate of the saturated tosylate. The insensitivity of allylcarbinyl tosylate to this change in solvent nucleophilicity strongly suggests that it is solvolyzing by an S_N1 mechanism. The solvolysis products are not all stable in 98% formic acid. They are more stable in the presence of sodium formate and, by extrapolation of the product mixtures obtained at varying sodium formate concentrations, an initial (kinetic) product mixture could be estimated as 45% cyclopropylcarbinyl, 45% cyclobutyl, and 10% allylcarbinyl formates:

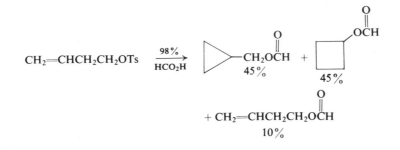

This product mixture agrees very well with that obtained from the formolysis of cyclobutyl tosylate [67]. Nitrous acid deamination of cyclopropylcarbinyl amine and of cyclobutyl amine gives the same mixture of alcohol products as does aqueous solvolysis of the chlorides [68]. Also, incomplete aqueous solvolysis of cyclopropyl-carbinyl chloride yields a similar mixture of rearranged chlorides [68]. Cyclobutyl and allylcarbinyl chlorides are unreactive under the conditions employed so that the isomeric alcohols were all formed from the cyclopropylcarbinyl chloride. The isolation of rearranged chlorides points to the formation of an ion pair intermediate in this reaction that collapses faster than solvolysis occurs.

Because similar product ratios are observed for the carbonium ions, it is reasonable to suggest a common intermediate. If we consider the reaction of cyclopropyl-carbinyl derivatives only, we might expect either the primary carbonium ion to expand the ring (thus forming a secondary cation and at the same time relieving ring strain) or else ring opening to occur and relieve strain completely. These processes might occur competitively or consecutively.

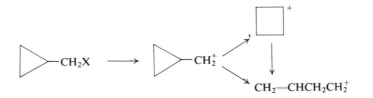

However, the matter cannot be this simple, because there is no apparent driving force for the conversion of the allylcarbinyl cation back to either ring compound, if relief of strain is the driving force leading to ring opening. Nevertheless, a rapid equilibrium between such ions has been proposed to account for the similar product spread observed with different isomers [70].

Rate results can shed some light on the nature of the intermediate expected to explain the above results. Saturated primary halides are essentially inert to solvolytic reactions as compared with allylic halides. This is confirmed by the lack of solvolysis of allylcarbinyl chloride at 50°C in 50% aqueous ethanol. Under these conditions, 2-methylallyl chloride reacts only 1/40 as fast as cyclopropylcarbinyl chloride and 2/3 as fast as the cyclobutyl chloride [68]. These strikingly fast reactions —cyclopropylcarbinyl chloride is estimated to ionize 10^9 times faster than primary chlorides [67]—must involve stabilization of the incipient carbonium ion and the most likely source of such stabilization is charge delocalization.

To find out whether the products obtained in the cyclopropenylcarbinyl-cyclobutyl cation system stemmed from a symmetrical intermediate, isotopic labeling was used [69]. Treatment of cyclopropylcarbinol-C^{14} with Lucas reagent (zinc chloride and hydrochloric acid) affords only allylcarbinyl chloride with completely scrambled C^{14}:

$$\triangleright\!\!-C^{14}H_2OH + ZnCl_2/HCl \longrightarrow ClC^{14}H_2C^{14}H_2CH\!\!=\!\!C^{14}H_2.$$

The three methylenes become equivalent in this reaction and therefore must either become equivalent or be rapidly equilibrating during the course of the reaction. To determine which of these possibilities was operative, an irreversible reaction must be employed. The nitrous acid deamination of amines was chosen. Both cyclopropylcarbinyl and cyclobutyl amines produce the same mixture of alcohols when the deamination is carried out in water [68]. Since the conditions are mild, product stability was no problem and, most importantly, the loss of nitrogen from the diazonium ion is certainly irreversible so that no reactant isomerization occurs. The deamination of cyclopropylcarbinyl-C^{14} amine led to almost, but not quite, complete equivalence of the methylene carbons [69]. Clearly, the reaction does not

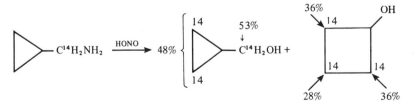

proceed through an intermediate or transition state where the three methylenes are equivalent.

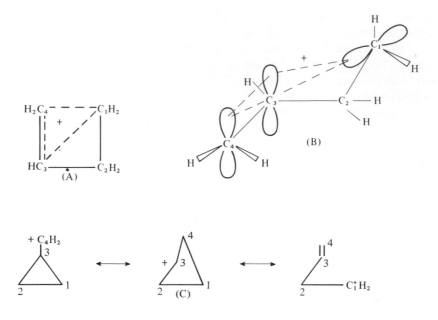

Fig. 13–5. Representations of bicyclobutonium ion.

To explain all of the above results a nonclassical intermediate was postulated, the bicyclobutonium ion [69], which is represented by several different methods in Fig. 13–5. In the first representation (A), the dotted lines are used to indicate the atoms that contribute atomic orbitals to a multicenter molecular orbital. These atomic orbitals are shown in B, where it is apparent that atoms 3 and 4 involve π overlap and atom 1 involves considerable σ overlap. Drawing C is an attempt to represent the ion as a resonance hybrid but we must use a highly unorthodox bent structure for the cyclobutyl cation. We shall use structure A in the following discussion. To use it for predicting products the dashed lines are removed from the atom that is attacked by a nucleophile, while the dashed line remaining forms a normal bond. Thus, nucleophilic attack at atom 1 leads to the formation of an allylcarbinyl product, attack at 3 produces a cyclobutyl compound, and at 4 it gives a cyclopropylcarbinyl product.

The deamination of C^{14}-labeled cyclopropylcarbinyl amine would give only 2-C^{14}-cyclobutanol by nucleophilic attack at atom 3 and cyclopropylcarbinyl alcohol labeled at the carbinyl position by attack at atom 4, if the reaction goes through the bicyclobutonium ion in Fig. 13–5:

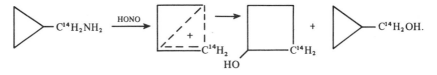

This does not agree with the observed distribution. It was suggested that a number of the ions are rapidly equilibrated [69]:

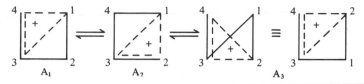

We might expect the conversion from A_1 to A_2 to be rapid, since it involves only a slight movement of atom 1 toward atom 4, but for conversion of either of these to the A_3 ion a new bond between atoms 2 and 4 must be formed and greater atomic movement is required. This is most easily seen by examining representation B in Fig. 13–5. If the ions can be trapped before complete equilibration, the methylenes do not become equivalent and we expect excess C^{14} in the carbinyl methylene group of the cyclopropylcarbinyl alcohol and excess C^{14} in the positions adjacent to the carbinol atom of cyclobutanol, both of which are observed.

Historically, the isolation of the same product mixtures from solvolysis reactions of both cyclopropylcarbinyl and cyclobutyl compounds and the anomalously rapid rates of these reactions were noted first [68]. Isotopic tracer techniques then demonstrated that reactions of the two ring compounds did not proceed through the same single intermediate [69]. In a highly imaginative attempt to account for both the accelerated ionization of the reactants and the observed rapid equilibrations, in the most economical way, the nonclassical bicyclobutonium ion was proposed as an intermediate. Finally, the formation of this ion from allylcarbinyl compounds was predicted and found [67]. Although the bicyclobutonium interpretation has been questioned [70, 71] and the problem is probably not yet solved, the approach used is typical of good mechanistic reasoning and experimental design.

Even more spectacular double-bond participation occurs in the norbornenyl system. The acetolysis of *endo*- and *exo*-5-norbornenyl sulfonates or halides leads principally to nortricyclyl derivatives as well as to small amounts of *exo*-dehydro-norbornyl derivatives [72]:

The *exo*-brosylate reacts about 8000 times more rapidly than the *endo* isomer [73]. This rate difference is probably due to anchimeric assistance to ionization in the *exo* isomer. The departure of the leaving group from the *exo* side projects a p orbital lobe in a direction favorable to σ overlap with the double bond. Departure from the *endo* position projects the p orbital lobe away from the double bond, so that assistance is not expected. The *endo* isomer probably ionizes to a classical ion, which rearranges to the nonclassical homoallylic bridged ion formed directly from the *exo* isomer.

Also, *endo*-brosylate affords slightly more *exo*-acetate than does the *exo*-brosylate, 17 *vs.* 11% [72], probably from a direct S_N2 reaction. The solvolysis mechanism is thus formulated [42] as:

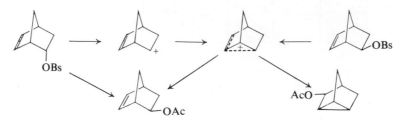

The bridged ion given in this scheme might be expected to rearrange:

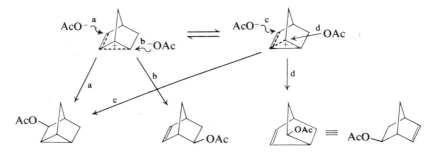

But it is also possible that the reaction proceeds through a symmetrical ion:

Again, the subtle technique of isotopic labeling was used to study this reaction [72]. When C^{14} was used as a label at C_2 and C_3, both *endo*- and *exo*-brosylates gave *exo*-dehydroacetate with C scrambling. If the symmetrical ion is the precursor to this product, there should be a loss of 50% of the C^{14} at positions C_2 and C_3, since reaction at C_2 and C_6 is equally probable:

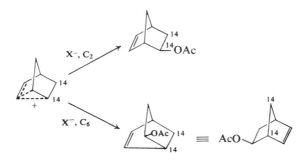

Only about 30% rearrangement occurred with the *endo*-brosylate and 38% with the *exo* isomer during acetolysis [72]. Formolysis of *exo*-brosylate gave 48% rearrangement [72]. We conclude that the symmetrical ion is not formed directly from the *exo* derivative. Either a slowly established equilibrium between the two unsymmetrical ions or formation of the symmetrical ion after the asymmetric ion is produced can explain these results. Unfortunately, because the exact positions of the C^{14} were not determined in the product, hydride shifts that would also produce scrambling cannot be excluded.

The 7-substituted norbornenyl tosylates also show rate enhancement. The *anti*-tosylate undergoes acetolysis 10^{11} times that of the saturated compound and is 10^7 times more reactive than the *syn* isomer [73, 74]:

anti   syn

The only product of acetolysis of the *anti* isomer is *anti*-acetate [73, 74]. The extreme rate increase and stereospecificity of this reaction support a bridged ion intermediate:

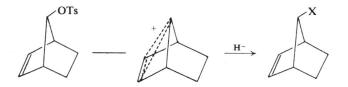

When strongly nucleophilic reagents are used, another product is observed. Thus, methanolysis of the tosylate yields 99.7% 7-*anti*-methyl ether but only a 48.5% yield of this material is obtained with 4 M NaOMe, the remaining product being an *endo*-tricyclic ether [75].

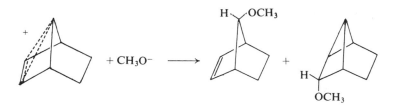

With poor nucleophiles the transition state of the product-producing step comes later than with strong nucleophiles, *cf*. Hammond's postulate. The transition state structure is determined by its similarity to the products. The *anti*-7-norbornenyl methyl ether is about 12.7 kcal/mole more stable than the tricyclic product. As the nucleophilic activity is increased, the transition state resembles the ion more.

Attack at C_2 and C_3 is favored by a statistical factor of two and by greater positive charge at these positions in the ion. The greater positive charge at C_2 and C_3 than at C_7 is shown by NMR spectroscopy [75, 76]. The stereospecificity of substitution at both C_2 and C_7, the rate enhancement, and the $C_2:C_7$ reactivity ratio can all be explained on the basis of a nonclassical bridged ion. Addition of a second double bond increases the rate of solvolysis still more. The hydrolysis of 7-norbornadienyl chloride in 80% acetone proceeds about 760 times faster than that of *anti*-7-norbornenyl chloride [77], i.e. about 10^{14} times faster than the saturated system. The bridged ion proposed as an intermediate in this reaction has been studied by NMR [75, 76, 78]. Atoms 2, 3 and 5, 6 do not become equivalent:

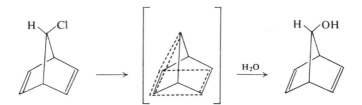

Brown and Bell [70] observed that *anti*-7-norbornenyl tosylate produces a 60% yield of tricyclo[4.1.0.0³·⁷]heptane

and that 7-chloronorbornadiene produces an 83% yield of tricyclo[4.1.0.0³·⁷]hept-4-ene

when treated with sodium borohydride in aqueous diglyme. These results led them to suggest an alternative to the nonclassical ion intermediate, proposing that sodium borohydride successfully served as a trap for a pair of rapidly equilibrating classical carbonium ions, e.g.

In the Brown mechanism for the solvolysis of the norbornenyl and norbornadienyl systems the nonclassical ions discussed above are considered to be the structure of the transition state between the two proposed classical ions rather than the structure of a single intermediate.

Finally, the acetolysis of *endo*-7-isopropylidenenorborn-5-en-2-yl tosylate proceeds about 2000 times faster than that of *endo*-5-norbornenyl tosylate [79]. The product is the unrearranged *endo*-acetate. The acetolysis of the *exo* isomer produces only rearranged acetate [79]. The results for the isopropylidene compounds are in accord with double-bond participation:

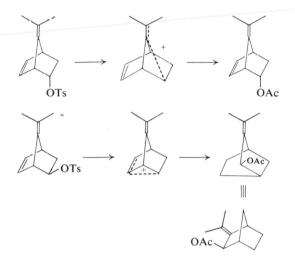

These results demonstrate that at least two different ions can exist at C_2. Their formation depends upon the stereochemistry of the reactant.

Benzonorbornenyl systems give results that qualitatively parallel those of the analogous norbornenyl systems. Acetolysis of either *exo*-or *endo*-2-benzonorborn-enyl brosylates produces *exo*-acetate [80]. The *exo* isomer is about 7000 times more reactive than the *endo* [80], a value very similar to the ratio obtained for the analogous 2-norbornenyl brosylates:

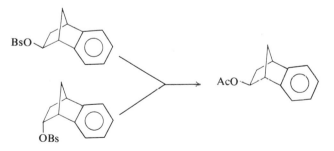

The *anti*-7 isomer yields the corresponding acetate at a rate 6×10^5 times faster than 7-norbornyl brosylate [80] –considerably less acceleration than is provided by a single double bond. This is not surprising if we consider that the interaction proposed requires a loss of aromatic stabilization:

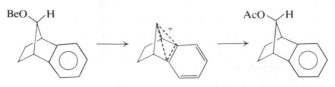

The structure of the proposed ion appears to be symmetrical, or at least the transition state leading to it must be. This has been demonstrated by a study of substituent effects [81]. Substitution of a methoxyl group in the aromatic ring at a position *meta* to the norbornyl system increases the rate of acetolysis by a factor of 54. This rate enhancement is consistent with either symmetrical or asymmetrical nonclassical or even classical bonding in the transition state. Addition of a second methoxyl group adjacent to the first will lead to different results, depending upon the transition state structure. If the transition state is not symmetrical, the second methoxyl should act as a *meta* substituent and perhaps even produce a slight rate retardation, with a value for σ_p^+ of -0.78 and for σ_m^+ of $+0.05$; if it is symmetrical, the second methoxyl should produce the same effect as the first. The observed effect is a further increase in rate by a factor of 55 [81]. Methyl substituents behave similarly, with the mono-methyl-substituted material being 5.7 and the dimethyl compound being 36 times more reactive than the unsubstituted benzonorbornenyl brosylate. In fact, these results are correlated by an Okamoto-Brown type plot, if σ^+ for a single substituent is taken as an average value, $(\sigma_p^+ + \sigma_m^+)/2$. The ρ-value of -5.1 [81] suggests considerable accumulation of positive charge on the C_2 and C_3 positions of the norbornyl system.

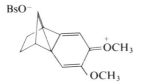

Classical

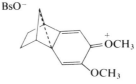

Asymmetrical nonclassical

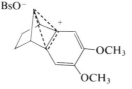

Symmetrical nonclassical

Many of the reactions discussed above have been explained in terms of a non-classical ion (electron-deficient) with one delocalized electron pair bonding three atoms by σ type bonds. We have examined systems in which the ion is formed by a double bond and an electron-deficient carbon atom—the π route to nonclassical ions [82]. The solvolysis of cyclobutyl and cyclopropylcarbinyl compounds was also explained on the basis of a nonclassical ion formed by what is called the σ route [82].

The most fully studied σ route to nonclassical carbonium ions occurs in the norbornyl system. Indeed, the greatest controversy concerning the role of nonclassical ions is centered on the norbornyl cation. Is the norbornyl cation nonclassical or is it an equilibrium mixture of classical (localized) ions? Both sides of the argument have recently been reviewed. For a more complete discussion of the problem in favor of nonclassical ions and for more comprehensive coverage of the chemistry of norbornyl compounds, the reader should examine the articles by Berson [83] and by Sargent [84]. Brown has succinctly stated the arguments favoring a classical interpretation [70, 85], as has Deno [71]. Since all these review articles are easily available we shall here sketch just a few of the approaches. It is hoped that the reader will refer to both the reviews and the original literature cited therein for greater detail.

NEIGHBORING CARBON AND HYDROGEN

The five criteria that have been used to suggest the occurrence of nonclassical ions during a reaction were discussed above for the bicyclobutonium ion without being specifically enumerated. They are: a) unusually fast reaction rates; b) stereospecifically formed products; c) racemization or its absence; d) internal return with rearrangement; e) rearranged products [84].

The rates of acetolysis of norbornyl tosylates and brosylates depend upon the configuration of the starting material [86]. Thus, the *exo* isomer reacts 350 times faster than the *endo*-brosylate at 25°C [86]:

exo   *endo*

This titrimetric rate ratio does not provide the best measure of the rates of ionization, however, since the *exo*, but not the *endo*, isomer involves internal return. Polarimetric rate constants give an ionization rate ratio of 1600 in favor of the *exo*-brosylate [87]. Winstein and Trifan [86] argued that the rate difference was due to anchimeric assistance in the *exo* isomer. They took the ionization of *endo*-norbornyl compounds as "normal," and the *endo*-brosylate reacts at nearly the same rate as cyclohexyl brosylate [86]. If, on the other hand, the ionization rate of the *exo* isomer is considered normal, then the *endo* material solvolyzes at an abnormally slow rate [70, 85]. To support his hypothesis that the *exo*-brosylate reacts normally, Brown suggests that cyclopentyl derivatives provide better models for ionization and points out that *exo*-norbornyl brosylate acetolyzes only 12.4 times faster than cyclopentyl brosylate [85]. Similarly, the ratios for methanolysis and ethanolysis are 3.9 and 3.6 respectively [85]. Brown [70] suggests that the *endo* isomer solvolyzes abnormally slowly because of increased steric hindrance caused by the departing group passing very close to the *endo*-6-hydrogen. This causes the transition state for *endo* departing groups to be sterically destabilized relative to the reactant and results in an abnormally slow reaction:

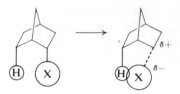

Substitution of an *endo*-methyl group should further slow the acetolysis rate because of the increased bulk of the interfering group. Indeed, 6,6-dimethyl-2-*endo*-norbornyl tosylate undergoes acetolysis at only 1/19 the rate of *endo*-2-norbornyl tosylate [88]. The rate of the *exo*-tosylate is also decreased by the introduction of two methyl groups at the 6 position, the dimethyl tosylate reacting 25 times slower than the unsubstituted tosylate [88]. The *exo* to *endo* ratio for the dimethyl compound (206) is nearly as large as that for the unsubstituted tosylate (280). Similar studies have been carried out with deuterium as a 6 substituent [89, 90]. The observed kinetic isotope effect was not dependent upon whether the deuterium atom was *endo* or *exo* but did depend upon the orientation of the brosylate. Thus both 6-*endo*-d-2-*endo*-norbornyl tosylate and 6-*exo*-d-2-*endo* tosylate showed a negligible or slightly inverse isotope effect for acetolysis, $k_H/k_D = 0.99 \pm 0.02$ [89]. This is consistent with ionization to a classical ion but is not consistent with steric deceleration of ionization. Deuterium, being smaller than hydrogen, should not show the same steric effect as hydrogen at the *endo*-6 position. Solvolysis of the 6-d-2-*endo*- and 6-d-2-*exo*-tosylates gave a large isotope effect, $k_H/k_D = 1.10 \pm 0.02$ [89], that was also independent of the deuterium orientation. The difference in isotope effects between the *endo*- and *exo*-brosylates is hard to explain using current classical ionization theory.

Solvolytic products obtained from both *exo*- and *endo*-norbornyl brosylate have been found to be exclusively the *exo* form [86, 87]. While the product obtained from optically active *exo*-tosylate is found to be completely racemic, that obtained from optically active *endo*-brosylate is optically active. The optical activity of the product decreases with decreasing nucleophilicity of the solvent, ranging from values of 13% inversion in 80% aqueous acetone at 75°C to 3% inversion in formic acid at 25°C [87]. In addition, we should recall that *exo* isomers show $k_\alpha/k_t > 1$, indicating that racemization occurs in the reactant, but no internal return was observed for the *endo* isomer [86]. Although the solvolytically substituted product is pure *exo* starting from either isomer, some hydrocarbon is also obtained as a result of an elimination reaction. *Exo*-brosylate yields 4% hydrocarbon, 98% of which is nortricyclene [87].

These results have been interpreted [86, 87] as demonstrating the direct formation of a nonclassical ion from the *exo* isomers to give racemic *exo* products. The *endo* isomers are said to ionize to a classical ion that is presumed to leak predominantly into the nonclassical structure while the remainder is bled off to inverted *exo* product.

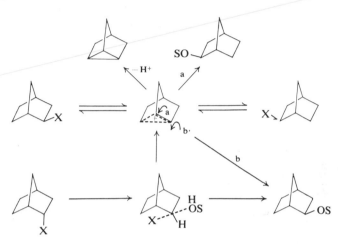

There are a number of other ways to account for the racemization of the norbornyl compounds. Hydrogen migrations, either a 6,2 or a 3,2 shift, can convert the norbornyl cation into its enantiomer:

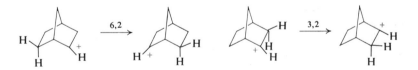

Similarly, a rapid equilibrium of the classical 2-norbornyl cation by a Wagner-Meerwein migration will give a racemate:

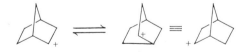

To distinguish between some of these alternatives and to establish their importance, an isotopic tracer technique was used [91]. If carbon atoms 2 and 3 of *exo*-2-norbornyl brosylate were labeled with isotopic carbon and solvolyzed in acetic acid, a 3,2

Table 13–17. Predicted and Observed Isotopic Distributions for the 2-Acetate Formed from *exo*-2-Norbornyl Tosylate Labeled at C_2 and C_3

Mechanism	Activity at			
	C_2, C_3	C_1, C_4	C_7	C_5, C_6
3,2 Shift	100	0	0	0
6,2 Shift	50	0	0	50
Bridged ion	50	25	25	0
Equilibrated classical ions	50	25	25	0
Observed [91]	40	23	22	15

hydrogen shift would result in no scrambling, since the bridged ion would place 25% of the isotope at each of the 1, 2, 3, and 7 positions. However, classical ions rapidly equilibrated by a Wagner-Meerwein shift would give the same result, so this evidence cannot be used to distinguish between these two proposals. The predictions of each possible mechanism and the observed scrambling are given in Table 13–17. Clearly, hydride shifts alone cannot account for these results. The presence of isotopic carbon at C_5 and C_6 does establish a 6,2-hydride shift during the reaction. To account for the observed distribution, a nortricyclonium ion intermediate was proposed [91]. If this ion of three-fold symmetry is formed after the original bridged ion or competitively with it and if 45% of the acetolysis results from reaction of the nortricyclonium ion (the rest resulting from capture of the preceding unsymmetrical bridged ion), the observed isotopic scrambling can be accounted for.

Nortricyclonium ion

It may also be accounted for by considering the nortricyclonium ion structure as that of a transition state [86] between equilibrating bridged ions. The role of the nortricyclonium transition state structure was questioned recently when it was shown that 6,2-hydride shifts occur purely *endo-endo* [92] in some rearrangement reactions.

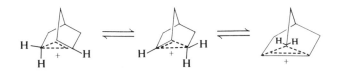

The scrambling results fail to substantiate the 3,2-hydride migrations that have been demonstrated by NMR studies [93]. At $-120°C$ the 2-norbornyl cation formed in liquid sulfur dioxide shows three peaks with relative areas of 4:1:6 [93], but above $-5°C$ the spectrum is a single line, indicating the equivalence of all hydrogens. The nonequivalence at low temperature stems from the freezing out of the 3,2 shift [93].

Although much additional work has been carried out in an attempt to distinguish between classical equilibrating and nonclassical norbornyl ions, no absolutely definitive experiment has yet been devised. The reader is again referred to the reviews cited above for more complete coverage of this interesting problem [83–85].

Migration of alkyl groups in acyclic systems frequently occurs. There is no evidence of rate enhancement by methyl, e.g. neopentyl, derivatives but this is sometimes observed in more highly substituted systems. It is not at all clear whether neighboring group participation or relief of steric strain leads to this rate increase [42].

Hydrogen also migrates to electron-deficient carbon atoms. It has been claimed that hydride shift involves hydrogen participation in the transition state [93]. Perhaps of more interest is the extreme rapidity with which hydride ion migration occurs. Whiting has stated that a reaction of a secondary system that occurs without hydride shift must involve no electron-deficient intermediate but must involve an S_N2 transition state [15]. This view, if correct, provides still another criterion for distinguishing between S_N1 and S_N2 routes.

ELIMINATION

The substitution reaction is nearly always accompanied by elimination of H—Y. Elimination may involve H bound to the same carbon as Y (α elimination) or H bonded at an adjacent carbon (β elimination) [94]. The α elimination process is not of great importance under most substitution reaction conditions and we will not discuss it. On the other hand, β elimination may be the predominant reaction occurring under conditions expected to yield a substitution product and elimination products may thus suggest the mechanism of substitution.

Many elimination reactions carried out in the presence of base are kinetically first-order in both base and eliminating substrate. Two mechanisms involving these moieties in the rate expression appear applicable. The first, called an E2 mechanism, is a synchronous removal of the β-H by base, formation of an incipient double bond, and splitting off of the leaving group:

$$B: H—CR_2CR_2—X \rightarrow BH^+ + R_2C=CR_2 + X^-.$$

The second, known as the E1cB mechanism, is a two-step process involving an equilibrium proton removal followed by a unimolecular loss of the leaving group from the conjugate base of the substrate:

$$B + H—CR_2CR_2X \rightleftharpoons BH^+ + \overline{C}R_2CR_2X$$
$$\overline{C}R_2CR_2X \rightarrow R_2C=CR_2 + X^-.$$

To distinguish between these two mechanisms, 2-phenylethyl bromide was converted to styrene by sodium ethoxide in deuterated ethanol [95]. After about 50% of the reaction has taken place, both the unreacted bromide and the styrene formed are free of deuterium, so that the E1cB mechanism can be ruled out in this reaction. Of course, if collapse of the carbanion to alkene is fast relative to the collapse to reactants, no mixing would be expected. The E2 mechanism is thought to prevail for simple structures while the E1cB mechanism occurs in a few rare cases [94]. The transition state of the E2 elimination, however, may have considerable carbanion character.

The stereochemistry of the E2 reaction has been studied in a number of systems. The preferred mode of elimination has the departing groups in the same plane and on opposite sides of the incipient double bond. Thus, elimination from the diastereo-meric 1,2-diphenyl-1-propyl halides afforded only alkene arising from *trans* elimination [96]:

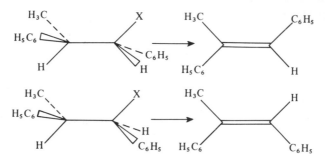

Although the *trans* planar arrangement is normally favored, coplanar *cis* elimination may occur almost as rapidly. The *cis* and *trans* isomers of 2-phenylcyclopentyl tosylate both undergo elimination with potassium *tert*-butoxide in *tert*-butyl alcohol [97]. The *cis* isomer eliminates *trans* while the *trans* isomer must eliminate *cis*. The *trans* elimination occurs only 9.1 times faster than the less-favored *cis* elimination:

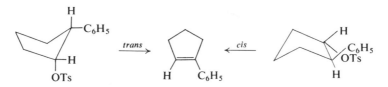

When HBr is eliminated from 2-butyl bromide, two alkenes can form. When ethoxide ion is the base, 19% 1-olefin and 81% 2-olefin result [98]. This is an example of the familiar Saytzeff rule—that dehydrohalogenation of secondary and tertiary halides favors formation of the most substituted alkene. This is the most stable product and probably suggests that the transition state involves considerable double-bond character [94]. There are many clear violations to the Saytzeff rule when steric factors are important. Thus, when *tert*-butoxide is the base, 2-butyl bromide eliminates to give 53% 1-olefin. Table 13–18 illustrates the role of the size of the base in determining the direction of elimination. The last entry clearly shows that the steric hindrance may result from substituents in the substrate as well as in the base. When large groups are departing, the least substituted olefin is generally formed. This may account for the Hofmann rule: when onium salts decompose, the alkyl group with the largest number of β-hydrogens will be eliminated. Thus, ethylene is the predominant product when n-propylethyldimethylammonium hydroxide is heated. Similarly, *tert*-butylethyldimethylammonium hydroxide affords a 93% yield of isobutylene [99]. Both the steric effect and the acidity of the β-hydrogens are important in determining the Hofmann elimination [94]. This interpretation, of course, implies considerable carbanion character in the transition state.

Table 13–18. Percentage of 1-Alkene Formed in E2 Reactions*

Compound	Base			
	EtO$^-$	*tert*-BuO$^-$	*tert*-AmO$^-$	Et$_3$CO$^-$
CH$_3$CH$_2$CHBrCH$_3$	19	53		
(CH$_3$)$_2$CHC(CH$_3$)BrCH$_3$	21	73	81	92
CH$_3$CH$_2$CBr(CH$_3$)$_2$	30	73	78	89
(CH$_3$)$_3$CCH$_2$CBr(CH$_3$)$_2$	86	98		97

* From Brown and Moritani [98], Table II (in part).

Of greatest interest to our discussion of nucleophilic substitution reactions is the fact that the E2 elimination is a side-reaction to any S_N2 process for which it is possible (a result of the basicity of most nucleophiles). The result of the direct competition of these processes depends upon several factors. We have previously pointed out that S_N2 reactions are retarded by substitution at either the α- or β-carbon atoms and this substitution increases the rate of E2 reactions. Therefore, increasing substitution at either α or β positions favors elimination. This is shown in Table 13–19. The E2 reaction is also favored by bulky bases and by strong bases. The effect of solvent changes can be predicted by applying the principles used in substitution reactions. Finally, the activation energy of E2 reactions is normally larger

Table 13–19. Alkene Yield in E2 Reactions of Alkyl Derivatives with Ethoxide Ion*

Compound	T, °C	Alkene, %
CH$_3$CH$_2$Br	55	0.9
CH$_3$CH$_2$CH$_2$Br	55	8.9
(CH$_3$)$_2$CHCH$_2$Br	55	59.5
(CH$_3$)$_2$CHBr	25	80.3
(CH$_3$)$_3$CBr	25	> 97

* Data from Dhar *et al.* [100].

than that for S_N2 reactions. This results in an increased ratio of elimination to substitution with increased temperatures.

As we have seen, when a reaction is carried out in the presence of a base, the product composition is dependent upon the leaving group. When no base is present, i.e. in solvolytic conditions, the departing group has little effect upon the product mixture (Table 13–20). This common composition of product mixture (nearly the same, within experimental error) strongly suggests a common intermediate. The intermediate is the carbonium ion formed by a slow ionization, which then loses a proton to form alkene. This process, called an El mechanism, represents another reaction of carbonium ions. (We shall not repeat our earlier discussion of the formation of carbonium ions.)

Table 13–20. Product Composition for Reactions of
$CH_3CH_2C(CH_3)_2X*$

X	Conditions	Products		Alkene, %
Br	EtO⁻	71	29	
Me₂S⁺	EtO⁻	14	86	
Br	EtOH	82	18	41
Me₂S⁺	EtOH	87	13	48

* Data from references 100–102.

There is competition between elimination and substitution reactions of the carbonium ion whenever the ion bears a β-hydrogen. This competition normally favors substitution, but to increase elimination the temperature can be raised and a less-nucleophilic solvent employed. All the other reactions of carbonium ions cited earlier are also competitive with elimination.

The *sec*-butyl system is an interesting one, giving some information on the conformational requirements of the transition states in elimination reactions [103].

$$CH_3CH_2CHXCH_3 \longrightarrow \underset{CH_3\ \ CH_3}{\overset{H\ \ \ \ H}{>\!\!=\!\!<}} + \underset{CH_3\ \ H}{\overset{H\ \ \ \ CH_3}{>\!\!=\!\!<}} + CH_3CH_2CH=\!CH_2$$

The ratio of the three isomeric alkenes is taken as a measure of the relative rates of elimination, which may then be related to the population of the transition state conformers that can lead to elimination. Concerted eliminations give a *trans*-2-butene to *cis*-2-butene ratio of 1.8 to 3.0 [103]. The favoring of *trans*-olefin is attributed to the higher population of the more stable conformer in a *trans* elimination and the more stable conformer

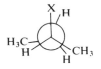

for eliminations that proceed by a *cis* mechanism such as acetate pyrolysis:

When elimination is stepwise or when the C—X bond is at least almost broken, a *trans* to *cis* ratio of about unity is observed. Thus, solvolysis of 2-butyl tosylate affords *trans*- and *cis*-2-butene in the ratio of 1.1:1 [104]. The E1 reaction only shows appreciable steric effects when eclipsing groups are bulky [94], so the two conformers of the transition states leading to alkene are about equally populated, owing to the trigonal nature of the carbonium ion.

It has been argued [103] that the *trans*- to *cis*-butene ratio may be taken as a measure of the C—X bond-breaking in the transition state. The ratio of 1- to 2-alkene may be taken as a measure of C—H bond-stretching in the transition state. A high yield of butene-1 suggests little C—H stretching in the transition state leading to olefin. If the C—H bond is unaffected at the transition state, we should expect the ultimate loss of hydrogen to be statistically controlled and the 1- to 2-butene ratio from this statistical value to reflect the stability of the incipient double bond. The 1- to 2-butene ratio is 1.3 for pyrolysis of the acetate at a high temperature, 450°C [105], but only 0.20 at 200°C [106], whereas solvolysis of the tosylate gives a value of 0.11 [104], a somewhat surprising result. This approach permits us to compare transition state structures of reactions that are not rate-determining steps.

We have by no means done justice to the literature of elimination reactions. We have seen, however, that eliminations are common side-reactions during a substitution process and that a common intermediate is formed in the E1 and the S_N1 processes. Therefore, elimination reactions can, and must, be examined whenever a carbonium ion intermediate is anticipated.

MOLECULAR ORBITAL CORRELATIONS

If we take the carbonium ion as a suitable model for the transition state of an S_N1 reaction, we can use it to calculate possible reactivity indices. Probably the most appropriate guide to reactivity is the π electron energy difference between the original hydrocarbon ArH and the carbonium ion $ArCH_2^+$ [107]. If the π energy of a system is expressed as $n\alpha + M\beta$, the change in π electron energy can be obtained from the bonding energy coefficients by $M_{ArCH_2^+} - M_{ArH} = \Delta M$. The use of this parameter is illustrated by the results obtained for the solvolysis of arylphenylmethyl in 90% acetone [108]. Figure 13–6 is a graphic representation of the results given in Table 13–21.

Table 13–21. Relative Rates of Solvolysis of Arylphenylmethyl Chlorides in 90% Aqueous Acetone at 25°C*

Ar in Ar CHClC$_6$H$_5$	No. in Figs. 13–6 & 13–7	k/k_0	ΔM	q_r
Phenyl	1	1.00	1.301	0.400
2-Triphenylyl	2	4.66	1.317	0.379
2-Naphthyl	3	4.71	1.317	0.379
4-Biphenylyl	4	6.97	1.327	0.372
1-Phenanthryl	5	3.72	1.362	0.344
9-Phenanthryl	6	4.69	1.370	0.334
1-Naphthyl	7	6.39	1.369	0.336
6-Chrysyl	8	12.8	1.388	0.314
1-Pyrenyl	9	292	1.410	0.286
9-Anthryl	10	829	1.477	0.235

* From Verbit and Berliner [108], Table II (in part).

From Fig. 13–6 it will be noted that the compounds may be grouped into two classes, with the 9-anthryl point falling below both lines, which are nearly parallel. The slower line is fitted by all the compounds that have a 1-naphthyl-like structure and a hydrogen *peri* to the side-chain. The lower reactivity of these compounds has been attributed to steric hindrance in the transition state, either solvation or co-planarity or both [107, 108]. Similar behavior has been observed in other cases [107]. The 9-anthryl compound has two *peri* hydrogens and, interestingly, falls about as far below the slow line as that line falls below the fast line—suggesting, as we might expect, that steric effects are additive.

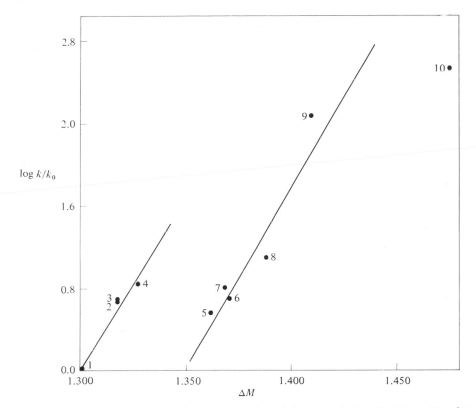

Fig. 13–6. Correlation of solvolysis rates of arylphenylmethyl chlorides with ΔM values. (From Verbit and Berliner [108], Fig. 1.)

A more tenuous correlation might be based upon the charge density at the exo-cyclic carbon atom [108]. The lower the charge density at this atom the more the charge is dispersed into the aromatic system. The greater this dispersal, the more stable the carbonium ion and the more reactive the chloride from which the ion is formed. If this argument is reasonable, we should expect a correlation of rates with charge density. Values for the charge density are given in Table 13–21, but the correlation with q_r (Fig. 13–7) is no better than that with ΔM. The 9-anthryl point fits the slow line better but the vagueness of the model process does not permit us to assign any meaning to this observation.

The correlation of rates of substitution reactions with molecular orbital param-eters is only fair. Because of the rather poor results, any mechanistic conclusions drawn from such correlations should be considered only as guides for further experimentation. We should point out, finally, that an S_N2 reaction of arylmethyl chlorides with KI in acetone correlates as well with ΔM as solvolysis reactions do, although a relatively low value for the slope is obtained [107].

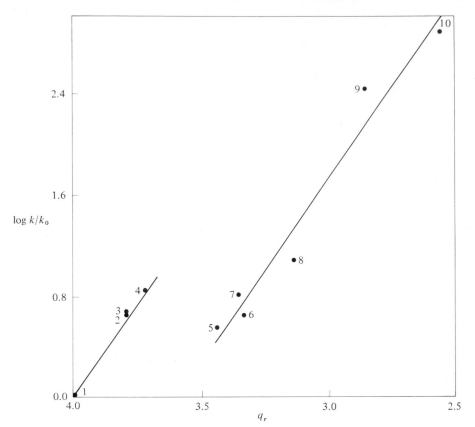

Fig. 13–7. Correlation of solvolysis rates of arylphenylmethyl chlorides with q_r values.

PROBLEMS

1. In 25% aqueous dioxane, addition of 0.0462 M NaN_3 does not affect the rate of solvolysis of 0.018 M 2-octyl brosylate but diverts 31% of the product to azide of inverted configuration. Give a reasonable mechanism to explain this.

2. The rate of hydrolysis of *tert*-butyldimethylsulfonium ion is unaffected by added OH^- but at 50°C reacts 3.2 times faster in EtOH than in water. Explain.

3. Acetolysis of both 2-phenyl-3-pentyl tosylate and 3-phenyl-2-pentyl tosylate affords the same mixture of products, 57% 3-phenyl-2-pentyl and 43% 2-phenyl-3-pentyl acetates. Explain.

4. The reaction of α-phenylethyl chloride with silver nitrate in benzene gives a 94% yield of pure α-phenylethyl nitrate with retention of configuration. In cyclohexane, inversion of configuration is observed. Explain the retention in benzene and relate

these results to those where π complex formation has been demonstrated in aromatic substitutions.

5. Explain the following order of reactivity, commenting on each compound in the acetolysis reaction at 50°C.

Compound	Relative rate
2-Butyl brosylate	1.00
3-Phenyl-2-butyl brosylate (*erythro*)	0.58
(*threo*)	0.66
3-Methyl-3-phenyl-2-butyl brosylate	36
3-(*p*-Anisyl)-2-butyl brosylate	45

6. The second-order rate constant for reaction of NaOH with allyl chloride is faster in 40% dioxane–60% water than in 60% dioxane–40% water at 65°C. What can you conclude about the transition state of this reaction? Predict the effect of a γ-methyl group on the rate (crotyl chloride *vs.* allyl chloride). Indicate your reasoning.

7. The acid-catalyzed dehydration of 2,2-dimethylcyclohexanol affords product A. Give a mechanism for this reaction.

A

8. In the solvolysis reaction, 80% EtOH at 25°C, of the following chlorides the alkene obtained is as follows. Give a reasonable explanation of this order.

	Alkene, %
tert-Butyl chloride	16
2-Chloro-2-methylbutane	34
2-Chloro-2,3-dimethylbutane	62
3-Chloro-2,3,4-trimethylpentane	78

9. The acetolysis of 2-(cyclopent-3-enyl)ethyl *p*-nitrobenzenesulfonate proceeds 74 times faster than the saturated analogue. The yields of *exo*-norbornyl derivatives were high.

CH₂   CH₂
ONs   ONs

a) Explain the rate enhancement.

b) The introduction of a methyl group at the double bond results in a further 7-fold rate enhancement. Explain this rate enhancement.

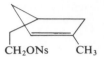

CH₂ONs   CH₃

c) On the basis of your answer to (b), can you explain a further 5.5-fold rate enhancement on the addition of a second methyl group? If not, provide a consistent explanation for all of the results.

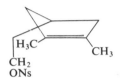

H₃C   CH₃
CH₂
ONs

d) What rate effect would the double bond in 2-(cyclopent-2-enyl)ethyl nosylate be expected to produce relative to that of the 3-enyl isomer? Why?

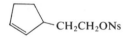

CH₂CH₂ONs

e) Can these results be satisfactorily explained using only classical carbonium ions?

10. The hydrolysis of optically active 2-octyl brosylate in 75% aqueous dioxane affords inverted 2-octanol of 77% optical purity. Addition of sodium azide leads to the production of 2-octyl azide and 2-octanol, the latter being 100% inverted.
a) Suggest a mechanism to account for these results.
In the absence of sodium azide 2-octyl brosylate is solvolyzed in pure methanol to give 2-octyl ether with 100% inversion. Methanol is more polar than 75% aqueous dioxane.
b) Is this result consistent with your mechanism?
The amount of inverted 2-octanol decreases with an increase of the percentage of dioxane in the solvent.
c) Propose a mechanism consistent with all of the data.

REFERENCES

1. L. Fowden, E. D. Hughes, and C. K. Ingold, *J. Chem. Soc.*, 3187 (1955).
2. C. K. Ingold, *Structure and Mechanism in Organic Chemistry*, Cornell University Press, Ithaca, N. Y. (1953).
3. H. Eyring, H. Gershinowitz, and C. E. Sun, *J. Chem. Phys.*, **3**, 785 (1935).
4. S. Sato, *J. Chem. Phys.*, **23**, 592 and 2465 (1955).
5. A. Streitwieser, *Chem. Revs.*, **56**, 571 (1956).
6. a) P. Walden, *Ber.*, **26**, 210 (1893) and subsequent papers;
   b) H. Phillips, *J. Chem. Soc.*, **123**, 44 (1923).

7. E. D. HUGHES, F. JULIUSBERGER, S. MASTERMAN, B. TOPLEY, and J. WEISS, *J. Chem. Soc.*, 1525 (1935).

8. C. A. BUNTON, *Nucleophilic Substitution at a Saturated Carbon Atom*, Elsevier Publishing Co., New York (1963).

9. J. L. GLEAVES, E. D. HUGHES, and C. K. INGOLD, *J. Chem. Soc.*, 236 (1935).

10. E. D. HUGHES, C. K. INGOLD, and A. D. SCOTT, *J. Chem. Soc.*, 1201 (1937).

11. V. GOLD, *J. Chem. Soc.*, 4633 (1956).

12. E. D. HUGHES, C. K. INGOLD, R. J. L. MARTIN, and D. F. MEIGH, *Nature*, **166,** 679 (1950).

13. A. STREITWIESER, T. D. WALSH, and J. R. WOLFE, *J. Am. Chem. Soc.*, **87,** 3682 (1965).

14. A. STREITWIESER and T. D. WALSH, *J. Am. Chem. Soc.*, **87,** 3686 (1965).

15. M. V. WHITING, *Chem. Brit.*, 482 (1966).

16. W. E. DOERING and H. H. ZEISS, *J. Am. Chem. Soc.*, **75,** 4733 (1953).

17. P. VON R. SCHLEYER and R. D. NICHOLAS, *J. Am. Chem. Soc.*, **83,** 2700 (1961).

18. R. C. FORT and P. VON R. SCHLEYER, *J. Am. Chem. Soc.*, **86,** 4194 (1964).

19. R. D. HEYDING and C. A. WINKLER, *Can. J. Chem.*, **29,** 790 (1951).

20. K. A. COOPER, M. L. DHAR, E. D. HUGHES, C. K. INGOLD, B. J. MACNULTY, and L. I. WOOLF, *J. Chem. Soc.*, 2043 (1948).

21. S. G. SMITH, A. H. FAINBERG, and S. WINSTEIN, *J. Am. Chem. Soc.*, **83,** 618 (1961).

22. J. E. LEFFLER and E. GRUNWALD, *Rates and Equilibria of Organic Reactions*, John Wiley & Sons, New York (1963), Chaps. 8 and 9.

23. E. M. ARNETT, W. G. BENTRUDE, J. J. BURKE, and P. McC. DUGGLEBY, *J. Am. Chem. Soc.*, **87,** 1541 (1965).

24. N. T. FARINACCI and L. P. HAMMETT, *J. Am. Chem. Soc.*, **59,** 2544 (1937).

25. L. C. BATEMAN, M. G. CHURCH, E. D. HUGHES, C. K. INGOLD, and N. A. TAHER, *J. Chem. Soc.*, 979 (1940).

26. L. C. BATEMAN, E. D. HUGHES, and C. K. INGOLD, *J. Chem. Soc.*, 960 and 1014 (1940).

27. S. WINSTEIN, M. HOJO, and S. SMITH, *Tetrahedron Letters*, 12 (1960); S. WINSTEIN and J. S. GALL, *Tetrahedron Letters*, 31 (1960); S. WINSTEIN, J. S. GALL, M. HOJO, and S. SMITH, *J. Am. Chem. Soc.*, **82,** 1010 (1960).

28. H. L. GOERING and J. F. LEVY, *J. Am. Chem. Soc.*, **85,** 3059 (1963); *J. Am. Chem. Soc.*, **86,** 120 (1964).

29. S. WINSTEIN, P. E. KLINEDINST, and E. CLIPPINGER, *J. Am. Chem. Soc.*, 4986 (1961) and earlier papers.

30. S. WINSTEIN, B. APPEL, R. BAKER, and A. DIAZ, *Organic Reaction Mechanisms*, Special Publication No. 19, The Chemical Society, London (1965), p. 109.

31. E. GRUNWALD and S. WINSTEIN, *J. Am. Chem. Soc.*, **70,** 846 (1959).

32. J. D. REINHEIMER and J. F. BUNNETT, *J. Am. Chem. Soc.*, **81,** 315 (1959).

33. G. F. SMITH, *J. Chem. Soc.*, 521 (1943).

34. J. O. EDWARDS and R. G. PEARSON, *J. Am. Chem. Soc.*, **84,** 16 (1962).

35. R. F. HUDSON and G. KLOPMAN, *J. Chem. Soc.*, 5 (1964).

36. N. KORNBLUM, R. A. SMILEY, R. K. BLACKWOOD, and D. C. IFFLAND, *J. Am. Chem. Soc.*, **77,** 6269 (1955).

37. R. GOMPPER, *Angew. Chem. Int. Edn.*, **3,** 560 (1964).

38. R. C. KERBER, G. W. URRY, and N. KORNBLUM, *J. Am. Chem. Soc.*, **87,** 4520 (1965).

39. N. KORNBLUM, W. J. JONES, and D. E. HARDIES, *J. Am. Chem. Soc.*, **88,** 1704 (1966); N. KORNBLUM and D. E. HARDIES, *J. Am. Chem. Soc.*, **88,** 1707 (1966).

40. H. M. R. HOFFMANN, *J. Chem. Soc.*, 6753 and 6762 (1965).

41. P. B. D. DE LA MARE, L. FOWDEN, E. D. HUGHES, C. K. INGOLD, and J. D. H. MACKIE, *J. Chem. Soc.*, 3200 (1955) and earlier papers.

42. B. CAPON, *Quart. Rev. (London)*, **18,** 45 (1964).

43. D. J. CRAM, *J. Am. Chem. Soc.*, **71,** 3863 (1949); **74,** 2129 and 2137 (1952).

44. W. B. SMITH and M. SHOWALTER, reported in reference 5.

45. D. J. CRAM, *J. Am. Chem. Soc.*, **86,** 3767 (1964).

46. H. C. BROWN, K. J. MORGAN, and F. J. CHLOUPEK, *J. Am. Chem. Soc.*, **87,** 2137 (1965).

47. H. C. BROWN, R. BERNHEIMER, C. J. KIM, and S. E. SCHEPPELE, *J. Am. Chem. Soc.*, **89,** 370 (1967).

48. S. WINSTEIN, B. K. MORSE, E. GRUNWALD, K. C. SCHREIBER, and J. COURSE, *J. Am. Chem. Soc.*, **74,** 1113 (1952).

49. S. WINSTEIN, M. BROWN, K. C. SCHREIBER, and A. H. SCHLESINGER, *J. Am. Chem. Soc.*, **74,** 1140 (1952).

50. R. BAIRD and S. WINSTEIN, *J. Am. Chem. Soc.*, **85,** 567 (1963).

51. G. A. OLAH, E. NAMANWORTH, M. B. COMISAROW, and B. RAMSEY, *J. Am. Chem. Soc.*, **89,** 711 (1967).

52. G. A. OLAH, N. A. OVERCHUK, and J. C. LAPIERRE, *J. Am. Chem. Soc.*, **87,** 5785 (1965).

53. P. D. BARTLETT, *Nonclassical Ions*, W. A. Benjamin, New York (1965).

54. S. WINSTEIN and H. J. LUCAS, *J. Am. Chem. Soc.*, **61,** 2845 (1939).

55. S. WINSTEIN, E. GRUNWALD, and L. L. INGRAHAM, *J. Am. Chem. Soc.*, **70,** 821 (1948).

56. E. GRUNWALD, *J. Am. Chem. Soc.*, **73,** 5458 (1951).

57. H. L. GOERING and K. L. HOWE, *J. Am. Chem. Soc.*, **79,** 6542 (1957).

58. R. M. ROBERTS, J. CORSE, R. BOSCHAN, D. SEYMOUR, and S. WINSTEIN, *J. Am. Chem. Soc.*, **80,** 1247 (1958).

59. R. H. DEWOLFE and W. G. YOUNG, *Chem. Revs.*, **56,** 753 (1956).

60. C. A. VERNON, *J. Chem. Soc.*, 4462 (1954).

61. P. B. D. DE LA MARE and C. A. VERNON, *J. Chem. Soc.*, 3555 (1953).

62. G. STORK and W. N. WHITE, *J. Am. Chem. Soc.*, **78,** 4609 (1956).

63. C. A. VERNON, *J. Chem. Soc.*, 423 (1954).

64. W. G. YOUNG, S. WINSTEIN, and H. L. GOERING, *J. Am. Chem. Soc.*, **73,** 1958 (1951).

65. J. K. KOCHI, *J. Am. Chem. Soc.*, **84,** 3271 (1964).

66. J. B. ROGAN, *J. Org. Chem.*, **27,** 3910 (1962).

67. K. L. SERVIS and J. D. ROBERTS, *J. Am. Chem. Soc.*, **86,** 3773 (1964).

68. J. D. ROBERTS and R. H. MAZUR, *J. Am. Chem. Soc.*, **73,** 2509 (1951).

69. R. H. MAZUR, W. N. WHITE, D. A. SEMENOW, C. C. LEE, M. S. SILVER, and J. D. ROBERTS, *J. Am. Chem. Soc.*, **81,** 4390 (1959).

70. H. C. BROWN, *The Transition State*, Special Publication No. 16, The Chemical Society, London (1962), p. 155; H. C. BROWN and H. M. BELL, *J. Am. Chem. Soc.*, **85,** 2324 (1963).

71. N. C. DENO, in *Progress in Physical Organic Chemistry*, Vol. 2, (Eds. S. G. Cohen, A. Streitwieser and R. W. Taft), Interscience Publishers, New York (1964), p. 129.

72. J. D. ROBERTS, C. C. LEE, and W. H. SAUNDERS, *J. Am. Chem. Soc.*, **77**, 3034 (1953).

73. S. WINSTEIN and M. SHATAVSKY, *J. Am. Chem. Soc.*, **78**, 592 (1956).

74. S. WINSTEIN, M. SHATAVSKY, C. NORTON, and R. B. WOODWARD, *J. Am. Chem. Soc.*, **77**, 4183 (1955).

75. A. DIAZ, M. BROOKHART, and S. WINSTEIN, *J. Am. Chem. Soc.*, **88**, 3133 and 3135 (1966).

76. H. G. RICHEY and R. K. LUSTGARTEN, *J. Am. Chem. Soc.*, **88**, 3136 (1966).

77. S. WINSTEIN and C. ORDRONNEAU, *J. Am. Chem. Soc.*, **82**, 2084 (1960).

78. P. R. STORY and M. SAUNDERS, *J. Am. Chem. Soc.*, **84**, 4876 (1962); P. R. STORY, L. C. SNYDER, D. C. DOUGLAS, E. W. ANDERSON, and R. L. KORNEGAY, *J. Am. Chem. Soc.*, **85**, 3630 (1963).

79. C. H. DEPUY, I. A. OGAWA, and J. C. MCDANIEL, *J. Am. Chem. Soc.*, **83**, 1668 (1961).

80. P. D. BARTLETT and W. P. GIDDINGS, *J. Am. Chem. Soc.*, **82**, 1240 (1960).

81. H. TANIDA and H. ISHITOBI, *J. Am. Chem. Soc.*, **88**, 3663 (1966).

82. S. WINSTEIN and P. CARTER, *J. Am. Chem. Soc.*, **83**, 4485 (1961).

83. J. A. BERSON, in *Molecular Rearrangements*, Part 1, (Ed. P. deMayo), Interscience Publishers, New York (1963), pp. 111–231.

84. G. D. SARGENT, *Quart. Rev. (London)*, **20**, 301 (1966).

85. H. C. BROWN, *Chem. Brit.*, 199 (1966); *Chem. Eng. News*, **45**, 87 (1967).

86. S. WINSTEIN and D. TRIFAN, *J. Am. Chem. Soc.*, **71**, 2953 (1949); *J. Am. Chem. Soc.*, **74**, 1147 and 1154 (1952); S. WINSTEIN, B. K. MORSE, E. GRUNWALD, H. W. JONES, J. CORSE, D. TRIFAN, and H. MARSHALL, *J. Am. Chem. Soc.*, **74**, 1127 (1952).

87. S. WINSTEIN, E. CLIPPINGER, R. HOWE, and E. VOGELFANGER, *J. Am. Chem. Soc.*, **87**, 376 (1965).

88. P. VON R. SCHLEYER, M. M. DONALDSON, and W. E. WATTS, *J. Am. Chem. Soc.*, **87**, 377 (1965).

89. B. L. MURR, A. NICKON, T. D. SWARTZ, and N. H. WERSTIUK, *J. Am. Chem. Soc.*, **89**, 1732 (1967).

90. J. M. JERKUNICA, S. BORCIC, and D. E. SUNKO, *J. Am. Chem. Soc.*, **89**, 1732 (1967).

91. J. D. ROBERTS and C. C. LEE, *J. Am. Chem. Soc.*, **73**, 5009 (1951); J. D. ROBERTS, C. C. LEE, and W. H. SAUNDERS, *J. Am. Chem. Soc.*, **76**, 4501 (1954).

92. J. A. BERSON and P. W. GRUBB, *J. Am. Chem. Soc.*, **87**, 4016 (1965).

93. V. J. SHINER and J. G. JEWETT, *J. Am. Chem. Soc.*, **87**, 1382 (1965).

94. D. V. BANTHROPE, *Elimination Reactions*, Elsevier Publishing Co., New York (1963).

95. P. S. SKELL and C. R. HAUSER, *J. Am. Chem. Soc.*, **67**, 1661 (1945).

96. D. J. CRAM and F. A. A. ELHAFEZ, *J. Am. Chem. Soc.*, **74**, 5851 (1952).

97. C. H. DEPUY, G. F. MORRIS, J. S. SMITH, and R. J. SMAT, *J. Am. Chem. Soc.*, **87**, 2421 (1965).

98. H. C. BROWN and I. MORITANI, *J. Am. Chem. Soc.*, **78**, 2203 (1956).

99. A. C. COPE, N. A. LEBEL, H. H. LEE, and W. R. MOORE, *J. Am. Chem. Soc.*, **79**, 4720 (1957).

100. M. L. DHAR, E. D. HUGHES, C. K. INGOLD, and S. MASTERTON, *J. Chem. Soc.*, 2055, 2058 and 2065 (1948).

101. E. D. HUGHES, C. K. INGOLD, and L. I. WOLFF, *J. Chem. Soc.*, 2084 (1948).

102. K. A. COOPER, E. D. HUGHES, C. K. INGOLD, and B. J. MACNULTY, *J. Chem. Soc.*, 2038 (1948).
103. J. K. KOCHI, *J. Am. Chem. Soc.*, **85,** 1958 (1963).
104. H. C. BROWN and M. NAKAGAWA, *J. Am. Chem. Soc.*, **77,** 3614 (1955).
105. C. H. DePUY, C. A. BISHOP, and C. N. GOEDERS, *J. Am. Chem. Soc.*, **83,** 2151 (1961).
106. R. BORKOWSKI and P. AUSLOOS, *J. Am. Chem. Soc.*, **83,** 1053 (1961).
107. A. STREITWIESER, *Molecular Orbital Theory for Organic Chemists*, John Wiley & Sons, New York (1961), Chapter 12.
108. L. VERBIT and E. BERLINER, *J. Am. Chem. Soc.*, **86,** 3307 (1964).

PHYSICAL AND CONVERSION CONSTANTS

PHYSICAL CONSTANTS

Avogadro's number	$N = 6.023 \times 10^{23}$ mole^{-1}
Boltzmann's constant	$\mathbf{k} = 1.380 \times 10^{-16}$ erg. deg^{-1}
Planck's constant	$h = 6.625 \times 10^{-27}$ erg. sec
Gas constant	$R = 8.314 \times 10^7$ erg. mole^{-1}. deg^{-1}
	0.08206 liter. atm. mole^{-1}. deg^{-1}
	1.987 cal. mole^{-1}. deg^{-1}
Mass of an electron	$m = 9.108 \times 10^{-28}$ gm
Mass of a proton	$M = 1.672 \times 10^{-24}$ gm
Electronic charge	$e = 1.662 \times 10^{-10}$ Coulombs
	4.803×10^{-10} esu
Velocity of light	$C = 2.998 \times 10^{10}$ cm. sec^{-1}

ENERGY CONVERSION FACTORS

1 electron volt $= 8066.0$ cm^{-1}
1.602×10^{-12} erg. molecule^{-1}
23.06 kcal. mole^{-1}
1 cm$^{-1} = 1.988 \times 10^{-16}$ erg. molecule^{-1}
2.859×10^{-2} kcal. mole^{-1}
1.240×10^{-4} electron. volts
1 erg. molecule$^{-1} = 5.035 \times 10^{15}$ cm^{-1}
1.440×10^{13} kcal. mole^{-1}
6.242×10^{11} electron. volts
1 kcal. mole$^{-1} = 349.8$ cm^{-1}
6.947×10^{-14} erg. molecule^{-1}
4.336×10^{-2} electron. volts

APPLICATION OF GROUP THEORY: SYMMETRY SIMPLIFICATIONS

The principal difficulty with calculations of the type we have been carrying out is expanding the secular determinant. A large determinant can be reduced to several smaller ones if the molecule possesses an axis of symmetry. The process involves first choosing trial wave functions with different symmetry properties that are dependent upon the molecule. Each smaller determinant is formed from the trial functions belonging to the same symmetry species and these smaller determinants may then be solved by the method of cofactors or any other standard procedure.

We shall not be concerned with theory but only with the method as a tool. The proper definitions of the intermediate orbitals can be obtained with *group theory procedures*. To do this and ultimately to obtain the solutions sought, six steps should be followed:

1. Draw the π system, labeling the orbitals and indicating the nodal plane of the p orbitals.

2. Determine the type of symmetry involved and find the appropriate character table.

3. Carry out the symmetry operations. A symmetry operation is a rotation about an axis, a reflection in a plane, or an inversion through a center of symmetry that leaves the molecule unaltered. Atoms that are transformed into other atoms by the symmetry operation are given the character 0; an atom that is unchanged by the operation is given the character $+1$; an atom that is converted to minus itself, i.e. is turned upside down, is given the character -1. In this manner the reducible representation is obtained.

4. Determine the number of symmetry orbitals belonging to each irreducible representation.

5. Obtain the symmetry orbitals.

6. Convert these trial wave functions into secular determinants and solve.

Let us discuss each step while working examples. Although we can easily solve the determinant for allyl, this is also easily reduced to smaller determinants.

1. The first step is obvious (Fig. B–1). Because we do not consider nonneighbor interactions in the Hückel approach we could just as well draw allyl as a linear molecule, but then we would obtain a different symmetry for the molecule. Although this would serve our immediate purpose just as well as specifying the bent

316

geometry, we might as well make the approach as general as possible. Similarly, all atoms can be treated as spheres lacking the nodal plane of the molecule but this procedure also leads to incorrect symmetry species. Again, it is not difficult to obtain the correct results, although these simplifications can be used to obtain smaller secular determinants.

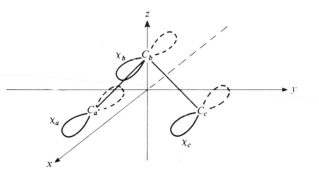

Fig. B–1. Coordinate system for allyl.

2. Finding the correct symmetry involved is more difficult but we shall make no errors if we assume less symmetry than a molecule actually has. For this reason we will not discuss all symmetry operations. Most secular determinants can be broken down by using only four symmetry operations. The first is the trivial one of leaving the molecule alone, the identity operation E. The second, rotation about an axis of symmetry, is designated as C_p and indicates a rotation of $360/p$ degrees about a p-fold axis. For simplicity we will look only for two-fold symmetry axes—those about which a rotation of $180°$ turns the molecule into itself. The third symmetry operation, reflection in a plane, is designated σ. If the plane is parallel to the axis of symmetry it is denoted as σ_v; if it is perpendicular to this axis it is σ_h. The fourth operation, i, is inversion through a point center of symmetry. These symmetry operations (together with their names and symbols) may be summarized as:

Symmetry operation	Symmetry element (name)	Symbol
1. Leave molecule alone	Identity element	E
2. Rotate about axis through $360/p$ degrees	p-Fold axis of symmetry	C_p
3. Reflect in a plane	Plane of symmetry	σ
a) If plane includes the axis of symmetry		σ_v
b) If plane is perpendicular to the axis of symmetry		σ_h
4. Invert through a point of symmetry	Center of symmetry	i

If a molecule has only a p-fold axis of symmetry it belongs to the point group C_p, but if it also has p two-fold symmetry axes perpendicular to the p-fold axis it belongs to the group D_p. If a compound has a p-fold axis of symmetry, no other two-fold axes, but a plane of symmetry parallel to the p-fold axis, the group is C_{pv} and if the plane is perpendicular to the p-fold axis, its group is C_{nh}. The character tables are labeled with these point-group names and the symmetry operations are given in the boxheads (Tables B–1 through B–4).

Table B–1. Character Table for C_{2v}

C_{2v}	E	C_2	$\sigma_v(zx)$	$\sigma_v(yz)$
A_1	1	1	1	1
A_2	1	1	-1	-1
B_1	1	-1	1	-1
B_2	1	-1	-1	1

Table B–2.
Character Table for C_2

C_2	E	C_2
A	1	1
B	1	-1

Table B–3. Character Table for D_2

D_2	E	$C_2(z)$	$C_2(y)$	$C_2(x)$
A	1	1	1	1
B_1	1	1	-1	-1
B_2	1	-1	1	-1
B_3	1	-1	-1	1

Table B–4. Character Table for D_{2h}

D_{2h}	E	$C_2(z)$	$C_2(y)$	$C_2(x)$	i	σ_{xy}	σ_{zx}	σ_{yz}
A_g	1	1	1	1	1	1	1	1
B_{1g}	1	1	-1	-1	1	1	-1	-1
B_{2g}	1	-1	1	-1	1	-1	1	-1
B_{3g}	1	-1	-1	1	1	-1	-1	1
A_u	1	1	1	1	-1	-1	-1	-1
B_{1u}	1	1	-1	-1	-1	-1	1	1
B_{2u}	1	-1	1	-1	-1	1	-1	1
B_{3u}	1	-1	-1	1	-1	1	1	-1

For allyl there is a two-fold axis and two planes parallel to this axis (Fig. B–2). Thus, allyl belongs to the C_{2v} point group and Table B–1 is the appropriate one. The tables also give further information. The A species are symmetric about the principal axis of rotation while B species are antisymmetric. The subscripts indicate species that are symmetric (1) or antisymmetric (2) with respect to reflection in C_{pv} or rotation about the two-fold axes in the D_p group. The g and u subscripts indicate species that are symmetric or antisymmetric with respect to a center of inversion. When there are three equivalent axes of symmetry, the B species which is symmetric with respect to rotation about the long z-axis is given the subscript 1, subscript 2 is assigned to that species symmetric with respect to rotation about the y-axis and the species symmetric with respect to rotation about the x-axis is assigned the subscript 3.

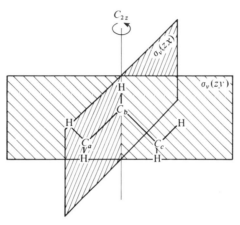

Fig. B–2. Symmetry of allyl.

3. In carrying out the symmetry operations it is a great help to adopt some systematic procedure. The trivial case of the identity operation leaves all atoms unchanged. Each atom therefore is assigned a value of 1. The C_{2z} operation converts atom a into atom c and atom c into atom a, so both atoms are given a value of 0. Atom b is inverted and given a value of -1. The two σ_v symmetry elements are treated in the same manner. The results are tabulated in Table B–5, which should not

Table B–5. Transformation for Allyl

Orbital	E	C_{2z}	$\sigma_v(zx)$	$\sigma_v(yz)$
χ_a	1	0	0	-1
χ_b	1	-1	1	-1
χ_c	1	0	0	-1
	3	-1	1	-3

be confused with the apparently similar character tables. Below the line we sum the numbers for each operation.

4. To obtain the number of irreducible representations (Γ) contained in the reducible representation (Table B–5), we sum the products of the numbers below the line in this table, the respective terms for each row in the character table, and the coefficients for each operation given at the top of the table (all one in this case) and then divide by the total number of symmetry operations. Thus, for allyl

$$n_{A_1} = \tfrac{1}{4}[3 \cdot 1 \cdot 1 + (-1 \cdot 1 \cdot 1) + 1 \cdot 1 \cdot 1 + (-3 \cdot 1 \cdot 1)] = 0.$$

There is no orbital of a_1 symmetry in allyl. Similarly, using the other irreducible representations, we obtain one orbital with A_2 and two with B_1 symmetry properties:

$$n_{A_2} = \tfrac{1}{4}[3 \cdot 1 \cdot 1 + (-1 \cdot 1 \cdot 1) + 1 \cdot -1 \cdot 1 + (-3 \cdot -1 \cdot 1)] = 1,$$
$$n_{B_1} = \tfrac{1}{4}[3 \cdot 1 \cdot 1 + (-1 \cdot -1 \cdot 1) + 1 \cdot 1 \cdot 1 + (-3 \cdot -1 \cdot 1)] = 2,$$
$$n_{B_2} = \tfrac{1}{4}[3 \cdot 1 \cdot 1 + (-1 \cdot -1 \cdot 1) + 1 \cdot -1 \cdot 1 + (-3 \cdot 1 \cdot 1)] = 0.$$

There is a determinant for each row in the character table of order equal to the numbers computed in this manner. Thus we have reduced the original 3×3 determinant to one 1×1 and one 2×2 determinant.

5. To obtain the trial wave functions we again carry out the symmetry operations but this time we write down the orbitals that are generated by the transformation using a minus sign to indicate that an orbital is inverted (Table B–6). We now take

Table B–6.

Orbital	E	C_{2z}	$\sigma_v(zx)$	$\sigma_v(yz)$
χ_a	χ_a	$-\chi_c$	χ_c	$-\chi_a$
χ_b	χ_b	$-\chi_b$	χ_b	$-\chi_b$
χ_c	χ_c	$-\chi_a$	χ_a	$-\chi_c$

the matrix product of the horizontal row of the character table for each irreducible representation and of the transformation of orbital table that we just obtained. Since we have no a_1 representation we need not carry out that multiplication. For the a_2 representation we obtain

$$a_2\Phi_1 = (\chi_a - \chi_c + \chi_c - \chi_a)\begin{pmatrix} 1 \\ 1 \\ -1 \\ -1 \end{pmatrix}$$

$$= \chi_a - \chi_c - \chi_c + \chi_a = 2\chi_a - 2\chi_c$$

and

$$a_2\Phi_{1'} = (\chi_b - \chi_b + \chi_b - \chi_b)\begin{pmatrix} 1 \\ 1 \\ -1 \\ -1 \end{pmatrix}$$

$$= 0.$$

For the b_1 representation

$$b_1\Phi_2 = (\chi_a - \chi_c + \chi_c - \chi_a)\begin{pmatrix} 1 \\ -1 \\ 1 \\ -1 \end{pmatrix}$$

$$= \chi_a + \chi_c + \chi_c + \chi_a = 2\chi_a + 2\chi_c$$

and

$$b_1\Phi_3 = (\chi_b - \chi_b + \chi_b - \chi_b)\begin{pmatrix} 1 \\ -1 \\ 1 \\ -1 \end{pmatrix}$$

$$= \chi_b + \chi_b + \chi_b + \chi_b = 4\chi_b.$$

All other products will either be zero or equal to one of these. The b_2 representation need not be used, since we have already found that it, like the a_1, does not contain an orbital.

The three trial orbitals that we have obtained must be normalized:

$$a_2\Phi_1 = (1/\sqrt{2})(\chi_a - \chi_c),$$
$$b_1\Phi_2 = (1/\sqrt{2})(\chi_a + \chi_c),$$
$$b_1\Phi_3 = \chi_b.$$

6. We are now ready to convert these trial wave functions into secular determinants. For the a_2 representation the determinant is 1×1 in the form

$$|H_{11} - E| = 0,$$

where $H_{11} = \int \Phi_1 H\Phi_1 \, d\tau$. For $a_2\Phi_1$ this is

$$H_{11} = \int \frac{1}{\sqrt{2}}(\chi_a - \chi_c)H\frac{1}{\sqrt{2}}(\chi_a - \chi_c) \, d\tau$$

$$= \tfrac{1}{2}\int \chi_a H\chi_a \, d\tau - \tfrac{1}{2}\cdot 2\int \chi_a H\chi_c \, d\tau + \tfrac{1}{2}\int \chi_c H\chi_c \, d\tau,$$

since $\int \chi_a H\chi_a \, d\tau = \alpha$ and $\int \chi_a H\chi_c \, d\tau = 0$. This becomes

$$H_{11} = \tfrac{1}{2}\alpha - 0 + \tfrac{1}{2}\alpha = \alpha$$

and the determinant is

$$|H_{11} - E| = |\alpha - E| = 0.$$

The 2×2 determinant for b_1 takes the form

$$\begin{vmatrix} H_{11} - E & H_{12} \\ H_{21} & H_{22} - E \end{vmatrix} = 0.$$

We need to determine H_{11}, $H_{12} = H_{21}$, and H_{22}. For Φ_2 and Φ_3 they are:

$$H_{11} = \int \Phi_2 H \Phi_2 \, d\tau = \int \frac{1}{\sqrt{2}} (\chi_a + \chi_c) H \frac{1}{\sqrt{2}} (\chi_a + \chi_c) \, d\tau$$

$$= \alpha$$

$$H_{12} = H_{21} = \int \Phi_2 H \Phi_3 \, d\tau = \int \frac{1}{\sqrt{2}} (\chi_a + \chi_c) H \chi_b \, d\tau$$

$$= \frac{1}{\sqrt{2}} [\int \chi_a H \chi_b \, d\tau + \int \chi_c H \chi_b \, d\tau]$$

$$= \frac{1}{\sqrt{2}} (\beta + \beta) = \sqrt{2}\beta.$$

Similarly, $H_{22} = \int \Phi_3 H \Phi_3 \, d\tau = \alpha$. The secular determinant is then obtained as

$$\begin{vmatrix} \alpha - E & \sqrt{2}\beta \\ \sqrt{2}\beta & \alpha - E \end{vmatrix} = 0 = \begin{vmatrix} x & \sqrt{2} \\ \sqrt{2} & x \end{vmatrix}$$

The two b_1 trial wave functions are a set of linear equations that correspond to the 2×2 determinant. If the orbitals that we are obtaining were the actual symmetry orbitals, each of the trial functions would lead to a 1×1 determinant. The 2×2 determinant may be solved for the values of χ to find the energy levels and then the coefficients of ϕ_2 and ϕ_3 may be obtained. As we have seen, these two trial wave functions have the same symmetry and may be recombined to give the wave function

$$\Psi = C_1 \phi_2 + C_2 \phi_3.$$

Since we have already obtained the coefficients for allyl, let us work them out for another molecule. We will also use fewer symmetry operations than are possible to see what is the effect of this upon our result. Let us select benzene, which is a highly symmetrical molecule, and go through the treatment again, following the six steps used for allyl.

1. We place the benzene ring in the XY plane, as shown in Fig. B–3.
2. Although benzene has a six-fold axis of symmetry, we shall ignore it and call the z-axis a two-fold principal axis. We shall also ignore the several planes of symmetry and the center of inversion and treat the x- and y-axes as two perpendicular two-fold axes. Thus, by this assignment, benzene will be treated with the D_2 point group and we will use that character table (Table B–3).
3. The D_2 transformation for benzene is given in Table B–7.
4. The irreducible representations are:

$$n_A = \tfrac{1}{4}[6 \cdot 1 \cdot 1 + 0 \cdot 1 \cdot 1 + (-2 \cdot 1 \cdot 1) + 0 \cdot 1 \cdot 1] = 1,$$
$$n_{B_1} = \tfrac{1}{4}[6 \cdot 1 \cdot 1 + 0 \cdot 1 \cdot 1 + (-2 \cdot -1 \cdot 1) + 0 \cdot -1 \cdot 1] = 2,$$
$$n_{B_2} = \tfrac{1}{4}[6 \cdot 1 \cdot 1 + 0 \cdot -1 \cdot 1 + (-2 \cdot 1 \cdot 1) + 0 \cdot -1 \cdot 1] = 1,$$
$$n_{B_3} = \tfrac{1}{4}[6 \cdot 1 \cdot 1 + 0 \cdot -1 \cdot 1 + (-2 \cdot -1 \cdot 1) + 0 \cdot -1 \cdot 1] = 2.$$

The 6×6 determinant is broken into two 1×1 and two 2×2 determinants.

Table B–7.

Orbital	E	C_{2z}	C_{2y}	C_{2x}
χ_a	1	0	-1	0
χ_b	1	0	0	0
χ_c	1	0	0	0
χ_d	1	0	-1	0
χ_e	1	0	0	0
χ_f	1	0	0	0
	6	0	-2	0

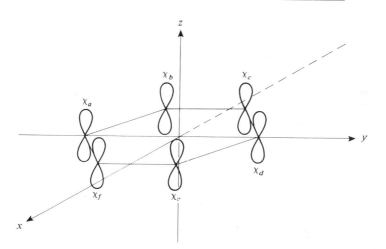

Fig. B–3. Coordinate system for benzene.

5. Transformation of orbitals gives the data in Table B–8.

Table B–8.

Orbital	E	C_{2z}	C_{2y}	C_{2x}
χ_a	χ_a	χ_d	$-\chi_a$	$-\chi_d$
χ_b	χ_b	χ_e	$-\chi_f$	$-\chi_c$
χ_c	χ_c	χ_f	$-\chi_e$	$-\chi_b$
χ_d	χ_d	χ_a	$-\chi_d$	$-\chi_a$
χ_e	χ_e	χ_b	$-\chi_c$	$-\chi_f$
χ_f	χ_f	χ_c	$-\chi_b$	$-\chi_e$

We now obtain the normalized trial functions

$$\Phi_1 a = \Psi_A = \tfrac{1}{2}(\chi_b - \chi_c + \chi_e - \chi_f),$$

$$\Phi_2 b_1 = \frac{1}{\sqrt{2}}(\chi_a + \chi_d),$$

$$\Phi_3 b_1 = \tfrac{1}{2}(\chi_b + \chi_c + \chi_e + \chi_f).$$

The last two trial functions have the same symmetry and can be combined to give

$$\Psi_B = \frac{C_1}{\sqrt{2}}(\chi_a + \chi_d) + \frac{C_2}{2}(\chi_b + \chi_c + \chi_e + \chi_f).$$

Furthermore,

$$\Phi_4 b_2 = \Psi_c = \tfrac{1}{2}(\chi_b + \chi_c - \chi_e - \chi_f),$$

$$\Phi_5 b_3 = \frac{1}{\sqrt{2}}(\chi_a - \chi_d),$$

and

$$\Phi_6 b_3 = \tfrac{1}{2}(\chi_b - \chi_c - \chi_e + \chi_f)$$

can be combined to give

$$\Psi_D = \frac{C_3}{\sqrt{2}}(\chi_a - \chi_d) + \frac{C_4}{2}(\chi_b - \chi_c - \chi_e + \chi_f).$$

6. The determinant for the a group will be of the form

$$|H_{11} - E| = 0$$

$$H_{11} = \tfrac{1}{4}\int (\chi_b - \chi_c + \chi_e - \chi_f)H(\chi_b - \chi_c + \chi_e - \chi_f)\, d\tau$$

$$= \tfrac{1}{4}[\alpha - \beta - \beta + \alpha + \alpha - \beta - \beta + \alpha] = \alpha - \beta$$

$$|\alpha - \beta - E| = 0; \quad E = \alpha - \beta$$

For the b_1 group we have a determinant of 2×2 form:

$$\begin{vmatrix} H_{11} - E & H_{12} \\ H_{21} & H_{22} - E \end{vmatrix} = 0$$

$$H_{11} = \tfrac{1}{2}\int (\chi_a + \chi_d)H(\chi_a + \chi_d)\, d\tau = \alpha$$

$$H_{12} = H_{21} = \frac{1}{2\sqrt{2}}\int (\chi_a + \chi_d)H(\chi_b + \chi_c + \chi_e + \chi_f)\, d\tau = \beta\sqrt{2}$$

$$H_{22} = \tfrac{1}{4}\int (\chi_b + \chi_c + \chi_e + \chi_f)H(\chi_b + \chi_c + \chi_e + \chi_f)\, d\tau = \alpha + \beta$$

$$\begin{vmatrix} \alpha - E & \beta\sqrt{2} \\ \beta\sqrt{2} & \alpha + \beta - E \end{vmatrix} = \begin{vmatrix} x & \sqrt{2} \\ \sqrt{2} & (x + 1) \end{vmatrix} = 0$$

$$x^2 + x - 2 = 0; \quad (x + 2)(x - 1) = 0; \quad x = 1, -2$$

$$E = \alpha - \beta; \quad E = \alpha + 2\beta$$

For the b_2 group it is:

$$H_{11} = \tfrac{1}{4} \int (\chi_b + \chi_c - \chi_e - \chi_f) H(\chi_b + \chi_c - \chi_e - \chi_f)\, d\tau = \alpha + \beta$$
$$|\alpha + \beta - E| = 0; \quad E = \alpha + \beta.$$

Finally, the 2×2 determinant for the b_3 group is:

$$H_{11} = \frac{1}{\sqrt{2}} \int (\chi_a - \chi_d) H(\chi_a - \chi_d) = \alpha$$

$$H_{12} = H_{21} = \frac{1}{2\sqrt{2}} \int (\chi_a - \chi_d) H(\chi_b - \chi_c - \chi_e + \chi_f)\, d\tau = \beta\sqrt{2}$$

$$H_{22} = \tfrac{1}{4} \int (\chi_b - \chi_c - \chi_e + \chi_f) H(\chi_b - \chi_c - \chi_e + \chi_f)\, d\tau$$
$$= \alpha - \beta$$

$$\begin{vmatrix} \alpha - E & \beta\sqrt{2} \\ \beta\sqrt{2} & \alpha - \beta - E \end{vmatrix} = \begin{vmatrix} x & \sqrt{2} \\ \sqrt{2} & x - 1 \end{vmatrix} = x^2 - x - 2 = 0$$

$$x = 2, -1$$
$$E = \alpha - 2\beta; \quad E = \alpha + \beta.$$

We have now obtained the energies of the six molecular orbitals.

To find the coefficients for the molecular orbitals, we treat each irreducible representation separately. For the A and B_2 representations, we already have the normalized wave functions:

$$A: \Psi_A = \tfrac{1}{2}(\chi_b - \chi_c + \chi_e - \chi_f),$$
$$B_2: \Psi_C = \tfrac{1}{2}(\chi_b + \chi_c - \chi_e - \chi_f).$$

For the B_1 representation we use the determinant obtained earlier and proceed as in Chapter 4:

$$\begin{vmatrix} x & \sqrt{2} \\ \sqrt{2} & x + 1 \end{vmatrix} = 0.$$

For $x = -2$,

r	A_r	A_r^2	C
1	-1	1	$-1/\sqrt{3}$
2	$-\sqrt{2}$	$\tfrac{2}{3}$	$-\sqrt{2}/\sqrt{3}$

$$\Psi_B = (C_1/\sqrt{2})(\chi_a + \chi_d) + (C_2/2)(\chi_b + \chi_c + \chi_e + \chi_f).$$

Substitution affords

$$\Psi_B = \left(-\frac{1}{\sqrt{3}}\Big/\sqrt{2}\right)(\chi_a + \chi_d) + \left(-\frac{\sqrt{2}}{\sqrt{3}}\Big/2\right)(\chi_b + \chi_c + \chi_e + \chi_f)$$
$$= -(1/\sqrt{6})(\chi_a + \chi_b + \chi_c + \chi_d + \chi_e + \chi_f).$$

For $x = 1$,

$\dfrac{r}{1}$	$\dfrac{A_r}{2}$	$\dfrac{A_r^2}{4}$	$\dfrac{C}{\sqrt{2}/\sqrt{3}}$
2	$-\sqrt{2}$	$\dfrac{2}{6}$	$-1/\sqrt{3}$

$$\Psi'_B = \frac{1}{\sqrt{3}}(\chi_a + \chi_d) - \frac{1}{2\sqrt{3}}(\chi_b + \chi_c + \chi_e + \chi_f).$$

Finally, for the B_3 representation, the wave functions

$$x = 2; \quad \Psi'_D = \frac{1}{\sqrt{6}}(\chi_a - \chi_b + \chi_c - \chi_d + \chi_e - \chi_f)$$

and

$$x = -1; \quad \Psi'_D = -\frac{1}{\sqrt{3}}(\chi_a - \chi_d) - \frac{1}{2\sqrt{3}}(\chi_c - \chi_d - \chi_e + \chi_f)$$

are obtained by the same procedure.

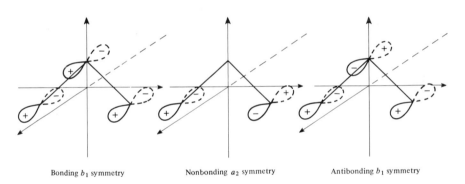

Bonding b_1 symmetry   Nonbonding a_2 symmetry   Antibonding b_1 symmetry

Fig. B–4. Symmetry species for allyl.

We might now ask what has been lost by not using all of the symmetry of benzene. If we had completed the solution for allyl, we would have found that the bonding and the antibonding orbitals are of b_1 symmetry and the nonbonding orbital is of a_2 symmetry (Fig. B–4). These are correct assignments. However, if we diagram our results for benzene we find that the orbitals are assigned to the wrong symmetry species (Fig. B–5). We must accept this incorrect assignment if we do not use all of the symmetry elements of a molecule. Nevertheless, the values of the coefficients are correctly obtained when less symmetry is assumed than actually exists and, since electron densities, bond orders, free valences, and charge densities are all obtained from the coefficients, these will be the same whether all of the symmetry is used or not. For spectroscopic purposes the complete symmetry classification must be used for the actual molecular geometry. If this is done, the approach described above will give the correct assignment.

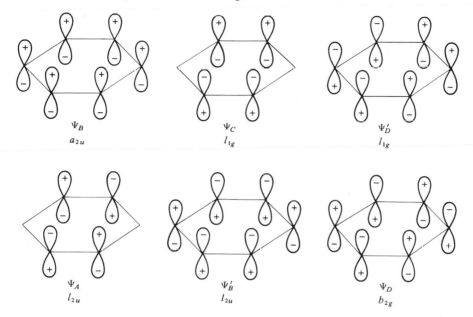

Fig. B–5. Molecular orbitals for benzene with correct classifications of D_{6h} symmetry. The symbol e is used for doubly degenerate species.

THE VARIATION PRINCIPLE

As stated in Chapter 3, the variation method is but one approach to finding approximate solutions of the wave equation. It is based upon the theorem that, if Φ is any normalized function such that $\int \Phi\Phi^* \, d\tau = 1$ and if the lowest eigenvalue of the operator H is E_0, then

$$\int \Phi^* H\Phi \, d\tau \geq E_0.$$

The proof of this theorem is not difficult. We begin with the integral

$$\int \Phi^*(H - E_0)\Phi \, d\tau = \int \Phi^* H\Phi \, d\tau - E_0 \int \Phi^*\Phi \, d\tau$$
$$= \int \Phi^* H\Phi \, d\tau - E_0.$$

We then expand the function Φ in a series of the eigenfunctions $\Psi_1, \Psi_2, \ldots, \Psi_i$ of H:

$$\int \Phi^*(H - E_0)\Phi \, d\tau = \int \left(\sum_i c_i^* \Psi_i^*\right)(H - E_0)\left(\sum_i c_i \Psi_i\right) d\tau.$$

We can substitute $E_i\Psi_i$ for $H\Psi_i$ because the Ψ_i's are eigenfunctions of H. Making this substitution gives

$$\int \Phi^*(H - E_0)\Phi \, d\tau = \int \left(\sum_i c_i^* \Psi_i^*\right)\left(\sum (E_i - E_0)c_i \Psi_i\right) d\tau$$
$$= \sum_i c_i^* c_i (E_i - E_0).$$

The product $c_i^* c_i$ is a positive number and E_0 was defined as the lowest eigenvalue of the operator H, so $E_i \geq E_0$. Thus,

$$\sum_i c_i^* c_i (E_i - E_0) \geq 0,$$

so

$$\int \Phi^*(H - E_0)\Phi \, d\tau \geq 0$$

and therefore

$$\int \Phi^* H\Phi \, d\tau \geq 0,$$

which is the original theorem. The equality sign can only hold when $\Phi = \Psi_0$, that is, where the eigenfunction Ψ_0 has the eigenvalue E_0.

The application of this theorem to the special case of linear combinations is given in Chapter 3.

AUTHOR INDEX

SUBJECT INDEX

ABCDE79876543210

ABCDE79876543210

HENRY SEEBOHM

THE BIRDS OF SIBERIA
TO THE PETCHORA VALLEY

ALAN SUTTON · Gloucester
HIPPOCRENE BOOKS, INC. · New York

First Published 1901

Copyright © in this edition 1985
Alan Sutton Publishing Limited

This edition first published in Great Britain 1985
Alan Sutton Publishing Limited
30 Brunswick Road
Gloucester GL1 1JJ

ISBN 0-86299-259-1

This edition first published in the U.S.A. 1986
Hippocrene Books, Inc.
171 Madison Avenue
New York, N.Y. 10016

ISBN 0-87052-188-8

Cover picture: Grey Plovers *by Carol Ogilvie*

Typesetting and origination by
Alan Sutton Publishing Limited.
Photoset Bembo 9/10.
Printed in Great Britain
by The Guernsey Press Company Limited,
Guernsey, Channel Islands.

PUBLISHERS' NOTE

For the purposes of this paperback edition the two parts of *The Birds of Siberia* have been printed as separate volumes under their individual part titles – *To the Petchora Valley* and *The Yenesei*.

The map and index from the original one volume format of 1901 have been included in *both* the paperback volumes. Inevitably they contain references to both parts, but it is hoped that their inclusion will enable the volumes to be read independently.

BIOGRAPHICAL NOTE

HENRY SEEBOHM (1832–95) was a Sheffield steel manu-
facturer. His successful business activities gave him the time
and the money to indulge in extensive travels throughout
Europe and parts of Asia. He became, by assiduous collecting
and acute observation, an ornithologist of great repute. His
two most remarkable journeys were those in 1875 and 1877 to
Siberia, to the basins of the Petchora and Yenesei Rivers
respectively. Here he found the hitherto unknown breeding
grounds of several birds, including Bewick's Swan, Grey
Plover and Little Stint. In addition he collected eggs and skins
of many rare or little known species and subspecies.

Seebohm wrote a number of definitive ornithological works
and a great many scientific papers. However the two books
about his Siberian journeys, *Siberia in Europe* (1882) and *Siberia
in Asia* (1884), subsequently reprinted in 1901 as a single
volume *The Birds of Siberia*, were written for a wider audience.
They combine the narrative of his often exciting experiences
with detailed accounts of the birds that he found. To get from
London to Yenesei took him two months, travelling by rail
and then sledge, drawn successively by horses, dogs and
reindeer. There are also charming descriptions of the people he
encountered and of their way of life. The successes, the
frustrations and the failures in his search for birds are all
recounted. These were not just collecting trips, however. The
detailed observations on nesting habits and behaviour are still
of interest coming as they do from a region that is hardly
better known to the English ornithologist today than it was a
hundred years ago.

MALCOLM OGILVIE

GREY PLOVER

CHAPTER I.

EARLY EXPLORERS.

John Wolley—Unknown Breeding-Grounds—Birds of Archangel and Lapland—Voyages to the Petchora in the Seventeenth Century—Schrenck's Visit in 1837—Castrén's Visit in 1842—Keyserling's Visit in 1843—Pelzam's Visit in 1874—Hoffmansegg's Visit about 1850—Outfit —Letters of Introduction.

THE history of British birds has been enthusiastically studied by ornithologists during the last half-century. In spring and autumn several species of birds annually visit our shores in considerable numbers, passing us in their migrations to and from unknown breeding-grounds. These migrations, and the geographical distribution of birds, have of late years occupied a large share of the attention of ornithologists. The name of John Wolley stands pre-eminent amongst the discoverers in this department of science. His indefatigable labours in Lapland are still fresh in the memory of the older generation of ornithologists, who will never cease to regret his untimely death. Notwithstanding his researches, there remained half a dozen well-known British birds whose breeding-grounds still continued wrapped in mystery, to solve which has been the ambition of many field naturalists during the past twenty years. These birds, to the discovery of whose eggs special interest seemed to attach, were the Grey Plover, the Little Stint, the Sanderling, the Curlew Sandpiper, the Knot,* and Bewick's Swan.

In 1872 my friend John A. Harvie-Brown accompanied E. R. Alston on an ornithological expedition to Archangel, the results of which were published in the "Ibis" for January 1873; and in 1874 I went with Robert Collett of Christiania to the north of Norway. Neither of these journeys added any very important fact to the stock of ornithological knowledge; but in each case they considerably increased our interest in Arctic ornithology, and gave us a knowledge of the notes and habits of many Arctic birds which was of invaluable assistance to us on our subsequent journeys. The difference between the birds found at Archangel and those at the north of Norway was so striking that we, as well as many of our ornithological friends, were convinced that another ten degrees east would bring us to the breeding-ground of many species new to North Europe; and there was also a chance that among these might be found some of the half-dozen birds which I have named, the discovery of whose breeding-haunts was the special object of our ambition.

* The Knot (*Tringa canutus*) was the only one of these six species of birds which we did not meet with in the valley of the Petchora. It probably breeds on the shores of the Polar Basin in both hemispheres, but its eggs were absolutely unknown until they were discovered on the west coast of Greenland a few years ago.

Harvie-Brown had been collecting information about the river Petchora for some time, and it was finally arranged that we should spend the summer of 1875 there together. We were under the impression that, ornithologically speaking, it was virgin ground, but in this we afterwards discovered that we were mistaken. So far as we were able to ascertain, no Englishman had travelled from Archangel to the Petchora for 250 years. In that curious old book called "Purchas his Pilgrimes," published in 1625, may be found the narratives of divers merchants and mariners who visited this river between the years 1611 and 1615 for the purpose of establishing a trade there in furs and skins, especially beaver, for which Ust-Zylma on the Petchora was at that time celebrated.

In 1837 Alexander Gustav Schrenck visited the Petchora under the auspices of the Imperial Botanical Gardens at St. Petersburg, and published voluminous information respecting the botany and the ethnology of this district.

In 1842 Castrén was sent out by the Swedish Government and collected much valuable information about the Samoyedes and the other races of North-East Russia. The following year, Paul von Krusenstern and Alexander Graf Keyserling visited the Petchora, and published an important work upon the geology and physical geography of the country, but none of these travellers seem to have written anything upon the subject of birds beyond a mere passing mention of ducks and geese. In St. Petersburg we learnt that Dr. Pelzam, from the Museum at Kazan, visited the Petchora in 1874, but he spent most of his time in dredging and paid little attention to birds. In Archangel we made a more important discovery. We there met the man who had been guide to Henke and Hoffmansegg about 1853. From him we learnt that these naturalists had spent a year or more on the Petchora, had there collected birds and eggs, and had been very successful.

Our outfit was simple. We determined to be trammelled with as little luggage as possible. Besides the necessary changes of clothing we took each a pair of Cording's india-rubber boots, which we found invaluable. To protect our faces from the mosquitoes, we provided ourselves with silk gauze veils, with a couple of wire hoops inserted opposite the bridge of the nose and the chin, like little crinolines. These simple *komarniks* proved a complete success. On a hot summer's day life without them would have been simply unendurable. Of course the heat and sense of being somewhat stifled had to be borne, as by far the lesser of two evils. Our hands we protected by the regulation cavalry gauntlet. We took two tents with us, but had no occasion to use them. Our net hammocks served as beds by night and sofas by day, and very luxurious we found them. We each took a double-barrelled breechloader and a walking-stick gun. Five hundred cartridges for each weapon, with the necessary appliances for reloading, we found amply sufficient. The only mistake we made was in not taking baking powder, nor sufficient dried vegetables and Liebig's extract of meat.

In travelling in Russia, it is of the utmost importance to be on good terms with the officials, and we were most fortunate in obtaining the best introductions. Our warmest thanks are due to Count Schouvaloff for his kindness in giving us letters that ensured us a welcome such as we could not have expected. They added greatly to the safety and success of our trip.

SLEDGING THROUGH THE SNOW

CHAPTER II.

LONDON TO ARCHANGEL.

London to St. Petersburg—Mode of Heating Railway Carriages—Frozen
Market at St. Petersburg—Bohemian Waxwings—Moscow to Vologda—
M. Verakin—Sledging from Vologda to Archangel—The Yemschik—
Post-houses—The Samovar—Angliski Russ—Modes of Harnessing
Horses—State of the Roads—Weather—Traffic—Birds seen *en route*—
Arrival at Archangel.

WE left London on the 3rd of March 1875. A journey
of four days and three nights, including a comfortable
night's rest at Cologne and a few hours each at Hanover
and Berlin, landed us in St. Petersburg. In Belgium it
was cold, but there was no snow. In Germany we saw
skaters on the ice, and there were patches of snow in
shady corners. As we proceeded eastward the snow and
cold increased, and in Russia the whole ground was from
one to two feet deep in snow, and sledges were the only

conveyances to be seen at the stations.   As far as Cologne
the railway carriages were heated by the ordinary hot-
water foot-warmer, and very comfortable they were, with
a temperature outside of about 40°.   From Hanover to
Berlin the carriages were heated with charcoal fires under
the seats, and the sense of oppression from foul air was
so intolerable, that we were only too glad to shiver with
the windows open and the thermometer down to 20°.
From Berlin to the frontier the carriages were heated by
steam-pipes, with an arrangement for regulating the heat,
and although the thermometer outside continued the
same, we were able to keep a comfortable temperature
of 60° without any sense of suffocation.   In Russia the
carriages were heated with wood fires, and we kept up
about the same temperature without any sense of dis-
comfort, although the thermometer had fallen to 5°
outside.   At Wirballen our letters of introduction saved
us from an immensity of trouble and formality, thanks to
the courtesy of M. de Pisanko and the other officials.

We spent four days at St. Petersburg, sight-seeing
and completing the preparations for our journey.   The
morning after our arrival was the last day of the "butter
fair," and we were very much amused and interested,
especially with the ice-slide, which is one of its great
features.   A most interesting sight to us was the frozen
market.   Here, one stall was full of frozen pigs, there
another was laden almost mountain high with frozen sides
of oxen and deer.   Part of the market was occupied by
rows of stalls on which the frozen fish lay piled up in
stacks.   Another portion was devoted to birds and game,
heaps of capercailzie, black grouse, hazel grouse (the
rabchik of the Russians), willow grouse (the *koropatki* of
the Russians), and others, with stacks of white hares, and
baskets full of small birds.   Amongst the latter we were

anxious to secure some Bohemian waxwings, in order, if possible, to throw some light upon the vexed question of the difference between the sexes. We bought a dozen of the most perfect skins for eighty kopecks. There were not many waxwings in the market, and all those we bought proved, on dissection, to be males. In winter these birds go in flocks, and it seems that the sexes flock separately, as is known to be the case with many other species.

On the evening of the 10th of March we left St. Petersburg, and travelled by rail all night to Moscow, where we spent a day. In the market we were told that waxwings were seen only in autumn. Jackdaws and hooded crows we found very abundant in Moscow. We left in the evening, and travelled by train all night and the whole of the next day, reaching Vologda at midnight.

We had previously written to the English Consul in Archangel, and he was kind enough to buy fur dresses for us and send them on to St. Petersburg. He also commissioned M. Verakin, a Russian merchant in Vologda, to furnish us with a sledge and provisions for the journey. M. Verakin treated us most hospitably, would not hear of our going to the hotel, and gave us every assistance in his power. Unfortunately, he spoke only his native Russ, but at last he found us an interpreter in the person of the German servant of a friend, and we were able through him to convey our thanks to our host for his kindness to us.

From 8 A.M. on Sunday morning, the 14th of March, to Thursday at noon, we travelled by sledge day and night from Vologda to Archangel, a distance of nearly 600 English miles. Our sledge was drawn by three horses, driven by a peasant called the *yemschik*. Both horses and drivers were changed at each station. There were thirty-six stages, varying in length from fifteen to

twenty-seven versts (ten to nineteen English miles).
The horses were generally good, though small. They
were tough, shaggy animals, apparently never groomed,
but very hardy. We had but one lazy horse out of the
108 which we employed on the journey, but another
broke down, and had to be left on the roadside to follow
as best it could. That this treatment was not a solitary
instance was proved by the fact that on one of the
stages (the one of twenty-seven versts) we passed two
horses which had evidently broken down and had been
cast aside in the same way, lying dead and frozen on the
road. The drivers were very civil and generally drove
well, urging on the horses rather by the voice than the
whip, often apparently imitating the bark of a wolf to
frighten them, and at other times swearing at them in
every variety of oath of which the Russian language is
capable. The yemschiks were perfectly satisfied with a
pourboire of one kopeck per verst. The horses were
charged three kopecks per verst each. There was
generally a comfortable room at the stations, and the
station-masters usually came out to receive us. Sometimes we did not quit our sledge, but if we were hungry
we carried our provision-basket into the station-house,
ordered the "samovar," and made tea. The samovar is
a great institution in Russia. Provisions are not to be
had at the station-houses, but we always found a samovar,
and we were generally able to procure milk. The
samovar is a brass urn, with a charcoal fire in a tube in
the centre, which boils water in a few minutes. We
found that about a dozen words of Russ sufficed to pull
us through very comfortably. Arrived at a station, we
generally allowed the station-master to have the first
say. As soon as a convenient opportunity occurred we
interposed, "*Tre loshedi saychass*," which being interpreted

means "Three horses immediately." We then produced some rouble notes, and asked, "*Skolko*"—"How much?" The station-master would again begin to talk Russ. We offered the amount due as appeared from the list of stations which had been provided for us by M. Verakin at Vologda. This proving satisfactory, we proceeded to pay the yemschik his *pourboire*. The station-master once more began to talk volubly in Russ. We waited until he had done, and then asked innocently, "*Fameelye?*" The station-master nodded his head and said, "*Da, da*"— "Yes." We then said, "*Brown Seebohm Angliski Vologda na Archangelsk.*" After the changes had been rung upon our names, it generally ended in our having to copy them upon a piece of paper for the station-master to write in his book; and the new yemschik having by this time got his team in order, we settled ourselves down again, cried "*Kharasho!*"—"All right!" and started off. With slight variations this course was repeated at each station. Our horses were harnessed in divers ways. Of course one was always in the shafts, but the other two were sometimes put one at each side of the shaft-horse; sometimes one on the near side, and the other in front; sometimes side by side in front of the shaft-horse; and sometimes all three were in single file. The roads in the Archangel province, where the snow-plough was used regularly, were generally very good. In the province of Vologda, where the snow-plough seemed to be unknown, the roads were at least twice as bad as the imagination of an Englishman can conceive. On the good roads the sensation of travelling was very pleasant, not unlike that in a railway carriage; on the bad roads our sensations were something like what Sancho Panza's must have been when he was tossed in the blanket. Our luggage was tightly packed with hay, and ourselves in fur, else both would have suffered severely. At first we expected to be upset at each lurch, and took it for granted that our sledge would be battered to pieces long before the 600 miles to Archangel were completed, but by degrees we began to feel reassured. The out-riggers of our sledge were so contrived that the seat might approach, but not quite reach, the perpendicular; and after we had broken a shaft once or twice, and seen the cool businesslike way in which our yemschik brought out his axe, cut down a birch-tree and fashioned a new shaft, we began to contemplate the possibility of the entire dissolution of the sledge with equanimity. The weather was very changeable; sometimes the thermometer was barely at freezing-point, sometimes we had a sort of November fog, and occasionally a snowstorm, but nearly half the time it was clear and cold with brilliant sunshine. The last night and day it was intensely cold, from 2° to 4° below zero. There was a considerable amount of traffic on the roads, and we frequently met long lines of sledges laden with hides, tar-barrels, frozen sides of beef, hay, flax, etc. Many peasants were sledging about from place to place, but we saw very few travellers with Government horses. The country was covered with about two feet of snow. It was rarely flat; at first a sort of open rolling prairie land with plenty of timber and well studded with villages, it afterwards became more hilly and almost entirely covered with forest. In many cases the road followed the course of a river, frequently crossing it and often continuing for some miles on its frozen surface. The track was then marked out with small fir-trees stuck into the snow at intervals. During the whole journey we met with only one person who could speak either English, French, or German. This was at Slavodka, where we bought some fancy bread and Russian butter from a German baker, who came from Hesse Cassel. Jackdaws and hooded crows were the commonest birds in the open country, feeding for the most part upon the droppings of the horses on the roads. They were in splendid plumage and wonderfully clean. Many of the jackdaws had an almost white ring round the neck, and are doubtless the *Corvus collaris* of some authors, but, so far as we were able to see, this cannot be regarded as a good species. We frequently saw almost every intermediate variety in the same flock. During the first few days we noticed many colonies of nests in the plantations, but whether these would be tenanted by rooks later on in the season, or whether the hooded crow breeds in colonies in this country, we were not able to ascertain. We occasionally saw ravens and magpies, the latter becoming more common as we travelled farther north. In the open country we frequently came across small flocks of yellow-hammers on the roads, and now and then a pair of bullfinches. In driving through the forest we occasionally caught sight of a crossbill, pine grosbeak, marsh-tit, jay, or great spotted woodpecker. On one occasion we had an excellent opportunity of watching a small covey of willow-grouse, almost as pure white as the snow upon which they were running. In the villages sparrows were common enough. At Vologda, we are under the impression that they were all the house sparrow. In the villages through which we passed after the first day they were certainly all tree sparrows.

Upon our arrival at Archangel we were most hospitably entertained by the British Consul, Mr. Charles Birse. We were delighted once more to sit down to a good dinner, to enjoy the luxury of a Russian bath after our long journey, and to have a good night's rest in a comfortable bed.

LITTLE STINT

CHAPTER III.

ARCHANGEL.

The White City, Archangel—Decline of its Commerce—Cheapness of Living—Peter Kotzoff—Father Inokentia—The Samoyedes and their Sledges—Their Physical Characteristics—Samoyede Names of Birds —National Songs—Election of Samoyede Chiefs—Their Ignorance of Doctors or Medicinal Plants—Piottuch—Birds—The Weather—Hasty Departure from Archangel.

WE spent nineteen days in Archangel completing the preparations for our journey, and picking up what information we could respecting the great river Petchora, and the routes thither. Everybody looked upon our expedition as a most formidable undertaking, but all were anxious to give us every assistance in their power. There is an excellent German club in Archangel, and we dropped a few roubles in practising *krasnoye po bielemou* and *bieloye po krasnomou* * with billiard-balls large enough for Hercules to have played with. Archangel, the white city, must have been christened in winter. Most of the houses are painted white, the streets were white, the Dvina was white, and as far as the eye could reach the whole country was white. The principal street, the Troitski Prospekt, is a long straight road flanked with low houses, separated by gardens. All the houses are constructed of wood, except in the centre of the town, where many of them are of plastered bricks. The population is said to be from fifteen to seventeen thousand in winter, increasing in summer to about half as many more. Archangel seems to be declining in importance as a commercial centre, doubtless in consequence of its isolation from the railway system of Russia. The number of large firms does not increase, and there are now only three export houses of importance. The chances of commercial success are consequently small, and most of the young men who can afford it leave the city. The cost of living is small. House-rent is very cheap, and provisions equally so. For example, the best joints of beef can be bought in winter for 3*d*. per lb., in summer at 3¾*d*. White bread costs 4½*d*. per lb., but brown bread can be had for ¾*d*. Butter is 7½*d*. per lb. Milk (unskimmed) 1*d*. per quart, and cream 3¾*d*. per pint. Game is ridiculously cheap, capercailzie being 7½*d*. each in autumn and 1*s*. 7*d*. each in winter; hazel grouse 4½*d*. per brace in autumn and 11¼*d*. in winter; hares 3*d*. each, and salmon 9*d*. to 1*s*. 3*d*. per lb. In spite of the long and severe winters, the price of fuel is not a very important item. Wood sufficient to serve a small family for a year costs about 10*l*.

For some days we sat in commission, examining

* Red upon white, and white upon red.

witnesses on the Petchora, the British Consul kindly acting as interpreter for us. We got the best information from Peter Kotzoff, a Russian pilot, who showed us a chronometer which was presented to him by the British Government for assisting in the rescue of the crew of the *Elizabeth*, which was wrecked at the mouth of the Petchora. He was for some years a pilot on the great river, and acted as guide to Count Wilczec on his return journey overland from the Austrian-Hungarian Arctic Expedition. Another interesting acquaintance which we made was that of Father Inokentia, the present archpriest of Archangel, who lived seventeen years in the Petchora, principally east of Ishma. He was sent out by the Russian Government as a missionary amongst the Samoyedes, to convert them from their so-called idolatrous faith to the Greek Church. He told us that he remembered meeting with Schrenck, and that Castrén stopped some time at his house, at Kolva, on the river Ussa. He left the Petchora in 1847, so that his information was somewhat out of date. Father Inokentia seemed to be a jolly fat friar of the old school, and was very kind and patient in answering our numerous questions. How far he succeeded in his mission it is difficult to say. Most of the Samoyedes on the west side of the Ural now profess to belong to the Greek Church, but we were repeatedly informed that many of them still secretly retain their old beliefs, and continue to practise their ancient rites. We went through most of the Samoyede vocabulary given in Rae's "Land of the North Wind," and found it to be on the whole correct. No doubt, in districts so widely separated as the Kanin peninsula and the valley of the Ussa, considerable differences of dialect must be expected. But perhaps the most interesting information which we obtained respecting this curious race of people was that which we got from the Samoyedes themselves. We had our first glimpse of them—it was little more than a glimpse —at St. Petersburg, where we found a single *choom* erected on the ice of the Neva. These were probably poor Samoyedes, owning only a few reindeer, and earning a scanty living during the long winter by selling various articles made from the skins and horns of these deer, and picking up a few kopecks by giving curious strangers a ride in their national sledges.

Near the villages round Archangel there were several Samoyede chooms. Two or more families were wintering about fifteen versts from Archangel, and came almost every day in their sledges to the town. On one of our shooting excursions we chartered a couple of these sledges to take us to an island on the Dvina, and thoroughly enjoyed this novel mode of travelling. The reindeer were very tractable, and we skimmed over the surface of the snow at a rapid pace. We had long conversations with several Samoyedes, the Consul, of course, acting as interpreter, and we invited them to the Consul's house, where they gave us freely all the information they could respecting themselves and the traditions of their race. They spoke Russian well and were by no means devoid of intelligence. They were all small men, with dark straight hair worn hanging over the forehead, thin moustache and beard, and little or no whiskers. Their features were irregular, with wide flat noses, high cheek-bones, and thick lips. The under jaw was coarse and heavy, the eyes brown, small, and oblique like those of the Chinese, and not unfrequently sore. They had small hands and feet, wide round heads, and sallow complexions We took some of them to the museum, where they

recognised many of the stuffed birds, and tried to
describe their habits and imitate their notes. They
gave us the following Samoyede names of birds in the
Petchora district :

Sandpiper	Suitar.
Willow Grouse	Hond-jy'.
Swan	Chouari.
Goose	Yebtaw.
Black Goose	Pardén Yebtaw.

They told us there were two species of swans in the
Petchora, the larger one common and breeding there, the
smaller one rare, and appearing only in autumn. They
represented the snowy owl as found on the tundra, but
did not recognise the Lapp or Ural owls. We found
later that these statements were substantially correct. On
one occasion the Samoyedes favoured us with some of
their national songs, monotonous chants which reminded
me very much of the songs of the peasants of the Parnassus. One, which was translated for us, was a sort of
Ossianic ditty, relating how the singer intended to make
a journey with reindeer, how he would select the four
fleetest bull reindeer from his herd, how he would always
be at the head of the party, how he would get plenty of
vodka, how he would barter his skins, and how he would
take care not to be cheated in the transaction. One of
the Samoyedes told us that they have a chief, residing in
the Ural, who is answerable to the Emperor for the
annual tribute, and that at his death his son succeeds
him, unless he is thought not worthy to be made king.
In this case another chief is elected by ballot, by putting
pieces of wood into a *pimü*, or boot. It is right to note,
however, that other Samoyedes whom we questioned had
never heard of this Ural chief. The Samoyedes have no
doctors, and use no medicinal plants, nor do they employ

any other medicines, unless the outward application of
goose or swan fat for frost-bites may rank as such.

At Archangel we were fortunate enough to secure the
services of M. Piottuch, a Polish exile, whom we engaged
to go with us to the land of the Samoyedes in the double
capacity of interpreter and bird-skinner. He spoke
Russian and bad French, and since Alston and Harvie-
Brown's visit to Archangel in 1872 had spent a considerable part of his leisure time in shooting and skinning
birds. Accompanied by Piottuch we made several excursions on snow-shoes into the neighbouring woods, but
saw remarkably few birds. Archangel contains a great
number of sparrows; most of the farmyards abounded
with them. Once or twice we identified a tree-sparrow,
but by far the greater number were the common house-
sparrow, many of the males being in splendid plumage.
The next commonest bird was certainly the hooded
crow. They were remarkably tame. In the market we
sometimes saw half a dozen perched at the same time on
the horses' backs, and we could almost kick them in the
streets. They are the scavengers of Archangel. Pigeons
were also common, now wild, but probably once domesti-
cated. They look like rock-doves, a blue-grey, with
darker head and shoulders, two black bars on the wing,
and a white rump; but in some the latter characteristic
is wanting. These pigeons are never molested, and are
evidently held to be semi-sacred, like those in the Piazza
di San Marco in Venice, or in the court of the Bayezidieh
mosque in Stamboul. Jackdaws, ravens, and magpies
were frequently seen. In the woods we found the mealy
redpoll, the marsh-tit, an occasional bullfinch, a pair of
lesser spotted woodpeckers, and a solitary hawfinch.
Some white-winged crossbills and waxwings were brought
alive into the town, but the peasant who had the wax-

wings asked eight roubles a pair, so, of course, we did not buy them. We were told that these birds were common near Archangel until towards the end of November, when they disappear as the weather becomes more severe.

During our stay in Archangel we had considerable changes in the weather. Soon after our arrival it was very cold, and on one or two occasions we noticed the thermometer as low as 27° below zero. If the weather was windy we felt the cold keenly, but at the lowest point there was not a breath of wind, and wrapped up in our furs we suffered from nothing but an attack of icicles on the moustache. Occasionally we had slight snow-storms, but brilliant sunshine was the rule, and we found the clear, dry air most invigorating. After April had set in the weather became more cloudy, and the thermometer once registered 37° in the shade. No signs of frost having been visible by the 6th, we made hot haste to be off before our winter road should break up, taking leave of our kind friends, Mr. and Mrs. Birse, with great regret. It has rarely been our lot to be received with such genuine hospitality as was shown us by this estimable gentleman and his wife.

SAMOYEDE KNIVES

UST-ZYLMA

CHAPTER IV.

SLEDGING TO UST-ZYLMA.

Bad Roads—Postal Service in Winter and Summer—Changeable Weather
—Scenery—Pinega and Kuloi Rivers—Snow Plains—The Forests—Birds
—Samoyedes—Mezén—A Polish Exile—Snow-Buntings—Jackdaws—We
leave Mezén—Scenery—The Mezén River—The Pizhma—Bad State of
the Roads—Piottuch's Accident—The Via Diabolica—Bolshanivagorskia
—Break up of the Road—Polish Prejudices—The Villages—Curiosity of
the Peasants—Greek Crosses—Love of Ornament—Employment and
Amusements—Samoyedes—Siberian Jays—Umskia—First View of the
Petchora—Arrival at Ust-Zylma.

THE journey from Archangel to Ust-Zylma on the
Petchora is between 700 and 800 English miles.
There are about forty stations, the distances between
them being somewhat greater than those on our previous
journey. Had we left Archangel a fortnight earlier,
before the sun was powerful enough to soften the surface

of the snow, we might have accomplished the journey
in much shorter time.   As it was, we took three days
and three nights to reach Mezén.   We stopped one
day and two nights in this, the frontier town of Siberia in
Europe ; and the remainder of the journey occupied five
days and four nights.   A fortnight later the snow became
impassable, the winter road was broken up, the horses at
the stations in the uninhabited portions of the country, a
distance of 250 versts, were sent home, and for two
months the valley of the Petchora was as effectually cut
off from all communication with civilised Europe as if it
had been in the moon.   The last 150 miles had become a
series of uninhabited, impassable swamps, across which no
letter, nor messenger, nor telegram, ever came.   The
postal service was suspended until the floods in the river
caused by the sudden melting of the snow had sufficiently
subsided to make it possible to row against stream.
The summer route from Mezén to Ust-Zylma is up the
Mezén River to its junction with the Peza, up that river
to its source, across the watershed, a porterage of sixteen
versts, by horses, to the source of the Zylma, and then
down that river to the Petchora.

We left Archangel on a Tuesday evening, in two
sledges or *pavoskas;* Harvie-Brown and I, with part of
the luggage in one, drawn by three horses, and Piottuch
with the remainder of the luggage in the other, drawn
by two horses.   That night and the whole of the following day were warm, the thermometer standing at 44° in
the shade.   In the sun it once went up to 70°.   The
wind was south-west, and in our inexperience we began
to fear that summer would be upon us before we reached
the Petchora.   Our progress was slow, and at this time,
including stoppages, we did not average much more than
seven miles an hour.   On Wednesday night we had a

smart frost, and began to congratulate each other on the
chance of our progress being more rapid.   But we soon
found that we were out of the frying-pan into the fire.
The great traffic to and from the fair at Pinega had worn
a deep rut for the horses' feet in the track, and one runner
of our sledge would persist in running in it, which threw
the sledge so much out of the level that the outrigger or
projecting spar, which is necessary to prevent the sledge
from being upset every five minutes, was continually
ploughing into the snow which formed a bank on each
side of the road.   As long as the snow was soft it was of
little consequence, but when the crust was hardened by
an hour or two of frost, the outrigger of the sledge went
" scrunch " into it with a sound almost like that of a man
turning wood in a lathe, and our progress was as much im-
peded by this unwelcome break as it had been by the giving
way of the snow under the horses' feet.   On Thursday
afternoon the sun was again hot, but fortunately it froze again
at night.   Friday was dull all day, with a slight thaw, and
we reached Mezén at 4 P.M. and found the roofs dripping.

The scenery on the route was much more varied than
we had expected to find it.   Most of the way we sledged
through the forests, a wide space being cleared on each
side of the track ; but sometimes the trees came close up
to the road, which was hilly and winding, and we seemed
to be lost in a dense wood.   Perhaps the most picturesque
scenery of the journey was that we saw in ascending the
Pinega River and descending the Kuloi, and we repeatedly enjoyed it for some versts at a time.   The Pinega
River is very broad, with what looked like cliffs of oolite
on each side, surmounted by pine forests.   The Kuloi
River is narrower, and there are no cliffs of any importance,
the trees coming down to the edge of the ice.   When we
passed the Kuloi near its source, soon after leaving

Pinega, the river was flowing through a strip of open country. In several places it was free from ice, and on two occasions we saw ducks swimming upon the open water. About thirty versts before reaching Mezén we crossed an immense plain of snow, as flat as a lake, extending east and west as far as the eye could reach. In almost every instance the flat plains were destitute of trees, being no doubt swamps or marshes, too wet for timber to grow in, whilst the hills were invariably covered with forests. We found that the roads were always deep in the forests. Our horses had firm footing, but the outriggers of the sledge " scrunched " unpleasantly. In the open plains the sides of the road were low, any deep tracks which might have been made being no doubt soon filled up again by the drifting snow, and we got on at a rapid pace so long as the snow did not give way under the horses' feet. The forests were principally spruce fir, and very spruce these fir-trees looked, as if they had just been combed and brushed, in striking contrast to the haggard larches, whose leafless branches were clothed with black and grey lichen like a suit of rags, and were torn and twisted by the winds into wild fantastic shapes, reminding one of a sketch by Gustave Doré. In many places birches and Scotch fir were common, and occasionally we saw a few willows. There were very few birds. The hooded crow was the commonest, principally close to the villages. Now and then we saw a jackdaw or a raven, or a pair of magpies. As we proceeded farther east, sparrows became less plentiful, but we noticed both species, the house and the tree sparrow. Soon after leaving Archangel we met with a flock of snow-buntings, and they gradually became more frequent as we neared Mezén, especially on the rivers. They seemed to be slowly migrating northwards, following the course of the rivers, where there was always a chance of their finding some open water. Not far from Pinega we got out of the sledge to chase a pair of great spotted woodpeckers, and succeeded in shooting the female. We also saw a pair of Siberian jays, but, not being provided with snow-shoes, we found it was no use attempting to follow the birds into the forests through the deep snow. Soon after leaving Pinega we saw a bird sitting on a cliff, and after a short chase shot it, and found it to be a common crossbill, a bird which, curiously enough, we did not meet with afterwards. A stage or two before reaching Mezén we saw a second pair of Siberian jays, and surprised a fine male capercailzie not far from the road.

At Pinega we found a party of Samoyedes from Kanin, with about twenty sledges, and we passed a larger party about halfway to Mezén. We met with no difficulties. Once or twice, on our arrival at a station during the night, we were told that there were no horses to be had, that they were all out; but on the presentation of the "Crown Padarozhnayas," with which General Timarsheff (the Minister of the Interior at St. Petersburg) had kindly provided us, horses were forthcoming at once. We paid for five horses on one occasion when we had only four, and at Pinega the station-master tried to make us take six, but our obstinate refusal to do so, lest it should become a precedent in future, prevailed.

We reached Mezén on the 10th of April, and spent an interesting day in this frontier town. The Ispravnik, to whom we had letters from the Governor of Archangel, called upon us and invited us to take tea at his house. He spoke a smattering of French, but had asked a Polish exile of the name of Bronza to meet us as interpreter. M. Bronza spoke German, and we endeavoured to get some information from him about the Samoyedes; but he

was so full of his own grievances, and so utterly without
interest in Russia and everything Russian, that we soon
gave it up in despair.   Poland is evidently the Ireland of
Russia.   Both the Irish and the Poles seem crazy on the
subject of home-rule, and in many other points show a
similarity of temperament.   They are both hot-blooded
races, endowed with a wonderful sense of humour, and
an intolerable tolerance of dirt, disorder, and bad
management generally.

At Mezén we were much interested in watching a
large flock of snow-buntings.   Their favourite resort was
the steep bank of the river, where they found abundance
of food in the manure which was thrown away.   In a
country where there is plenty of grass in summer and
very little corn is cultivated and where the cattle have to
be stall-fed for seven or eight months out of the twelve,
manure apparently is of little value, and hundreds of cart-
loads are annually deposited on the steep banks of the
river, where it is washed away by the floods caused by
the sudden melting of the snow in May.   The snow-
buntings were also frequently seen round the hole in the
ice on the river, where the inhabitants of Mezén obtained
their supply of water.   In both places the boys of the
village had set white horsehair snares, and seemed to be
very successful in their sport.   At this time of the year
these birds are fat and are excellent eating.   We were
told that in a fortnight they would be here in much
greater numbers, and would be sold for a rouble the
hundred, or even less.   None of the birds we got were
in full summer plumage, yet they looked extremely
handsome as they ran along the snow like a wagtail or a
dotterel, or fluttered from place to place with a butterfly-
like kind of flight.   We occasionally saw them hop, but
they generally preferred to run.   The most interesting

fact which we observed was that the snow-bunting occasionally perches in trees. We saw two in the forest, one of which perched in a spruce fir.

We found jackdaws very numerous at Mezén, but Piottuch told us that it is only during the last four or five years that the bird has been seen in this neighbourhood. He said that it is now a resident there. Piottuch in the days of his exile lived some years at Mezén, and had a considerable circle of acquaintance in the town, who made merry on the occasion of his revisiting them.

We left Mezén on Sunday morning at nine, glad to get away, as Piottuch's old friends were too many for him, and far too hospitable, and he was drinking more champagne than we thought prudent. During the previous four-and-twenty hours we had had violent wind and snowstorms, but the morning had cleared up, the sun shone brilliantly, and it was not cold. But at night snow came on again and continued till Wednesday evening, when the weather suddenly cleared up again, the thermometer falling from freezing-point to zero. During the three days, about four inches of snow had been added to the couple of feet already on the ground. Travelling during even a slight snowstorm is by no means so pleasant as when the sun shines on a mild day; but travelling in a sledge with the thermometer at zero is decidedly unpleasant, even with brilliant sunshine and no wind. If you expose your face to the air your nose is in danger, then the icicles that form continually upon your moustache are anything but comfortable, and the condensation of your breath upon your neck-wrappings is always irritating; while, if you subside altogether into your furs, the sense of semi suffocation is almost as bad. On the whole, however, we did not suffer so much from the cold as we expected.

The scenery on this journey was more varied than any we had previously met with. We alternated between forest, river, and open plain. The Mezén is a fine river, half a mile or more wide, with steep banks of what looked like red chalk about 100 feet high, clothed with forest to the edge, which is continually crumbling away and letting the pine-trees slip into the water. At intervals, and often with remarkable regularity, the cliffs were cut away down to the water's edge, probably by small temporary rivulets born of the melting snow. The Pizhma is a much smaller river, not half the size of the Mezén, and without rocky cliffs on the banks. There are two Pizhmas, on both of which we travelled. Both rise in the lake of Jam, the Petchorski Pizhma flowing north-east into the Zylma just before that river enters the Petchora, and the Mezénski Pizhma flowing south-west into the Mezén. On the rivers the roads were always good, except in one part of the Mezénski Pizhma where the river is very narrow and the current very strong. In one place we almost shuddered to see open water rushing along within nine feet of the sledge. Not long afterwards we stuck fast, and had to get out of the sledge on the snow in the middle of the river. It was nearly midnight and very cloudy. Piottuch with his lighter sledge had got safely over the dangerous part and stood grinning at us, as the yemschiks hacked the frozen snow off the runners of our sledge with their axes, and having added his two horses to our team, placed two little fir-trees across the path and flogged the horses until they dragged the machine through the snow and water on to firm ground. We had our revenge, however, shortly afterwards. A few stations farther on Piottuch's sledge came to grief, one of the runners breaking completely in two in the front. He was some distance in

advance of our sledge, and when we overtook him at the
station he came to us with a very long face to tell us of
the "*très mal chose.*" We soon set him upon his legs
again. We bought a peasant's sledge for a rouble and a
half, took off the sides, and removing the runners from
the broken sledge lashed the two together with a strong
cord. Piottuch started in high glee again, assuring us
that his sledge was "*beaucoup plus bon*" than ours. The
effect of the alteration however was, to raise the level of
his outriggers a few inches, which made all the difference
between safety and danger. He was soon fast asleep as
usual, for he had not yet quite slept off his Mezén champagne, when his sledge gave a greater lurch than it was
wont to do and capsized, waking him with a shower of
portmanteaus about his ears; and he was dragged out of
the deep snow by the yemschik amidst roars of laughter
on our part.

As before, we found the roads in the open plain
always good. These plains were a dead flat, with a tree
or two here and there. The rut worn by the horses' feet
was not deep, and the path was almost level with the
side. We glided along smoothly and luxuriously. The
roads in the forest were bad beyond all conception. The
banks were high, and were always in the way of the
outriggers, which "scrunched" against them with a most
irritating sound. Both laterally and vertically they were
as winding as a snake. Sometimes our sledge was on
the top of a steep hill, our first horse in the valley, and
our third horse on the top of the next hill. The motion
was like that of a boat in a chopping sea, and the sledge
banged about from pillar to post to such an extent that
we scarcely felt the want of exercise. The Russian
forest-road is not a *via mala*, it is a *via diabolica*.

At Bolshanivagorskia, upon entering the station-house,

we found the room occupied by a party, and the samovar in full operation. Fancying that some of the party looked English, I inquired if any of them spoke German, and the least Russian-looking gentleman among them replied that he did. I informed him that we were Englishmen, travelling from London to the Petchora, and I added that we were glad to find some one on the route with whom we could converse. I then asked him if he and his party were also travelling. He replied that they were stationed there for some time. I then asked if his name was Rosenthal. He said it was, and a hearty laugh followed at the success of my guess. We enjoyed his astonishment for some time, and then explained that we had been told by the Ispravnik at Mezén that there was only one man in the district who could speak German, the forest engineer, Herr Rosenthal. We spent an hour pleasantly together. Like every one we met who had not been to the Petchora, he exaggerated the dangers and difficulties of the journey. He was engaged in measuring the timber felled on Rusanoff's concession on behalf of the Russian Government, who receive so much per tree according to the quantity of available wood in it.

On the other hand, it is possible that we may have under-estimated the dangers and difficulties of our journey, seeing we had the good luck to pull through them so well. The roads were certainly giving way, and it may have been a happy accident in our favour that the weather changed again when it did. On one occasion the crust of snow not being firm enough to support the horses, they all three suddenly sank up to their bellies. Of course they were utterly helpless. We feared for a moment that our journey had suddenly come to an end and that we had hopelessly stuck fast. We alighted from the sledge, which had not sunk in the snow. The two yemschiks set to work in good earnest, and we doffed our malitzas and followed suit. The horses were un-harnessed, and we soon succeeded in making them struggle out on to firm ground. We had no difficulty in pushing the sledge after them, and were soon ready to start again. All this time Piottuch stood calmly by, never offering for a moment to render us the smallest assistance. The Russians we always found equal to any emergency, and ready to lend a helping hand on such occasions as an Englishman would. The Poles, on the contrary, seem to be a helpless, shiftless race of people, with a contemptible prejudice against manual labour. A similar accident did not happen again. We had many a stumble, but no irretrievable fall. Our horses were sure-footed and wonderfully plucky, and we seldom had a really bad animal. We started with five horses for the two sledges, which we reduced to four the latter half of the journey, and on one or more occasions we accom-plished a stage satisfactorily with only three.

The country is very thinly populated. After leaving Mezén the villages were small, and during the last 150 miles there were no villages at all, only a single station-house, where a change of horses could be obtained, and which would shortly be deserted altogether for the summer months. As we were the first Englishmen who had travelled on this road during the lifetime of any of the villagers, our appearance naturally excited great curiosity, and when we stopped at a station in the village to change horses, a crowd quickly gathered round the sledges. We found the peasants very inquisitive, asking the English names of various articles. They were extremely good-natured, enjoyed a broad joke, laughed heartily at our pigeon-Russ, and were, so far as we could judge, perfectly honest. We left our sledges with all our luggage, wraps,

and things unprotected, sometimes for an hour, at the
stations where we stopped for a meal, and on no occasion
had anything been stolen. In the villages on this part of
the journey we noticed a number of crosses, generally one
or two at the entrance, and one near the centre of the
village. They were made of wood, and were about ten
feet high, the ordinary Greek double cross, with an
oblique foot-bar, and most of them were protected by a
wooden roof to keep off the snow. Both the roof and
the cross itself were, as a rule, elaborately carved, and the
whole face of the cross was covered with inscriptions (no
doubt Slavonic) in about three-inch letters. Sometimes
in the poorer villages the crosses were not carved, and
the inscription and ornamentation were simply painted
upon the wood, generally in various colours. The Russian
peasantry in European Siberia seem to be fond of ornament. The majority of the houses are built with the
gable end to the street, and in the centre of the gable is
a window, opening on to a balcony. This balcony, the
framework of the windows, the ends of the rain-gutters,
and the ends of the ridge of the roof, were often elaborately carved and fretted, and sometimes painted in gay
colours. In nearly all the villages we noticed a conspicuous arrangement of railings for the drying of flax,
hay, or corn. In the station-houses we found the men,
and sometimes the women, engaged in spinning flax,
making nets, or weaving coarse linen. In the stations,
however, where there was no village, a draught-board of
very rude construction evidently served to while away the
long winter evenings. Several times during the journey
we saw Samoyedes, or Syriani, sledging along with their
reindeer, and in many places the snow was ploughed up
some distance from the road, showing that the reindeer
had been seeking for food. As we neared Ust-Zylma we

passed several of the chooms, or reindeer-skin tents, of these curious people by the roadside. During the greater part of the journey few birds were to be seen. In the villages magpies were the commonest birds, and occasionally we saw a few pigeons, hooded crows, and tree-sparrows. On the banks of the river flocks of snow-buntings were common. In the forests we saw a few capercailzie.

At Umskia, where we were fortunately detained six hours for want of horses, there was an abundant supply of birds. This station is a solitary house on the banks of the Petchorski Pizhma, about fifty-four versts from Ust-Zylma. The great attraction for birds in this place was doubtless the hole in the ice of the river, which had to be kept open to supply the station with water, and the dung which the horses dropped during the few hours they fed and rested outside the station. We shot five Siberian jays (*Perisoreus infaustus*), and had some opportunity of watching their habits. They were not at all shy, and were fond of perching upon or clinging to the trunks of the pines, and sometimes we saw them run up the stems like a woodpecker. Their song was by no means un-musical, a low warble like that of the starling, but not so harsh. These birds are early breeders, and the song is probably discontinued soon after incubation has begun, as we did not hear it afterwards, though we frequently came across the birds. Out of the five birds which we shot only one proved to be a female, with the ovary very small. There were a few snow-buntings always to be seen, but we did not think it worth while wasting powder and shot upon them, as we had selected a score of hand-some birds out of a lot brought to one of the stations by a peasant who had snared them. We could have bought almost any quantity alive or dead at ten kopecks the

score. I shot one by accident as it was feeding under a
larch-tree in company with a Siberian jay, a couple of
bullfinches, half a dozen other snow-buntings, and a few
redpolls. Harvie-Brown shot another as it sat perched
upon the branch of a larch, in order to be able to produce
the skin of a bird shot perching, as the fact that they do
ever perch in trees has been disputed. We had abundant
opportunity of seeing these birds in trees. We saw as
many as three or four in one tree at the same time, and
frequently observed them fly from one tree to another.
We saw plenty of the Northern bullfinches (*Pyrrhula
rubicilla*, Pallas) and shot five males in brilliant plumage.
They were all in pairs. We fancied that the call-note of
these bullfinches differed from that of our bird. Speaking
from memory, it seemed to us to be louder and harsher,
by no means so plaintive, and not badly represented by
the word "kak."

After leaving Umskia we looked anxiously out for the
first glimpses of the distant Petchora, and it was not long
before we crossed a low range of hills, from the ridge of
which we had a view of the mighty river. As we sledged
down the Zylma, and finally reached its junction with the
Petchora, the vastness of this river impressed us beyond
all our expectations. We were 300 miles from its mouth,
and to our left the huge flood stretched away in a broad
white stream as far as the eye could reach, and fifteen
times as wide as the Thames at Hammersmith Bridge.
On the opposite bank, a mile and a half off, we could
discern the churches and houses of Ust-Zylma, round
which the river swept to our right. Piottuch had arrived
at the town some hours before us, and we found comfortable apartments in the house of a Russian peasant of the
name of Boulegan, where we were visited by M. Znaminski,
the Preestáff of Ust-Zylma, and drank a toast (the success

of our visit to the Petchora) in a bottle of excellent Crimean champagne.

The total course of this great river covers nearly 1000 miles. It rises in the Urals, north of the government of Perm, not far from the important town of Tcherdin, which lies upon the watershed of the Petchora and the Kama. It drains nearly the whole of the northwestern slope of the Ural Mountains, and flows almost due north till its junction with the Ussa; here the river is a mile wide, and the Ussa is the larger stream of the two. The Petchora at this point makes a bend west; but after receiving the waters of the Zylma, it resumes its northward course, which it continues till it falls into the Arctic Ocean by a number of mouths opposite the islands of Novaya Zemlya.

OLD RUSSIAN SILVER CROSS

ANCIENT CHURCH OF THE OLD BELIEVERS

CHAPTER V.

UST-ZYLMA.

Ust-Zylma—Its Streets and Houses—Its Manure—Population of the Town—Its Churches—Our Quarters—The Banks of the River—The Old Believers—Their Superstition—Silver Crosses—Hospitality of the Officials—Shooting-parties—Captain Arendt and Captain Engel—Snow-shoes—Scarcity of Birds—The Snow-bunting—Redpolls—Winter.

UST-ZYLMA * is a long, straggling village, lying on the narrow strip of flat land on the north and east bank of the Petchora, where that river makes a sudden bend from west to north, about 300 miles from its mouth. Each homestead is a farmhouse with outbuildings,

---

* In "Purchas his Pilgrimes," the narrative of the voyage of Josias Logan, who wintered in the valley of the Petchora in 1611, contains the following description of this town : " Ust-Zylma is a village of some thirtie or fortie houses, and standeth in the height of 66° and 30 minutes. They have corne growing there, both barley and rye, and their barley is passing faire and white almost as rice."

including almost always a bath-house. They are irregularly scattered over the ground, sometimes at considerable distances apart, and sometimes in clusters. There is a principal road which one might by courtesy call the main street, which meanders through the village for perhaps two miles, with numerous side branches ; but the general appearance of the place is as if the houses had been strewed about at random, and each peasant had been left to make a road to his nearest neighbour as best he could. Towards the centre of the village there is here and there a wooden causeway, like those in Archangel. We found this wooden *trottoir* all but indispensable when the thaw set in. When we reached Ust-Zylma the streets were covered with a thick layer of frozen manure. The yards round the houses were in a still worse condition, and when the sun was hot it was difficult to walk dryshod in consequence of the pools of liquid manure, which filled every depression in the ground, and no doubt very frequently soaked into the wells. This manure makes Ust-Zylma one vast dung-hill, and would probably produce much disease, were it not for the fact that it is frozen for nearly seven months out of the twelve, and is in most years carried away soon after it thaws by the floods of the Petchora, which generally overflows its banks when the snow melts all at once with the sudden arrival of summer. It not unfrequently happens at this season of the year that half the village is under water, and the peasants have to boat from house to house. All the houses are built with this contingency in view. The bottom story is generally low, and consists of a suite of lumber-rooms, where the cattle are often housed in winter. The dwelling-rooms are on the second story, generally reached by a covered flight of stairs outside the house, leading from a porch below

to a gallery, which is carried round the house. Upon
this porch, staircase, and gallery a good deal of skill in
wood-carving is often expended. The winter is long,
and the length of time during which the cattle are stall-
fed so great, and the amount of land available for cultiva-
tion so small, that there is always a large surplus of
manure, which, as I have already stated, the peasants do
not think worth the cost of preservation. The cattle are
fed principally upon hay, which is cut upon the low lands
on the other side of the Petchora. These lands are
flooded every spring, and any manure placed upon them
would speedily be washed off: nor is it needed, as the
river itself is the great fertiliser in these low-lying
districts, exactly as the Nile is in Egypt. Of course, to
accumulate so much manure in the streets, the traffic
must be large. Long strings of sledges were often to be
seen drawing hay, pine logs for buildings, and smaller
timber for firewood. In the summer nearly every
peasant turns fisherman, and catches salmon and other
fish in the Petchora with a seine net. Neither farming
nor fishing seems to be very profitable. It is very easy
to get a living, but there is no market for surplus produce.
Beef fetches only $1\frac{1}{2}d$. per lb. retail. Most articles that are
worth the cartage, such as furs, feathers, down, frozen
meat, tar, and so forth, go to Pinega fair, and some are
even sent as far as Nishni Novgorod; but the cost of
transit absorbs the profit. Now and then you meet with
a merchant who has accumulated a handsome fortune;
but the peasants are on the whole poor, and will doubtless
remain so until railway communication with Moscow is
opened, or steamers run regularly from the mouth of the
Petchora, both of which projects seem at present to be
hopelessly improbable. The population of Ust-Zylma
probably does not exceed 1500 or 2000, increased in

winter by Samoyedes, who erect their chooms in the neighbouring forest. When we reached Ust-Zylma, and for a week or more afterwards, a great migration of these curious people was going on, and we often saw a score or more of their sledges in a day, and sometimes there were as many reindeer as horses to be seen in the streets.

The flat country on the banks of the Petchora, upon which the village is built, does not extend more than a few hundred yards. The land then rapidly rises, and these slopes are cultivated for some way up the hillside. We found the peasants busily employed in carting manure in sledges and spreading it on the snow. The monotony of the long village is broken by three churches, one a very ancient and picturesque structure, in some places rather artistically ornamented. This was formerly the church of the Old Believers, but it is now too rotten for use, and a more modern-looking building has been erected. The third church is that of the Orthodox Greek Church. All the houses in Ust-Zylma are of course built of wood, solid balks of timber with moss and tar in the joints, and notched into each other at the corner, and they are more or less carved and ornamented in various places. Sometimes the slopes of the hills are relieved by a large tree which has been left standing, and here and there is an old windmill. Beyond the cultivated ground is the forest, clothing the hilly country stretching away north, the trees gradually dwindling in size as far as the Arctic Circle, beyond which lies the mysterious tundra.

Our quarters in Ust-Zylma were two excellent rooms on the second floor of the best house in the village, for which we paid two roubles a month. No doubt we could have had them for half the money if we had taken them for six months. The house was built by M. Sideroff, the founder of the Petchora Timber-trading Company, and

was afterwards sold to M. Boulegan. Our windows
looked out across the street on to the Petchora, which we
calculated from two rough trigonometrical observations to
be a mile and a half wide. At Ust-Ussa, 200 miles
higher up, its width is said to be nearly a mile. A little
beyond the limits of the village at each end, the flat land
on the bank of the river ceases, and the forest comes up
to the edge of a cliff of sand, earth, and pebbles, varying
from 50 to 100 feet high. This bank drops nearly
perpendicularly on to the mud and pebbles on the edge
of the river. In some places the pebbly strand was bare
of snow, and we noticed pieces of granite, ironstone, and
limestone. Some of the latter was full of fossil shells,
and we found many pieces that looked like madrepore
and fossil coral. Soon after the high steep bank of the
river begins, the grand sweep which the Petchora makes
round the village ends, and the river stretches away
north-east for miles. The view from the top of the bank
looking up the wide white river is very fine. The high
banks, too steep in most places for the snow to rest upon,
and the dark pines on the top, form a striking contrast
to the pure white snow on the ice below, down which for
many versts may be seen the long winding line of dimi-
nutive fir-trees, marking the road, upon which the sledges
of the travelling peasants look like black spots in the
distance. It would, perhaps, be a very difficult subject
to make a fine picture of, the effect on the eye being one
of simple vastness, causing one continually to exclaim,
" What a great river! What a big country!"

Most of the peasants of Ust-Zylma and the villages
near are Old Believers, people who retain a very curious
form of Christian superstition, closely allied to the Greek
Church. Castrén calls them the " Raskolnicken " of
Ust-Zylma. They have not a good reputation amongst

the Germans, who have to hire labour for the timber-trade on the Petchora. They are represented as crafty and faithless, and as few of them are employed as possible. Their chief characteristic appears to be that they make the sign of the cross with the thumb touching the second and third, instead of the fourth and fifth fingers, as is the fashion of the Orthodox Church. They have a curious prejudice against tobacco, and will not smoke it themselves nor, if they can help it, allow other persons to smoke in their houses. They seem to have Jewish superstitions against pork and hare, neither will they use any plate, glass, or other article from which persons not of their religion have eaten or drunk. If you offer them vodka in your own glass they will refuse it if they be strict Old Believers, but we must do them the justice to say that, under circumstances of this kind, many we met were superior to their superstitions. But the most extraordinary feature of their religion is that it forbids the use of potatoes as food. They are not very diligent in their attendance at church nor much under the control of their priests, holding the doctrine that every man should be a priest in his own house, and should conduct divine worship there. Our host was very exemplary in this respect when he was sober, having an excellent religious library, and we often heard him and his family chanting Slavonic prayers. One of his books was a Slavonic MS., dating about 1740, and profusely illustrated with full-page coloured drawings, very carefully executed, although somewhat stiff. It appeared to be the history of some of the saints of the Greek Church. I tried very hard to buy this book, but nothing would induce M. Boulegan to part with it. In a corner of every Russian room is a sacred picture or *ikon*, before which every one on entering the room bows and crosses himself several times before speaking to the host. Some of these pictures are very old, being handed down from generation to generation, and sometimes there is quite a collection of these *ikona*, varied with brass and enamel triptychs of various ages and merit. Every peasant wears a silver or bronze cross. Some of these are of exquisitely delicate workmanship, frequently ornamented with enamel, and occasionally set with jewels. On the back of many of them are elaborate Slavonic inscriptions. A wonderful fertility of resource is found in the designs of these crosses, which are always chaste and artistic, never florid in the ornamentation or wanting in harmony of parts. The great centre of all this religious art is, we were informed, the monastery of Onega, on the south shore of the White Sea.

A peculiarity which we were told marked the Old Believers of Ust-Zylma is a habit which the women have of uttering cries, not loud but frequently repeated. This habit or disease is called "*equarter*," and is brought on immediately by the smell of tobacco smoke. Whether the cry is voluntary, and is intended as a mark of disapproval, or as an exorcism against evil influences, or whether it be a form of hysteria allied to St. Vitus's dance, we were not able to ascertain.

The officials at Ust-Zylma received us with the greatest hospitality. In addition to the letters with which the Governor of Archangel had provided us, it so happened that Piottuch was an old friend of M. Znaminski, the Preestáff, or highest military officer. He had made his acquaintance some years ago, in the days of his exile in Mezén, and both being fond of a day's sport, they had fraternised as sportsmen ought to do. M. Sakeroff, the postmaster, was the other great *chasseur* of Ust-Zylma, and these gentlemen were kind enough to plan several shooting-parties for our benefit. M. Znaminski was a stout handsome man, very dignified in his manners, but active in the field, and we were under very great obligations to him for his uniform kindness and hospitality to us. Another official who, as well as his charming wife, was most hospitable to us was the Public Prosecutor, M. Miranoff, the "Schlüdevatel," as Captain Engel always called him. We were also most kindly entertained by the "Maravoi," who appeared to be a gentleman of considerable education. Unfortunately none of these gentlemen spoke either English, French, or German, so that our communication with them was necessarily very limited. Interpreting was certainly not Piottuch's forte. Any information we got through him was so largely mixed with his own ideas and opinions, that we soon ceased to attach much value to it, besides which his bad French was often as difficult to understand as the original Russ.

We got a great deal of information respecting the country and its inhabitants from two gentlemen in the employ of the Petchora Timber-trading Company, Captain Arendt, the manager or "Provalychik" in the Petchora, residing temporarily at Ust-Zylma, and Captain Engel, the commander of the steamer belonging to the company, which was then lying in winter quarters at Habariki, about twenty-seven miles down the river. These gentlemen called upon us the day after our arrival, and we were indebted to both of them for innumerable acts of kindness.

Among our first purchases on our arrival at Ust-Zylma was a couple of pairs of snow-shoes, without which it is impossible to travel on the snow. No one can form the slightest idea how utterly helpless one is without snow-shoes when there is scarcely three feet of snow on the ground. To travel a mile would probably be a hard day's work, completely knocking one up. On snow-shoes we got along comfortably at the rate of three miles an hour, and we soon became tolerably at home on them. They were about seven feet long and six inches wide, made of birch wood, and covered underneath with reindeer skin, with the hair pointing behind. This is absolutely necessary to enable one to ascend a hill, the hair preventing effectually any sliding backwards. The great difficulty with which we had to contend at first was to avoid treading on our toes, but with a little practice we learnt to keep our shoes parallel. In going down hill we had to be careful lest our speed should increase to the point where we lost the control of our centres of gravity.

Every day we sallied out with our guns and snow-shoes in search of birds, but during the first week or so it was somewhat monotonous work, and we soon began to tire of winter. There were very few birds to be seen. In the village the hooded crow, the magpie, and the tree-sparrow were common, and now and then we saw a raven. The peasants brought us capercailzie and hazel grouse, which they shot with their rifles and offered us at twenty kopecks (about sevenpence) each for the capercailzie, and the same sum per brace for the hazel grouse. These birds are probably all residents, though Father Inokentia told us that the hooded crow was a migratory bird at Pustorzersk, arriving there about the 10th of May.

The commonest bird at this season of the year in the streets of Ust-Zylma is undoubtedly the snow-bunting (*Plectrophanes nivalis*). We were told that they arrived about the 1st of April. In spite of its abundance we could not help looking upon it with all the interest attaching to a rare bird. The brilliant contrast of the black and white on the plumage of these birds, then rapidly assuming their summer dress, was especially beautiful during flight. The flight itself is peculiar, somewhat like that of a butterfly, as if it altered its mind every few seconds as to which direction it would take. It can scarcely be called an undulating flight. The bird certainly does rest its wings every few seconds, but either they are expanded when at rest, or they are rested for so short a time, that the plane of flight is not sufficiently altered to warrant its being called undulatory. The snow-buntings in Ust-Zylma were principally in flocks, but now and then we saw a couple of birds together which seemed to have paired, and occasionally, when the sun was hotter than usual, a solitary specimen might be seen perched upon a rail attempting to sing, but we never heard them sing on the wing. Unfortunately we did not get far enough north to meet with these birds at their breeding stations. In 1874, when Collett and I were in Norway, we found the snow-bunting breeding on the island of Vadsö in the Varanger Fjord. We were too late for eggs, as this bird is a very early breeder, and the young were already in the nest by the middle of June; but we had many opportunities of watching the male birds. They would fling themselves up into the air almost like a shuttlecock, singing all the time a low and melodious warble, not unlike that of a shore-lark, or perhaps still more like that of the Lapland bunting, and they would immediately descend in a spiral curve with wing and tails expanded, and finish their song on a rock. Although we only once or twice heard the snow-buntings attempting to sing in Ust-Zylma, they were by no means silent birds, and were continually calling to each other. The call note is a *zh*, not unlike that of the brambling or greenfinch. The alarm-note is a loud *tweek*. As they fly together in flocks they merely twitter to each other, not unlike purple sandpipers on the seashore.

Flocks of redpolls (*Fringilla linaria*, Linn.) were also common, but consisting of much smaller numbers than those of the snow-bunting. Many of the males were beginning to assume the carmine breast, showing great promise of beauty when the full summer plumage should be attained. We were informed that these birds arrived about the same time as the snow-bunting. On the outskirts of the town we met with a few small parties of yellow-hammers (*Emberiza citrinella*, Linn.), and occasionally heard their familiar song. These birds are probably also migratory. They were comparatively rare, and as we never saw any farther north, we may assume Ust-Zylma to be about the extreme limit of their summer range. The forests were remarkably silent. Often there was not a bird to be seen for miles. Once or twice we had a distant glimpse of a Siberian jay, a marsh-tit, or a bullfinch, but we did not succeed in obtaining a shot. On the whole our first week in Ust-Zylma was not very encouraging from an ornithological point of view. After eight days work our list of identified birds in the valley of the Petchora stood as follows:

1. Hooded crow.	4. Tree-sparrow.	7. Yellow-hammer.
2. Raven.	5. Snow-bunting.	8. Capercailzie.
3. Magpie.	6. Mealy redpoll.	9. Hazel grouse.

—certainly a very meagre list. Notwithstanding such a bad beginning, we did not feel disheartened, but laid all the blame on the weather. We could not help smiling at our alarm in Archangel lest summer should come before we could reach the Petchora. Nearly three weeks had gone by, and summer and the summer birds seemed as far off as ever. The thaw made no progress. Sometimes

it was hot enough in the sun in the daytime, and the
glare of the sunshine on the white snow forced us to
wear snow spectacles, but it always froze again at night,
and if a few days sunshine made any impression on the
snow, a raw cold day, with a high wind and a more or less
heavy fall of snow, made everything look and feel as
winterly as before.   Piottuch went over to Ishma with
M. Znaminski, but did not shoot a bird.   He told us that
he saw two birds of prey, most likely hen-harriers, and
M. Znaminski informed us that we must not despair, as
a swan had been seen flying over.

OLD RUSSIAN SILVER CROSS

CHOOMS OF THE SAMOYEDES

CHAPTER VI.

THE ZYLMA AND ITS NEIGHBOURHOOD.

The Samoyedes—Reindeer—The Tundra—Nomad Life—Diseases of
Reindeer—Samoyede National Character—Trip to Umskia—Bad Roads
—Paucity of Birds—Easter Holidays—Drunkenness—Heavy Snowfall
—Our First Bird's-nest—Excursion to an Island in the River.

DURING this comparatively idle time we picked up what
information we could about the Samoyedes. Captain
Engel, who was a wild, harum-scarum, devil-may-care
fellow, and had been in most parts of the world, had
seen a good deal of the Samoyedes. Some years ago
he was wrecked in the lagoon of the Petchora, not
far from the island of Varandai, had been hospitably
received by these wandering people, had made his
way across country to Kuya, and had remained in the
district ever since. The information which we obtained

from Captains Arendt and Engel may be summed up as
follows :

The Samoyedes are a Mongolian race of nomad
habits. They live almost entirely upon reindeer. In
summer they live in tents made of birch-bark; in
winter their tents or chooms are made of reindeer-skins.
They eat the flesh of the reindeer and drink its blood.
Their dress is made of its skins, neatly sewn together
with its sinews. The wealth of a Samoyede consists
entirely in the number of his reindeer; each knows his
own by marks cut upon the animal's ear. In summer
the Samoyedes live on the tundras. Some go to the
Kanin peninsula, some to the Timanski Tundra or
Malyazemlia, and others to the northern shores of the
Great Tundra, the Bolshaizemlia of the Russians, the
Arkya-ya of the Samoyedes. These tundras are naked
tracts of slightly undulating land, rolling prairies of moor,
swamp, and bog, full of lakes, and abounding with
reindeer-moss, upon which the reindeer feed. In summer
the tundras are quite impassable for horses, but the reindeer, with their broad feet, will carry a sledge over places
where it would be impossible for a man to stand. The
Samoyedes are always on the tramp, seldom remaining
long in one place. A considerable portion of their lives
is spent in packing, unpacking, and travelling. In winter
the cold is too great for the reindeer to find food under
the frozen snow of the Arctic latitudes, and in summer
the poor animals would be driven frantic by the mosquitoes
which swarm in the more southerly regions. In summer
the Samoyedes occupy their spare time in shooting ducks
and geese, making their clothes, reindeer harness, etc.,
and in winter they come down to the towns and villages
—Kuya, Pustozersk, Ust-Zylma, Mezén, Pinega, and
others, and barter their surplus reindeer-skins, horns,

feathers, etc., with the Russian merchants for bread, vodka, and other articles. Those that come down to the more southerly towns have learnt the value of money, and prefer to sell rather than barter. They used to be very clever with the bow and arrow, but now they all use old-fashioned small-bore flint-lock rifles. Some of the Samoyedes are very rich. A reindeer is worth about seven or eight roubles, or an English sovereign. Some of the Samoyedes are said to possess as many as 10,000 reindeer. Of late years the reindeer have suffered much from disease. Captain Engel was of opinion that this disease was allied to cholera. The animals turn dizzy, and run round and round like sheep attacked by " sturdy." The reindeer also suffer much from a hideous parasite. One day, as we were passing a herd of them in the streets of Ust-Zylma, Engel took hold of one of the animals, and groping among the long hair on the small of the back, he presently squeezed out of the flesh one of these disgusting creatures. In a short time he produced a dozen of them. They varied in size from half an inch to an inch in length, the diameter being from half to a third of the length. The surface was covered with rudimentary scales. The lower part of the body was tapered, and the head rounded with two indistinct jaws. We did not notice even the rudiments of legs. They are, no doubt, the larvæ of some fly or beetle. Engel told us that they sometimes reached a length of four inches or more. Some herds of reindeer are perfectly free from these creatures, and others suffer very much from them.*

The Samoyedes are an acute and intelligent people, but on the whole they are not so sharp-witted as the Russians. They are good-natured and harmless, except when they are drunk, then they become quarrelsome and

---

* Probably the reindeer bot (*Hypoderma tarandi*), first described by Linnæus. —ED.

dangerous. They are passionately fond of vodka, a fairly mild, and to us by no means palatable spirit, distilled from barley, and they easily become intoxicated. In some places they distil an intoxicating drink from a fungus. If a drunken Samoyede quarrels, and calls for help, the other Samoyedes will at once help him. Engel's recipe for dealing with a dangerously drunken Samoyede was to supply him with more drink, when he speedily becomes maudlin and begins to sing. The Samoyede women are generally betrothed very young, about thirteen, and often have children at fourteen. Some Samoyedes have more than one wife, but this is very rare. The race is no doubt slowly dying out, and is to some extent becoming mixed. They are acquainted with the stars, and use them as a compass; but Engel told us of a very curious circumstance which came under his observation when he was brought across the tundra in the sledges of the Samoyedes. In stormy weather, when it was impossible to determine the direction, the Samoyede used to scrape away the snow down to the moss, which he examined, and altered his course accordingly. The Samoyedes do not live to be very old, but grey-haired old men and women are seen among them.

After we had been a week at Ust-Zylma without seeing any sign of summer or summer birds, we began to find time hang heavy on our hands. Picking up information about the Samoyedes and the Old Believers was such unsatisfactory work, from the contradictory nature of the reports, that we soon got tired of it, and longed for something better to do than shooting redpolls and snow-buntings. As we had not met with any Siberian jays or bullfinches at Ust-Zylma, we decided that the best way to while away the time was to go back again to Umskia for a day or two, in the hope of finding as many birds as we saw there before. We took the small sledge and a couple of horses, and travelled all the Friday night. The journey was a very eventful one. The sledge, it may be remembered, had turned over once with Piottuch, but he had travelled at least 100 miles in safety afterwards, and we had almost forgotten the circumstance. We soon found out, however, that something was radically wrong with the crazy machine. It must have dropped its centre of gravity altogether on the *via diabolica*, for between Ust-Zylma and Umskia (a distance of thirty-six miles) we were upset and tumbled over into the snow no less than fifteen times. This was altogether a new experience for us, but we survived it without any damage, thanks to the thickness of our malitzas and the depth of the snow.

Arrived at Umskia we were disappointed to see so few birds. The Siberian jays had disappeared altogether. The snow-buntings were represented by a solitary individual perched upon the summit of a lofty larch. Occasionally two or three redpolls were to be seen, and at long intervals during the day a pair of bullfinches put in an appearance. We saw a pair of white-tailed eagles (*Haliætus albicilla*, Linn.) soaring over the forest, but they never came within gunshot. The day was cold, with only occasional gleams of sunshine and continual threatenings of snow, and no birds seemed to be feeding. We took a long walk on the road, and made several excursions into the forest and down the river on snow-shoes, but scarcely a bird was to be seen. At this season of the year the most absolute silence reigns in these drear Siberian forests. In the afternoon we tightened up our "pavoska," and so far succeeded in restoring the centre of gravity that we returned home without a spill. We saw only two birds either in going or returning, a Siberian jay in going, and a capercailzie (*Tetrao urogallus*, Linn.) in returning.

On our arrival at Ust-Zylma at two o'clock on Sunday morning, we found service going on in the church in celebration of Easter Eve. We went with M. Znaminski to the 3 A.M. mass, and after service breakfasted with him, and at 7 A.M. turned into our hammocks for an hour or two's rest. The Easter holidays lasted three days, during which we saw plenty of eating and drinking, and some (but not much) drunkenness. The Russian peasantry in Siberia easily get drunk. They drink vodka neat, and two or three glasses are enough for most of them. There is one very curious circumstance about drunkenness in this part of the world. So far as we could ascertain, with the Russian peasants drunkenness never produces crime. When a Russian peasant is drunk, he is not quarrelsome like most Englishmen, but simply becomes obtrusively affectionate. He wants to embrace you, and kiss you, and be your very best friend. During these holidays, when we were returning from the hospitable boards of our Russian or German friends in the small hours of the morning, we would occasionally meet one or two victims of excess of vodka lying in the snow, their malitzas being warm enough to prevent them from being frozen to death.

On the Sunday night there was a very heavy fall of snow. At least a foot must have been added to the depth. On the Monday morning the weather was very stormy, and the fresh fallen snow was drifted into hills and valleys. The change in the appearance of the town was wonderful. The vast dunghill of Ust-Zylma had put on its Easter holiday attire, and was once more pure as the driven snow. Everything was covered with a layer of white powder, dry as dust, and white as (the only possible comparison)—white as itself. At night the effect was still more striking. The snow on the railings, on the house tops, and wherever it had been disturbed by footmarks, was white, and all the rest was a pale delicate cobalt-blue.

On Tuesday the 28th of April we got our first nest. It was brought in by some peasants. It was the nest of a Siberian jay, and contained four eggs. This bird is probably the earliest breeder in these parts, and no doubt winters in the Petchora district. The nest was not so flat as we expected, and was composed almost entirely of lichens, with a few pieces of matting, hair, and feathers. The foundation was made of slender pine twigs, and the inside was profusely lined with feathers.

The snowstorm having now ceased, we made an excursion on snow-shoes to an island on the Petchora. and afterwards visited the opposite bank of the river— *l'autre côte*, as Piottuch called it. It was remarkable how very few birds we saw. I twice came across a flock of bullfinches, all males, and shot three of them. I also saw and shot a solitary tit, very nearly allied to our marsh-tit. It is a greyer bird than ours, with the white cheeks much whiter, and the black hood extending much farther down the back. We also saw footmarks of hares, and found several snares set by the peasants to catch them. The next day we visited the same ground again. We did not see a single bullfinch, but caught a glimpse of a small spotted woodpecker. We crossed over to the banks of the Zylma, but the birch woods there produced nothing but a solitary marsh-tit, which I shot. The woods round Ust-Zylma seemed to be absolutely empty of bird life. Our first eight days had produced only nine species of birds. During the following ten days we increased our list by only three birds—the bullfinch, the Siberian jay, and the Siberian marsh-tit.

LASSOING REINDEER

CHAPTER VII.

THE SAMOYEDES.

Trip to Habariki—Samoyedes—Lassoing Reindeer—Dogs of the Natives—Samoyede Sledges—Reindeer Harness—The Chooms—Samoyede Hospitality—Marriage Ceremonies—Funeral Rites—Religion.

IT was quite obvious that we should make little or no progress in our ornithological researches until summer came. We accordingly laid ourselves out to pick up further information about the Samoyedes, so that our time might not be absolutely wasted. We had not yet visited any of their chooms, or tents, and we were glad to learn from Captain Engel that there were several in the neighbourhood of Habariki. On Thursday morning, April 29, we sledged over to that village, a distance of forty versts. The road was about two-thirds on the Petchora, and the remaining third across country, principally islands. It was so good that we accomplished the distance in four hours, stopping for half an hour midway to feed the horses. We scarcely saw a bird on the whole journey.

Habariki is a poor little village, without a church, and containing not more than a dozen houses. The sandy banks of the river are about fifty feet higher than the level on which it is built, and keep it out of the reach of the floods that come with the thaw. The village was admirably adapted for the winter quarters of Sideroff's steamer, which lay below the bend in a little creek running back out of the Petchora, protected there from danger of being smashed to pieces by the blocks of ice that crash down on the breaking up of the river.

After a good lunch we hired two sledges and started in search of the Samoyedes with Captain Engel and a Russian, the engineer of the steamer. We had ascertained that there were some chooms about four versts off, but just as we arrived at the place we found everything ready for a move northward. The chooms were taken down and packed on sledges, and the reindeer, to the number of about 500, were collected together; and before we had been there ten minutes the order to march was given. We were informed that they were not going far that afternoon, and would probably erect their chooms in the course of the evening within a verst of Habariki, but that before doing so they were going to take out fifty of the reindeer which belonged to a Russian. We were anxious to see the operation of lassoing, and drove with the Samoyedes in our sledges to the place selected for the purpose. As soon as we left the road our horses stuck fast with the snow up to their traces, and we were glad to give up our almost ineffectual struggle to get along on foot, and seat ourselves on one of the reindeer sledges, which soon brought us to the spot. It was admirably chosen—a large open space—perhaps half a mile across, sufficiently hollow to give it the effect of a natural amphitheatre surrounded by forest. In the centre was a slight elevation, where three or four sledges were stationed, commanding a fine view of the herd of reindeer gathered round. A little below us in the hollow were about a score of sledges with the women and the baggage.

The Samoyedes proved themselves expert in throwing the lasso. In the left hand they held a small coil of rope, in the right hand the larger half. The lasso was thrown with an underhand fling, and nearly always successfully over the horns of the animal at the first attempt. The left hand was then pressed close to the side so as to bring the shock of the sudden pulling up of the reindeer at full speed against the thigh. When a reindeer found itself caught, it generally made desperate efforts to escape, but was usually on its haunches gasping for breath in a few seconds. The Samoyede then hauled in the rope, or, if it had run out nearly to its full length, another Samoyede came up and began to haul it in nearer to the animal. When he was close to the deer he took hold of its horns, and with a side twist brought it down on to the snow. The Russian to whom the fifty reindeer belonged then approached, and taking a thong of three-plait matting from a bunch at his belt, tied one of the animal's forelegs to the hind leg on the same side; crossing the feet, but keeping the legs parallel at the point of ligature.

As soon as the reindeer was left, he made wild efforts to rise and walk; and sometimes succeeded in hobbling a few paces. Finding his strength give way with his frantic efforts to escape, he generally rested with his fore-knees on the snow for a time; and finally lay down quietly. A dozen reindeer were soon on the ground.

The scene became quite exciting; the reindeer were wheeling round and round in circles. The dogs tied to the sledges barked furiously and evidently wished to have a share in the sport. The dogs selected by the Samoyedes to help them to get within lasso range of the deer rushed frantically about at the command of their masters, whose loud cries added to the excitement of the scene. Sometimes a herd of reindeer ran over a place where the snow was unable to bear their weight; and it was interesting to watch them snorting and plunging. As the number caught increased, the difficulty also increased of identifying and catching the remaining few of the fifty that belonged to the Russian, and the Samoyedes with the lassos were driven about in sledges at a rapid pace to get within reach of the animals they wanted. The deer kept together; if one ran out of bounds a dog was sent after it and soon brought it back again. In one respect the reindeer resemble sheep; wherever one goes, the rest try to follow.

In this herd the greater number were females (*vah' shinka*), with good horns; these they do not cast till they drop their young. A few were males (*horre*), their new horns just appearing. Those chiefly used in the sledges were cut reindeer (*bück*), also without horns. Some of the hornless animals leaped right through the lasso and others were caught by the leg.

The lasso is a cord about 100 feet long, made of two thongs of reindeer-skin plaited together, so as to make a round rope three-eighths of an inch in diameter. The noose is formed by passing the cord through a small piece of bone with two holes in it. The lasso passes freely through the hole, while the end is fastened to a little bone peg with a bone-washer to prevent it slipping through the other hole.

The dogs were all white except one, which was quite black. They were stiff-built little animals, somewhat like Pomeranian dogs, with foxlike heads and thick bushy hair; their tails turned up over the back and curled to one side.

The next morning we turned out of our hammocks at four and strolled in the brilliant sunshine, hoping to meet with some birds; but, with the exception of the hooded crows, magpies, snow-buntings, and redpolls, we met with none feeding. In the woods we saw an eagle, a pair of marsh-tits, a pair of Siberian jays, and occasionally a pair of ravens.

After breakfast we visited the chooms, and very picturesque they looked in the white landscape in the dazzling sunshine. Here and there a few willows dotted the undulating ground near a winding rivulet. The reindeer were not to be seen, all were away feeding. Two chooms stood a few feet apart from the rest; in front of these the sledges were drawn up, twenty-three in number, some light and elegant in shape, with four carefully hewn ribs on each side, and a low sloping back. In these the Samoyedes and their families travelled. Others were not quite so finely finished, and had only three ribs on each side; these were used for the lighter baggage, reindeer-skins, malitzas, and so forth, covered over in some cases with a tarpaulin made of pieces of birch-bark, neatly sewn together with reindeer-sinew. Other sledges again were of much stronger and clumsier make, with only two ribs on each side, adapted for the heavy baggage. Some of these were a simple gantry upon runners, carrying casks of reindeer-meat, others a wooden chest with an angular roof like the recognised Noah's ark model, containing loaves of black bread and other perishable articles.

The harness of the reindeer is very simple. The saddle is a plain band of tanned reindeer-leather, about eight inches broad, hanging a few inches below the body on each side. About six inches from each end a double thong of reindeer-skin is attached, and forms the belly-band. The thong passes through the saddle, and is fastened to a button (*stchorlak*) made of reindeer-horn or bone. These buttons are about two inches in diameter, with two oval holes near the centre for the thong to pass through. Some of them are round, others square with the corners off, others hexagonal, and others again hexagonal with every alternate side concave, whilst some are merely irregular rhomboids. All the buttons are bevelled on the edge, and generally slightly hollowed to fit the curve of the reindeer's side. On the near side of the near reindeer is a piece of carved bone, into which the reins can be hitched, called *halsü* (the *h* pronounced slightly gutturally). This part of the harness is of divers shapes and patterns, and seems to be especially the part on the ornamentation and variation of which the Samoyedes expend their spare time and taste.

The simplest form is a hook to receive the reins. A more elaborate one is a double hook, the reversed hook being obviously added only for the sake of ornament. Others again have the double hook, with a variety of ornamental carving added. On the off side of the saddle, opposite the *halsü*, is a leather loop to which the bridle-rein of the next deer is attached. The collar is a narrow band about three inches wide, also of tanned leather, passing round the neck. The two ends of this collar are fastened together by the trace which passes from the sledge, between the hind legs of the deer, between the body and the belly-band which hangs rather loosely, then between the forelegs to the breast, where it passes

through the two ends of the collar, and is secured to a
bone peg or a *paysik* of simple construction. The head-
piece or halter (for no bit is used) is called *syahney*. That
of the leading deer consists of a square straight piece of
bone or horn, about four inches long, on the right cheek,
under the root of the horns, with a hole at each end, and
a second piece of horn, a semicircular or half-round
section, bending nearly rectangularly, not quite in the

REIN RESTS

middle. This piece of horn is hollowed or deeply
grooved on the flat side, and has a hole bored through at
each end, and a third hole about half an inch from that
one at the long end. The position of this piece of horn
is with the short end halfway across the forehead and
the long end in a similar position to the straight piece of
horn on the other side of the head. Both pieces are
more or less ornamented with simple carving ; they are
fastened together, the ends about a couple of inches apart,
by a short thong of plain or plaited leather, passing
through the holes at one end of each piece, and tied

across the forehead. To the other ends of the pieces of
bone, plain thongs of leather are attached, one passing
behind the horns, the other under the neck. Through
the third hole, in the long side of the bent piece of horn,
passes a thong fastened to the single rein, either with a
simple tie or with an intervening swivel made of horn,
called by the Samoyedes the *sürnye*. The head-pieces
of the other deer are slightly different. The bone pieces
under the horns are slenderer, but slightly curved, and
both alike. They are tied together across the forehead,
as is the head-piece of the leading deer, but the other
ends are tied to the apex of a piece of bone or horn,
shaped like an isosceles triangle, with the angles cut off
square, the angle at the apex being very obtuse, and the
basal line slightly concave. These triangular pieces are
placed nearly over the jugular vein, and are fastened at
one end under the neck, and at the other at the back of
the head. The bridle-rein is attached at one end to the
thong passing at the back of the head, and the other to
the saddle of the deer to the left or near side. The wood
or bone blind pulley through which the traces run. is
called *pate-chay*, it is so arranged that any deer not doing
its fair share of the pulling drops behind against the
sledge. The animals are urged on by a long pole, with
which they are hit or poked ; it is called the *toor*, and the
bone button at the end of it the *toor-mahl*. Behind each
sledge, on each side, there is a thong of leather passing
through a hole pierced through one end of a bit of bone
about nine inches long. A second thong of leather forms
the link connecting this to a second bone, which can be
fastened to the head-piece of the deer of the following
sledge, which thus requires no driver. This rude chain
is called the *pooinye*. The swivel is occasionally a
brass one, bought from the Russians. Now and then a

brass ring is seen on the head-piece, and sometimes tassels of plain leather, shaped like luggage labels and stained vermilion, ornament it.

The chooms were shaped like ordinary regulation tents, about twelve feet in diameter and height; they were supported inside by some thirty slender birch poles, converging to a cone, tied together in a bunch at the top. This skeleton was covered with old, dirty, and much-patched reindeer-skins, sewn together and lined with coarse and half-rotten canvas, probably old sails. Some cords of twisted reindeer-sinew strengthened the structure, and an opening about a foot wide was left at the summit of the tent to serve as a chimney. We drew back the covering overlapping the opening used as a door and entered. Snow, heaped up to the height of about a foot, protected the choom from bottom draughts. A wood fire burned in the centre upon a thin metal plate; an ordinary gipsy kettle was suspended over it by a simple arrangement. Mats of slender birch-bark, woven together every six inches by a warp of string, were placed on either side of the fire; over these were stretched another mat made of some kind of rushy grass. Around were packed various articles of clothing, wooden bowls and spoons of Russian origin, a Russian box containing a china tea-service; a heap of reindeer giblets, part of which were doubtless stewing in the kettle, and sundry other articles. Exactly opposite the door there hung one of the Onega bronze bas-reliefs of saints or virgins, framed in a rudely carved piece of wood, shaped somewhat like a cross.

After purchasing some reindeer harness, we were invited to drink a cup of tea and to eat a kind of spiral biscuit. Our hostess had just been sewing; a steel needle, a tailor's thimble, and thread of reindeer-sinew lay in a corner of the tent. The smoke annoyed us when we stood up, but we did not feel it much when seated. The Samoyedes sat cross-legged on the ground, and tea was served on a little table about six inches high, just large enough to hold half a dozen cups. As usual, we found our hosts very ready to give us any information we asked them.

The Samoyedes never seemed annoyed at our taking notes among them; they struck us as a good-tempered, somewhat phlegmatic race. They carried old-fashioned Russian flint-lock rifles, but we could not rouse their interest in our breech-loaders; they do not appear to work much in metals. They always carry a knife, no doubt of Russian make, but they are very ingenious in making handles and in ornamenting them. Patterns of various grades of elaboration are carved upon them, and the patterns filled up with melted tin. They use a small saw, a rude form of brace and bit, and also the indispensable axe.

Like the Russians, the Samoyedes have beautifully white and regular teeth. They are very fond of chewing the resin which they get from the Scotch fir, which doubtless assists in keeping the teeth clean.

As we are now on the subject of this strange race, we may as well insert here some details we gathered a few days later, after our return to Ust-Zylma, from a Samoyede who drove up in his reindeer sledge from a choom near Habariki. Our interpreter was a Polish Jew, banished by his father to Siberia, because he had adopted the religion of the Greek Church. He translated the Samoyede's bad Russian into worse German.

We were informed that when a young Samoyede desires to marry, and has come to some understanding with the damsel of his choice, he visits her father's choom, and with a short stick taps him, and then the mother of the maiden, on the shoulder. He then demands the girl in marriage, and offers the father and mother a glass of vodka, which he has brought with him. As a token of his goodwill the father drinks the vodka ; he tells the young man he has no objection, but that he must ask the girl's consent. The preliminary ceremony of asking papa having been gone through, the young man retires. A few days later he comes again to the choom ; this time accompanied by what servants he has, and provided with plenty of vodka. His retinue remain outside, while he enters the choom, and seats himself by the side of his lady-love. The father hands the young man a glass of vodka ; he drinks half, and hands the half-full glass under his left arm to the girl, who finishes it. The father then gives his daughter a glass of vodka, who in like manner drinks half of it, and presents the remainder with her left hand under her right arm to her lover, who drains the glass. After this the father hands a piece of raw flesh to the young man, who eats it, and then takes a piece from the floor, eats half, and presents the other half under his left arm to the girl to finish. She, in her turn, takes a piece of raw flesh from the floor, eats half, and likewise hands the other half under her right arm to the young man to finish. Then follows the eating and drinking that in barbarous, as in civilised nations, is considered necessary to ratify the ceremony. Before night an old man, called a *shaman*, a kind of magician or medicine-man, carrying a drum, visits the choom ; of him the bridegroom asks certain questions concerning his bride. If the old man knows nothing against her he begins to play upon his drum, and the marriage is completed. If, however, the magician speaks evil of the girl, the young man has the option of leaving her there and then, or if he be still enamoured of her charms, it is open to him to bargain with her father to take her for a month or a year on trial. At the expiration of the time agreed upon, if the pair suit each other, they consider themselves married for life. On the other hand, should they not agree, they can separate at the end of the time specified; but in that case the man must provide for any children born within the period. After the marriage festivities are over, the young couple are left alone in the choom of the bride's father.

It is customary for the bridegroom to present his bride with the skin of a black fox. The girl's father gives his son-in-law a choom, with all its appurtenances, and five, ten, twenty, or thirty reindeer, according to his wealth. If the bridegroom be rich, he gives his father-in-law money to the amount sometimes of two hundred roubles.

Since the adoption of the Russian faith by the Samoyedes they bury their dead. Previous to their conversion, when one among them died he was fully dressed and, in his best malitza and soveek, was laid flat on his back on the tundra. His favourite *bück* reindeer was killed and laid by his side, with his best harness and his driving-pole and bow.* The choom is taken down at once, and the camp is broken up amidst much weeping and lamentation. If possible, the place is never re-visited. The Samoyedes believe that if the dead man's property were not left with him his spirit would follow them.

The Samoyedes used to have wooden idols, to which

---

* Captain Hall, in his "Life with the Esquimaux," mentions a similar custom existing among them. The Innuits seal up their dying in snow-huts, or *igloos*, where they are allowed to die alone. The blubber-lamp, as well as the fishing and hunting instruments of the dead, are always laid by his side, and the place is abandoned.

they sacrificed reindeer.* In order that the reindeer may reach the unseen god, of whom the wooden idol is evidently considered but the symbol, it must be killed in a peculiar fashion. A running noose is made in the middle of a cord and put round the horns of the deer; a Samoyede holds the two ends. Another noose is put round the animal's hind feet, and while he is thus held at full stretch, he is stabbed in both sides with two pieces of wood (not with a knife); then the spirit of the reindeer is supposed to be sent to the god. The greater number of Samoyedes have adopted the Russian faith, and have been baptized into the Greek Church, but many of these still retain their ancient beliefs, and sacrifice to their idols, while in the more easterly parts of the vast region inhabited by this people, many have not yet been "converted."

* William Govedon, who wintered at Pustozara, 1614–15, tells us that the Samoyedes had then " no true knowledge of God, but worship blocks and images of the deuill, unto which they strangle tame deere."—*Purchas his Pilgrimes*, lib. iii. ch. 12.

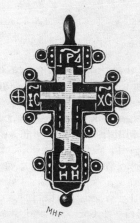

OLD RUSSIAN SILVER CROSS

A SPILL IN THE SNOW

CHAPTER VIII.

LIFE IN UST-ZYLMA.

May-day—Snow-buntings—Jackdaws—Game—Birds of Prey—Sunday
at Ust-Zylma—A Fire—Marriage Ceremony—Tenure of Land—The
Commune—Preparations for Summer.

ON May-day the thaw continued in real earnest. A warm
wind and a hot sun made great havoc with the snow. All
traces of the heavy fall of the previous Sunday night
soon disappeared, and a considerable portion of the old
accumulation of winter melted. Ust-Zylma became once
more a vast dunghill, and on the hills, where the snow in
some places lay exceptionally deep, it was too soft to bear
our weight, even on snow-shoes. We attempted our
usual ramble in the woods at the back of the town; but
travelling was very laborious, and we returned to our
quarters with broken snow-shoes, and without having

remarked anything of special interest. With the excep
tion of a yellow-hammer, which was making a feeble
attempt to sing, we scarcely saw or heard a bird. One
effect of the thaw was to banish the snow-buntings from
the town to the country. Although this bird is thick-
billed, and undoubtedly feeds on grain and seeds during
the winter, it appears to change its diet to some extent
during the breeding season. When I was in Lapland I
found it nesting among the rocks on the island of Vadsö,
in the Varanger Fjord. Not far distant, down by the
shore, was the great whaling establishment of Mr. Foyne,
where on an average three whales a week were cut up.
The snow-buntings constantly visited the yard, which
abounded with insects attracted by the offal; and the
stomachs of some which I shot and skinned proved to be
full of these.

During this sloppy season we confined our walks
pretty much to the town itself, carrying our walking-stick
guns in case a new bird should turn up. On the 3rd of
May we were rewarded by seeing for the first time a pair
of jackdaws. It was contrary to law to shoot in the
streets, and the birds were within a stone's-throw of the
house of the public prosecutor. I shot one of them, as I
thought, very cleverly, on the sly, but I found that my
attempt at concealment had been a failure, for a day or
two afterwards, whilst discussing our walnuts and wine
with the chief magistrate at the public prosecutor's
hospitable table, we were kindly cautioned to shoot as
little as possible in the streets.

The liberal hospitalities of our friends helped to
beguile the time during the thaw; and occasionally the
peasants offered us birds, which provided variety for our
larder, and sometimes interested us and found employment for Piottuch We bought four capercailzies for

eighty kopecks from one of our friends the Samoyedes
who had shot them with ball. Hazel-grouse (*Bonasa
betulina*) were also frequently brought to us, at twenty
kopecks per brace. They are most delicate eating, and
are considered by many to be the finest game that can
be brought to table.

Winter returned on the 4th of May, when a raw west
wind brought a heavy storm at noon, after which snow
and bitter cold continued, with occasional high wind, till
the 8th. We went out, notwithstanding, struggling on
snow-shoes across deep ravines and through bushes and
plantations. We also made an excursion within the
island in search of birds. For some days the snow-
buntings remained outside the town in such immense
flocks that when they rose the whirring of their wings
could be heard at some distance. On the 6th the
snow drove them back into Ust-Zylma, also small parties
of redpolls, which follow the buntings very much as
starlings follow rooks. When we first met with the
flocks of snow-buntings we found them to consist principally of males, but as the season advanced the females
largely predominated. On the 4th of May we saw a
white-tailed eagle and a hen-harrier, and on the following
day we had an excellent sight of a merlin. Magpies
were as abundant as ever, but, like the snow-buntings,
they had moved into the country, and on the 5th we discovered a nearly completed nest in a spruce fir, built
about five feet from the ground. The birds were most
vociferous, and used every artifice to decoy us away from
their property.

On the 8th of May summer seemed farther off than
ever. On the previous day the weather had been very
changeable—alternately warm, snowing, hailing, sleeting,
with an occasional gleam of sunshine, and a cold wind,

but on the whole a thaw. The next day the morning was bitterly cold, with the north wind blowing hard. In the afternoon the wind veered to the west, with a heavy fall of snow. At midnight the wind dropped, the sky became clear, and the thermometer went down to 16°. The landscape was again white and frost-bound. It looked exactly like mid-winter, except that at that hour of night we could see to read a newspaper out of doors. The climate of these regions is very curious at this time of the year. The change is sudden and violent—a leaping from mid-winter into summer, without any intervening spring.

We strolled out in the morning, not expecting to see anything new. We shot a tree-sparrow and a yellow-hammer, and were returning home somewhat disheartened, in spite of our unexpectant mood at starting, when a hen-harrier suddenly put in an appearance. He did not, however, come within range, and we went into a little valley, there to wait for him or a chance raven. By-and-by a small hawk crossed in front of us. We followed it up the hillside, caught sight of it again, watched it alight on a heap of manure, quietly stalked it, and shot it. It turned out to be a female merlin. Whilst we were carefully putting it away, an eagle passed almost within shot of us. In one of the cottages a peasant showed us the skin of an eagle-owl (*Bubo maximus*). The next evening we strolled out on the banks of the Petchora. Brilliant sunshine flooded the earth, not a cloud was in the sky; but it was cold and winterly as Christmas. Flocks of magpies and of hooded crows were almost the only birds we saw. They passed us on the wing, evidently going to their resting-places in the woods.

The week had not brought us many birds, but we knew summer was at hand, and we waited patiently.

Meanwhile we mingled with the inhabitants of Ust-Zylma and observed their ways. Sunday seemed a day devoted to calling, and many sledges used to drive up to the house where we were from the neighbouring villages. The peasants combined business with these visits to town, and we bought four skins of white fox and one of grey fox for nine roubles and a half, from one of Boulegan's visitors.

Once we had an opportunity of seeing the people of Ust-Zylma turning out to extinguish a fire. A small conflagration burst out in the house of Captain Arendt. All the villagers trooped to the spot, armed with axes, wooden shovels, and boat-hooks. It is the law that in case of fire every peasant should assist in putting it out. On each house a board is nailed up, on which is roughly sketched the article its inhabitants must furnish to assist in extinguishing the flames. The people keep to their primitive ways and habits. We watched a peasant one day shooting at a mark with a flint-lock rifle. The barrel was very thick, and the bore the size of a large pea. He carried a spiral coil of lead, and, when he wanted a bullet, bit a piece off with his perfectly white regular teeth, and chewed it into a rough sphere. His gun, which he told us was worth five roubles, was ornamented all over the stock with by no means inartistic carvings.

On one occasion we assisted at a wedding in the Orthodox Greek church. The marriage ceremony took place in the afternoon, and was sufficiently imposing. The priest met the couple at the vestibule of the church. After going through a form of prayer, he presented the bride and bridegroom with a lighted taper, which he had first crossed over their bowed heads; the rings likewise were crossed over their heads, as were also a pair of gold crowns before being placed upon them. The bible and the crucifix were kissed. A silver cup of wine was quaffed by the plighted pair, each drinking from it alternately. Censers · of incense were swung. The priest, the happy couple, and the assistants bowed and crossed themselves continually, and between each part of the ceremony prayers were offered.

We were not very successful in our attempts to obtain accurate information as to the tenure of land. It was sometimes difficult to reconcile conflicting statements. Most of our informants, however, agreed that they or their ancestors were formerly serfs of the Crown, that after their emancipation the land remained the property of the Crown, and was leased to the village or commune at a nominal rent. The affairs of the commune are managed by a parliament or town council, composed of every householder, electing a mayor or *starrosta* (literally, oldest man), whose term of office is three years, and who is responsible to the Government for the rent or taxes payable by the commune. Every three years a redistribution of land takes place, the arable land being divided amongst the householders in lots proportionate to the number of individuals living in each house. Five hundred roubles will build a handsome habitation in Ust-Zylma. We were informed that every peasant was annually entitled to a fixed number of cubic yards of firewood without charge, and to a limited number of balks of good building timber, which he was free to sell if he did not require to use it.

The near approach of summer was the signal for unusual exertions on the part of the peasants. Procrastination seems to be a Russian national vice. Now, when the horses were nearly worn out by long feeding upon bad hay, and when the roads were very heavy by reason of the thaws, the poor animals had to work double time. A quantity of last year's fodder still lay on the flat land on the other side of the Petchora, which, if left, would inevitably be swept away when the frozen river broke up ; the cattle had to be taken across the ice and housed in a place of safety, there to wait until the floods subsided on these flat stretches and the new rich pasture had begun to spring up. The women and children had also to be transported across, to look after the cattle ; whilst the men went down the river to fish, leaving Ust-Zylma as deserted for three months as a winter village in the Parnassus.

OLD RUSSIAN SILVER CROSS

SHOOTING WILD GEESE

CHAPTER IX.

THE ADVENT OF SUMMER.

Mild Weather—Bear-tracks—Saddle of Bear—First Rain—Six New Migratory Birds—Magpie's Eggs—Cessation of the Winter Frost—Return of Winter—A Wild-goose Chase—Cachets—Night on the Banks of the Petchora—The Silent Forest.

ON the 10th of May we had for the first time real summer weather, which continued for some days. It thawed in the shade as well as in the sun; but, as there was not much wind, the snow melted slowly. We drove up the Zylma and took a long walk in our snow-shoes, returning across the island; but the pine and birch woods were still almost deserted. We shot a pair of marsh-tits, heard the cry of a great black woodpecker, and saw four wild geese flying over our heads. On the island we fell in with a small flock of shore-larks (*Otocorys alpestris*), and

succeeded in shooting four while feeding upon the bare
places on the banks of the island.   We also started a pair
of wild geese and a large owl, probably the snowy owl,
which alighted on a heap of snow in the middle of the
Petchora.   Its flight resembled that of the glaucous gull,
but it occasionally skimmed close to the snow for some
distance.

We traced along the snow the footprints of a bear and
its cubs, about a day or two old.   The traces of Bruin's
presence had an added interest to us from the fact that
for the last two days we had been breakfasting and dining
on a saddle of bear, and most excellent we had found it,
much better than beef.   The animal we had been feasting
on was about a year old ; it had been turned out of its
place of hybernation by some woodcutters, who had cut
down the tree at the root of which it was sleeping. I bought
the skin, and had an excellent hearth-rug made of it.

Summer now seemed to have suddenly burst upon us
in all its strength, the sun was scorching, the snow in
many places melted so rapidly as to be almost impassable.
The mud banks of the Zylma were steaming from the
heat.   On the 12th of May, about noon, the weather
grew hazy, with a very conspicuous halo around the sun-
like a dull circular rainbow ; the wind was warmer than
it had yet been, and in the afternoon there came on a
steady rain, the first rain we had seen since we left home.
Sancho Panza says that one swallow does not make a
summer ; but the arrival of six species of migratory birds
within two days ought to have some significance.   On
the 11th we saw for the first time a pair of swans.   The
same day, on the half-open land between the Petchora
and the Zylma, we saw some flocks of wild geese, and,
near a pool of water on the ice, half a dozen Siberian
herring-gulls (*Larus affinis*, Rheinh.).   Their cry seemed

to me to be exactly the same as that of the common and Mediterranean herring-gulls. On the 12th a little detachment of white wagtails came to the village, and we shot six during the day. In each instance they were on the roof of the houses. We also shot a redstart (*Ruticilla phœnicurus*, Linn.) occupying the same position. Another new arrival was the meadow-pipit, of which we shot a solitary example. The shore-larks had already been some days in Ust-Zylma, and by this time were in large and small flocks in the fields on both sides of the town. All those we shot proved to be males. Three or four small hawks, probably merlins, were hovering about, and a snowy owl was brought in to us, apparently just killed. A white-tailed eagle, his white tail looking grey against the snow, was perching on an ice-block in the Petchora, and at a little distance off we could distinctly see a raven picking a bone. Morning and evening we watched the gulls, without being able to get a shot at them. The redpolls had disappeared altogether, and we saw the snow-buntings only once or twice. The signs of coming summer were surrounding us, small flies were on the wing, twice we came upon a tortoiseshell butterfly ; we visited the magpie's nest, which we had discovered some days previously in a spruce, and found that it contained seven eggs. But even the approach of summer has its accompanying drawbacks : we had to give up at this time all hope of more winter posts, and two months might elapse before the summer ones would arrive. This break in the communication with civilised Europe is one of the trials to be endured by explorers in these districts.

The little spurt of mild weather, however, turned out to be a delusion. Our six species of summer migrants proved no more reliable than Sancho Panza's solitary swallow. On the 13th a strong gale from the north brought winter back again, and drove away our newly arrived visitors to more genial latitudes. The snow-buntings and the shore-larks became very wild during this spell of bitter wind; towards evening it dropped, and when we came upon a flock of the former, they were so tame that they allowed us to walk about within ten and sometimes five yards of them. The flock was composed mostly of females; one male that we observed amongst them was in more mature plumage than any we had yet seen. Birds of prey appeared in unusual numbers. We saw hen-harriers, both male and female, numerous merlins, which often perched upon the heaps of manure in the fields, and, for the first time, a peregrine falcon. Piottuch was fortunate enough to shoot a fine snowy owl on the goose ground between the Petchora and the Zylma. A hard frost in the night, followed by a cold east wind with bright sunshine, was most unfavourable to the arrival of migratory birds. We were deliberating as to what would be the least unprofitable mode of spending the day, when the Preestáff sent in to inquire if we would join him and the postmaster in an excursion four and twenty miles up the Petchora to shoot geese, and we accepted their invitation gladly. We ordered a horse and sledge, packed up provisions, tents, and wraps, and were soon *en route*.

About halfway we descried two swans on the snow of the Petchora. We started our sledge in pursuit, and approaching the birds in a spiral curve, we came within range, fired, and missed. The birds, very large and very white, flew about a verst across the river, and again alighted. Here they were joined by a third swan. Slowly we crept up again in a spiral curve within range; this time two rifles fired, and both missed; a third time the rifles came within range, but with no better result; after which the swans flew right away.

We then visited a small lake close to the banks of the Petchora, but it was completely ice-bound, and declared to be *niet dobra* (good for nothing). Finally, we selected a spot where there was open water in two places. Geese flew about in small flocks at intervals during the afternoon, and we all expressed confident hopes of a bag after sunrise. The horses were taken from the sledge, a fire was lit, supper with unlimited tea followed, and was over by eleven. We then selected places supposed to be favourable for the cachets; at each place a hole was dug in the snow, which was piled up to the height of three or four feet, and planted round with willow twigs. "Cocksure" (the nickname we gave to Piottuch, a bad pun on his name),* who was in high glee, drove across the Petchora with the postmaster, where he was "cocksure" of finding plenty of geese.

After a final cup of tea and a smoke, we separated at one o'clock, each departing to his cachet, to take, if he felt so inclined, a sleep in the snow for a couple of hours. I did not feel sleepy, and was curious to watch a whole night on the banks of the Petchora; so doffing my malitza, axe in hand, I set to work to turn my cachet into a turreted castle, some six feet high inside. It was a keen frost, and the surface snow was easy to hew out into square blocks, which I joined together with soft snow from below, and soon my castle was one solid mass of frozen snow. The exercise kept me warm. I planted my last piece of willow twig and put on my malitza just as the sun appeared above the horizon, amidst lake and vermilion clouds, behind the steep mudbanks on the other side of the Petchora. Behind me rose a thick

* " Piatookh " is the Russian for a cock.

wood of willow and decayed or decaying birch, a pine showing here and there between. Presently I spied, from between my turrets of snow, a marsh-tit silently searching for food on a willow; I changed one of my cartridges for dust-shot, put my feet into my snow shoes, sallied forth, and shot it. His mate soon began to call, and in half a minute I secured her also, and returned to my cachet.

An hour passed by; now and then I heard the distant "gag, gag" of the geese, or the wild cry of some far-off swan, but nothing came within range of less than cannon-shot of me. Fourteen large glaucous gulls slowly flew up the Petchora; I watched a pair of swans on the ice through my telescope, and listened to the distant call of some smaller gulls; whilst redpolls and white wagtails often passed over me, all flying up wind. At length I got tired of waiting and watching, and made an excursion on my snow-shoes into the wood. All around was dead silence; nothing was to be heard but the gentle rattling of the east wind amongst the leafless branches of the willows. The wood seemed as empty of bird-life as the desert of Sahara.

I returned to my cachet, and waited and watched with no better result than before. A flock of snow-buntings came fluttering up the Petchora and alighted on some willow-trees; this was interesting. I now made an excursion to the cachet of my companions. I had forgotten to wind my watch, and made this an excuse for my visit. Halfway to it, I came upon a small flock of reed-buntings amongst some willows, and missed a shot at one of them. My companion had stuck heroically to his cachet, but had had no better luck than mine. As we were chatting, we heard the note of a bird, which I took to be a redstart.

I followed the sound to some distance, but could not overtake the bird on my snow-shoes. Setting out to return to my cachet, I was interrupted by a flock of reed-buntings; I got a shot at one, but the cap missing fire, away they flew. I was returning disconsolately by the side of a thick but narrow plantation, when I heard a "gag, gag" through the trees, and descried seven geese, apparently flying straight for my companion's cachet; and on returning I learnt that he had brought down a bean-goose.

On my way back to my cachet I met another party of reed-buntings, one of which I bagged; then I sat in my hiding-place for an hour, waiting for geese that never came within range. At eight I found I had taken a wink of sleep. I could stand it no longer, so set off in search of my companions, and bagging another reed-bunting and wagtail on my way, we returned together to our encampment, where we soon had the kettle boiling with *tchai*.

The postmaster and "Cocksure" turned up as we were breakfasting, and reported a blank night. The Preestáff, we found afterwards, had fared no better. Deciding that we had had enough of this wild-goose chase we harnessed our sledges and returned home in a steady rain. Our horse was done up, and we were six hours on the road, through four of which we slept soundly, waking up just in time to bag a score of shore-larks.

Notwithstanding its inglorious results, we enjoyed our trip as a novelty, and had many hearty laughs over divers "spills" out of and over the sledge; but as ours was the only one that brought home a goose, the best of the laugh was on our side. We had, moreover, bagged a new migrant, and "Cocksure" had seen a black wood-pecker and a common snipe.

THE BANKS OF THE ZYLMA

CHAPTER X.

THE BREAK-UP OF THE ICE.

Gulls—Species new to Europe—Fresh Arrivals—Duck-shooting—Bird-
life in the Forest—Gulls perching on Trees—Break-up of the Ice on
the Zylma—On the wrong Bank of the River—Dragging the Boats
across the Ice—Final break-up of the Ice on the Petchora.

THE same evening, as we sat at the window of our rooms
writing up our journals, and now and then looking up
to glance through the rain at the ever-impressive scene
before us, we suddenly descried upon the ice a flock
of, perhaps, 200 gulls. In the twinkle of an eye we
had donned our indiarubber boots and were wading
through the streets of Ust-Zylma. As we neared the
birds we made sure, from their note, that the larger
number of them were the common gull, with possibly
a dozen herring-gulls among them. We discharged four
cartridges of our goose-shot into them. Our broadside,

fired from a distance, left one dead and one wounded on the field. The smaller bird was undoubtedly the common gull, but it was not at first so easy to determine to what species the larger gull belonged. The colour of the mantle was intermediate between that of the lesser black-backed gull and the Mediterranean herring-gull, but the wing pattern resembled that of the latter species. Upon our return home, however, we cleared up the difficulties surrounding our bird, and finding that it had no colloquial name in our language we ventured to christen it the Siberian herring-gull. The species was not new to science, but we may claim to have been the first to add it to the list of European birds.

Another species new to our list was the golden plover, which also arrived in flocks. These birds were special objects of our attention, partly because they were a valuable addition to our larder, and still more so because we were anxiously on the look-out for the arrival of the grey plover, the eggs of which were one of the possible prizes which we hoped to obtain. All our efforts to obtain even a glimpse of the latter species on migration proved, however, in vain. As we subsequently met with them on the tundra, we can only suppose that they migrate to their breeding-quarters by a different route, probably following the coast-line. If they do fly across country, they must travel at such a high elevation that they are rarely observed inland.

Wild geese and swans increased in numbers daily, and about this time flocks of wild ducks began to fly up the Petchora. So far as we could judge, they seemed to be principally pintail ducks, though we succeeded in shooting a teal.

Pipits also began to arrive in great numbers. They were wild and difficult to shoot, apparently all flying up wind; evidently eager to continue their journey and rarely alighting on the ground. Both species were represented, but they appeared to migrate in separate flocks, and the red-throated pipit was much more abundant than the meadow-pipit. We occasionally heard both species singing, but they were by no means in full song, being evidently intent on migration.

Fieldfares and redwings also arrived and soon became very numerous; and among the flocks of shore-larks which continued to pass through the district a few Lapland buntings were generally to be seen.

The flocks of shore-larks had by this time become more numerous, and consisted of males and females in nearly equal numbers. These birds were very tame, frequenting for the most part the fields at the back of the village, feeding and running about in the stubble, and occasionally attempting to sing on the ground. The snow-buntings and redpolls had disappeared, and in the streets their place appeared to be taken by white wagtails. Fresh flocks of these charming little birds in full breeding plumage arrived daily; and in a large flock consisting of from thirty to forty birds we noticed an Arctic yellow wagtail (*Motacilla borealis*).

Three whimbrels passed over us. My companion whistled to them, so cleverly imitating their note that they approached within fifty yards of him, when he shot them. A peasant also brought us a rook, the only one we saw during our journey. At this time we ascertained positively the presence of a bird which we had long suspected to be on the roof of the Preestäff's house next door to ours—a no less important bird than the common sparrow. We shot two males and three females. This is an extraordinary instance of the extreme localness of birds. We never by any chance saw these common sparrows among the tree-sparrows in our yard, nor had we any reason to think that they were to be found elsewhere in the town.

On the 19th we received an invitation from our friends who had assisted us in our late wild-goose chase, to join them in a duck-hunt. M. Znaminski had a *maisonnette* a few versts up the Zylma, which he turned to use on such occasions of sport. He and M. Sacharoff were already there. We accepted the invitation, and after sledging across the Petchora, and perhaps four versts up the Zylma, we reached our host's quarters at about 3 A.M. We had made a somewhat circuitous road up the Zylma, for there were many ugly-looking places in the ice which had to be avoided. On arriving we dismissed our yemschiks, who returned to Ust-Zylma with orders to come with five sledges to fetch our whole party back on the following day at noon.

The shooting-ground was a flat piece of country lying between the Petchora and the Zylma. It bore traces of its annual submersion for a week or two under the waters of the great river when it breaks up. The larger part was covered with a forest of birch, willow, and alder ; many of the trees were dead, perhaps in consequence of the flood, and drift-wood was scattered or accumulated in piles all around.

It was heavy work walking in these woods, or rather wading through the water and snow in them. Every now and then we came to a lake or an open swamp, or found ourselves on the banks of a *kuria* or creek where the snow had melted, and the walking was easier. Few or no trees grew by the side of these kurias ; the banks of the Zylma also were bare, the forests near the rivers being shorn off by the ice, which sometimes mows down the stoutest trees as a man mows grass with a scythe. On the low ground between the Zylma and the forest land, pollard willows grew, many of which had been knocked down by the floating blocks of ice.

It would be impossible to estimate the number of ducks we saw. They seemed to fly over us by hundreds and thousands. Small and large flocks continually passed us on the wing. In the evening the shores of the Zylma and a piece of open water opposite were almost black with them; sometimes they filled the air like a swarm of bees. They were very wild, but the old pollard willows gave excellent opportunities for concealment, and a good shot would have made a heavy bag in a short time. My companion shot seven in about an hour: six pintails and one teal. Nearly all these ducks were pintails; we identified hundreds through our glasses, and saw only a few teal.

My companion identified a small flock of shovellers, one of which flew quite close to him. He also distinctly made out a pair of golden-eyes, which came within shot while we were dining. Through the glass he also recognised a wigeon. We also saw a few geese and swans. We met with the greenshank more than once, and had a fine view of a peregrine falcon. A small flock of shore-larks and a few red-throated pipits, too busy migrating to stop to be shot, nearly complete the list of birds we saw in the open country.

I spent most of my time in the woods. Three weeks previously we had made a long round through them on our snow-shoes and found them deserted; not a bird to be seen but a solitary marsh-tit or an occasional "hoodie." Now, in the early morning, these woods were full of life and abounded in interest for the ornithologist. In the afternoon they were more quiet, and the interest was not sufficient to repay the toil of wading through water, snow, mud, and drift-wood. The commonest and noisiest bird was the redpoll. Next to it, strange to say, was the meadow-pipit. This bird behaved in every way like the tree-pipit, being occasionally seen on the ground, but mostly up in the trees; sometimes singing on the ground, sometimes when on the wing, but oftener in the branches overhead.

We had just decided that these birds were, or ought to be, tree-pipits, when we shot down half a dozen from among the branches, and finally satisfied ourselves that they were the meadow-pipit. Our astonishment was still greater, however, when we beheld three gulls quietly perched upon the top of a tall birch in the wood. We watched them for some time, examining them through our glasses; at last they rose and flew over our heads, and by their cry we recognised them to be the familiar *Larus canus*. Shortly afterwards we shot one.

Fieldfares and redwings were sprinkled through the woods; we could almost always hear the song of the latter bird, as well as the loose cry of the former, and its starling-like note before alighting. My companions saw a couple of redstarts chasing each other, and I followed a willow-wren, which was in full song, for at least an hour, but did not succeed in shooting it. Many white wagtails flew past, and reed-buntings were also common. Where the birches were largest we heard the tapping of woodpeckers. We shot a pair of Siberian lesser spotted woodpeckers (*P. pipra*, Pall.); and of a pair of three-toed woodpeckers that we saw we succeeded in shooting the male. We also shot a pair of marsh-tits.

When I returned on the morning of the 20th after a five hours' solitary ramble in the woods, I found the sportsmen still fast asleep. My entrance roused them, and we soon proceeded to make tea. We were sitting down to our pipes after our late breakfast, when we were startled by the appearance of M. Znaminski, who had just gone out, and now came hurrying back in a state of great excitement, beckoning to us to come.

We seized our guns, expecting to see some great or rare bird; we rushed to the door, and there we paused and stood still, gazing before us in mute astonishment. Our road was in movement, and was going to Ust-Zylma at the rate of two or three miles an hour. There was no doubt about it, the Zylma was breaking up. The scene was wild and picturesque. In a few hours it was very impressive. The ice had broken into the Petchora at the mouth of the Zylma. Here and there piles of it lay upon the banks. Finally it had blocked, and gradually the Zylma became a confused mass of jammed ice and tree-trunks, while an occasional ice-floe, thicker than the rest, formed where the water had been stiller and deeper, rising above the level. While the ice moved the sound was like that of a waterfall : as it cracked on the Petchora, the noise was as that of rumbling thunder. The water was rapidly rising, and our predicament was serious. It was obvious that no horses could reach us. The Russians, who at first did not realise the situation, soon began to look grave. We took counsel together, and we decided to transport ourselves and our baggage to some houses that stood on higher ground, halfway towards the mouth of the Zylma. It took us some hours to do this. We were beginning to make preparations for a week's camping in the midst of floods, when towards four o'clock we discerned in the distance the figures of our yemschiks. They were coming, but they were coming without horses. When they reached us we learned from them that the ice had broken up on both shores of the Petchora. They had come across in a boat, which they had dragged for a couple of versts in a sledge across the central field of ice, being forced to leave it on the shore five or six miles off. We determined to put the bulk of our baggage under the charge of two yemschiks and to return with the other men in the boat.

We felt rather nervous as we entered the boats and put to sea on the open water across which we had sledged so recently, and we had some little difficulty in finding a solid piece of ice on which to land. The central ice of the Petchora was evidently on the eve of breaking up. Every nerve was strained to drag the boats across the mile of ice, and relaunch them on the safe side of the river without a moment's unnecessary loss of time. It was past midnight, and at any moment the crash might come. The ice was obviously under great pressure. Cracks running for miles with a sound like distant thunder warned us that a mighty power was all but upon us, a force which seemed for the moment to impress the mind with a greater sense of power than even the crushing weight of water at Niagara, a force which breaks up ice more than a mile wide, at least three feet thick, and weighted with another three feet of snow, at the rate of 100 miles in the twenty-four hours. It was eight o'clock in the morning when we landed in Ust-Zylma, and heartily thankful we were to find ourselves once more safe in our quarters. We were hungry and dead tired after the excitement was over, and after a hasty breakfast we were glad to turn into our hammocks. We slept for a couple of hours, and then, looking out of the window, we found the crash had come ; the mighty river Petchora was a field of pack-ice and ice-floes, marching past towards the sea at the rate of six miles an hour. We ran out on to the banks to find half the inhabitants of Ust-Zylma watching the impressive scene.

DIFFICULTIES WITH SNOW-SHOES

CHAPTER XI.

PEASANT LIFE IN UST-ZYLMA.

Religious Processions—Costumes of the Peasants—A Russian Holiday
—Drunkenness—Prejudices of the Old Believers—Field Work—House-
building—New Birds—The Siberian Chiffchaff—Prices of Provisions—
Arrival of Waders.

THE 21st of May was St. Michael's Day, one of the
greatest holidays in this country. A long procession of
Old Believers, consisting mostly of women and children
carrying banners and pictures, wended its way through
the town. The women were dressed in their best, and
decked with all the jewellery that they possessed, some
of which was very ancient and valuable. Many of the
dresses, too, were antique—heirlooms handed down from
mother to daughter. Some of these were gorgeous, none
were vulgar, the colours being always sober, rich and

clear. The wealthier peasants' wives and daughters were arrayed in velvet and gold, silk and satin; those of the poorer in linen and cotton, almost entirely of Russian manufacture. The women, as a rule, wore the *rubakha*, which is simply a skirt put over the fur malitza, coming down to within a few inches of the ground; their *chaussures* consisted of high boots, and their head-dress of an orientally coloured handkerchief, tied behind. We had already noticed this Eastern taste for colour among the peasantry. A few days previously an imposing wedding procession had passed our window. The larger number of the party were on horseback, two on each horse. All were brightly dressed: the men wore knots of ribbons on their shoulders; the women, gaily apparelled, had on various and curious head-dresses, ornamented with gold braid. Yet, for all their brilliancy, the colours did not look garish, a little touch of grey being always introduced to subdue the effect.

On St. Michael's Day it is customary to make presents to the Church. The peasants brought various sorts of offerings, cows, sheep, gloves, ribbons, etc., which were afterwards sold by auction. Then the afternoon was spent in merry-making, and, as is too often the case on a Russian holiday, the revellers all got more or less drunk.

We found the condition of things wonderfully altered at Ust-Zylma by the breaking up of the ice of the Zylma and the Pizhma. Despite the map, the latter river flows into the Petchora, and is not a tributary of the Zylma. The thaw of the two rivers together had been too much for the Petchora. The ice was broken up for three or four versts on either side of the town; most of it had disappeared, perhaps beneath the other ice. Already several boats were out, and the men were fishing in open water. The breaking-up of the ice went on steadily for

days. By the 25th of May the great river was entirely
free. Summer had come as suddenly as usual, and the
people were hard at work; the women and children
carting manure on the land, using sledges, although the
snow had disappeared except where it lay in drifts; the
men breaking up the ground with an antediluvian-looking
plough, sowing corn broadcast, or harrowing in the seed
with a wooden-toothed harrow.

A good deal of building was also going on. The
year before the peasants had made large earnings out of
the fisheries, and were now spending larger sums than
usual in erecting houses. We found the demand for
labour was great, and wages were high. Few men could
be got under 10s. per week. We spent our days, as
usual, on the look-out for the arrival of new migratory
birds, in watching the habits of those at hand, and in
adding to our collection. We saw no snow-buntings
after the 18th, and the merlins disappeared with them.
Nor did we see any gulls after the 21st. The shore-
larks and the Lapland buntings were also growing scarce.
Occasionally small flocks of them would appear in the
fields behind the house, sometimes so busy feeding as to
allow us to approach very near them.

On the 21st of May we were surprised to find a pair
of wheatears. In England they are the earliest birds of
passage to arrive in spring, but of course they winter
farther south than the snow-buntings and shore-larks,
and we might reasonably expect them to arrive later in
such northerly breeding-grounds.

On the 22nd we added another familiar British
migrant to our list, the tree-pipit, a bird which usually
arrives rather late with us. A more important addition
to our list was, however, the Siberian chiffchaff (*Phylloscopus tristis*, Blyth), a little warbler which frequented

the low willows, uttering a plaintive call, a single note repeated at intervals. We were under the impression that we were adding a new bird to the European list, but we afterwards found that our discovery had been forestalled by M. Meves of Stockholm, who had found it some years previously in the government of Perm. A third specimen which we added to our list was a skylark. On our return home we found that Znaminski had also been out shooting, and had bagged some very interesting birds for us—five green wagtails, three meadow-pipits, two red-throated pipits, and a stonechat, the latter not the European but the Indian species (*Pratincola maura*, Pall.), a new and interesting addition to the European fauna. Znaminski's hunting-ground had been a marshy piece of land just behind the town, sprinkled over with small spruce firs, bushes of stunted birch, juniper, and dwarf rhododendrons (*Ledum palustre*). To this spot we betook ourselves the next morning, and found it to be a favourite resting-place of migratory birds. We shot a red-throated pipit on the ground, solitary among a company of meadow-pipits. We secured a green wagtail and a short-eared owl. In this favoured spot the willow-warblers congregated and were in full song; the blue-throated warblers were also there, but their song was not so full; it resembled sometimes the warble of the pipit and sometimes that of the whitethroat. We secured, besides, a brace of golden plover and a reed-bunting.

During the afternoon we visited the skirts of the pine-forest in the valley, and there I shot two male wheatears. The day before, a male and female wheatear had flown past me and perched on the summit of a tall pine. Out of a spruce fir in the wood we now heard a loud, clear "chiff-cheff-chaff." We thought it was the cry of the chiffchaff; but we failed to find the bird.

Shortly after we heard a warbler singing. For a moment we fancied it was a willow-wren, but before the song was half finished we felt convinced that we were unacquainted with it. It was not unlike the "chiff-cheff-chaff" of our bird when it makes the third variation it occasionally does in its notes, but these notes were more musical, repeated rapidly without intermission, running into a song. This bird was also perching in a spruce fir, but a long shot brought it down. It proved to be the Siberian chiffchaff. For days afterwards we heard several of these birds singing, and, on further study of their note, we found it very distinct from that of the chiffchaff. Our bird's note is not badly represented by its name, with an equal accent on both syllables. The note of the Siberian chiffchaff is better represented by the word "chivit," with a decided accent on the first syllable. It is seldom uttered singly, but generally repeated "chiv-it, chiv-et," or oftener "chivit," followed by two notes of its song. The bird seemed very partial to the spruce fir, perching on its topmost bough. In comparing its habits and those of the willow-warbler, we found the Siberian chiffchaff easy to shoot, while the latter was as wild as possible.

Another song that greatly roused our curiosity was a melodious whistle, reminding us both of the song of the blackbird and of the redwing. We expected the songster would turn out to be some rare Siberian thrush. The bird was by no means shy, so we had no difficulty in following its song, and in approaching within easy shot, as it perched sometimes on the top, sometimes near the summit of a spruce fir. Once we observed it hopping on the ground. We obtained six specimens, and were somewhat disappointed to find such melodious and thrush-like notes proceeded from the pine-grosbeak.

It is a curious fact that the day following, on returning to the spot where we had seen and shot so many various birds, we found it deserted; there was nothing but willow-warblers on it. Red-throated pipits passed over singly and in flocks, but none seemed disposed to alight. In a plantation hard by we heard a chaffinch sing, but we did not get a shot at it. We fell in there with a small flock of bramblings, and secured a male that was not yet in full breeding plumage. On the following day a thick mist came up the Petchora, which cleared up about noon, and was followed by a north-west breeze with gleams of sunshine and threatenings of rain. Birds were few and sang little, the note of the warblers being almost the only one we heard. We had an excellent opportunity of identifying a white-tailed eagle, which came almost within shot of us. Two cranes (*Grus communis*, Bechst.) passed over us, and I recognised them as birds I had seen two or three days before. By this time all the hooded crows and magpies had gone into the woods to breed, and the town was deserted by them. During the week there had apparently been an arrival of house-sparrows in Ust-Zylma, for they abounded in Znaminski's yard. Strangely enough, we could not meet with any in other parts of the town.

On the 26th the weather changed. A cold north-east wind blew, and it was a day unpropitious for bird-shooting. So little did we anticipate meeting with any, that we spent the morning in buying provisions for our journey. It may be useful to record the prices we paid :

Salt beef	1.70 rouble	per poud	(1¼*d*. per lb.).
Butter	6.50 roubles	,,	(4¾*d*.	,,).
Tea	2	,,	per lb.	(5*s*. | ,,).
Coffee	.55 rouble	,,	(1*s*. 4*d*.	,,).

We also bought a *nvelma*, or white salmon, for our

present use.   In its stomach were several small fishes. It weighed 15 lb., and cost 10 kopecks per lb.   We were told that later the price would be 5 kopecks per lb. This fish sometimes reaches the weight of 60 lb.   We found it very nice eating, but failed to recognise its boasted superiority to salmon.   We acknowledge, how-ever, that the cooking may have been in fault.

In the afternoon we went out in the cold wind, not expecting to shoot anything ; but to our astonishment we found a number of new birds in the town itself.   We secured a wood-sandpiper out of a flock of four, and a Temminck's stint, of which there were several.   We saw a common swallow twice, and shot a pair of ringed plovers.   We had also an excellent view of two oyster-catchers.   All these were new arrivals.   Many green wagtails were to be seen, and we shot four males and two females.   In the village we met a shore-lark, the first we had seen for many days in the streets.

The unfavourable-looking day proved one of the most interesting we had yet had.

OLD RUSSIAN SILVER CROSS

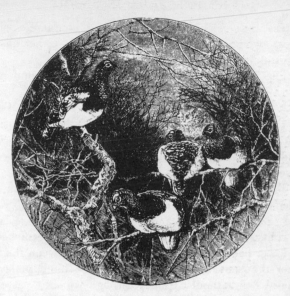

WILLOW-GROUSE

CHAPTER XII.

THE PETCHORA IN FLOOD.

Samoyede Names—The Blue-throated Warbler—Toads—Birds Resting on Migration—Sparrow-hawk—The Petchora Free from Ice—A New Song—Ceremony of Blessing the Steamer—Rambles in the Woods—Appearance of the Mosquitoes.

WHILST we were waiting for the flood in the Petchora to subside sufficiently to make it safe for us to proceed down the river in a small boat, we met with a Samoyede somewhat more intelligent than usual, and from him we were glad to learn something more concerning the names of various articles connected with reindeer and sledging which we had collected. It is somewhat difficult to express the exact sound in English characters, since almost every Samoyede word is pronounced either nasally or gutturally.

The Samoyede for sledge is *khăn*, the *kh* pronounced like *ch* in German, and the *n* like *ñ* in Spanish.

A reindeer is *tū*, the *u* like the German *ü*. There are three sorts of reindeer : *khōra-tü*, the entire male reindeer; *khăb-tü*, the cut reindeer; and *yāh-tü*, the female reindeer. These adjectives are also used in reference to horses and other cattle.

The piece of leather over the body of the animal which takes the place of our saddle is called the *yōde'-yĕnă*. The narrower band round the neck, in place of the collar, is the *pōde'-yŭr*. The single trace attached to the lower part of the collar, and passing between the legs under the body, is called the *să*. The blind pulley, or pulley-block without a pulley through which it passes, is the *pyat'-say'*. The halter, or bridle without a bit, is the *syāhn*. The halter of the leading reindeer is the *nyes'-mĭn dye syāhn*. The halter of the other reindeer is the *pyelay' syāhn*. The rein with which the leading reindeer is guided is the *mĕtănye*. The hook on the side of the saddle-band on which the rein rests is the *khălsōōlă*. The swivel or universal joint by which the rein is attached to the halter is the *sŭr'nye*. A button which serves to fasten the trace to the collar, or the belly-band to the saddle, is the *pāysĭk*. The long pole with which the reindeer are driven is the *tōōr*, and the bone or ivory knob at the end of it the *tōōr-māhl*. The rein connecting the leading reindeer with the one next to it is the *poo-inye*. A lasso is called a *teēn-zāy'*, and the bone noose through which it runs is the *sah'mĭk*. The tent or choom is the *myah'-kăn*, and a dog is called a *vŏĭnyekō*.

The Samoyede who gave us this information was one

of the poorer men of his tribe. All the richer families had migrated north with their herds of reindeer before the snow had melted. The poorer families remained behind, hanging on to the skirts of the Russians, helping them with their fishing, and receiving for pay such food as their employers chose to give them. One cannot help pitying these poor people. Their nation is gradually dying out. Like the North American Indians, they are doomed to destruction, for, like them, they cannot refuse spirits. In the struggle for existence they have no chance with the cunning Russian, who in all matters of business has no more conscience than a Greek or a Jew.

During this time the birds were few. On the 27th we took a walk in the forest, and the only ones that were singing were the willow-warblers, an occasional pine-grosbeak breaking in now and then. We secured, however, a pair of bramblings out of a flock. We shot a blue-throated warbler, a yellow-hammer, a female reed-bunting, a Siberian jay, a stonechat, and a red-throated pipit, and out of a number we brought down a brace of golden plover. We saw a solitary shore-lark, a gull (apparently the common species), and a fine male bull-finch. In the town we got a couple of wood-sandpipers; then the green wagtails were common, and we came upon a large party of Lapland buntings, all apparently females. In the evening the wind dropped and a frost set in. At midnight, when we went to bed, the thermometer marked only 30°. The next day was bright, but cold, with a light north wind blowing. We went for another long tramp through the pine-woods, but very few birds were to be seen. We shot a pair of grosbeaks, a fieldfare, and a blue-throated warbler (*Cyanecula suecica*, Linn.). We saw a Siberian jay, for whose nest we had a long search, which resulted in our finding two old ones. Whether these were nests of the Siberian jay or of the pine-grosbeak we could not, however, determine. Twice we heard the note of the Siberian chiffchaff, but we could not see or get a shot at the birds.

The smart frost returned during the night. In the morning, however, the wind veered round to the east, and it was warm; in the afternoon it was very hot. Five hours hard walking through the woods in the early morning resulted in nothing. I did not bring down a single bird. My companion shot two blue-throated warblers; they had now grown as common as the willow-warbler. The blue-throated warbler has been not inaptly called the Swedish mocking-bird. Sometimes it is shy and retiring, seeking food in the densest thickets and bushes, haunting the marshy grounds sprinkled over with small spruce fir, dwarf willows and juniper; but when newly arrived from its winter home, and beginning to sing, it is an easy bird to see, and not difficult to shoot. On its first arrival it often warbles in an undertone so low that you fancy the sound must be muffled by the thick tangle of branches in which you think the bird is concealed, while all the time it is perched on high upon the topmost spray of a young fir, this very conspicuousness causing him to escape detection for the moment. His first attempts at singing are harsh and grating, like the notes of the sedge-warbler, or the still harsher ones of the whitethroat; these are followed by several variations in a louder and rather more melodious tone, repeated over and over again, somewhat in the fashion of a song-thrush. After this you might fancy the little songster was trying to mimic the various alarm-notes of all the birds he can remember—the "chiz-zit" of the wagtail, the "tip-tip-tip" of the blackbird, and especially the "whit-whit" of the chaffinch. As he improves in voice, he sings louder and longer, until at last he almost approaches the nightingale in the richness of the melody he pours forth. Sometimes he will sing as he flies upward, descending with expanded wings and tail, to alight on the highest bough of some low tree, almost exactly as the tree-pipit does. When the females have arrived, there comes at the end of his song the most metallic note I have ever heard a bird utter. It is a sort of "ting-ting," resembling the sound produced by the hitting of a suspended bar of steel with another piece of the same metal.

Our afternoon walk was more fruitful of result than that of the morning. I had followed for some time the shore of the overflowing Petchora, when, after having bagged a brace of wood-sandpipers and a ring-dotterel, I crossed a sandbank to a marshy pool. The muffled croak of numerous toads or frogs kept up a sound resembling that of gurgling water. On my approach the whole tribe disappeared and hid in the mud. After I had waited a while, three slowly put up their noses above the surface. I fired ineffectually upon the reptiles, but I started seven or eight sandpipers and a red-throated pipit, upon which I set off at once in pursuit of the last bird. I presently found myself on a marshy piece of ground, covered with grassy hillocks, in the narrow trenches between which pipits were sitting. As I walked on they rose at my feet on all sides, and I soon had half a dozen within shot. I brought down a bird with each barrel, reloaded, and, as I walked up to my victims, there rose between me and them two or three pipits, who evidently preferred being shot to being trodden upon. Unfortunately I had but two cartridges left, so, bringing down another brace, I went back to our quarters

for more ammunition.   On returning to the open marshy
ground, I found the birds still there, and very soon
secured another half-dozen.   My last shot was a double
one.   As I was getting over the soil upon which some
pipits had been sitting, a hawk rushed past clutching a
bird in its claws.   A dozen wagtails set off after it in
vociferous pursuit.   I followed more quietly, and soon
had the satisfaction of laying a male sparrow-hawk upon
its back, with a half-eaten sparrow beside it.   Some wagtails remained perched upon the railing behind which the
hawk had retired to finish the devouring of its prey.
They uttered cries, which might be interpreted either as
doubting the supposed escape of their foe, or as a pæan
of rejoicing over its downfall.   The sight of their enemy
lying motionless on its back rendered them deaf to the
sound of my gun and blind to my presence.   They
remained undismayed within a few yards of me, not
stirring until I had packed away the hawk.   At this
juncture my companion came up.   He had been more
fortunate than I in his raid upon the reptiles, and had
secured a couple, which we found to be a species of toad,
with whitish and black spots and stripes on the back.
At this pool I now secured a Temminck's stint, and my
companion another pipit, making the eleventh shot that
day.   For weeks we had never succeeded in shooting
more than one out of a flock.   They had abounded
during the last fortnight in the fields and in the open
ground about the town.   We had seen hundreds, and
yet, during those two weeks, we had not secured more
than five males and one female; now in a couple of
hours we had bagged ten males and one female out of a
single flock.   We had found them wild, and seldom
disposed to settle on the ground.   It was curious that
these pipits should have been so different from the

others; but what was still more curious and interesting was their behaviour during the raid we made upon them. After repeated shots, bringing down several of their numbers, the remainder would get up, settle on the railings, on the adjoining house-roof, or perch upon the slender branches of a willow-tree hard by.

The same day I saw again the barn-swallow, which seemed to be the only representative of its species at Ust-Zylma. I watched a flock of shore-larks and Lapland buntings on the stubble. As a rule, they ran along the ground like the wagtails, but I also marked both birds hopping for some distance.

For the first time, on Sunday, 30th of May, the Petchora was free from ice. The steady march-past of the frozen blocks had lasted just one week. The wind that day was warm, blowing from the south, but the sky was cloudy. A peasant brought us three young Siberian jays, and another rowed across the river, the bearer of a ruff, the first we had yet seen; and of some eggs—six duck's eggs, doubtless those of the pintail, and four of the hooded crow. The following day the warm south wind continued, with sunshine and cloud. We took a long round in the valley, where a few days before we had seen so many Siberian chiffchaffs. The blue-throated warblers were singing lustily, but we failed to hear or see the bird we were specially in search of. As we were making our way home, through a swamp thickly studded over with willows, birch, and fir, I heard a song quite new to me. It closely resembled that of the yellow-hammer, whose note is popularly supposed to say " Lit, lit, lit, little bread and no cheese." This bird cried " Lit, lit, lit, in as tay." I shot the strange songster, and brought down my first little bunting (*Emberiza pusilla*, Pall.). Twice during the day we visited the marshy spot, upon which forty-eight hours previously the red-throated pipits had swarmed, but we found it utterly deserted. The flock was evidently resting after a long stage of migration, and had now resumed its northward progress.

The next day a visit to the same spot brought the same result; not a red-throated pipit was to be seen upon it. On the 1st of June I saw a common scoter for the first time, flying down the Petchora close past Sideroff's steamer. I was on deck at the time, one of a crowd waiting to witness the ceremony of sprinkling the vessel with holy water ere it set out on its summer voyage. The ship had arrived the evening before from its winter quarters in the bay behind Habariki. The ceremony was effective. Flags were flying, cannons firing, guests assembled; a breakfast was prepared, then came the procession of robed priests, candles burning and censers swinging; prayers were chanted, the crucifix was kissed, and then the sprinkling began. Everybody and everything was sprinkled with holy water from a rod, apparently made of fine gilt wire. The paddle-boxes were sprinkled, the deck was sprinkled fore and aft, the cabins were sprinkled, the sailors were sprinkled; the captain and the engineer each received a whisk from the brush, which made them wince, for at that moment a detachment of ice, probably from the Ussa, was passing down the river, chilling the water not a little. Then all was over except the breakfast, when a practical joke was played upon the guests. A course of bear-flesh was served up incognito, so deliciously cooked that all ate of it with gusto, suspecting nothing. Our amiable friend, the wife of the public prosecutor, alone suspected, but wisely kept her counsel.

After our dissipation we spent the evening packing skins, and retired to our hammocks about midnight; but whether owing to Captain Arendt's hospitality or to the effect of the arsenic in the skins, we could not sleep. At three o'clock, finding that the sun had been up some time, we bethought ourselves that we could not do better than follow his example, so we accordingly arose, and shouldering our guns, marched off to the Siberian chiffchaff valley. We chose good positions in the wood, and disposed ourselves to watch and wait. Before long I heard the distant *chivit* of the much longed-for bird, rising from the bottom of the valley. I pressed forward cautiously through the trees, and caught sight of the little warbler's white throat glistening in the sunshine, as it uttered its unpretentious song, perched on the top of a pine. I could not approach it nearer than within sixty yards without making a considerable *détour* to avoid the stream with its high mud walls, crumbling down on all sides, so I risked a shot. It was too far and missed. Meanwhile a second Siberian chiffchaff set up its *chivit*. I started off in pursuit of the cry and soon came within shot of the bird, perched, as usual, on the summit of a spruce fir. I fired, ran to the tree, searched diligently through the moss at the foot, but found nothing. Whistling for my companion to come up, I began to run the tree over with my telescope, when, to my great delight, I caught sight of my bird lying dead on a spray within six inches of the top. We saw no more of these birds during the morning, but shot two wheatears, which had by this time grown common, a pair of blue-throated warblers and a willow-wren. Nearly all the green wagtails which we saw had more or less brown on the breast; they were doubtless last year's birds which had not yet assumed the full mature plumage. On our return a peasant brought us three young ravens and some duck's eggs, probably pintail's. That day I recorded in my journal, with many groans, the first appearance of the mosquitoes. Horrid-looking beasts, with bodies a third of an inch long, monsters, the *Culex damnabilis* of Rae, with proboscis "*infernali veneno munita.*" I foresaw that we should have opportunities enough to study the natural history of these bloodthirsty creatures to our hearts' discontent.

OLD RUSSIAN SILVER CROSS

THE FLOODED BANKS OF THE RIVER

CHAPTER XIII.

A TRIP TO HABARIKI.

Trip to Habariki—Forest Scenery—Tarns in the Woods—Changeable
Weather—New Birds identified in the Forests—Golden Eagle—Osprey—
Hobby—Cuckoo—Yellow-headed Wagtail—Bohemian Waxwing—Great
Snipe—Terek Sandpiper—Goosander—Smew—Black-throated Diver.

WE were fast asleep the next evening when we were
roused up by Captain Engel's invitation to go down with
him by the steamer to Habariki to stay there three days.
We had barely time to dress and fill our pockets with
cartridges. The current of the river was in our favour;
it was running at the rate of four miles an hour, and we
accomplished the twenty-seven miles in two hours.
Arrived at Habariki we scarcely recognised the place
again. The snow had disappeared, all but a patch or
two on the Timanski hills, fifty miles off. The Petchora,
freed from ice, had risen some twenty feet or more, and

had flooded the island in front of the village, the willows
and pine-tree tops being just visible above the surface.
Inland, half the country at least was under water, a vast
network of lakes and swamps with forest between. In
some places the skirts themselves of the forest were
flooded. As we had not brought our wading-boots we
had to confine our explorations to the woods. These
proved an inexhaustible source of interest to us, and one
in no wise lacking in variety. There was much beauty
in these woods. Under foot spread a carpet of soft green
moss and lichens, the thick moss predominating in the
older and thicker parts of the forest, while the reindeer-
moss and the many-coloured lichens abounded in the
younger and more open woods. Stray shrubs of arbutus
and rhododendron, bushes of bilberry, crowberry, cran-
berry, the fruit of which was preserved by seven months'
frost, clumps of carices, and other vegetation decked the
shady aisles. The monotony of the great pine forest was
varied by the delicate hues of willow and alder thickets,
by plantations of young pines and firs, by clumps of tall
spruce and haggard old larches, while here and there a
fine birch spread abroad its glossy foliage, or a gaunt
Scotch fir extended wide its copper-coloured arms. All
around lay strewn trunks and branches of timber, fallen
or felled, in every stage of decomposition, from the hoary
log, moss-covered and turned to tinder, to the newly
lopped branches of some lofty forest patriarch, whose
magnificent boughs had been wantonly cut up to furnish
firewood for Sideroff's steamer. The most curious features
in these forests were open and slightly hollow places, like
tarns, or half dried-up tarns, the bed carpeted with moss
and a network of last year's *Potamogeton*. The shallow
places were quite dried up, but the deeper ones had still
a lakelet glistening in the centre. These hollows are

doubtless filled with water when the Petchora reaches its highest flood point in June, and many are not yet dried up when an early winter sets in, and the remaining water becomes ice-bound.

Our three days stay at Habariki was marked by very variable weather. Thursday was calm and warm, with bright sunshine. Friday was bitterly cold, with a strong gale from the north, and only occasional gleams of sunshine, and slight storms of rain and snow. On Saturday morning the gale had subsided, and the greater part of the day the sun shone, but a violent hailstorm fell during the afternoon, and in the evening we had a dead calm. Notwithstanding the generally unfavourable weather we saw a vast number of birds, and added to our lists in these three days more than half as many species as we had seen during the whole of our stay at Ust-Zylma.

We saw several eagles, but only one near enough for identification. It showed no traces of white on the tail, and we concluded it might be a golden-eagle or a white-tailed eagle of the first year. We identified an osprey as it flew past us overhead. We fired at it, and it dropped a large bunch of damp moss that it was doubtless carrying for nesting purposes. On a bare larch-trunk towering high above the surrounding wood we could see, about fifteen feet from the top, a large nest, which we presumed was that of this bird.

I rose a dark-winged hawk from the ground, which I have no doubt was a hobby. Some hours later we saw a similar-looking bird, perched high on the naked branch of a dead larch, and a long shot brought it down. It proved a fine male of this species.

Many of the ancient stems of the larches contained old nest-holes of woodpeckers, and the bark of some trees was riddled from top to bottom with small holes, evidently made by these birds when feeding.   One of our sailors shot a male.   We saw soon after a pair of three-toed woodpeckers, but did not then succeed in securing either of them.   On another occasion we heard the tapping sound of the woodpecker's beak ; a tap, then a slight pause, followed by a rapid succession of taps, and, after a second slight pause, a final tap.   I imitated the sound as well as I could with a cartridge on the stock of my gun. The bird immediately flew to a dead larch-trunk, close to where we were standing, and perched, its head thrown back listening, some fifty feet from the ground.   In this position it fell to my companion's gun.   It was a female.

We heard the cuckoo's familiar note repeatedly every day ; the first time it was near midnight, soon after our arrival at Habariki.

The hooded crow and magpie were as abundant as usual in this part of Europe.   The Siberian jay was very common in the wood, and very noisy ; all the more so, perhaps, for the number of young birds among them.   I saw on one occasion an old jay feeding a young one.   I shot the latter ; it was in the full plumage of the first year. The old birds were very tame and easy to secure, for they were in full moult.   The body bore no appearance of it, but the wing and tail feathers were "in the pen."   The flight of the Siberian jay is noiseless, resembling somewhat that of the owl, sailing with wings and tail expanded before alighting.   These birds like ascending from branch to branch, close by the stem of a birch or fir.   When they cannot hop from one bough to another they ascend the trunk in the fashion of the woodpecker.   This habit we both of us specially noted.   We did not hear their song, but they were constantly uttering harsh loud cries, some of which reminded us of those of the peregrine at its nest, while others resembled the scream of the woodpecker. During the season of incubation the Siberian jay seemed shy and silent.

A flock of tree-sparrows was always to be seen among the few houses in the village, sometimes perched on the railings, at other times gathered in a bunch on the roofs. We saw no evidence of their having begun to think about building. The pine-grosbeak was one of the commonest, if not the commonest bird at Habariki, and the mealy redpoll also was common. The little bunting was not rare, but its shy and retiring habits often caused us to overlook it. We rarely heard it sing, yet frequently noticed its quiet call-note. We also often came upon it feeding on the ground near the swampy edge of the forest tarns, in company with yellow wag-tails, fieldfares, and bramblings. We saw several reed-buntings, and shot a male. They usually frequented the willows on the edges of the marshes and lakes. The green wagtail was common, and still kept together in flocks ; we constantly saw them in trees.

The yellow-headed wagtail (*Motacilla citreola*) was a bird we had neither of us met with before. The alighting of a small party of five on an alder-bush surprised us. We secured a male, but the remainder disappeared among some alders and willows growing on an impassable piece of flooded land close to the Petchora, which was also full of floating driftwood. So, unfortunately, we saw them no more.

We noticed a few white wagtails, principally near the village. Fieldfares were numerous, sometimes in flocks, generally in pairs. They scarcely seemed to have yet begun to breed. We had two nests brought us, how-ever, each containing one egg. We found plenty of old isolated nests, but no traces of colonies. The fieldfares were singing far more in the woods about Habariki than I had heard them doing during the breeding season in Norway.

The redwing was decidedly commoner than the fieldfare, and its rich wild notes constantly resounded in all parts of the forest. Its usually plaintive whistle was only occasionally heard, the note which it more frequently uttered resembled rather that of the song-thrush, but was very short. We shot one, to make sure that it was a bird of no other species. Its low warble often came following the notes just mentioned; but sometimes it was given without the preliminary note, and once we heard it utter a loose alarm-cry like that of the fieldfare. It is evidently an earlier breeder than the latter bird. We got four or five of its nests, containing four eggs each; one had five eggs. We found one nest in a spruce-fir built nine feet from the ground, but in no instance did we find a nest nearer than eighteen inches to the ground, nor is it likely that there would be any built lower in a country comparatively flooded. All the redwings were in pairs; we saw no signs whatever of their habits being gregarious.

The blue-throated warbler was very common and tame, allowing us to approach near as it sang perched on a low bush or fed on the ground. It was in full voice, and the variety of its notes formed a perfect medley of bird-music. It frequented marshy ground, whether amongst alders and willows, or in the forests of pines or other trees. We saw several handsome male redstarts, and came upon a pair or two of wheatears in the open sandy pinewood near the village.

In the same locality we saw a few pairs of stonechats. Willow-warblers were very abundant. At Habariki, for the second time, I heard this bird utter a note different from any I had heard in England. It is like the *t-r-r-r* of the chiffchaff, but it is very difficult to describe it exactly on paper. The nearest letters denoting it are perhaps *z-z-z;* it reminded me very much of the spitting of a cat. We heard the song and also the "*chiv-it*" of the Siberian chiffchaff several times, and succeeded in shooting one bird. When silent we always found it busily engaged feeding like a tit, usually among spruce-firs. Of the Lapp-tit (*Parus cinctus*, Bodd.) we saw two pairs and a few solitary birds.

The note of the waxwing had long been familiar to me, for I had once kept a pair in a cage for some months. I was delighted to hear it once more resounding from the lofty spruce and larch trees in the forest. We succeeded in shooting one pair only ; nor were they in very good plumage, having very few and small wax-like appendages on the secondaries. The eggs in the female were very large, and the testes of the male very fully developed. It is therefore probable that they were on the point of building, if they had not already begun. As the yellow on the primaries was I-shaped and not V-shaped, I judged it to be a young bird.

We saw one solitary barn-swallow, and shot it, and came upon many droppings of the capercailzie, but did not see the bird. Several traps were set in the forest to catch the hen, for the cock is not eaten. The peasants call the latter *gluká*, and the female *taitaióra*. Willow-grouse and hazel-grouse, we were told, were abundant in some seasons.

We saw one pair of golden plover on the newly sown cornfields behind the village, and noticed two or three pairs of ringed-plover frequenting the ploughed land below Habariki and the grassy banks of a little stream running out of the Petchora. We rose a pair of double snipe from the young wood on the sandy ground beyond the fields, and bagged one of them. These were the first examples we had yet seen of the species.

We did not succeed in securing a common snipe, but we often heard their peculiar *tic-tuc* note, and the sound of their drumming high in the air. My companion identified a snipe with his glass as belonging to this species; it was uttering the characteristic note, and later, when it dropped to the ground, it rose again with the zigzag flight belonging to this bird. We were not a little surprised the first time we saw a common snipe perched upon the topmost upright twig of a bare larch seventy feet above ground. We soon grew familiar to the sight; indeed, after what we witnessed of the arboreal habits of birds we are not accustomed to see perching in England, we ceased to feel surprise at the circumstance. The origin of this habit is doubtless due to the flooding of the great tracts of country by the annual overflow of rivers at the time of migration. We saw but one flock of Temminck's stint, feeding on the marshy ground near one of the forest trees. We shot them all, hoping to discover the Little stint amongst them, but we were disappointed.

We found the greenshank and dusky redshank (*Totanus fuscus*) abundant, but did not succeed in shooting an example of either species.

Wood-sandpipers were common, frequenting the edges of the marshes and the forest tarns. This bird, like Temminck's stint, elevates its wings when alighting, until they almost meet. There is a likeness also in the song of the two birds. The note of the wood-sandpiper is decidedly musical. We shot specimens from the summit of high bare trees sixty-five feet at least from the ground.

We shot half a dozen Terek sandpipers, the first we

had yet seen. The favourite resort of these pretty birds
was the grassy margin of the stream before mentioned,
where they fed on the edge of the water and on the
shoals of driftwood which lined it in many places. We
also came upon them in the marshy ground round some
of the forest tarns. They were extremely tame. Like
the wood-sandpiper, they would allow us to come and
talk within a few yards of them, letting us take up a
position where, by a little patience, a double shot could
be obtained. We thoroughly identified the ruff on the
marsh, although we failed to obtain a specimen of it.

We saw a bean-goose, which had been shot a day or
two before our arrival. We also saw a pair of swans,
and identified the skin and head of one shot by a sailor a
week or two before our arrival as belonging to the common
wild species, *Cygnus musicus.*

Wigeons were by no means uncommon on the lake,
the larger forest tarns, and the open water in the marshes
We shot a female off the nest, and took from it five eggs
and the down : it was built under a couple of fallen trees
crossing each other. The nest had been used the previous
year, as old egg-shells were under the down. Several
other specimens of this bird were brought to us.

The pintail was the commonest duck about Habariki.
We shot a female from the nest, taking nine eggs and the
down. This nest also was under a prostrate tree, and
not far from the wigeon's. We had one nest of teal
with down brought us, together with a male bird. They
were not rare. The golden-eye was a common duck,
generally seen in pairs on the open water in the marshes
and larger forest tarns. We shot a female, and took
a perfect egg from her. A nest in the hollow stump
of a tree some twenty feet from the ground was shown
to us, and we were told that these birds bred there

every year.   The nest contained ten eggs and plenty of
down.

We saw several goosanders, distinctly identifying one
pair on the water of the marsh behind Habariki.   The
smew was rather a common duck ; we saw many pairs on
the pools, the large marsh, and the woodland tarns, and
secured a fine male.   We were told that they breed in
low stumps of trees.

We identified the black-throated diver for the first
time on the 2nd of June.   We saw it several times and
heard it flying overhead.

We occasionally saw one or two common gulls and
one pair of Siberian herring-gulls.   In addition to the
above-mentioned birds we frequently saw others that we
were unable fully to identify.   Thus we often came upon
large sandpipers on the marsh whose cry was like that of
the redshank ; they were probably the dusky redshank.
We also saw a large flock of ducks of a heavy species
flying overhead which we imagined to be the eider-
duck.

In the woods and forests of Habariki we did not once
meet with the raven, the bullfinch, or the yellow-hammer,
or with any species of pipit or lark.

THE DELTA OF THE PETCHORA

CHAPTER XIV.

OUR VOYAGE TO THE DELTA.

Return to Ust-Zylma—Wedding of the Engineer's Son—Scarlet Bullfinch
—Last Days at Ust-Zylma—Our Boat—We Sail to Habariki—Birds' Eggs
—Smew's Eggs—Snipes in Trees—Down the Petchora—Sedge-warbler—
Blackcock—Arctic Tern—Willow Swamps—We Cross the Arctic Circle
—A New Bird—Arrival at Viski—The Delta—Double Snipe—Pustozersk
—The Tundra—Arrival at Alexievka.

WE returned to Ust-Zylma on Sunday, the 6th of June,
and attended the wedding of the son of the engineer of
Sideroff's steamer. It took place in the church of the
Old Believers, but the ritual did not differ much from
that of the orthodox ceremonial. The bridal party afterwards sat in state in the house of Sideroff's manager.
Coffee was first served, then sherry, afterwards champagne. All the quality, as an Irishman would say, were
present, except the public prosecutor. It was an exceed-

ingly formal and slow affair, the only feature of interest
being the assemblage of villagers outside, who sang a
melancholy tune, while two or three couples slowly
walked round each other in a depressed fashion, the
gentleman taking hold of one of the lady's arms by the
elbow, the other arm interlaced in hers.   The girls wore
their hair plaited in a pigtail behind, at the end of which
a cross-bar was attached, from which dangled half a dozen
broad ribbons like a banner screen.   They kept their
eyes fixed on the ground as they danced, and lifted a
handkerchief of many colours to their mouths.   All the
time vodka was served from a tin can, and through the
afternoon and evening the part of the room near the door
was filled with an ever-changing crowd of peasant maidens
who came to have a good stare at the bride and bridegroom and, having gazed their fill, retired to make way
for others, who entered and did likewise.

The next morning a stroll up the chiffchaff valley
resulted in nothing, but as we were returning home I
heard the song of a bird that was quite new to me—four
notes loud and clear.   I shot the little songster, and it
proved to be a male scarlet bullfinch (*Carpodacus
erythrinus*).   It was in company with another bird, but
this one escaped us.   We heard the cuckoo in our
morning ramble.   Four eggs of the wood-sandpiper were
brought to us, and the next day four eggs of the oyster-
catcher, one of which was slightly set.   All that day we
worked hard at our eggs ; we had blown 143 in all,
including the egg of a peregrine falcon which a Samoyede
brought us on the 27th of May.   He said he found it in
a nest built on the ground, containing three others, which
he had the clumsiness to break.   At night we turned out
for a breath of fresh air along the banks of the great
river.   During our walk we shot a pair of Terek sand-

pipers, the first we had yet seen in Ust-Zylma. We also brought down two Temminck's stints, and afterwards secured our solitary example of the Little ringed-plover (*C. minor*). I shot at it as it rose from and again alighted upon a swampy, hummocky strip of tundra land. The next day a peasant brought us a fine cock willow-grouse, our first, clothed in about half its summer costume. We had also a nest given to us of the wheatear, with one egg in it, and the female bird caught upon it.

We had for some time been on the look-out for a boat in which to make the journey down the river, and by the exertion of Piottuch and the kind help of M. Znaminski, who was much interested in our expedition, we succeeded in obtaining one which suited us very well. A wooden cabin, not unlike a large dog-kennel, occupied the centre, and was just large enough for us to recline in at full length ; and at the back of it was a covered space, where our baggage could be packed secure from the heavy rains which occasionally occur in summer. It had one mast, on which we could hoist a square sail whenever the wind was favourable. The current would of course usually be in our favour, but we were also provided with four oars, which, though incapable of propelling the boat at much speed, would be useful in crossing the stream, and in giving her way enough to make the rudder of some use in a calm. We engaged four boatmen, two Russians, a Samoyede, and a half-breed, all of whom possessed some knowledge of the river, while the latter had the additional advantage of being what passed in this district as an enthusiastic sportsman. We left Ust-Zylma on Thursday, the 10th of June, and sailed down to Habariki with a fair wind and a strong current. The banks of the river were covered with birch and spruce woods, alternating with willow-swamps. On our way we landed at

several places, but met with nothing of special interest.
Everywhere we found the bluethroat, the redwing, the
brambling, the fieldfare, the little bunting, and the
willow-warbler common.   We saw a solitary sand-martin.
The peasants at Habariki had collected eggs for us ;
among them those of the redwing, the redstart, the hooded
crow, and various ducks.   The best nest contained eight
eggs.   It had been found by two boys, who had divided
the eggs and the down between them.   Four of these
eggs, cream coloured, of a smaller size than the pintail's,
were first brought to us, and with them some pale grey
down.   The lad who brought them said he had found
the nest in the old stump of a tree, and the fragments of
rotten wood scattered in the down seemed to corroborate
his statement.   We then sent for the other sharer of the
spoil ; he had already sold the eggs, along with another
duck's nest, containing six eggs.   On our inquiry as to
what he had done with the down, he immediately went
off for it, and soon brought it to us.   It was very pale
down, containing small fragments of wood, the exact
counterpart of the other portion in our possession.   We
found, however, that the down of the second nest was
mingled with it.   We had no difficulty in separating it,
for it was brown, and evidently that of the pintail.   Ultimately we purchased the batch of ten eggs from Sideroff's
manager, who had bought them from the lad.   Four
exactly matched the four we had secured from his companion ; the other six were the same in size but greenish
in colour, and similar to eggs of the pintail duck which
we afterwards obtained.   Upon showing the boys some
skins of ducks, they at once identified the smew as the
duck which belonged to the whiter eggs with the pale
grey down.   These eggs are extremely rare in collections,
and we were not a little elated with our prize.

At three the following morning we shouldered our guns and went on shore. We had sat up late blowing eggs, but the excitement of finding ourselves in a locality where rare eggs and birds might be expected made any attempt to sleep fruitless, and we decided to gratify our curiosity without further delay. We shot a Siberian chiffchaff singing and "chiviting" lustily amongst the pines, and heard several cuckoos. The snipes were drumming on the marshes, and three times we marked th m perched high up on trees; once upon a dead trunk, and twice on the slender dead branches near the summit of larches. These trees were at least seventy feet high. To put an end to all dispute concerning their species, we settled the question by dropping a common snipe with a No. 4 cartridge. It was shot from the topmost twigs of a lofty larch, just budding into leaf. My afternoon walk, which was a long round on the marsh, resulted in very little. I rose a reeve from her nest, and shot her as she was silently shuffling off. The nest was a rather deep hole upon a grass tussock, lined with dry grass, and in it were four eggs and two feathers. A quantity of yellow wagtails were running along the swampy ground, and perching freely upon the birches growing on the islands formed in the marsh. Their usual cry was a loud *nc* or *ns*, but what seemed the call-note to the female resembled the sound *i-i-i-k;* the song is a low chatter like that of the swallow. Ducks were constantly coming and going to and from the open places on the swamp. The wigeon, judging from the frequency of its cry, seemed the commonest species; its loud *m-e-e e'-yu* was continually to be heard.

In the evening we left the little village of Habariki and proceeded down the river. All the next day we crept slowly down the mighty Petchora, a strong current in our

favour, but the wind contrary, and with only a couple of
oars propelling us along. The scenery was often interesting. The west bank, lofty and steep, was now and
then clothed to the water's edge with forests of birches
and pines ; the east bank at that part was a dead flat
covered with willows. Numberless islands studded the
water, *kurias* running up amongst them, sometimes of
great picturesqueness. The *tirrr'-eek'* of the Terek sandpiper resounded continually ; and sometimes we heard
the cry of the common sandpiper. We shot a brace of
the latter, the first we had secured ; we found the species
very wild. Two or three times during the day we pulled
up on an island or on the mainland. On a sandy island
thinly covered with grass we came upon a party fishing
with a seine net ; we watched and saw the net twice
drawn without result. On this island we shot a hen-
harrier, a cuckoo, and a short-eared owl. A few gulls
were flying about—the common gull and the Siberian
herring-gull. As we pulled on, I saw a party of six
waxwings flying north. Willow-warblers abounded ; I
watched one for some time that allowed me to approach
within six feet of it. I noticed that some appeared to
have a whiter throat and a more rapid song than usual.
One I heard vociferously uttering a note unlike any that
I have heard from the willow-warbler, *tuz-zuk*. These
observations convinced me that two species of willow-
warblers exist in these parts, and upon a careful examination of our skins afterwards, I found that I had shot an
Arctic willow-warbler (*Phylloscopus borealis*). Swans,
geese, and ducks, especially the latter, were to be seen in
the ponds behind the fringing belts of willows ; amongst
these we clearly identified the scaup and the black scoter.
We found six ducks' nests, most of which were those of
the wigeon. In one of these dense willow-swamps lining

the east bank of the river I found for the first time the
sedge-warbler.   On several occasions, especially at night,
we heard its harsh notes, but the bird kept very close,
and was very difficult to see.   I shot two ; one was flying
out of a birch-tree, in which it had descended, singing
after the manner of the bluethroat.   We also secured a
red-throated diver, the first added to our list.   We saw a
rough-legged buzzard, the only one of the species we
clearly identified.   It was sitting in a low willow-tree,
and we shot it, as we silently drifted past, about midnight.   We stopped soon after, anchoring in a little
creek.   A steady rain began to fall, which continued all
the following day ; we just managed to creep down to the
river Yorsa, where again we pulled up *en route*.   We
saw very few birds, but in the evening we got on shore,
and a turn in the rain was not without result.   We
seemed entangled in a network of willow swamps, lakes,
and *kurias* running out of the winding Yorsa.   Here and
there rose a few taller willows and birches.   After a
while we came upon a little house, the abode of the hay-
cutters in autumn, which our boatmen were now glad to
make use of for the night.   All around it were long
straggling meadows, upon which the grass was just
beginning to come up.   My companion shot a second
yellow-headed wagtail, a male ; he saw the female also,
but lost her.   He also saw a small owl, probably Tengmalm's owl.   I secured a fine male goshawk, the only
one we identified on our journey.   It was in a thick
alder-bush when I disturbed it, in the act of devouring a
female wigeon.   In the same place I shot a short-eared
owl.   Reed-buntings abounded.   I took a nest containing
four eggs ; it was built inside an old fieldfare's nest, and
was nine feet from the ground, in a willow-tree.   This is
another example of the manner in which birds accommo-

date themselves to the circumstances of a flooded country. We found the little bunting very common, and just beginning to build. Once or twice a white-tailed eagle hovered overhead. In long grass covering the raised bank of the island we discovered a blackcock's nest containing five eggs; also a wigeon's nest, with seven eggs, and a teal's with six.

The next afternoon we left the Yorsa River: the day was fine, but the wind contrary. We stopped for an hour at Churvinski Ostroff, and had a short stroll on shore armed with walking-stick guns. My companion shot a tree-sparrow, and I a small spotted woodpecker. We also started a three-toed woodpecker out of its hole in a tree; I shot it, when immediately the female came up, and I secured her also. We whistled for our boatmen, who, by our orders, cut down the tree. The bird's hole was about fifteen feet from the ground, descending nine inches perpendicularly; there was no lining in it, except plenty of saw- or rather beak-dust. It contained two newly hatched birds and one egg. On our way back we shot a pair of yellow-headed wagtails; the female had dry grass in her beak, which she was evidently carrying to build her nest. The male was not fully mature, having the nape brown, and dark feathers amongst the yellow of the crown. The yellow of the hen-bird was much less brilliant than that of her mate, and the head and cheeks were greenish-brown, with the exception of a pale yellow streak over each eye, meeting across the forehead. A few miles lower we brought down two little buntings and an oyster-catcher; we also took a brambling's nest and a duck's, both containing eggs. That evening we saw our first Arctic tern. We spied them from a distance, and brought them within range by imitating their notes. We suspected this species by the ash-grey colour of the lower parts. Later in the night we had the opportunity of procuring both birds and eggs, and verifying our previous recognition. We had pulled up at one of the islands to boil the kettle for tea and cook some fish. After this meal we began to explore. We shot three terns, and found three nests, securing five eggs in all. As I was in the act of taking up one of these nests, a hare ran up, stood in mute amazement gazing at me for a second or two, and then turned and bolted. On this island we shot an oyster-catcher; it was evident the nest was there, but we could not find it.

Rain and contrary winds accompanied us all the next day; and at night we stopped at Abramoff. We got from the peasants there eggs of the common gull and some of the white wagtail, besides those of the wigeon, golden-eye, fieldfare, and redpoll. We also saw a couple of young ravens. We shot a ringed-plover, a Temminck's stint, and a pair of yellow-headed wagtails. We were now leaving the more hilly country and the forests of pine, and were entering a waste of willows. Far as the eye could reach, on all sides of us, stretched this never-ending, almost impenetrable willow-swamp, with winding *kurias* and lakes. The only break in the monotony was here and there a straggling bit of pasture-land, on which stood a house or two, where a cow fed and the peasants fished, and where, in the autumn, they would make hay. Terns, gulls, and oyster-catchers were now not unfrequently seen, in addition to the almost numberless ducks that were breeding everywhere. On the shores would occasionally appear a Terek sandpiper, a Temminck's stint, or a dotterel. In the thickets the bluethroat was giving way to the sedge-warbler, but the willow-wren remained the commonest bird. The notes of the redpoll, the brambling, and the redwing still sounded. The fieldfare and the reed-bunting, as well as the yellow-headed, yellow, and white wagtails were still often to be met with, the little bunting being especially plentiful. That day I took my first nest of the Terek sandpiper. I was walking in a wood of tall willows, when the bird rose at my feet and silently fluttered away. There were four eggs laid in a slight hollow, lined with broad grass. We also found the nest of an oyster-catcher, containing four eggs.

We were now a little to the north of the Arctic Circle, and at three in the morning moored our boat on the shores of an island among whose willows grew an occasional birch or alder. I spent five hours upon it. Sedge-warblers were singing lustily, and sometimes so melodiously that we almost took them to be bluethroats. Soon, however, my attention was arrested by a song with which I was not familiar. It came from a bird singing high in the air, like a lark. I spent an hour watching it. Once it remained up in the sky nearly half an hour. The first part of the song was like the trill of a Temminck's stint, or like the concluding notes of the wood-warbler's song. This was succeeded by a low guttural warble, resembling that which the blue-throat sometimes makes. The bird sang while hovering; it afterwards alighted on a tree, and then descended to the ground, still continuing to sing. I shot one, and my companion an hour later shot another. Both birds proved to be males, and quite distinct from any species with which either of us was previously acquainted. The long hind claw was like that of the meadow-pipit, and the general character of the bird resembled a large and brilliantly coloured tree-pipit. It was very aquatic in its habits, frequenting the most marshy ground amongst the willows.

On our return home five skins of this bird were

submitted to our friend Mr. Dresser, who pronounced it
to be a new species, and described and figured it in a
work which he was then publishing on the birds of
Europe. In honour of my having been the first to
discover it he named it after me, *Anthus seebohmi*,* but,
alas for the vanity of human wishes, I afterwards
discovered that the bird was not new, but had been
described some years before from examples obtained
on the coast of China. I had subsequently the pleasure
of working out its geographical distribution, as the reader
who cares to peruse the accompanying footnote may
learn. The honour of having added a new bird to the
European lists still remains to us, and is one of the
discoveries made upon our journey on which we pride
ourselves.

In the evening we reached Viski, a small town with a
church built upon a flat piece of pasture-land. It was
the first village containing more than half a dozen houses

---

* The Siberian pipit (*Anthus gustavi*, Swinhoe) was perhaps the most interesting
discovery which we made during our journey. It was first described by Swinhoe
in 1863, from specimens obtained at Amoy, in South China, on migration. It is
seldom that the history of an obscure bird is so suddenly and completely worked
out as has been the case with this species. In 1869, G. R. Gray, of the British
Museum, redescribed the species as *Anthus batchianensis*, from skins collected by
Wallace on the island of Batjan in the Moluccas. In 1871 Swinhoe announced
the identity of Gray's birds with the species with which he had previously described
from South China. Three years later he identified the species in North China
on migration, and also obtained a skin from Lake Baikal. The year after our visit
to the Petchora, Drs. Finsch and Brehm found it in the valley of the Ob, a little
to the north of the Arctic Circle, and I afterwards found skins in the British
Museum from Borneo and Negros in the Philippine Archipelago, and also obtained
information that it had been procured in winter at Manila and in Celebes. In
1877 I found it breeding in considerable numbers in the valley of the Yenesei
in latitude 70½°, and on my journey home I identified skins in the Museum
at St. Petersburg, collected by Baron Maydell in Tschuski Land, north of
Kamtschatka, and on Bering Island to the east of the peninsula, collected by
Wossnessensky. We may therefore conclude that the Siberian pipit breeds on
the tundras beyond the limit of forest growth, from the valley of the Petchora
eastwards to Bering's Strait, that it passes through South-Eastern Siberia and
East China on migration, and winters in the islands of the Malay Archipelago.

and the first church that we had seen since leaving Ust-Zylma. It is reputed to be the residence of several rich peasants, one of whom is the owner of 10,000 reindeer valued at a sovereign each. Without exception it is the dirtiest place I have ever been in. The peasants keep cows, but as they have no arable ground the manure is valueless and is thrown outside the house to be trodden under foot. There was an excellent shop in the place, where we laid in a store of tobacco, white flour, etc. In the village we saw a sand-martin and a magpie, but no sparrows.

On leaving Viski we entered upon the true delta, a labyrinth of water and islands, one almost as dead a flat as the other. The islands—which but a little while ago had lain three or four feet deep under the overflow of the great river—were almost all alike. They were monotonous willow-swamps, with here and there narrow strips of sandy land appearing, thickly covered with grass and sparingly sprinkled with willows and alders. Everywhere were the winding *kurias* and chains of lakelets. On the dry places ducks of various sorts were breeding. We identified a shoveller, and there were wigeons, scoters, and teal. On one island we found two pintails' nests with eggs, and I shot our first tufted duck, a species which we found very rare in the Petchora. As soon as I fired there rose between me and it a flock of red-necked phalaropes, which alighted between me and the floating body. I shot five : they were the first we had yet secured, but later in the day we brought down four more. My companion meanwhile was exploring another island, where he fell in with a flock of ruffs at their " lecking " place. He shot two. Geese were becoming more and more plentiful ; in one instance we marked aflock of fifty at least. Swans often passed us by twos and threes. The sandpipers, the Terek, and Temminck's stints were as common as ever. We watched one of the latter to its nest, shot it, and secured the four eggs. Early next morning I brought down a skylark, the second only that we had seen. I also shot a blue-throat, a species which by this time had grown very rare. The commonest warbler, abounding in some places, was the sedge-warbler, next to it was the willow-warbler. Now and then also we heard the red-wing, and generally where we stopped there would greet us the song of the new pipit pouring down from the sky. The bird would remain up in the air for a long time, then fly down and alight in the middle of a dense willow swamp, rendering it impossible for us to secure another specimen. A red-throated pipit that my companion shot out of a tree furnished us with the best possible evidence that this species is much more arboreal in its habits than the meadow-pipit. The yellow-headed wagtail had now become quite a common bird, but occasionally we still saw the white wagtail. At one island we shot a pair of small spotted woodpeckers, which must have found the alder and willow-trunks very small for their nests. I found also two fieldfares' nests, one with four, the other with six eggs. Late in the evening we came upon a large flock of great snipe, and in the course of half an hour we had shot ten. They were flying about in companies of about six, continually alighting on the ground, where the sound of their feeding was often heard. One or two common snipe were also hovering overhead and frequently drumming. On one island we saw signs that the breaking up of the Petchora did not take place so silently in the delta as it had done at Ust-Zylma. On the flat shore we discovered a small range of miniature mountains some eighteen to twenty feet high. We took them at first from a distance to be low sandhills, but on nearer approach found them to be a pile of dirty blocks of ice.

We arrived at Pustozersk at midnight on June 18, and spent the night shooting. The country was a sort of rolling prairie, rising here and there into dry moorland, on which grew birches, junipers, and a few pines. The lower land remained a willow-swamp. Among the sand-hills we found a couple of terns' nests and one of the Terek sandpiper. Plenty of Temminck's stints were about, but we failed to find any nests. We shot a couple of sand-martins preparing to build. In a walk that I took on the dry moorland I stalked a couple of willow-grouse sitting upon a birch-tree, very conspicuous objects for a mile around. I also rose a shore-lark from its nest, in which I found four young birds, and secured a golden plover, one of whose axillary feathers was blotched with brown. In this part of the moor the yellow-headed wagtails abounded. Down in the marshy ground I shot a ruff, and saw several others, besides a number of red-necked phalaropes ; but of all the birds the most interest-ing were the pipits. Our new pipit was here by no means uncommon ; two or three would sometimes be singing together. We secured two more specimens, one of which must have been trilling its roundelay up in the air for nearly an hour before we were able to shoot it. These pipits poured their song indifferently from the sky, or perching on a bough, or down upon the ground. The red-throated pipit we also found settling freely in trees. In the swampy ground we saw many sedge-warblers, fieldfares, and redwings, and one or two blue-throats. The next night we again spent shooting in a willow-covered island just opposite Kuya. We had grown very weary of these islands, and somewhat disappointed in the result of our ornithological experience of the delta. We had indeed secured some interesting species of birds, but each island had proved almost a repetition of the others —the same landscape, the same conditions, the same bird-life. We were nearing Alexievka, however, and on the eastern side of the river we could almost distinguish the low outline of the skirts of the great Zemelskaya Tundra, stretching away, we knew, on the east to the Ural Mountains, on the north-east to the gates of the Kara Sea ; and the tundra was the unexplored land, the land of promise.

On this island we took the nest, containing seven eggs, of a pintail, shooting the bird as she was flying off. We found also those of the red-necked phalarope, the great snipe, and the reed-bunting. Our most exciting nest-discovery was that of a swan. It was a large nest, made of coarse grass lined with a little down and a few feathers, and containing three eggs. It was placed upon a bank between two marshes, half-concealed by willow-scrub. The most interesting birds we shot were a black scoter, a herring-gull, and a long-tailed duck, the first we had yet seen on our travels. Its cry was not unlike the word " colguief." Of all species of ducks it is the tamest and yet one of the most difficult to shoot, for it is an expert at diving, and eludes the sportsman's aim by its rapid and repeated plunges under the surface of the water.

Just before reaching Alexievka we anchored for an hour at another island, about which seven swans were sailing. The graceful birds, however, did not give us the chance of a shot. Upon this island we had an excellent view of our first great black-backed gulls, and also of Buffon's skua. The former were sitting amidst several Siberian herring-gulls, but their superior size allowed us to identify them at a glance. The Arctic tern was breeding on this island, while ruffs, phalaropes, and Temminck's stint abounded upon it. On one part, covered with dwarf willows, interspersed with taller trees, I heard to my astonishment the warble of the Siberian chiffchaff, two specimens of which I secured. The red-throated pipits were there perching, as usual, in the boughs, and I noticed also one or two of our new pipits and a number of reed-buntings.

This bird-haunted island was our last stoppage before reaching Alexievka. We arrived at our destination on the evening of the 19th of June, after ten days voyage down the great river and through the intricacies of the monotonous delta.

PLOUGHING AT UST-ZYLMA

ALEXIEVKA FROM THE TUNDRA

CHAPTER XV.

ALEXIEVKA.

Alexievka—The Timber Rafts—The Island—Nests and Eggs—Buffon's Skua—Sailing for the Tundra—Description of the Tundra—Its Vegetation—Nests of Lapland Bunting and Red-throated Pipit— First Sight of the Grey Plover—Its Nest—Omelette of Grey Plover's Eggs—Birds seen on the Tundra—Eggs collected during the Day—Nest of *Anthus gustavi*.

ALEXIEVKA is the shipping-port of the Petchora Timber-trading Company. It is a group of houses built upon an island in the delta of the great river, where the ships are laden with larch for Cronstadt. The larch is felled in the forests 500 or 600 miles up the river, and roughly squared into logs varying from two to three feet in diameter. It is floated down in enormous rafts, the logs being bound together with willows and hazel-boughs. These rafts are manned by a large crew, some of whom help to steer it down the current with oars and poles, while others are hired for the season to assist in loading the ships at Alexievka. Many of the men bring their wives with them to cook for the party; sleeping huts are erected on the raft, and it becomes to all intents and purposes a little floating village, which is frequently three months in making the voyage down the river. Marriages have been known to take place on these rafts. Occasionally a funeral has to be performed, and sometimes all hands are engaged in helping to keep the raft under the lee of an island or a promontory to avoid the danger of having it broken up by the violence of the waves. With the greatest care in the world this will sometimes happen. The Russian has a good deal of the fatal facility to blunder which characterises the Englishman, and shiploads of stranded logs of larch are strewn on the islands of the delta and on the shores of the lagoon of this great river.

When we landed on the island of Alexievka it was a rapidly drying-up willow-swamp of perhaps half a dozen square miles, some six feet above the level of the Petchora, which swept past it with a rapid current. In some places the willow-swamp was impenetrable, in others bare grassy oases varied the flat landscape, and there were one or two largish lakes on the island. During the floods which accompanied the break-up of the ice, the whole of the island was under water, and men were busily clearing away the mud which had deposited itself on the floors of the houses. An extensive series of wooden fortifications protected the various buildings from being carried away by the ice. For four months of the year the village was a busy scene, full of life and activity, but for the remaining eight months a solitary man and a dog kept watch over the property of the Company, and even they had to desert their charge and escape to the shore during the breaking-up of the ice.

Three rooms were generously placed at our disposal, and we proceeded to make ourselves as comfortable as the circumstances would permit. Our first care was to buy a brace of willow-grouse and a bean-goose for the pot; our next to purchase eggs of the yellow-headed wagtail, bean-goose, willow-grouse, and long-tailed duck. A nest of the white wagtail which we found contained remarkably brown eggs; it was made chiefly of roots and a little stalky grass, and was lined with reindeer hair. The next day peasants brought us two nests of the yellow-headed wagtail, which were also composed of fine roots and dry leafy grass, the inside lined with reindeer hair; one had, besides, two small feathers and a piece of duck-down.

The mosquitoes, which of late had tried us severely, were now giving us a respite, driven back by the cold north wind and occasional snowstorms. All day I kept indoors, going out but for half an hour, when I bagged a Siberian chiffchaff and a red-throated pipit perched in a tree. The nests came in plentifully. The first day of our stay there were brought to us those of the blue-throat, the redpoll, the reed-bunting, the willow-warbler, two of the bean-goose, with the goose snared upon it, and one of the pintail duck. With these were brought two wigeon's eggs. The weather continued very cold; the Petchora looked sullen and tempestuous under the dark sky and bleak wind. The next day we again kept indoors, profiting by our enforced captivity in having a general overhauling of our skins. We found the Siberian chiff-chaff the commonest warbler amongst the willows of Alexievka. Its note is a "ching-chevy" repeated three or four times in rapid succession with the accent laid on the "ching," and the warble generally, but not always, ending with a final "ching." Probably owing to the

coldness of the weather we did not then hear it in full
song, as we did at Ust-Zylma and Habariki. We found
Buffon's skuas numerous in Alexievka ; they were usually
in flocks of five or six. There seemed to be only one
common sparrow in the place, and this I shot.

The 22nd of June was inscribed in our journal as a
red-letter day. We were dead tired when we turned
into our hammocks at half-past ten the night before, and
slept the clock round and an hour over, rising at half-
past eleven. When we woke we found it was a bright
warm day, the wind had dropped, and the great river
looked no longer like an angry sea. We decided to
cross it, ordered our men to get the boat ready, made a
hasty breakfast, and set sail at last for the land of promise,
the mysterious tundra. We pictured this great land to
ourselves as a sort of ornithological Cathay, where all
sorts of rare and possibly unknown birds might be found.
So far we had been just a little disappointed with the
results of our trip. July would soon be upon us, and we
had not yet solved one of the six problems that we had
proposed to ourselves as the main objects of our journey.
We had not seen the least trace of the knot, the curlew
sandpiper, the sanderling, or the grey plover. Some
birds that we had at first fancied might be Little stints in
full breeding plumage, we were now thoroughly convinced were nothing but Temminck's stints, and as we
had hitherto met with but one species of swan, we had
reluctantly come to the conclusion that we had not yet
seen Bewick's swan. We congratulated ourselves that
our observations on the arrival of migratory birds at
Ust-Zylma were not without interest. We were much
pleased that we had shot one specimen of the Arctic
willow-warbler. The abundance of yellow-headed wagtails, and the prospect of bringing home many of the

eggs of this rare bird, was a source of considerable
satisfaction to us.   Our two best things were undoubtedly
the new pipit and the Siberian chiffchaff.   We hoped
that both these birds might be new, but our acquaintance
with the various Indian species that might possibly migrate
into this region was not sufficient to warrant us in enter-
taining more than a hope.   We therefore looked forward
to our first day on the tundra with more than usual anxiety
and interest.

The tundra forms the east bank of the Petchora, and
we anchored our boat under a steep cliff, perhaps sixty
feet high, a crumbling slope of clay, earth, sand, gravel,
turf, but no rock.   We looked over a gently rolling
prairie country, stretching away to a flat plain, beyond
which was a range of low rounded hills, some eight or
ten miles off.   It was in fact a moor, with here and there
a large flat bog, and everywhere abundance of lakes.
For seven or eight months in the year it is covered with
from two to three feet of snow.   Snow was still lying in
large patches in the more sheltered recesses of the steep
river-banks, and on one of the lakes a large floe of ice,
six inches thick, was still unmelted.   The vegetation on
the dry parts of the tundra was chiefly sedges, moss, and
lichen, of which the familiar reindeer-moss was especially
abundant.   In some places there was an abundance of
cranberries, with last year's fruit still eatable, preserved
by the frost and snow of winter.   Here and there we met
with a dwarf shrub, not unlike a rhododendron, with a
white flower and aromatic-scented leaves (*Ledum palustre*),
a heath-like plant with a pale red flower (*Andromeda
polifolia*), and dwarf birch (*Betula nana*) running on the
ground almost like ivy.   The flat boggy places had evidently been shallow lakes a few weeks ago after the
sudden thaw, and were now black swamps ; water in the

middle, grown over with yellow-green moss, and sedges towards the edge. They were separated from each other by tussocky ridges of moor, which intersected the plain like the veins on the rind of a melon. We found no difficulty in going where we liked ; our indiarubber waterproofs were all-sufficient. We crossed the wettest bogs with impunity, seldom sinking more than a foot before reaching a good foundation, a solid pavement of ice. Birds were but thinly scattered over the ground, but there were sufficient to keep our curiosity on the *qui vive*. The commonest bird was the Lapland bunting, and we took two of their nests in the tussocky ridges between the little bogs. The next commonest bird was the red-throated pipit, and we found two of their nests in similar positions. As we marched across the tundra we fell in with some dunlins, and took a couple of their nests. This was encouraging. The dunlin was a bird we had not seen at Ust-Zylma, and one possibly that migrated direct across country to Ust-Ussa. We had not walked more than a couple of miles inland before we came upon a small party of plovers. They were very wild, and we found it impossible to get within shot of them ; but a distant view through our binocular almost convinced us that we had met with the grey plover at last. On going a little farther other plovers rose, and we determined to commence a diligent search for the nest, and offered half a rouble to any of our men who should find one. Our interpreter laughed at us, and marched away into the tundra with a "C'est impossible, monsieur." We appealed to our Samoyede, who stroked his beardless chin and cautiously replied, " Mozhna." The other men wandered aimlessly up and down, but the Samoyede tramped the ground systematically, and after more than an hour's search found a nest on one of the dry tussocky ridges intersecting the bog, containing four eggs about the size and shape of those of the golden plover, but more like those of the lapwing in colour.   The nest was a hollow, evidently scratched, perfectly round, somewhat deep, and containing a handful of broken slender twigs and reindeer-moss.   Harvie-Brown concealed himself as well as he could behind a ridge, to lie in wait for the bird returning to the nest, and after half an hour's watching shot a veritable grey plover.   Soon afterwards another of our men found a second nest, also containing four eggs, in an exactly similar situation.   Harvie-Brown took this nest also in hand, and in about an hour succeeded in shooting the female.   The third nest was found by the Samoyede. This time I lay down behind a ridge some thirty yards from the nest, and after waiting a quarter of an hour caught sight of the bird on the top of a distant tussock. Presently she ran nearer to another ridge, looked round, and then ran on to the next, until she finally came within fifty yards of where I was lying.   I had just made up my mind to risk a shot when she must have caught sight of me, and flew right away.   In a quarter of an hour I caught sight of her again, approaching by short stages as before, but from an opposite direction.   I must have been in full sight of her.   When she had approached within fifty yards of me, as near as I could guess, I fired at her with No. 4 shot and missed.   I remained reclining where I was, with little hope that she would try a third time to approach the nest, and whiled away the time with watching a Buffon's skua through my glass as it cautiously approached in my direction.   Turning my head round suddenly I caught sight of the grey plover running towards the nest within fifty yards of me.   I lifted my gun and fired again, but was so nervous that I missed her a second time.   I was so vexed that I got up and

walked towards the skua, which still remained *in statu quo*.
I missed a shot at it too, spent some time in a vain search
for its nest, and returned to my old quarters. In ten
minutes I saw the grey plover flying up. It took a wheel
in my direction, coming almost within shot, and evidently
took stock of me, and satisfied itself that I was a harmless animal practising with blank cartridge, and having no
evil design upon its eggs. It alighted about fifty yards
beyond the nest, and approached less timidly than before.
When it came within fifty yards of me I fired, this time
with No. 6 shot, and laid the poor bird upon its back.
As we returned to our boat Harvie-Brown found a fourth
nest, and, after watching as before, secured the bird. We
accidentally broke two of the eggs belonging to the third
nest, but reached Alexievka at midnight with fourteen
identified grey plover's eggs. Two sittings were quite
fresh, and made us an excellent omelette for breakfast
the next morning. The other two were very slightly
incubated.

On the tundra we saw several Buffon's skuas, and
shot two. I also shot a willow-grouse on a piece of
swampy ground near a lake, where a few dwarf willows
were growing. On the lakes we saw many pairs of long-
tailed ducks. A few pairs of yellow-headed wagtails,
which evidently had nests, a redwing, a Temminck's
stint, a few pairs of bean-geese, a redpoll, and a hawk,
which, as far as I could make out with my glass, was a
male peregrine—this completed the list of birds we saw
on the tundra.

On our return to headquarters we found that the price
we had paid for the eggs to the workmen had induced
many of them to go out bird-nesting, and at night our
bag for the day stood as under, as far as eggs were concerned :—

Grey plover	14
Dunlin	7
Great snipe	4
Lapland bunting	25
Red-throated pipit	39
Yellow-headed wagtail	10
Mealy redpoll	16
Reed-bunting	12
Redwing	3
Bean-goose	11
Wigeon (with down)	17
Temminck's stint	4
	162

This was a grand haul. Any little lingering feeling of disappointment which we had experienced was now completely gone. The grey plover eggs alone would have made our trip a success. They were unquestionably the first that had ever been taken in Europe. We spent the next two days in blowing our eggs and writing up our journals, occasionally strolling out among the willows on the island to bag a few yellow-headed wagtails and other birds to keep Piottuch employed. We found that the swans' eggs that we had brought from Kuya were perfectly fresh. The eggs of the bean-goose, on the contrary, some of them more than a week old, were mostly considerably incubated. The ducks' eggs were all fresh, or nearly so. Most of these were wigeon's, pale cream-coloured eggs; the down large, dark brown, very distinctly tipped with white and with pale whitish centres. The red-throated pipits and Lapland buntings' eggs were, many of them, too much sat upon to be easily blown, as were also the dunlins' eggs. The eggs of Temminck's stint, red-necked phalarope, yellow-headed wagtail, and most of the redpolls were all fresh or very slightly sat upon. The eggs of the gulls, both those of the common species and of the Arctic herring-gull, were quite fresh, whilst some of those of the Arctic tern were fresh, and some considerably incubated. During these two days we found several nests of the fieldfare on the island, a nest of the willow-warbler, and one of the yellow-headed wagtail. The latter was on the ground, concealed amongst the old tangled grass which the floods had twisted round a stake. It was principally composed of dry herbage, with one or two feathers in the lining. Our two *raræ aves*, which we christened the Petchora pipit, and the Siberian chiffchaff, were by no means uncommon, but we failed to find either of their nests. Amongst the nests, however, which our excellent coadjutors the Zyriani brought us was one which we at once concluded could belong only to the Petchora pipit (*Anthus gustavi*). It contained five perfectly fresh eggs, larger than those of the red-throated pipit, and similar in colour to those of the meadow-pipit. The nest was somewhat larger than that of the red-throated pipit, composed of more aquatic-looking flat-leaved grass, and containing fragments of *Equisetum* in the lining. Our collection of eggs increased rapidly. We had now 145 sittings, numbering 681 eggs.

MHF

OLD RUSSIAN SILVER CROSS .

STANAVIALACHTA

CHAPTER XVI.

STANAVIALACHTA.

The Tundra near the Yushina River—Golden Plover's Eggs—Abundance
of Nests—Lapland Bunting—Richardson's Skua—Means of Propelling
our Boat—The Tundra near Stanavialachta—Eyrie of a Peregrine Falcon
—More Nests—Abundance of Willow-grouse—Nest of the Willow-grouse
—Visit to two Islands in the Delta.

THE next day we left Alexievka in the morning to spend
a few days exploring the tundra in the neighbourhood of
Stanavialachta, the old loading-place of the Petchora
Timber-trading Company, about forty versts down the
river, where we learnt there were several wooden houses
that we could occupy. We sailed about twenty versts
down to the mouth of a small tributary called the
Yushina. The tundra here was less marshy, the ground
more hilly, and upon it were more willows. The
country looked so inviting that we cast anchor and went

on shore for a stroll. We soon saw some plovers, and were in hopes of a second haul of grey plovers' eggs. After a time our Samoyede discovered a nest, but the eggs in it were of a much lighter ground colour than those we had found before. We waited and shot the bird, but to our disappointment it turned out to be a golden plover. We afterwards saw several more. We could not detect any difference in the habits of the two species at the nest. We secured a bean-goose off its nest with seven eggs, and were very successful in finding nests of small birds. We took eggs of reeve, ringed-plover, willow-warbler, Lapland bunting, red-throated pipit, blue-throated warbler, redwing, Temminck's stint, and willow-grouse. The redwing's nest contained six eggs. It was in a willow about four feet from the ground. Redpolls were common, and oftener to be met with on the ground than in the willow and birch-bushes. The Lapland bunting we constantly saw both running and hopping on the ground. These charming birds were very tame and very numerous. They perched freely in the bushes. They were busily employed in the duties of incubation, and we rarely, if ever, heard them sing. In Finmark I used to hear their song constantly ; but then they were only just beginning to breed. We saw many red-throated pipits, carrying flies in their mouths, evidently destined to feed their young, and if we came inconveniently near their nests they would fly uneasily from bush to bush. Near a couple of deserted turf huts we noticed the white wagtail and the wheatear. The yellow-headed wagtail was also frequently met with on the tundra, but not in anything like the numbers in which we found it on the islands of the delta. On the banks of the great river numerous Siberian herring-gulls were slowly sailing past, and we shot four. I shot a Richardson's skua, which heedlessly flew within range of my gun. This was the first example of this species which we had yet seen. It was as white underneath as the Buffon's skuas, but the centre tail-feathers were much shorter. Curiously enough we never met with the dark-bellied variety of Richardson's skua in the Petchora. It must be the western form. I found it by far the commonest variety in Finmark. We saw a few Arctic terns, and got one egg. On the lakes the long-tailed duck was common, and I shot two males. These birds are very quarrelsome, and by no means so shy as the other ducks. My companion identified a red-breasted merganser, but did not succeed in shooting it. I saw a great snipe, a large flock of red-necked phalaropes, a few pairs of fieldfares, and several black-throated divers. Every day the tundra became gayer with flowers, and we continually regretted that we were not botanists. I noticed *Equisetum variegatum* for the first time. The evening, or what ought to have been the evening, turned out so cold, with a strong contrary wind, against which our stupid keelless boat could make little headway, that finding the tide was also against us, we cast anchor in a creek for a night's rest. In the morning, by dint of hard rowing for some time, then of thrusting with a pole, as is done in the flat-bottomed boats on the Grecian lagoons, then turning out two of our men, and making them drag us along, canal-boat fashion, we at length arrived at Stanavialachta. We spent the day in making the Company's deserted houses sufficiently waterproof to afford us good shelter for a few days. In the evening we turned out for a stroll; the tundra in this locality was much more hilly, and was diversified with more lakes than in the neighhourhood of Alexievka. The high ground was very dry, and we seldom came upon any impassable bog. The vegetation also was more abundant, the flowers more varied, and the willows and dwarf birch-trees more numerous. The weather was very unfavourable; a strong gale was blowing from the west, and it was very cold, with occasional attempts at rain, yet we saw many birds. The red-throated pipit was by far the commonest. My companion shot a meadow-pipit from a tree, and caught another sitting on its nest. We saw several golden plover, a flock of seven or eight Buffon's skuas, a pair of dotterel, and one or two shore-larks, besides securing the nest of a bean-goose containing two eggs. On the grassy top of a mound, half-way down the mud cliffs overlooking the great river, and within sight of the Arctic Ocean, I came upon the eyrie of a peregrine falcon. It contained four eggs, one of which was much lighter in colour than the others. This mound had probably been used for some years as a nesting-place by the falcons, since the grass was much greener upon it than upon the surrounding places. A little way off there rose another mound, just similar to it, and this was apparently the falcons' dining-table, for scattered all about it were feathers of grouse, long-tailed duck, and divers small birds.

While I remained near the nest, the two falcons hovered around, uttering sharp cries; when I approached nearer still, they redoubled their screams, hovered over me, closed their wings, and descended perpendicularly till within a few yards of my head. Their movements were so rapid that I wasted half a dozen cartridges in trying to secure them, and had at last to leave them, baffled in the attempt. My companion and I returned to the charge on the following day; but again we were defeated. A mile up the river, however, we found a second eyrie upon an exactly similar green-topped

mound. The nest contained three eggs, and the behaviour
of the birds as we neared it was the same as had been
that of the falcons of the day before. My companion
succeeded in shooting the male. We found many nests
of other birds. Our Samoyede in the morning brought
us one of the black-throated diver, containing two eggs,
and in the course of the day we found a second. We
also secured nests of the golden plover, long-tailed duck,
wheatear, Temminck's stint, blue-throat, and Lapland
bunting; in the latter were young birds. Our most
interesting find, however, was the nest with two eggs of
Richardson's skua, placed on a tussock of mossy ground.
It was lined with some reindeer moss and leaves of the
surrounding plants. The devices of the birds to deceive
us, as we came near it, attracted our attention and revealed
its vicinity. They often alighted within fifteen yards of
us, shammed lameness and sickness, reeled from side to
side as if mortally wounded, then when we persisted in
our onward course they flew boldly at us and stopped
repeatedly.

We again saw the dotterels, but apparently not yet
nesting. Willow-grouse were as plentiful on this part of
the tundra as red grouse on the Bradfield moors on
the 12th. Their white wings and their almost entirely
white bodies made them very conspicuous objects. They
usually rose within shot from a patch of willow cover.
Sometimes we saw a pair knocking about the tundra like
two big white butterflies, with a peculiar up-and-down
flight, then they tumbled into a willow-grown knoll
on the hillside. It might be owing to their extreme
conspicuousness that their flight always seemed so much
more clumsy than that of the red grouse. One of their
nests, which we found on the ground, contained a baker's
dozen of eggs. It was a mere hollow scraped in the turf,

lined with a leaf or two, a little dry grass, and a few feathers. The next day we succeeded in shooting the female peregrine on the first eyrie we had discovered, then, after taking a sketch of the place, we set out for Alexievka, visiting on our way a couple of islands on the delta. The first on which we disembarked was very marshy, and covered with small willows. On this island the willow-warblers were rare, but we occasionally heard the Siberian chiffchaff, and we noticed one almost incessantly repeating "*chi-vit'-che-vet'*." The yellow-headed wagtail was common, the shore-lark had disappeared altogether, the Lapland bunting was represented by a solitary bird. Red-throated pipits were still numerous ; but we did not see the meadow-pipit. The sedge-warbler abounded. We also saw several Temminck's stints, phalaropes, a flock of eight Buffon's skuas, and ducks of various sorts. The other island was almost entirely a grassy marsh, interspersed with spaces of open water. A flock of Siberian herring-gulls hovered about a party of fishermen, who were catching with a seine net a small fish exactly resembling the herring. Temminck's stints congregated in great numbers on the dry or drying mud, but we could find no trace of their nests. Phalaropes single and in flocks were common ; we took three of their nests, also one of a tern. Ducks as usual abounded ; we noticed among them a pair of shovellers, and carried off a nest, containing three eggs and a little down, which belonged to this bird. On the river we continually passed flocks of scaup and black scoter.

The sketch of Stanavialachta at the head of this chapter was taken from one of the peregrines' eyries ; the second eyrie was half-way down the point to the extreme left. To the right in the distance is the eastern boundary of Bolvanskaya Bay ; to the left, the outer islands of the delta.

GREY PLOVER'S NEST AND YOUNG

CHAPTER XVII.

AFTER GREY PLOVERS AT WASILKOVA.

Examination of our Nests—Excursion to Wasilkova—Search for Breeding Haunts of Bewick's Swan—News from England—Grey Plover's Eggs—Flock of Buffon's Skuas—Black Scoter's Nest—Watching for Skuas' Nests—Another Nest of Grey Plover—Scaup's Eggs—The Zyriani.

ON the 29th of June the weather was very wet. We spent the day in blowing eggs and examining our nests. We had now five nests which we were pretty sure were those of our new pipit; they were entirely distinct from that of the red-throated pipit. Instead of being composed of fine round grasses they were made of flat-leaved grass, knotted water-plants and small leaves, and in two of them were *Equiseta*. The eggs in them were larger, more lark-like, a dark ring circled the larger end, and they were all more or less mottled, especially those of the lighter variety.

Buffon's skua, we found, had been feeding upon beetles and cranberries. Another fact worth noticing was that the ten great snipes which we shot near Pustozersk were all males.

The following morning proving fine we set off on an excursion to Lake Wasilkova, which at high flood was but a bay of the Petchora. The tundra inland was the usual stretch of rolling moorland, swamp, and bog, interspersed with lakes and ranges of low sandy hills. On the swamps we found dunlins, on the moors golden plover, and once we saw a grey plover. In both localities we met the Lapland bunting and the red-throated pipit, and the dry grassy hills were haunted by shore-larks. On one of the lakes and along the coast we came upon Siberian herring-gulls; longtailed ducks abounded on the stretches of open water, but we failed to find a nest. We came to a spot on the shore where a pair of peregrines had built their eyrie, but the peasants had taken the eggs away for food. Under a low willow bush we shot a black scoter as she sat on her nest. Once we saw a hen-harrier beating up the hillsides, and caught sight of a white-tailed eagle as it flew overhead. Among the willows in the low swampy ground we shot a pair of wood-sandpipers, and caught three of their young, apparently a couple of days old. We also saw a raven and many Buffon's skuas. During the day the mosquitoes were very troublesome in the sheltered parts of the tundra, but a cold north wind kept the hilltops clear.

Hitherto, we had been unable to identify the swans that during our voyage had flown overhead, or settled on the ice in the river. We were convinced that there were two different sizes, but had been unable to establish the fact. On an island near Kuya we had found one nest

A SWAN'S NEST

containing four large eggs, but we had failed to secure the bird. To determine the breeding haunts of Bewick's swan was one of the principal objects of our journey, but as yet the offer of five roubles reward for any swan's eggs accompanied by the parent bird had resulted only in two or three nests being brought to us without the bird. Our Samoyede now brought us two swan's eggs that he had found thrown out of a nest, and advised us of a second nest containing four eggs. We despatched him at once to the latter with a trap to try and catch the bird. That day we also bought two very small swan's eggs, smaller than those of the ordinary wild swan, from a fisherman. He told us that his mate had the skin of the parent bird, which he had caught at the nest. The fishing encampment from which he came was lower down the river, on an island opposite the hamlet of Stanavialachta. We could not think this was a made-up story, for the man could not have heard of the reward we had offered for eggs accompanied with the captured parent bird, as we were the first to speak to him on his arrival. We therefore at once determined that if we did not discover Bewick's swan in the neighbourhood of Alexievka, we would make an excursion to Stanavialachta for the express purpose of obtaining the head and skin of the bird whose eggs we had just bought.

The following day our Samoyede returned from his excursion in quest of the swan. He had failed to secure her. From the appearance of the trap it seemed as if the swan had shuffled up to her nest on her belly, after the manner of a diver, for the trap had gone off and only secured a few breast-feathers. Simeon set off on a second expedition. The first time the nest had been discovered the eggs were exposed to view, this time they were carefully covered with down. Simeon now reset the trap, this time laying it over the eggs, and carefully concealing it with the down. His hope was that the bird would remove the down with her beak and be snared by the neck. On the morrow he came back to us, however, with the four eggs and no swan ; she had never returned, having apparently forsaken her nest, as we had feared she would. Simeon brought with him four ducks' nests, but the down was all mixed and the find was therefore valueless. These are some of the disappointments caused by the clumsy mismanagement of untrained men.

A cold east wind that blew all day prevented us doing much ; we went out for an hour only, and shot a few yellow-headed wagtails and a phalarope. We had plenty to interest us, however, in reading the letters and papers that had reached us from England. The steamer had arrived from Ust-Zylma the day before, bringing us tidings of home from April 4th to May 13th, inclusive. The post had reached Ust-Zylma on the 26th ; the last letters had therefore been five weeks *en route*, and so far as we know they had not been delayed in Archangel. From Ust-Zylma to Alexievka they would have taken more than another week to travel had it not been for the steamer. On the 13th of May the Consul at Archangel wrote that the ice on the Dvina was expected to break up in seven days. A letter dated the 26th described the Dvina as quite free from ice for some days past, showing that it and the Petchora broke up within a day or two of each other.

The cold north-east wind that continued blowing kept us near home, but as it also kept the mosquitoes at bay we did not complain very bitterly of it. In the face of the cutting gale we crossed over to the tundra on the following day, in search once more of the grey plovers. On the way we visited an island and took a nest of the ringed plover. Soon after landing at our destination we heard the note of the birds we were in search of, and saw two or three, but could not discover any signs of their having a nest. After our previous experience we decided to vary our tactics. Hitherto we had found the nests by sheer perseverance in searching, and had afterwards watched the female to the nest and shot her. We now decided to watch the female on to the nest in the first instance, and, having by this means found it, to secure the female afterwards as a further and more complete identification of the eggs. It was also perfectly obvious that the extreme care we had taken not to alarm the bird was unnecessary. Our little manœuvre of walking away from the nest in a body, leaving one behind lying flat on the ground to watch, under the impression that the bird could not count beyond three, and would think that we had all gone, was clearly so much artifice wasted. The birds were evidently determined to come back to their nests in spite of our presence; nor was there any cover to hide us if the contrary had been the case. Our care not to handle the eggs until we had secured the bird was also of no use, as we often proved afterwards. On a marshy piece of ground I shot a reeve; and then we struck across a very likely piece of land—little flat pieces of bog with mossy ridges between. Presently Harvie-Brown, who was in front, whistled, and as I was coming up to him I saw a grey plover to my left. He called out to me that he had put up a pair near where he was standing. I soon caught sight of another bird on the ground, lifting its wings as if to attract me from its nest. It then quietly ran off, and I went to the spot, but finding nothing lay down to watch. Harvie-Brown did the same about eighty yards off. It was not long before I caught sight of both birds at some distance. One, which I at once concluded must be the male, remained in one spot, the other was running towards me, stopping on some elevation every few yards to look round. By-and-by it flew between Harvie-Brown and me, and alighted on the other side of me. The other bird soon followed, and remained as before, apparently watching the movements of the restless bird, which I now felt sure must be the female. To this latter bird I now confined my attention, and kept it within the field of my telescope for more than half an hour. It was never still for more than a minute together; it kept running along the ground for a few yards, ascending the ridges, looking round, and uttering its somewhat melancholy cry. It crossed and recrossed the same ridges over and over again, and finally disappeared behind a knoll about forty yards ahead of me, and was silent. I now adjusted my telescope on a tussock to bear upon the place in case I lost its position, and was just making up my mind to walk to the spot when I again heard its cry, and saw it running as before. The male was still stationary. The crossing and recrossing the ridge upon which my telescope was pointed then continued for another quarter of an hour, and at last the bird disappeared behind the same ridge as before. I gave her a quarter of an hour's grace, during which she was perfectly silent, and then sat up to see if Harvie-Brown was satisfied that she was on the nest. His point of sight was not so favourable as mine; and, thinking I had given up the watch as hopeless, he fired off his gun as a last resource, and came up to me. As soon as he fired both birds rose almost exactly in front of the knoll upon which my telescope pointed. Upon his arrival to learn what I had made out, I told him the nest was forty or fifty yards in front of my telescope. We fixed one of our guns pointing in the same direction, so that we could easily see it. We then skirted the intervening bog, got our exact bearings from the gun, and commenced a search. In less than a minute we found the nest with four eggs. As before, it was in a depression on a ridge between two little lakes of black bog. The eggs in this, our fifth nest, were considerably incubated, which was probably the reason why the birds showed more anxiety to lure us away.

On our way back towards the river we crossed a marsh where we saw some dunlins, and secured one young one in down. On the higher part of the tundra, nearer the water's edge, were several golden plovers : we shot one, and noticed a pair of grey plovers amongst them. The two species were quite easy to distinguish even at some distance without the help of a glass. On a piece of low tundra near the Petchora we came upon a large flock of Buffon's skuas. My companion stopped to watch the grey plovers, and I marched after the skuas. We had usually seen these birds hawking like terns over the tundra, in parties of seven or eight, and now and then we had met a pair alone on the ground. They were always wild and difficult to approach, and hitherto we had succeeded in shooting a few only. As I neared the spot where the large flock was assembled I watched them alighting on the banks near the great river. I walked towards them, and soon caught sight of a score of herring-gulls on the shore to the right. Before I had got within a hundred yards of the latter they all rose and flew towards me, the skuas also rose and followed them. I let the gulls go by and aimed at the nearest skua as soon as it came within range. Fortunately I brought it down, for in a moment I was surrounded by about 100 or 150 skuas, flying about in all directions, generally about ten of them within shot. They were very noisy, uttering a cry like "hack, hack" as they darted towards me, or screaming wildly as they flew about. This lasted about twenty minutes, during which I finished what remaining cartridges I had, some of which were dust. I missed several birds, but left seven killed and wounded on the field. My companion now joined me ; he brought down four more and a Richardson's skua ; the birds then all retired except one that kept flying from one to the other of us, every now and then making a downward swoop, like a tern, over our heads. We soon discovered the cause of its anxiety ; a young skua in down, a day or two

old, lay on the ground at our feet. Our search for nest
or eggs was vain. As it was getting late, after shooting
a pair of dunlins on a space of marshy ground, and a
willow-grouse among some dwarf willows, we returned
to our boat, resolving to renew our search for eggs of
Buffon's skua and grey plover on the morrow. We
turned to look towards the place of our encounter with
the former : the whole flock had returned to it ; they
looked like great black terns on the wing as they hovered
over it with their peculiar kestrel- or tern-like flight. On
several occasions afterwards we observed that the skuas
have many habits in common with the terns.

The north-east wind continued to blow the next day,
but the sunshine was bright and warm. When evening
came and the sun got low down in the horizon—for of
course it never set—the wind increased and we felt it
very cold. We spent our morning blowing eggs. In the
afternoon we sent Cocksure on another expedition after a
swan, whose nest with four eggs had been found and
brought to us by one of our men. Towards four we
crossed the river to the tundra. Our crazy old flat-
bottomed boat could only sail with the wind dead on her
stern, so we had to row with the stream for about a mile
down the river, and then sail up again with the wind.
By the appearance of the surrounding landscape we
calculated that since we had last been on that part of the
Petchora, the water must have fallen four feet at least.
Some of the islands had doubled in size, and new sandbanks lay bare. We landed near a deserted house called
Bugree, and soon afterwards shot a black scoter off her
nest. It contained six eggs and an abundance of down
and lay in a little hollow sloping towards the river,
entirely concealed amongst dwarf birch. The scoter
apparently does not breed on the islands, but prefers a

drier situation on the tundra, upon some sloping bank overlooking a river or a lake, and sheltered by dwarf birch or willows.

We first paid a visit to the marshy ground and saw many dunlins, Lapland buntings, and red-throated pipits; one of the latter was carrying in its bill a caterpillar at least an inch long. Our next resort was to the sandy banks, where we found a ring dotterel's nest. We then visited the Buffon's skua ground. The large flock had left, but about a dozen remained behind. We watched them for an hour, and shot one. They were mostly hawking up and down the moor, occasionally resting on the ground. Suddenly, a skua uttered its alarm note; it sounded as if we had approached too near its nest. I whistled for my companion to come, and we lay down, about 120 yards apart, for an hour. The skua did not run about on the ground, but kept uneasily flying from one spot to the other, seldom remaining long in one place. One spot, however, it visited four times, and rested longer on it than on the others. The third time it visited it I made up my mind the nest was there, and carefully adjusted my gun on a hillock to cover the spot in case I lost it. The fourth time the bird visited it, Harvie-Brown and I got up together, each followed our bearings, and in about a minute we crossed each other at the nest, in which were two eggs. The bird was near at hand, shamming lameness to attract our attention. My companion walked up to it and shot—to our disappointment and disgust, not a Buffon's, but a Richardson's skua.

After this we turned our attention to the grey plover ground. We found one of our men trying to watch one of these birds to the nest. We lay down, one fifty yards to his right, and the other as much to his left. The birds

behaved exactly as those we watched the day before.
After the female had crossed and recrossed one hillock
many times, and finally disappeared behind it, I made up
my mind that the nest was there, and rose. My sudden
appearance alarmed the male, who flew up, showing his
black axillaries very distinctly in the evening sunshine as
he skimmed over my head. We then all three rose, and
in less than a minute met at the nest, which contained
three eggs. I sat down to pack the eggs; and Harvie-
Brown followed the male, who came up as we found the
nest. Whilst I was packing the eggs and warming my
hands, and talking "pigeon-Russ" with the man, the
female came within range, and I took up my gun and
shot her, thereby completing the identification of the
eggs. On our return home we found that Cocksure had
sent word that the swan had not revisited her nest as yet,
and begged one of us to go to relieve guard. My
companion accordingly, after a substantial meal, set off
at midnight; meanwhile the men we employed to help us
brought in the results of their day's work: a red-throated
diver, trapped on the nest, with two eggs; half a dozen
phalaropes' eggs, a duck's nest, containing seven large
olive-grey eggs, with down which was almost black.
These, they assured us, were the eggs of the *bolshaya
tchornaya ootka* (the great black duck). We recognised
them, however, to be the same as those our Samoyede
had brought home on the 2nd, and on which he had shot
a female scaup. The next take was a long-tailed duck's
nest, with five eggs. Then a man came in bringing us
four small nests of *malenkya petēētza* (small birds), a
sedge-warbler's, a red-throated pipit's and two willow-
warblers'.

The men who had collected these spoils were in
the employment of the Company, to whom belong the

steamers, the yacht or cutter, everything upon the island of Alexievka, and even the island itself. The Company has a large and profitable trade in timber, which is shipped principally to Cronstadt for the Russian Government. Whether the company be Mr. Sideroff or Mr. Iconikoff, or both, or neither, remains one of those commercial secrets so common in Russia, which nobody can ever get to the bottom of. These *employés* in Alexievka were all Zyriani from Ishma, a race of people said to be of Finnish origin. Some were reported to be very rich, the proprietors of large herds of reindeer. Like the people of Ust-Zylma, they are peasants, but were described to us as being more luxurious in their living and in the furniture of their houses. They were also said not to get drunk so often as the Ust-Zylma folk, but when inebriated, not to be good-natured and obtrusively affectionate as these are prone to be, but quarrelsome and given to fighting. They have the reputation of being better workmen, and certainly beat the Ust-Zylmians hollow at birds'-nesting. In feature or size the two do not differ much; perhaps the eyes of the Zyriani are more sunken and their cheek-bones a little more prominent; and there may be a greater number of red- and yellow-haired men among them. There were several fishing encampments of these peasants in different places down the river, and we found that it was customary in the wealthier families for one son to go in summer on the tundra, with the reindeer and the Samoyede servants. The language of the Zyriani is totally different from Russian, and belongs to the agglutinative family of languages. The tribe belongs to the Orthodox Greek Church, and not to that of the Old Believers.

KUYA

CHAPTER XVIII.

STANAVIALACHTA REVISITED.

Second Visit to Stanavialachta—Peregrine Falcons—Plague of Mosquitoes
—Midnight on the Tundra—Nest of the Velvet Scoter—Little Feodor
sent in Quest of the Swan's Skin—A Russian Bath—Feodor's Return—
Identification of Eggs of Bewick's Swan—Mosquito Veils—Our Eighth
Nest of Grey Plovers—Our Servants—Our Ninth Nest of Grey Plovers
—The Tenth and Eleventh Nests.

ON the following morning, when my companion returned
from his watch at the swan's nest, which had turned out
a complete failure, we consulted with Piottuch as to what
was to be done. The swan had evidently forsaken her
nest. Time was rapidly flying, and we feared the
breeding season would be over before we had obtained
identified eggs of the smaller species. It did not appear
as if we could do anything at Alexievka; we had evidently yet to learn how swans could be trapped at their
nests on the Petchora; and we came to the conclusion

that our wisest course was to go in search of the peasant who owned the skin of the swan belonging to the two small eggs we had bought some days ago. When we last heard of him he was fishing at one of the islands in the delta which we had visited, not far from Stanavialachta, and we determined to make a second expedition to this locality. Fortunately for us, an opportunity occurred on the following day to run over to this place in the steamer belonging to the company. Outside the bar in the lagoon the cutter was cruising about with pilots to bring any ship which arrived up the river to Alexievka. The steamer had to visit this cutter to take the men a fresh stock of provisions, and we were delighted to make arrangements with Captain Engel to take us with him, to drop us at Stanavialachta, and pick us up on his return.

We left Alexievka on the 6th of July and landed at our old quarters, but learnt to our disappointment that the peasant we were in quest of had found the fishing so bad that he had given it up in disgust and returned to his native village of Mekitza, some miles north of Alexievka. We were determined to settle the question if possible ; we ascertained that he had not sold the swan's skin, but had taken it with him, so we decided to send one of our men to Mekitza as soon as we returned to Alexievka. In the meantime we started for the tundra to revisit our previous shooting-grounds. We stopped a few minutes on the shore to watch a family of Samoyedes fishing with a seine-net. They seemed to be catching nothing but a small fish resembling a herring, and even these did not appear to be at all plentiful. Leaving the shore, our curiosity led us first to visit the eyries of the two pairs of peregrine falcons, at each of which we had shot one of the birds. We found that the male of the first had paired with the female of the second ; a fresh lining of feathers had been put into the latter's nest, and doubtless there would soon be eggs. The dotterels still haunted the hillsides. We shot some near each of the deserted houses—two by one, three by the other. Doubtless the right thing to have done would have been to lie down and watch the birds to their nests and to have taken the eggs. But in the first place a dotterel is very difficult to see through a mosquito-veil, and in the next to lie down and become the nucleus of a vast nebula of mosquitoes is so tormenting to the nerves that we soon chose to adopt the consolatory conclusion that the grapes were sour and not worth the trouble of reaching after ; or, in plain words, that the birds had not begun to breed, and it was no use martyrising ourselves to find their eggs. The mosquitoes were simply a plague. Our hats were covered with them ; they swarmed upon our veils ; they lined with a fringe the branches of the dwarf birches and willows ; they covered the tundra with a mist. I was fortunate in the arrangement of my veil, and by dint of indiarubber boots and cavalry gauntlets I escaped many wounds ; but my companion was not so lucky. His net was perpetually transformed into a little mosquito-cage ; his leggings and knickerbockers were by no means mosquito-proof ; he had twisted a handkerchief round each hand, but this proved utterly insufficient ; had it not grown cooler on the hills, as the sun got low, he would certainly have fallen into a regular mosquito fever. We were told that this pest of mosquitoes was nothing as yet to what it would become later. "Wait a while," said our Job's comforter, "and you will not be able to see each other at twenty paces distance ; you will not be able to aim with your gun, for the moment you raise your barrel half a dozen regiments of mosquitoes will rise between you and the sight." When the coolness of evening set in we had pretty good shooting for an hour or two ; but after nine or ten o'clock we found nothing. There is very little to be met on the tundra or anywhere else at midnight, for in spite of brilliant sunshine, the birds retire to roost at the proper time and all is hushed. Our best find was the nest of a velvet scoter. We shot the female as she rose from it ; there were eight eggs in it and a good supply of down. It was placed under a dwarf birch, far from any lake or water. We shot three willow-grouse

WATCHING GREY PLOVERS THROUGH A CLOUD OF MOSQUITOES

and caught three young birds in down. While we were seeking for them the male frequently flew past within easy shot, and the female ran about with head depressed and wings drooping, coming sometimes within two or three yards of us. We saw two pairs of wood sandpipers who had established themselves in a small space of marshy ground. They evidently had young, for they were continually flying round and alighting upon the willows. To search for young in down, through long grass, wearing mosquito-veils must prove a vain quest and we did not long pursue it. We caught the young of the Lapland bunting, and shot one of this year's shore-

larks, a very pretty bird. We saw a few divers, a large
harrier or eagle, and on the shore of the Petchora we
watched a flock of Siberian herring-gulls stealing fish
from the nets of the Samoyedes, and as we went down
river we came on another flock similarly employed. We
saw no swans on the tundra, but they were common on
the islands in the river ; one or two pairs were frequently
in sight, and still there continued to fly overhead flocks
of migratory ducks, always going north. All the day it
had been a dead calm, but for the slight southerly breeze
that had risen towards evening. The next morning a
long-unfelt pleasant breath of wind was blowing down
the river ; it was not enough, however, to drive back the
visitation of mosquitoes that was almost making us wish
for the blustering north gale back again.

Despatching little Feodor, our most intelligent man,
by the steamer to Kuya, we bade him walk over to
Mekitza, then ferret out the peasant and the swan's skin,
and bring us home the latter. Meanwhile we spent the
day blowing eggs. In the evening we took a Russian
bath—an experience worth describing. We lay down
upon a platform in a wooden house ; a primitive stove
was in it, built of stones loosely piled one upon the other ;
a hole in the side of the house with a sliding door let out
the smoke. A wood-fire was kindled in the stove ; it
was allowed to go out when the stones were thoroughly
heated ; the steam resulting from the pouring of a glass
of cold water upon them soon cleared the room of all foul
air and smoke. As we lay stretched on the platform we
occasionally threw water upon the hot stones, and flogged
ourselves with a small broom composed of birch-twigs,
still clothed with leaves ; after which we rubbed ourselves
down with matting, sponged all over with cold water,
and then went into another apartment to cool ourselves,

smoke a few *papyros*, and dress.   The peasants frequent these bath-houses, and often walk out of the hot steam naked, the colour of boiled lobsters, to plunge into the Petchora.

The next day was one of our red-letter days.   Little Feodor, our boatman, returned, bearing with him the longed-for trophy—the swan's skin.   He told us he had gone to Mekitza, only to learn there that the peasant whom he sought had departed to another island to fish. Going to his house he found, however, that the man had left the skin with his wife, and she, good soul, had cut off the beak and given it to her children for a plaything. Feodor paid her a rouble for the skin, with the feet still attached to it, and got the beak into the bargain.   There was no other swan's skin in the house, nor, as far as we could ascertain, was there another in the village ; this one was still soft and greasy, showing the bird had been but recently killed.   This, undoubtedly, was the skin of a Bewick's swan ; the beak also was equally indisputable. The eggs in our possession were exactly the size one would expect a swan so much smaller than the wild swan would lay.   We had every reason to believe and none to doubt that this was, indeed, the skin of the bird caught upon the nest containing the two eggs we had purchased. The chain of evidence connecting them was complete, and the identification of the eggs satisfactory.   Let us recapitulate and go over the links of the narrative, the more fully to establish the conclusion we had arrived at. Two peasants are fishing together at Pyonni, an island near the mouth of the delta of the great river, twelve versts north of Stanavialachta.   They find there a swan's nest, containing two eggs, and they set a trap for the bird, which they succeed in catching.   In the division of spoil, one takes the eggs, the other the swan.   One peasant, wearied out by the pertinacity of the cold north-east wind, goes up stream to fish in smoother waters. On his way he stops at Alexievka, where we are, and we buy from him a number of ducks' and gulls' eggs, also two swans' eggs unusually small. As we purchase these we tell him that we shall be glad to pay the price of any swan's skin he can get us. He replies that the skin of the swan whose eggs he has just sold to us is in the possession of his partner, that the bird was trapped at the nest before they were taken out of it, adding that he has left his mate fishing on an island opposite Stanavialachta. On inquiry we find that two of our boatmen know this man, that we have seen him ourselves on the island where we found the two shoveller's eggs; we remember that he made a haul with a seine net of a small basketful of fish resembling herrings, which he presented to one of our men. We now take the first opportunity to go down to Stanavialachta and learn there that this peasant, disgusted as his comrade was by the prevalence of the cold north-east wind, has returned home to Mekitza. We send our most intelligent man to his house and get the skin.

The relative size of the two birds is very different, as may be appreciated at a glance, without the help of measurements. The bill of Bewick's swan is more than half an inch shorter than that of the larger species; the lengths of the wing, measuring from the carpal joint, are respectively $20\frac{1}{4}$ inches and $23\frac{1}{2}$; the lengths of the middle toes $5 \cdot 15$ and $6 \cdot 1$. Our eggs of Bewick's swan were about $3\frac{9}{10}$ inches long. We have eggs of other swans, doubtless of the large species, which measure $4\frac{1}{10}$, $4\frac{3}{10}$, $4\frac{4}{10}$, and $4\frac{5}{10}$ inches; these measurements make it seem probable that exceptionally large eggs of Bewick's swan might be of the same size as exceptionally small eggs of the common wild swan. The eggs appear to vary very little in shape.

That afternoon I took a walk on the island, armed with my walking-stick gun. Birds were extremely tame. The yellow-headed wagtail seemed more abundant than ever. Reed buntings also were common. I got a shot at a swan, but the distance was a trifle too great. The weather was very hot, and the mosquitoes were swarming. Our home-made mosquito veils proved a great success ; they and our cavalry gauntlets just made life bearable in these Arctic regions ; still we longed for the cold winds back again to expel the plague of blood-sucking insects. Veils are necessary evils, but they interfere sadly with work, and much increase the difficulty of finding the shot birds among the long grass.

The next morning a swan's egg made us an excellent omelette for breakfast, after which I turned out for half an hour amongst the willows to shoot a few yellow-headed wagtails. They abounded on the marshy ground. I also secured two or three redpolls, some reed buntings, and a phalarope.

We set sail at noon, with a north-east wind, to visit the tundra eight or ten versts higher up the great river. For some distance before we landed the coast was very flat, with willows down to the water's edge. Amongst these dwarf trees we repeatedly heard our two especial favourites, the Petchora pipit and the Siberian chiffchaff. As soon as we got beyond the willows we landed on the tundra, and started in pursuit of a large flock of Buffon's skuas, but were soon stopped by a pair of grey plovers, which showed by their actions that we were near their nest. We lay down as before, forty or fifty yards apart, and watched the birds. They ran about, up and down, and all around us ; and at the end of half an hour we were no wiser than at first. There was evidently something wrong. Harvie-Brown then shouted to me, " Have you marked the nest ? " I replied by walking up to him and comparing notes. We then watched together for another half-hour with exactly the same result. I suggested that we must be so near the nest that the bird dare not come on, and advised that we should retreat to the next ridge, which we accordingly did. We had not done so many minutes before the female made her way on to the ridge where we had been lying. She then ran along the top of the ridge, passed the place where we had been stationed, and came down the ridge on to the flat bog towards where we then were. I whispered, " She is actually crossing over to us." Suddenly she stopped, lifted her wings and settled down on the ground. We both whispered, almost in the same breath, " She is on the nest." I added, " I saw her lift her wings as she settled on to the eggs." Harvie-Brown replied, " So did I," and added, " I can't hold out any longer against the mosquitoes." I replied, " I am perfectly satisfied ; she is within range, take her." He lifted his gun to his shoulder. She ran off the nest to the top of the ridge and stood there until my companion shot her. We then walked up to the nest, the first we had seen on the flat. The eggs were quite fresh, or nearly so ; and the nest must have been made nearly a fortnight later than those we had previously taken. During that time the bogs had become much drier, so that we could cross them without much difficulty ; and this was probably the reason why this nest was placed lower down. The eggs had all the appearance of a second laying, being less blotched than usual, one of them remarkably so. It is worth noticing that whilst we were watching in our first position, very near the nest, the birds were almost quite silent, and did not call to each other as they usually do.

After carefully packing the eggs, we walked on, and speedily started another pair. This time we lay down together, as nearly as we could tell, on the spot from which the birds rose, which seems to be generally from forty to fifty yards from the nest. The clouds of mosquitoes formed such a mist on the tundra that we had some difficulty in marking our birds ; but by raking the horizon with our binoculars and getting well bitten through our veils in the process, we soon found the female, and watched her to a ridge just opposite to us. She soon settled down ; and within a quarter of an hour after we had lain down we were both perfectly satisfied that she was on the nest. We gave her a few minutes grace, and then walked up to the nest, without making any effort to shoot the bird, having perfectly identified her, and being almost tired out by the mosquitoes. The eggs in this nest were considerably incubated. The nest was placed, as before, in a hollow on a ridge. The ground on this ridge was not so mossy as usual, and there was much bare brown turf to be seen. Whether this had anything to do with the colour of the eggs it is difficult to say ; but the fact is that these eggs are quite brown in ground-colour.

It was very late, or rather very early morning when we returned to our quarters, and we had to spend an hour slaughtering mosquitoes before we could make the room habitable ; then we had our dinners to cook and our pipes to smoke before we could retire to rest. At noon I turned out of my hammock and spent the day indoors. The wind was north-west, and there were continual hints of rain. Our men were tired after the long row the day before. They were not in good condition, nor could it

be expected they should be. They had now reached the
last day of a four weeks' fast, during which they were
supposed to eat nothing but bread and water, with fish if
they could get it. During the period of probation it was
intensely ludicrous to watch the expression on our steers-
man's face when he held up as many fingers as there still
remained days of fasting to be gone through, opening his
mouth wide the while, then grinning all over as he said,
" Moi skaffum." " Skaffum " is pigeon-English for " eat,"
derived, we were told, from the Swedish (*skaffa*, to
provide).* This fellow's name was Feodor; he was a
good-natured simpleton, indescribably lazy and always
thinking of his stomach—we had nicknamed him " Moi
skaffum." Gavriel, our other Russian, was not very
much sharper, but was by no means lazy when directed
in his work, though he had not the sense to discover for
himself what wanted doing. Our half-bred Samoyede,
also called Feodor,—Malenki Feodor we dubbed him—
was a sharp, active lad, always finding out something to
do ; with a little training, indeed, he would have made an
excellent servant. He learnt while with us to skin birds
well, and was by this time a fair nester. Simeon, our
thorough-bred Samoyede, was a philosopher—stolid,
phlegmatic, and a good worker. He was our birds'-nester
par excellence. He knew the tundra well and the birds
upon it ; for three years he had lived in Varandai, and in
his palmier days had reindeer of his own. Nothing
moved Simeon ; success did not elate him, nor failure
depress him. He would take the extra rouble we always
gave him when he brought us a rare bird's nest as a
matter of course, without a " thank you." And when, as
we witnessed once, he steadied the boat for a drunken

* The universal *skoff* (= " food " and " to eat ") of the British sailor seems a
more probable derivation.—ED.

German captain, who brutally trod upon his hand, evidently thinking it a fine thing to show his contempt for the poor Samoyede, Simeon equally took the insult as a matter of course, did not offer to withdraw his hand nor move a muscle of his face. If Simeon had any hot blood in him, the veins of it must have run very deep under his sallow skin.

The next day I did not do much either, but Cocksure being out of birds, I turned out amongst the mosquitoes and got him a few. I shot several yellow-headed wagtails, which were as abundant as ever, and also three Terek sandpipers, the first we had secured, although we had occasionally heard their notes on the island. A nest of shoveller's eggs, quite fresh, was brought to us during the day.

Our ninth nest of the grey plover we took on the 12th of July. A stiff warm gale from the east, with occasionally a smart shower of rain, kept the air clear of mosquitoes in the morning. In the afternoon the wind fell, and the mosquitoes were as bad as ever; but we were too busy to heed them much. At eleven we crossed to the tundra. We soon came upon a pair of grey plovers, which rose a couple of hundred yards ahead of us, their wings glittering in a gleam of sunshine after a smart shower. These birds have frequently a very curious flight as they rise from the nest, tossing their wings up in the air, reminding one somewhat of the actions of a tumbler pigeon. We lay down as near as we could to the spot from which they rose, and were somewhat puzzled at their behaviour. The male seemed equally, if not more anxious than the female, running about as much as she did, continually crying, and often coming very near us, and trying to attract our attention by pretending to be lame. The female rarely uttered a note.

We suppose this must have been because one of us was too near the nest. Harvie-Brown moved his post of observation after we had spent some time without being able to discover anything; and then the female behaved as usual, and I soon marked the position of the nest. We walked straight up to it, and found the four eggs chipped ready for hatching. We had no difficulty in shooting both birds, and afterwards hatched out two of the eggs, obtaining a couple of good specimens of young in down. With a little practice this mode of finding birds' nests becomes almost a certainty. One has first to be quite sure which is the male and which is the female. When the birds are near enough, and one can compare them together, the greater blackness of the breast of the male is sufficient to distinguish him; but we found that the females varied considerably in this respect, and that it was better to notice the habits of the birds. The female generally comes first to the nest, but she comes less conspicuously. She generally makes her appearance at a considerable distance, on some ridge of mossy land. When she has looked round, she runs quickly to the next ridge, and looks round again, generally calling to the male with a single note. The male seldom replies; but when he does so it is generally with a double note. When the female has stopped and looked round many times, then the male thinks it worth while to move; but more often than not he joins the female by flying up to her. The female very seldom takes wing. She is very cautious, and, if she is not satisfied that all is safe, will pass and repass the nest several times before she finally settles upon it. The female rarely remains at one post of observation long; but the male often remains for ten minutes or more upon one tussock of a ridge, watching the movements of the female.

We walked some distance before we came upon a second pair; but at length we heard the well-known cry, and got into position. We spent nearly two hours over this nest, and were quite at sea at the end of the time. We changed our position several times, but to no purpose. The female went here and there and everywhere, as much as to say, " I'm not going on to the nest as long as you are so near." By-and-by the mosquitoes fairly tired us out, and we gave up the watching game and commenced a search. At last we found out the secret of the bird's behaviour. We picked up some broken egg-shells, and concluded at once that the bird had young. We tried to find them, but in vain. These two hours, however, were not wasted. The birds came nearer to me than they had ever done before. I often watched them at a distance of not more than ten yards, and was able to hear their notes more distinctly. The note most frequently used is a single plaintive whistle, *köp*, long drawn out, the *ö* pronounced as in German, and the consonants scarcely sounded. This I am almost sure is the alarm-note. It is principally uttered by the female when she stops and looks round and sees something of which she disapproves. If the male shows any anxiety about the nest, which he seems to do more and more as incubation progresses, he also utters the same note. The double note, *kl-ee* or *kleep*—the *kl* dwelt upon so as to give it the value of a separate syllable—is also uttered by both birds. It is evidently their call-note. I have seen the female, when she has been running away from the male, turn sharp round and look towards him when he has uttered this note, exactly as any one might do who heard his name called. Whilst we were watching this pair of birds a couple of other grey plovers came up, and called as they flew past. The male answered the call and flew towards them. On the wing this whistle is lengthened out to three notes. I had some difficulty in catching this note exactly. It is not so often uttered as the two others I have mentioned, and is generally heard when you least expect it; but I am almost sure it is a combination of the alarm-note with the call-note—*kl-ee-köp*. If I wanted to make a free translation from Ploverski into English I should say that *kl-ee* means " Hallo! old fellow," and *köp* means " Mind what you are about!"

We procured our tenth nest of the grey plover the same afternoon. It was found by our Samoyede, who brought us three eggs and the male and female shot at the nest. He accidentally broke the fourth egg. As it contained a live young bird, we placed these three eggs in our hatching basket, where we had made a snug nest of bean-goose-down.

By this time we were pretty well tired with tramping the tundra. The ceaseless persecution of the mosquitoes, and the stifling feeling caused by having to wear a veil with the thermometer above summer heat, had taxed our powers of endurance almost to the utmost; and we turned our faces resolutely towards our boat; but a most anxious pair of grey plovers were too great an attraction to us to be resisted. We watched them for some time, during which a pair of ringed plovers persisted in obtruding themselves impertinently between us and the objects of our attention. This pair of grey plovers also puzzled us, and we concluded that they possibly had young, and consequently we gave up the search. We had each marked a place where we thought a nest might be; and we each of us went to satisfy ourselves that it was not there. The two places were about fifty yards apart. The birds first went up to Harvie-Brown and tried to draw him away by flying about and feigning lameness.

Then they came to me and did the same.   They were so
demonstrative that I felt perfectly certain of finding the
nest, and shot at the female.   She dropped in the middle
of a wet bog.   I then shot the male, walked up to him,
and left him with my basket and gun to struggle through
the bog to pick up the female.   Before I got up to her, I
saw her lying on the turf on her breast with her wings
slightly expanded.   I was just preparing to stoop to pick

MOSQUITO VEIL

her up, when she rose and flew away, apparently unhurt.
I must have missed her altogether, as she was evidently
only shamming to draw me away.   I returned to search
for the nest, and was unable to find it.   Whilst I was
looking for it Harvie-Brown came up; so I gave up the
search, and we again turned towards the boat.   When
we had got about halfway towards the spot where Harvie-
Brown had been looking, I caught sight of a young grey
plover in down, almost at my feet.   Stooping to pick it
up, I saw the nest with three eggs not a yard from me.

This was the last and eleventh nest of these rare birds which we found. The young in down are very yellow, speckled with black, and are admirably adapted for concealment upon the yellow-green moss on the edges of the little bogs, close to which the grey plover seems always to choose a place for its nest.

Our attempt to hatch the highly incubated eggs, and thus obtain specimens of young in down, was successful. We soon had five young grey plovers well and hearty, and secured three or four more afterwards.

OLD RUSSIAN SILVER CROSS

LITTLE STINT'S NEST, EGGS AND YOUNG

CHAPTER XIX.

THE GOLIEVSKI ISLANDS.

Trip to the Golievski Islands—Shoal of White Whales—Glaucous Gull—
Dunlins and Sanderlings—Black Scoter—Dvoinik—Little Stint—Curlew
Sandpiper—Snow Bunting—Overhauling our Plunder—The Company's
Manager—Discussions concerning the Stints—Probable Lines of Migra-
tion followed by Birds.

ON the 13th of July an opportunity presented itself of
visiting the Golievski Islands at the entrance of the

lagoon.   These islands are little more than sandbanks, and the beacons erected upon them for the guidance of vessels entering the river are washed away every spring by the ice.   To re-erect these beacons and to inspect others on various promontories on the shores of the lagoon, the steamer makes a trip every July.   Captain Engel asked us to accompany him, and we gladly accepted the invitation.

Passing Stanavialachta and Cape Bolvanski, we sailed almost due north to the bar, where the lead announced scarcely thirteen feet of water.   We then steered nearly east to within three miles of the shore, whence we afterwards kept in a north-easterly direction.   A few miles after passing Cape Constantinovka we altered our course to north, and made Island No. 4 about midnight.   Off Cape Constantinovka we came upon a shoal of white whales or beluga, which played like porpoises round the steamer.

We stayed a couple of hours on Island No. 4, erecting the beacon upon it.   The night was foggy at intervals, but the midnight sun shone bright.   The island is a flat desert of sand, unrelieved by a blade of grass.   It may be a couple of square miles in extent in the summer time, and is not much affected by the tide, which rises only four or six inches.   We found a large flock of glaucous gulls upon it, but we could only discover two nests.   They were heaps of sand, hollowed slightly at the apex and lined with some irregularly disposed tufts of seaweed. The young in down were running about on the flat sandbank.   We secured half a dozen and shot four old birds. The young were less spotted than those of most gulls ; the old birds were pure white, with delicate, dove-coloured mantles, paler than those of our herring-gull. The legs and feet were pale flesh-tinted pink ; the beak and the line round the eye were straw-yellow.   The

point of the beak was horn-colour, with the usual dark
vermilion spot on the angle of the lower mandible.   The
pupils of the eye were blue-black, and the irides very pale
straw-yellow.   The interior of the mouth was of the same
colour as the legs and feet.   The birds to whom the two
nests belonged were easily shot ; they made repeated
downward darts upon us like terns.   The rest of the flock
kept well out of range, soon settling down at a point on
the extreme end of the island, and, on being fired at there,
flew right away.   Among these glaucous gulls were two
immature birds and, one or two Siberian herring-gulls.
After the dispersion of the flock that had engaged all our
attention, we began to notice the presence of small parties
of sandpipers feeding about the island.   They were very
wild, running about on the low, wet sandbanks which
rose hardly a couple of feet above high-tide level, and
about the margins of the little pools in the lower parts
of the island.   Among them were some dunlins ; we
succeeded in shooting a couple of these, and one or two
sanderlings.   These birds were peculiarly interesting to
us.   We had scarcely hoped to come across them.   We
saw no evidence, however, of their breeding upon the
island ; they seem to have settled upon it merely to feed.
The only nests we found were those of the glaucous gull.
The shores of the island were devoid of all material for
nest-building, except sand and a very slight quantity of
seaweed.   A few whelks, some broken mussels, and
other bivalves lay sparingly scattered about ; with here
and there a few pieces of driftwood, and near the south
shore the decaying body of a seal, probably the harp seal.

At two o'clock we returned on board, and after a
couple of hours' sleep, we woke to find ourselves lying at
anchor in a thick fog that completely hid Island No. 3
from us.   The sun, however, was shining brilliantly over-

head. After an early breakfast we watched the fog lifting, and gradually we caught sight of the island, over which a flock of thousands of black ducks was whirling and circling. This island we computed to be some eight or ten miles in length. It appeared to be exactly the same sandy desert as Island No. 4, but we were told that some persons who have visited it declare that grass grows upon it. Unluckily for us its beacon had not been carried off, only laid upon its side by the ice, so that in an hour's time it was repaired and set up on its legs again and all hands ordered back on board. Near it lay another dead seal, apparently the common one, in a condition described by Cocksure as having "beaucoup d'aroma." A few herring and glaucous gulls were upon the island, and we found two empty nests; but what interested us most was the presence of large parties of dunlins and small flocks of sanderlings. Numbers of black ducks continually passed like clouds overhead. The large flocks did not come near enough for identification, but we made out among smaller ones the long-tailed duck and the black scoter, and were inclined to think that the large flocks were composed of the latter species.

At eight o'clock we had a more substantial breakfast than that partaken of in the earlier hours, and then went to lie down on sofas in the cabin. All day we drifted down a sea almost as smooth as a mirror; not a breath of wind stirred during the night or day. We had also left the mosquitoes behind, and only saw one or two after leaving the delta of the Petchora. The steamer returned to No. 4 Island as we slept to get into the right course and deposit a "carabas" on the William Bank, and a long pole (with a besom on the top and a stone at the foot) upon the Alexander Bank.

We commenced our next day at 4 P.M. It was a very

short one, but it proved very eventful. After a refreshing wash and a promenade on deck for half an hour, we dined and smoked a pipe. By that time the boats were ready, and we went on shore a couple of versts south of the river Dvoinik, there to erect another beacon, which we were afterwards told the Samoyedes had pulled down.

Harvie-Brown and I struck off at once for the tundra in the direction of the Pytkoff Mts. (580 feet high), about fifteen miles distant. The tundra was very flat, and we soon came upon ground exactly similar in character to that tenanted by the grey plovers near Alexievka. We had not walked far when we heard the well-known cry, and there rose four grey plovers. My companion soon after met with another pair and lay down to watch them. We parted company here, and I heard later that, feeling ill—the effect probably of irregular meals and sleep—he soon after returned to the ship, having met with nothing of interest, except the grey plovers and a few Buffon's and Richardson's skuas, and also picking up the feathers of a snowy owl.

After leaving him I went on for about a quarter of an hour, then finding the tundra "flat, stale, and unprofitable," I turned sharp to the north, towards what I took to be a large lake, but which in the maps is set down to be a bay of the sea. *En route* I saw nothing but an occasional Lapland bunting or red-throated pipit. Arrived at the water's edge, however, I spent an interesting hour. A large flock of sandpipers were flying up and down the banks. They looked very small and very red, and in order to watch them I hid amongst some dwarf willows, teeming with mosquitoes. I did not heed their bites, for my hopes and doubts and fears made me for the time mosquito-proof. Presently some birds swirled past, and I gave them a charge of No. 8. Three fell—three Little stints—the real Simon Pure at last. I now waited a few minutes, and soon heard their notes again. This time a small flock passed me over the water, and I dropped a couple into it. I endeavoured to wade in after them, but the mud was too much for me; a smart north wind was blowing also, so I turned back and waited on the shore; there I spent the time examining every dunlin that came within the range of my glass in the hopes of discovering one without a black belly. After a while I walked on, not caring to shoot more, but desirous of finding some evidence of the Little stint's breeding haunts. At a short distance before me rose sandhills sprinkled over with a sort of esparto grass, and towards these I now walked. The intervening ground was covered with thick, short, coarse grass, and was studded with little pools of water. I had not gone far before I came upon some sandpipers feeding on the edge of a small island in the bay. There was no kind of cover near; so approaching as close as I dared, I fired. There must have been six or seven birds; all rose but one, who tried to follow the rest, but was wounded, and he dropped into the water, fluttering feebly on till he reached another island. The mud on the banks was so deep and sticky that it was with difficulty I again got within range, and with a second shot laid him upon his back. When I managed to reach him, my pleasure was great on picking him up to find a curlew sandpiper. This was the single specimen of the species that we obtained on our journey. I now hastened on to the sandhills. The mosquitoes had by this time forced me to wear my veil, but when on reaching the hills I saw a number of small waders running hither and thither, I threw it back; still I could detect nothing but ringed plovers. I shot one to be certain of my identification, and hoping also that the report would rouse rarer game. A shore-lark in first plumage was the only other bird that rose at the sound. I secured it. Wandering on farther I was still disappointed. Beds of wild onion and large patches of purple vetch had replaced the coarse grass. I returned on my footsteps to the edge of the bay, and missed a shot at a swan; a snowy owl also flew past out of range. The curlew sandpipers had disappeared. The flock of Little stints was still there, but I left them to follow a snow-bunting, the first I had seen since leaving Ust-Zylma. I shot it. Then to my consternation I discovered through my glass that the last man had left the beacon, and that I must return. A pair of black-throated divers were sailing about the bay, one or two herring-gulls were flying about, but my time was up. I was a good mile from the ship, so turning by the sandhills I made my way to the beacon, bagging a fine male grey plover as I went. As soon as I got on board we started for Alexievka.

My wonderful success at the last moment determined us by some means or other to return to this land teeming with rare birds. We marked, as we steamed along, that the sandhills continued on the north side of the river Dvoinik as far as Cape Constantinovka. It was probable that the breeding-ground of the Little stints might be found on these coasts or on the mountains. Those I had seen might be last year's birds, not breeding this year, but haunting the neighbourhood of the older ones, as is the case with the flocks of dunlins. It was tantalising to have to hurry away from what seemed the Promised Land, and as we looked at the old washing-tub that usually carried us on our trips to the tundra, and knew that for its life it could not dare cross Bolvanskaya Bay, we felt inclined to parody Richard III.'s cry, and exclaim aloud, " A boat! a boat! my kingdom for a boat!"

Our young grey plovers in down, when we visited them, we found thriving. There were five small birds in excellent condition.

The five sanderlings that we had shot on the islands were three males and two females. The testes of the former were small, the latter had eggs about the size of a pin's head. Both males and females showed signs of moult; they had some bare places almost like sitting-spots, but no recent ones.

The curlew sandpiper turned out to be a female, with very small eggs, and showed no signs of having been breeding this year.

The five Little stints in our possession proved to be all males. Temminck's stints were very common at Alexievka. They were breeding abundantly : sometimes we found them in single pairs, sometimes almost in colonies, but we had never met with flocks of these birds since leaving the neighbourhood of Habariki. Those that we had come upon afterwards had never failed to show us by their ways that we were intruding upon their breeding quarters. When Harvie-Brown visited Arch-angel in 1872 he found Temminck's stints breeding on one of the islands of the delta of the Dvina. This was probably not far from the southern limit of their breeding range. He also continually observed this species in other localities, congregating in small flocks together, and evidently not breeding. These might have been the birds of the preceding year. If, as it is pretty well established, few sandpipers breed until the second year, and the young birds flock, during their first summer, somewhere near the southern limit of the breeding-stations, it might also be augured that the Little stints I had seen were probably breeding at no great distance from the spot I had visited the previous day. The thought of the probable vicinity of the nests, the discovery of which had been one of the strong motives of our journey, excited us so much that we did not go to bed, but spent the night plotting and planning the possibilities of getting to Dvoinik again. There were difficulties in the way. Unluckily for us the company's manager was a very impracticable man. It was his first year in office ; he was young, inexperienced, and comparatively uneducated. For the nonce he was absolute monarch of Alexievka, and the absoluteness of his power was too much for him. A German from Revel, he had yet so much of the Russian in him that, when scratched, the Tartar would out. He was very unpopular, and one glimpse behind the scenes revealed to us rebellion "looming in the distance." There were allowances to be made for the man. No gentleman would come to such a place as Alexievka, or face the existing muddle, for the sake of the miserable pay "la pauvre compagnie," as Cocksure calls it, gives. The Provalychik had a plentiful crop of cares under his crown. So far as we could see he was plotting and being plotted against. He was not backed up by the Bureau at St. Petersburg. His domestic affairs looked ugly, and amongst his subordinates he had scarcely one reliable man he could trust. The whole situation was a specimen of what the Germans call "Russische Wirthschaft." We knew the man could render us an invaluable service without exposing the company to the slightest loss, but as yet we had not been able to make him see with our eyes. We longed for the arrival of Sideroff, fearing, however, he would come too late. Meanwhile we tried to work the oracle, and had not yet given up the task in despair.

Whether the birds that I had seen in flocks on the tundra were those of the year before or not continued a matter of discussion between my companion and myself. He considered that maritime birds that feed principally when the tide falls, have consequently a periodical dining-hour and a special dining-room, and therefore get into the habit of flocking together at dinner-time. I remained still of the opinion that birds of the same species were breeding not far off, probably on the coast between Bolvanskaya Bay and Varandai, or it might be on the Pytkoff mountains. We had also many debates concerning the probable line of migration followed by the grey plover, the Little stint, the curlew sandpiper, and the sanderling; and in this we began to question the usually received theory that these birds migrate up the Baltic and along the coast of Norway to their breeding haunts. My own notion had long been that birds migrate *against* the prevailing winds; that they migrate *to* their breeding-ground in a narrow stream, returning from them in a broad one. If these birds, therefore, winter on the shores of the Mediterranean, they probably leave by way of the Black Sea, cross by the Sea of Azov to the Volga near Sarepta, follow the Volga to Kasan, thence along the Kama to Perm, then over the low hills of the Ural to the Ob, and so on to the Arctic Ocean. Some breed near the mouth of the Ob, others on the eastern or the western coast. The stragglers who wander off as far as Archangel and the North Cape may be barren birds with nothing else to do.

After starting this hypothesis we bethought ourselves that we had with us a list of the birds of Kasan, in a book lent to us by M. Znaminski. These chapters are headed "Materials for making a Biography of the Birds of the Volga," and the work itself is entitled, "Descriptive Catalogues of the High School of the Imperial University at Kasan," edited by MM. Kovalevski, Levakovski,

Golovinski, and Bogdanoff; published at Kasan in 1871. From this book Cocksure drew for us the following information :—

"*Little and Temminck's stints* are seen in flocks during the first fortnight in May on the Volga, from Simbirsk to Kasan, and on the Kama as far as Uffa. They are not seen during the summer, but are found again at Simbirsk in the middle of August.

"*Curlew sandpipers* are seen in Kasan in spring and autumn only, both on the Volga and Kama.

"*Sanderlings* are seen in autumn at Kasan, and have been seen in spring on the Sarpa.

"*Grey plovers* are seen in small flocks in May and September near Kasan, but are not to be met with every year.

"*Yellow-headed wagtails* arrive at Kasan with the common species, viz., middle of April ; a few pairs are seen until the beginning of June."

These extracts prove that part of the migration of these species takes place across country ; but probably the main stream follows the coast, especially in autumn, as I was myself an eye-witness, the year after my return from the Petchora, on the island of Heligoland.

THE LIGHTHOUSE AT
HELIGOLAND ON
A MIGRATION NIGHT

CHAPTER XX.

THE MIGRATION OF BIRDS.

Hybernation of Birds—Migration of Birds—Reed-warblers—Origin of
Migration—Transvaal Warblers—The Mammoth Age—Insect Life—
Lines of Migration—Heligoland and its Ornithologists—Variety of Birds—
Wind and Weather—The Throstle-bushes—Migration by Sight—Order of
Migration—Stray Migrants—The Yellow-browed Warbler—Migration on
Heligoland—Skylarks—Migratory Instincts—Other Facts of Migration.

IT is very difficult to realise the fact that no longer ago
than towards the close of the last century the belief in
the hybernation of swallows was held by many ornithologists. That certain species of mammals spend the winter
in a torpid state is proved beyond all possibility of doubt;
but there is no evidence of the hybernation of any species
of birds. Never was theory founded on more flimsy
substratum of supposed facts, or supported by weaker
logical argument. Swallows made their appearance in

spring, no one knew how or whence. During the summer they were remarkable for being almost constantly on the wing, but late in the autumn a noticeable change took place in their habits. They were observed more and more to congregate in large flocks, and towards evening to perch in numbers on houses, and frequently in trees. Finally they collected in thousands on the reeds and willows on the banks of the Thames, and disappeared during the night. In the morning not a swallow was to be seen, and ornithologists came to the startling conclusion that they had plunged into the dark waters of the river, and buried themselves in the mud at its bottom, to reappear the following spring, refreshed by their winter's sleep. And this theory was gravely accepted as one among many other unfathomable secrets of Nature! After a time it was, however, discovered that the disappearance of many of the summer resident birds from their breeding-grounds in this country was the signal for their appearance in some parts of Southern Europe or Northern Africa, and the theory of migration was accepted as resting upon a basis of indisputable fact when birds were seen in the act of migrating. At certain stations, such as Gibraltar and Malta, and notably on the island of Heligoland (all, curiously enough, under British rule), birds were seen passing over, not in small flocks only, but by thousands and tens of thousands, so that no possible doubt could remain as to the great fact of migration. The periodical disappearance of the swallow remained, however, almost as great a mystery as before. The impulse of migration was called an instinct, but did not the less remain an unfathomable secret of Nature, and the only cause that could be assigned for it was that it must have been originally implanted in certain species at their creation and denied to others.

The discoveries of Darwin and Wallace have placed the facts of migration in an entirely new light, and added a new interest to a subject which has always been one of the most fascinating departments of ornithology. The origin of the habit of migration is still involved in much mystery. It is probably a fact in the history of birds of comparatively modern date. It is not confined to any one geographical region, nor to any one family of birds, nor can we assume that it will be present or absent in every species of the same genus. The birds of the Nearctic region are as migratory as those of the Palæarctic. Many birds visit South America and Australia only during the breeding-season. If we include as birds of the tropical regions those species which visit them after having bred in the cooler regions, they will also contain a considerable proportion of migrants, even though no bird migrates there to breed. We may lay it down as a law, to which there is probably no exception, that every bird breeds in the coldest regions of its migrations. No bird migrates to the tropics to breed because there is no hotter region for it to migrate from. The stories of birds breeding a second time in the place of their winter migration probably have the same scientific value as the stories of swallows having been found hybernating in caves and hollow trees, or of toads having been found in the recesses of otherwise solid rocks.

Many birds, such as the robin, the blackbird, and others, which are for the most part resident in England, are migratory in Germany. There is every probability that it is only within comparatively recent times that these birds have ceased to migrate in England, and we may fairly conjecture that, should the English climate remain long enough favourable to the winter residence of these birds, they will develop into local races, which will eventually have rounder and shorter wings than their continental allies.

In some genera of birds it is comparatively easy to determine the geographical range from an examination of the shape of the wing. In the genus *Acrocephalus*, or reed-warblers, for example, *A. turdoides* is noticeable for its very pointed wing. Its migrations extend from South Sweden to the Transvaal. *A. orientalis*, again, is scarcely distinguishable except in having a slightly less pointed wing. Its migrations extend from Japan to Borneo. *A. stentoreus* has a decidedly more rounded wing, and the limits of its migrations are from Turkestan to India ; whilst *A. syrinx* has the roundest wing of all, and appears to have become a resident in the island of Ponape. In the smaller species of the genus the fact is equally striking. The sharp-winged *A. schœnobænus* ranges from the Arctic Circle to South Africa, whilst the more rounded-winged *A. dumetorum* and *A. bæticatus* have very limited ranges.

There is a considerable difference of opinion as to the origin of migration, some ornithologists holding that the original home of a species was its winter quarters ; others supposing that before the instinct of migration was formed the species was a resident in the district where it now breeds. Both views have their difficulties ; but the preponderance of evidence seems to me to be largely on the side of the latter theory. In turning over a box of Transvaal skins, shot during the breeding season between September and March, it seems impossible to come to any other conclusion. Throwing aside the brilliant birds of the district, we shall find, especially if the box comes from Potchefstroom, a variety of reed-warblers and allied birds, which speak of swamps abounding with insects, where birds of this kind delight to breed and find unlimited food.   As a matter of fact most of these birds do breed there, and, because the winter is so mild, remain there all the year round.   But mixed up with these African types we shall find a fair sprinkling of our own reed-warblers, who have gone down there to avoid our cold winters.   These birds are not breeding; they have migrated to the Transvaal to enjoy the mosquitoes of the Potchefstroom swamps, and when the Potchefstroom birds have finished breeding and begin their six months rest from family cares, they will some of them migrate to the Arctic regions of North Europe to breed amongst the mosquitoes which swarm on the river-banks on the outskirts of the tundra.   We can scarcely conceive it possible that these species were ever resident birds in the Transvaal.   It seems much more rational to conclude that they were once resident birds in the subarctic regions of Europe, and now by the change in the winter temperature of their original home have come to South Africa as migrants, apparently out of season in regard to their breeding habits, to mix amongst birds, many of whom are closely allied to, if not congeneric with, themselves.   The cause of migration is want of *food*, not want of *warmth*.   The feathers of a Siberian jay or a Lapp tit are proof against any cold.

Admitting that the various species of birds that breed in countless thousands in the Arctic regions were once residents there in the days when the climate was much warmer than it is now, we still find some difficulties to explain.   In the first place, the Mammoth age does not appear to have been so very much warmer than the present.   It is said that the remains of the foliage of conifers, such as now exist in Siberia, have been found in the stomachs of frozen mammoths.   In the second place, the question may be fairly asked : How about the three months' night? Would that be no bar to the wintering of so many birds in the Arctic regions? But are we sure that there was three months night? May it not be possible that the obliquity of the earth's axis to its orbit was much less in those ages, and that this was one cause of the comparative mildness of the winters, whilst the summers were for the same reason cool enough for the growth of conifers? An increase in the obliquity of the earth's axis would possibly account for the glacial period which destroyed the mammoths and compelled the birds to migrate.

It is alleged that many birds leave their winter quarters because in southern climates the heat dries up everything, and lessens the production of insect life. Many of our European birds winter on both shores of the Mediterranean. In wandering through the valleys of Asia Minor, or the mountain-gorges of the Parnassus, or on the islands in the lagoon of Missolonghi, in May and June, I noticed no absence of insect life. On the contrary, insect life appeared to be superabundant. Vegetable life appeared to be threatened by innumerable grasshoppers. One of the prominent features of the district was the countless thousands of beetles which swarmed on every plant; and, if we may judge from the number and size of their webs, the countries I have named must be a perfect paradise for spiders. That these districts are suitable for the maintenance of insectivorous birds during summer is proved by the fact that soon after the *Phylloscopi* which have wintered there have left, their place is filled with birds belonging to the allied genus *Hypolais*, so that the olive-trees are well supplied with insect-eating birds both winter and summer. One species of swallow winters in Greece, one is found there all the year round, and three other species are summer migrants to that country. In some cases no doubt the weaker birds are turned out by the stronger. Swallows arrive in Düsseldorf early in April. For some weeks they circle over the town, like a swarm of bees. Early in May the swifts arrive, and soon become as abundant as the swallows were, whilst the latter birds are rarely seen during the summer.

Too much has probably been made of the great lines of migration, the highways which lead from the summer to the winter quarters.* It has been asserted that there is a connection between these routes and the position of submerged continents across which the birds migrated in past ages. Probably there is some such connection, but in all probability an accidental one. To prove the case it would be necessary to show that migratory birds chose a longer route across a shallow sea in preference to a shorter route across a deep sea. It would be necessary also to prove that the habit of migration is older than the subsidence of the submerged land.

I venture to think that the *modus operandi* of migration has been to a large extent misunderstood. Few birds migrate by day. By far the greater number of species migrate by night. The number of places where nocturnal migrations can be systematically observed is very small. Two circumstances are requisite to make such observations successful. First, a sufficiently large population sufficiently interested in the event to permit no nocturnal migration to pass undiscovered. Second, a sufficiently intelligent naturalist to record the sum of many years' observation. Probably in no place in the world are these desiderata so exactly fulfilled as upon the

---

* This and the following paragraphs have been left intact, but how much Mr. Seebohm was afterwards led to modify his views on the subject of migration may be seen by reference to page 418 in Part II. of this volume.—ED.

island of Heligoland.   Soon after my return from the
valley of the Petchora, Mr. Gätke, the celebrated ornithologist and artist, who resided for so many years
on Heligoland, invited me to visit the island, to renew
the acquaintance of the grey plover, the Little stint, the
blue-throat, the shore-lark, the little bunting, and others
of my Petchora friends, and to see something of the
wonderful stream of migration which sets in every autumn
from the Arctic regions to the sunny South, and flows
abundantly past the island.   Heligoland is a very small
place, probably not much more than a hundred acres in
extent.   It is an isolated triangular table of red sand-
stone, with perpendicular cliffs two or three hundred feet
in height, dropping into a sea so shallow, that at low water
you can scramble round the island at the foot of the cliffs.
Most of the surface of this rock is covered with rich soil
and grass.   About a mile from the island is a sandbank,
the highest portion covered over with esparto grass, and
the lower portions submerged by the sea at high tide,
reducing the island from perhaps fifty acres to twenty-
five.   The resident birds on Heligoland and Sandy
Island probably do not exceed a dozen species ; but in
spring and autumn the number of birds that use these
islands as a resting-place during migration is so large,
that as many as 15,000 larks have been known to have
been caught there in one night, and the number of species
of birds obtained on these two small plots of land equals,
if it does not exceed, that of any country of Europe.
There are several species of Siberian and American birds
which have never been obtained in any part of Europe
except upon the island of Heligoland.   The list of
Heligoland birds is so varied, that many ornithologists
have doubted its accuracy.   No one can visit the island,
however, without being convinced of the *bona fides* of all

concerned. The authenticity of the Heligoland skins is beyond all possible question. During the time I spent on the island, from the 23rd of September to the 18th of October, I either shot or saw in the flesh such a variety of birds that I could almost agree with my friend Mr. Gätke when he stated that he would willingly exchange his collection of rare birds shot in Heligoland for those which had passed over the island without being obtained. It is probable, however, that the latter bear a much smaller proportion to the former in Heligoland than in any other place.

The fact is that this little island is the only part of the world of which the ornithology has been properly worked. Every little boy in the island is a born and bred ornithologist. Every unfortunate bird which visits the island has to run the gauntlet of about forty guns, to say nothing of scores of blowpipes and catapults. The flight and note of every bird is familiar to every islander. Each bird has its own local name in the Heligoland language. A new bird is instantly detected. The fisherman steers with a gun by his side; the peasant digs his potatoes with a gun on the turf, and a heap of birds on his coat. On an island where there are no cows, and sheep are kept for their milk only, meat is of course very dear, especially as it has to be brought by steamer from Hamburg, one of the dearest cattle-markets on the continent of Europe. Birds therefore naturally form an important article of diet to the Heligolanders. Every bird which appears is whistled within range with marvellous skill. The common birds are eaten, the rare ones sold to the bird-stuffer, and the new ones taken to Gätke. Many of the Heligolanders are clever shots. Long before sunrise the island is bristling with guns; and after dark the netters are busy at their throstle-bushes; whilst at midnight the birds commit suicide against the lighthouse. When we consider that this has been going on for a quarter of a century, and that the results have been most carefully chronicled for that length of time, the wonder is not that so many species of birds have occurred on Heligoland, but that so many have hitherto escaped detection. This must be accounted for on the theory that, after all, the appearance of birds on Heligoland is only accidental. Comparatively little migration is observed by the casual visitor who frequents the restaurant to enjoy the oysters and the lobsters, or rows across to Sandy Island to bathe on the shore, and take a constitutional on the "dunes." Now and then a flock of waders may be detected hurrying past; flocks of pipits occasionally land on the island, feed for an hour or two, and then pass on; and sometimes a scattered and straggling stream of hooded crows, of heavy and laborious flight, will continue all day long. But by far the most important migration will be found to have taken place "while men slept." Every flock which passes over probably drops a few tired or hungry birds, and a walk through the potato-fields in the morning after a migration night sometimes turns up the most curious and interesting variety of species which have sought the only cover on the island to feed or rest. Perhaps the first bird you flush is a skylark; the report of your gun starts a golden plover, or a jack snipe; then you observe some small birds skulking in the potatoes, and you presently secure a little bunting, an aquatic warbler, and a shore-lark. Your next shot may be a corncrake, followed by a ring ousel or a Richard's pipit.

Every night, however, is not a migration night. Sometimes for a week together you may diligently tramp the potatoes without finding a bird. Migration is a question of wind and weather. Aeuckens, the bird-stuffer on Heligoland, told me that birds migrate north-east in spring, and south-west in autumn. Gätke, on the other hand, maintains that the directions are due east and west. Both agree that birds dislike an absolutely favourable or absolutely contrary wind. The former ruffles their feathers and chills them; the latter, if too strong, impedes their progress. They prefer a side wind, and probably alter their course slightly to accommodate themselves to it. It is even said that they will sometimes tack. Weather is perhaps as important as wind. Under ordinary circumstances a bird does not require to rest on Heligoland, and the arrivals for the most part are said not to be from any point of the compass, but perpendicularly from the sky. The islanders describe with great gusto the sudden arrival of thrushes in this manner. There are scarcely any trees on the island, so the peasants make artificial bushes with a net on one side into which the poor thrushes are driven with sticks and lanterns as soon as they alight. Some hundreds are thus frequently caught in one night. By long experience the Heligolanders know when to expect an arrival of birds. Aeuckens related to me how they would watch on favourable nights by the throstle-bushes, when on a sudden, without a moment's warning, a rush and whirl of wings would be heard, and the throstle-bush would swarm with thrushes, not dropped, but apparently shot like an arrow from a bow, perpendicularly down from the invisible heights of mid air. It is supposed that migration takes place for the most part at a high elevation, beyond the range of our vision; that the birds migrate by sight, and not, as has been assumed, by blind instinct; that they are guided by prominent landmarks with which they have gradually become familiar; and that many birds which

are not gregarious at any other time of the year become
so during the periods of migration, in order to avail
themselves of the experience of the veteran travellers of
their own or of other species.   The desire to migrate is
a hereditary instinct originally formed and continually
kept up by the necessity to do so, in order to maintain a
struggle for existence against the changes of temperature,
but the direction in which to migrate must be learned
afresh by each individual.   The theory that migration
ordinarily takes place at high elevations is supported by
the fact that it is only in dark or cloudy weather that
migration on a large scale is observed.   It is supposed
that the landmarks being obscured by clouds, the birds
are obliged to descend to see their way, for it is observed
that as soon as the clouds begin to break, the migration
apparently comes to an end.   On dark nights the stream
of migration suddenly stops when the moon rises.   Each
bird has its time of migration.   Weather has, apparently,
nothing to do with this date.   Good weather does not
seem to hasten the birds to their breeding haunts, nor
bad weather retard their starting.   If the suitable conjunction of circumstances occur during the season of a
certain bird's migration, that bird visits the island.   If
the season goes by without such conjunction, the bird
does not visit the island.   The period of its migration is
over.   The migration of this species has taken place at
high altitudes, it may be, or by other routes ; and it is in
vain to look for it until the next season of migration
comes round, when, given the necessary wind and
weather, the appearance of the bird may confidently be
expected.

The period of migration of each species lasts about a
month.   In spring, during the first week, the flocks consist principally of adult males ; during the second week,

they principally consist of adult females; in the third
week, follow the birds of the year; whilst finally, during
the last week, arrive the cripples—birds which have lost
their toes, birds with half a tail, birds with one mandible
abnormally long, or birds with some other defect. In
autumn the order of migration is somewhat different.
For weeks before the regular period of migration is due
stragglers in various stages of plumage arrive, loaf about
in a desultory manner for a few days, and then disappear.
Some of these birds are in summer plumage, some of
them in their winter dress, whilst others are in a transition stage, moulting as they migrate. These *avant-
coureurs* are supposed to consist of barren birds, odd
birds who have been unable to find a mate, or birds
whose nests have been destroyed too late in the season
to allow of a second nest to be made. Having nothing
else to do, the hereditary instinct to migrate not being
checked by the parental instinct, they yield to its first
impulses, and drift southwards before the general body of
their species. When the period of migration sets in in
earnest, astounding as the fact is, it is nevertheless true
that the birds of the year are the first to migrate, birds
which of course have never migrated before. This
circumstance, which all the Heligolanders with whom I
conversed agreed in corroborating, may to a large extent
account for the fact that the rare stragglers recorded as
visiting Heligoland and other countries are for the most
part birds of the year on their first autumn migration. It
is not to be wondered at that on their first journey they
should frequently stray from the direct course. Probably
the mortality amongst birds of the year is very great,
especially amongst those who take the wrong road on
their first migration. The yellow-browed warbler (*Phylloscopus superciliosus*, Gmel.) breeds in immense numbers

on the Arctic circle in Siberia.   The main line of
migration of this, as well as of several other species of
birds breeding in the same district, is eastwards, passing
through North China and conducting them to South
China, Burma, and the eastern portion of India, where
they winter in abundance.   Several birds, some nearly
allied, and one congeneric, migrate west instead of east
from the same breeding-grounds, and with these a few
yellow-browed warblers appear annually to mix and find
their way to Europe, passing Heligoland in small numbers
nearly every autumn.   Probably most of these wanderers
perish during the winter, as they have been observed in
spring on Heligoland only once every few years.   This
charming little bird has once been recorded from the
British Islands.   I saw one or two during my short stay
on Heligoland, and was fortunate enough to shoot one.
For nearly a week, whilst I was visiting this interesting
locality, the weather was unfavourable.   There were
scarcely half a dozen birds on the island.   I used to take
a constitutional with my gun twice or thrice a day, spending most of the rest of the time in Mr. Gätke's studio,
chatting about his birds, visiting regularly Aeuckens, the
bird-stuffer, to inquire if any one else had had better luck.
On the 11th of October I shot three shore-larks.
Aeuckens told me that the appearance of this Arctic
species was a very good sign, that he had often noticed
that a few birds always preceded the favourable weather,
and that we might soon expect a change and plenty of
birds.   The next day the west winds, which had prevailed for a week, slackened a little.   In the afternoon
it was a calm, with a rising barometer; in the evening
a breeze was already springing up from the south-east.
I called upon Gätke, who advised me to go to bed, and
be up before sunrise in the morning, as in all probability

I should find the island swarming with birds. Accordingly I turned in soon after ten. At half-past twelve I was awoke with the news that the migration had already begun. Hastily dressing myself, I at once made for the lighthouse. As I crossed the potato-fields birds were continually getting up at my feet. Arrived at the lighthouse, an intensely interesting sight presented itself.

HELIGOLAND

The whole of the zone of light within range of the mirrors was alive with birds coming and going. Nothing else was visible in the darkness of the night, but the lantern of the lighthouse vignetted in a drifting sea of birds. From the darkness in the east, clouds of birds were continually emerging in an uninterrupted stream; a few swerved from their course, fluttered for a moment as if dazzled by the light, and then gradually vanished with the rest in the western gloom. Occasionally a bird wheeled round the lighthouse and then passed on, and occasionally one fluttered against the glass like a moth against a lamp, tried to perch on the wire netting and was caught by the lighthouse man. I should be afraid to hazard a guess as to the hundreds of thousands that must have passed in a couple of hours ; but the stray birds which the lighthouse man succeeded in securing amounted to nearly 300. The scene from the balcony of the lighthouse was equally interesting ; in every direction birds were flying like a swarm of bees, and every few seconds one flew against the glass. All the birds seemed to be flying up wind, and it was only on the lee side of the light that any birds were caught. They were nearly all skylarks. In the heap captured was one redstart and one reed-bunting. The air was filled with the warbling cry of the larks ; now and then a thrush was heard : and once a heron screamed as it passed by. The night was starless and the town was invisible, but the island looked like the outskirts of a gas-lighted city, being sprinkled over with brilliant lanterns. Many of the larks alighted on the ground to rest, and allowed the Heligolanders to pass their nets over them. About three o'clock A.M. a heavy thunderstorm came on, with deluges of rain ; a few breaks in the clouds revealed the stars ; and the migration came to an end or continued above the range of our vision.

The conclusion I came to after my Heligoland experience was that the desire to migrate was an hereditary impulse, to which the descendants of migratory birds were subject in spring and autumn, which has during the lapse of ages acquired a force almost, if not quite, as irresistible as the instinct to breed in spring. On the other hand, the direction in which to migrate appears to be absolutely unknown to the young birds in their first autumn, and has to be learnt by experience. The idea that the knowledge of where to migrate is a mysterious gift of Nature, the miraculous quality of which is attempted to be concealed under the semi-scientific term of instinct, appears to be without any foundation in fact. It appears that each individual bird has to find out its own proper winter quarters for itself, and learn the way thither as best it may. That birds have keen organs of sight is a fact well known to all who have watched them obtaining their food or eluding their enemies. That they must have wonderful memories for place is shown by the distance they roam from their nests which, however well concealed, they seem to have no difficulty whatever in finding again. Amongst true migratory birds, that is amongst birds which have a winter as well as a summer home, as distinguished from gipsy migrants who perpetually loaf about on the outskirts of the frost during winter, continually changing their latitude with the temperature, it appears to be a general rule that the farther north a species goes to breed the farther south it goes to winter. It is not known if this applies to individuals as well as to species. The various times of arrival of many species of birds in most latitudes of Europe are well known and carefully recorded, but of the dates of departure from the various latitudes of Africa where they winter we know little or nothing, otherwise this question might easily be settled. It is obviously much easier to record the date of arrival of a bird than of its departure. In the one case a single entry is sufficient; in the other, memoranda may have to be daily recorded for weeks. At Valkenswaard, in Holland, I noticed that the earliest migrants were those with the widest range. Birds whose breeding-range extended to or beyond Britain were the earliest to breed, whilst those whose eggs I was most anxious to obtain, those whose breeding-range did not extend to our islands, were very late in arriving. It seems to be a curious fact that, as a general rule—though subject, no doubt, to many exceptions—the birds who have come from the longest distance arrive the earliest. The facts of migration are, however, so many, and the theories which they suggest are so various, that we must bring this rambling, if not irrelevant chapter to an end, and return to the narrative of our doings in the valley of the Petchora.

OLD RUSSIAN SILVER CROSS

DOING ROBINSON CRUSOE AT DVOINIK

CHAPTER XXI.

IN CAMP AT DVOINIK.

Trip to Kuya—The Prahms—Travelling in a *Rosposki*—The Birds *en route*—Arrival of the *Triad* at Alexievka—We Win over the Manager—The *Ino*—Doing Robinson Crusoe in a Wrecked Ship—Nest of the Long-tailed Duck—Our First Little Stint's Nest—The Tundra—Sunset and Sunrise—Little Stint's Eggs—The Tundra near Bolvanskaya Bay—Phalaropes—Interior of the Tundra—Change of Plumage in Phalaropes—An Early Morning Start—Confusion of Time—The Snowy Owl—Two more Nests of Little Stint—A March of Geese on the Tundra—An Old Grave.

A DAY or two after our return from the Golievski islands, a chance suddenly turned up of making a trip up stream to Kuya. The rafts, which ought by this time to have reached Alexievka, had not arrived, and ill-natured rumours of their having run aground were brought down by some fishermen. The manager of the company had also run out of various *articles de luxe*, which his soul

lusted after; so the steamer was ordered to Kuya, and
we gladly accepted berths in her. On the way we met
one of the rafts coming down from Kuya. We drove on
to Mekitza to visit the prahms; queer-looking vessels,
something like canal-boats, carrying a gigantic mast in
the centre, and an arched roof above. Each vessel is
a shop, where miscellaneous merchandise is sold or
bartered, and the owners who come down every summer
from Tcherdin, near Perm, are sometimes very wealthy
men. The goods fetch high prices on board. We paid
elevenpence per pound for sugar, and six shillings for
tea. The merchant from whom we bought our provisions
was reputed to be worth a million sterling. Nor was
it extraordinary, considering the amount of trade he
managed to secure. He had come down to Mekitza
with three prahms, had cleared the cargo of two, and
sold the vessels, and very few goods now remained in
the one in which he intended to make his journey homeward. In the villages the prices were much lower than
those asked on the prahms. Thus we paid only $1\frac{3}{4}d.$
per lb. for excellent fresh beef.

At Kuya several timber-rafts passed us, proceeding to
Alexievka; these we waylaid. They were carrying a batch
of letters for us, up to June 7th. Having secured this welcome prize, we set our faces towards our headquarters.

The five versts between Kuya to Mekitza and back
we travelled in a *rosposki*, a machine composed of
four wheels, about two feet in diameter, the axle-trees
of which are connected by three parallel poles, upon
which we sat. This vehicle is, without exception, the
most uncomfortable carriage it has ever been my ill-luck
to travel in. There is no support for the back, nothing
to hold on by at the sides; only three bare poles to sit
on, and not height enough from the ground to swing one's

legs about in peace. On the way we saw sand-martins, hooded crows, arctic terns, common gulls, ringed plover, and Temminck's stints. We got young in down of the ringed plover and arctic tern, and shot a long-tailed duck with her brood of ducklings. At Kuya we saw both the common and the tree sparrow.

The morning had been intensely hot; in the afternoon the wind rose, veered round to the north, and the night was stormy and cold. The next day the chill continued, and for the time being the plague of mosquitoes was stayed. It was a pleasant surprise, on reaching Alexievka, to find an English schooner, the *Triad*, Captain Taylor, anchored in the river. She had come over from Iceland, whither she had carried coal, and was now chartered for larch to Cronstadt. We at once secured berths in her. She intended to sail in ten days, hoping to make Elsinore in a month.

The cold weather continued the next day. We spent two hours at Wassilkova, but saw little of interest. The red-throated pipits were in full moult, but we brought home some of their young, also those of the yellow-headed wagtail and dunlins, and a pintail duck and its half-grown ducklings. The next day my companion secured another specimen of our new pipit, for which we had been looking in the neighbourhood. The day was memorable for having brought successfully to a conclusion our negotiations with Captain Arendt, the manager of the company. A watch, a revolver, a musical box, and a ten-pound note had brought him round, and on the morrow the steamer was to be placed at our disposal. We were in high spirits, shouting, "Hurrah! for Dvoinik and the Little Stint!" The next morning we were fairly off by 10 A.M. It was damp and chilly, with a light breeze from the north-west. As we neared the bar, we sighted a brig under full sail. We hoisted a *rendezvous* flag, and went on board. Though flying Danish colours, we found she was an English vessel—the *Ino*, from Newhaven. The captain told us he had been some days trying to get into the Petchora, but he was unable to reach it by steering between islands Nos. 3 and 4, owing to the ice, and had come round the east passage between islands 7 and 8 and Varandai. This ice accounted for the extraordinarily cold weather we had been having since the previous Sunday.

About four we landed at Dvoinik, and took possession of a stranded vessel that was lying high and dry upon the beach. It was settled that the company's steamer should call for us on the following Tuesday, Wednesday, or Thursday, according to the final arrangements for the starting of our schooner, the *Triad*, in which we were to make part of our homeward passage. Meanwhile we were to live at Dvoinik, in regular Robinson Crusoe fashion. The deserted vessel looked very comfortable, and we anticipated a jolly time.

Leaving the men to sweep up the hold, we started off in high glee for a raid upon the Little stints. We hastened over the tundra, making for the marshy ground upon which I had seen the dunlins, but not one was there. Possibly, we thought, the young could fly by this time, and had joined their parents on their favourite feeding-ground. On the brackish lake close by we shot a brood of long-tailed ducks, and afterwards found an empty nest in the short, coarse grass, placed exactly at high-tide water-mark. It contained down enough to identify the species. There was no cover to the nest, except a margin of thin turf, that looked as if it had been turned up by a spade. On the lake there were, as before, a couple of black-throated divers. I waited for a short while, hiding in the cleft of the bank, as I had done on the previous occasion when I had shot the Little stints, but none were to be seen. I then skirted the margin of the bay to its narrow entrance, having spied a grey plover or two, a pair of Arctic terns, and a few herring-gulls. When there, a small number of dunlins passed rapidly overhead, and I repeatedly saw flocks of Little stints. However, these might have been the same flock passing and repassing. They were very wild, and I could not get a shot. Some time before, my companion and I had parted company. We now met at one of the capes at the southern extremity of the high promontory. Cocksure was with him. On comparing notes I found their experience had been much the same as mine, only Cocksure shot a Temminck's stint, near the sandhills. In returning we separated again to cover more ground ; and again when we met, and compared notes, we found that to each the sandhills, the lakes, and the shores had proved a blank, destitute of bird-life.

We then separated for a stroll on the tundra. I had not gone far before I heard our interpreter Piottuch shouting in a state of great excitement. Harvie-Brown was the first to come up ; and I joined them shortly afterwards. I found them sitting on the ground, with a couple of Little stints in down. I sat down beside them, and we watched the parent bird as she was fluttering and flying and running all round us, sometimes coming within a foot of one of us. After securing the old bird we went on a short distance, and Piottuch again made loud demonstrations of delight. This time it was nest and eggs. The nest was like that of most sand-pipers, a mere depression in the ground, with such dead *maroshka* (cloudberry) leaves and other dry materials as were within easy reach, scraped together to serve as lining. The position was on a comparatively dry extent of tundra, sloping from the top of the little turf cliffs that rise from the lagoon down to the sandhills at the twin capes, between which the tide runs in and out of a little inland sea. These sandhills are flanked on the side next the sea with piles of drift-wood of all sizes and shapes— lofty trees which have been mown down by the ice when the great river broke up and in many places overflowed its banks, squared balks of timber washed away by the floods from the stores of the Petchora Timber-trading Company, and spars of luckless ships that have been wrecked on these inhospitable shores. They are sparingly sprinkled over with esparto grass, and soon run into an irregular strip of sand and gravel. This part of the coast, however, did not seem to have any attraction for the Little stints. There were plenty of ringed plover upon it, and a few Temminck's stints; and we saw a pair of snow-buntings with five young, which had probably been bred amongst the drift-wood. At Dvoinik, however, for perhaps a verst from each twin cape, between the sand and the mouth of the little inland sea, is an extent of dead flat land, covered over with thick short grass, and full of little lakes, mostly very shallow and filled with black or coffee-coloured mud with an inch or two of brackish water upon it. Some of these pools are covered with aquatic plants, and others are open water. These lakes and pools seem to be the real point of attraction; and on their edges the Little stints feed, in small flocks of from half a dozen birds to a score, as they happen to meet from the tundra. The large flock of perhaps a hundred or more birds, which was occasionally seen, might possibly have been last year's birds and not breeding; but more probably it consisted entirely of males, which, so far as we had an opportunity of observing, do not take any part in incubation. The ground where the nests were placed was full of tussocks or hummocks, close together, the swampy ground between being almost hidden, or traceable only by rows of cotton-grass. The nests were within a hundred yards of the place where I shot the five Little stints on July 14, on a comparatively dry extent of tundra gently sloping towards the north-east, lying between the lagoon and the inland sea—exactly the place in which one would expect them to breed, not too swampy, but probably the coolest place the birds could have chosen. The Pytkoff Mts., though at a considerably greater elevation (513 feet above the level of the sea), are no doubt warmer, because more inland. The sandy shore, having little or no cover, would also be hotter from the sun. Facing the north-east, this part of the tundra catches the most of the prevailing winds at this season of the year, and the least sun; and no doubt the large bay or inland sea on one side, and the open water on the other, help to cool the air.

We had already given names to the different sorts of ground on the tundra. The dry, grassy hills were the shore-lark ground; the dead, flat bog, intersected with tussocky ridges, was the grey plover ground; the swampy marsh, covered with long grass, was the reeve ground. Where the grass was shorter and more tangled and knotted, it became dunlin ground; and where this short grassy swamp was sprinkled over with tussocks of dryer earth, covered over with moss and flowers, it was the Lapland bunting or red-throated pipit ground. The part where the tussocks lay so close together that they reminded one of the hundred domes of the Stamboul bazaar seen from the minaret of Santa Sophia, and the swampy ground was almost hidden, or traceable only by

rows of cotton-grass, we agreed to call for the future the
Little stint ground. The hummocks were covered with
green moss, mingled here and there with a little hoary
reindeer moss. This undergrowth was concealed by the
maroshka (the cloudberry), a species of rush, sedges,
the dwarf sweet-smelling daphne, and other shrubs and
flowers of the tundra.

The last few days had been almost winter, but on the
following day it was summer once again. The wind
had dropped and the clouds had gone from the sky.
This was the bright side of the change ; the reverse was
the swarm of mosquitoes that hung over the tundra.
Brown and I visited the Little stint ground again, on
the principle of "stick to your covey" ; but not a bird
or a nest could we see upon it. We shot a wheatear
on the shore, saw a pair of sanderlings, dropped a fine
glaucous gull, a reeve, and some other birds, and then
returned to our quarters. Our Samoyede brought us
a couple of nests of long-tailed ducks, one containing
three eggs, the other five. We were tired out, so
having cooked a duck for dinner, we went to bed at
4 A.M., to rise at 11 A.M. We began our day (let the
reader forgive the Irishism, it is only a Petchorski bull),
by watching the sun set and rise again in the space of an
hour or so ; then we set off, hoping to get the start of
the mosquitoes. It was a dead calm, and taking the
boat, we crossed over to the north twin cape. We found
the sand barren of special interest, as it had been on the
other side ; only the intrusive ringed plover made as
much hubbub as a hundred Little stints or grey plovers
would have done, evidently considering its eggs were
the only ones we could possibly be in search of. The
lakes and pools were very similar in shape and appearance to those on the south cape. Temminck's stints were

somewhat more abundant, and we fell in with one small party of Little stints. Before leaving this ground we devoted an hour to duck-shooting for the pot, and bagged three long-tailed ducks, and one pintail with two young in down. We then turned our attention to the tundra, which rapidly rose some forty feet or so, afterwards sloping gradually down apparently to the Pytkoff hills, distant some fifteen miles. In many places a white mist lay over the landscape, resembling far-away lakes. There were numerous small pools of water, but we could not distinguish them until within a short distance. In suitable ground the grey plover abounded, and we shot young Lapland buntings; yet on the whole the tundra did not look inviting—grey plovers and their eggs were not sufficient attraction to lure us to face the mosquitoes; so turning away from it we began to explore the shores of a river winding inland. On its high steep grassy banks we found shore-larks, old and young, and what was even more to the purpose and acceptable in our present Robinson Crusoe situation—an abundance of leeks or eschalots, of which we laid in a plentiful supply. We recognised an eagle soaring overhead, we saw some skuas, ringed plovers, Temminck's stints, and redpolls, but nothing of special interest. It was now about eight o'clock, so we rowed back to the entrance of the inland sea, intending to cross over to our quarters on the south cape, when suddenly a dense white mist, coming from the Arctic ice, fell upon us. We hastened to run our boat ashore, stopping to shoot a sanderling on a sandbank, and soon after an Arctic tern.

Our next nest of the Little stint was taken on the 24th of July. Harvie-Brown and I had been up all night, shooting by the light of the midnight sun, hoping to avoid the mosquitoes, and were returning home to our wrecked ship in a thick white morning mist. I stopped behind to refresh myself with a bath, and afterwards turned towards the Little stint ground. Just as I reached it I was glad to see Piottuch emerge from the white mist, with the intelligence that he had found another nest of this bird, containing four eggs, about three versts off, and had shot the bird, leaving the nest and eggs for us to take. We walked on together a short distance, when I heard the now familiar cry of a Little stint behind me, a sharp *wick*, almost exactly the same as the cry of the red-necked phalarope, or that of the sanderling. Turning quickly round, I saw the bird flying past as if coming up from its feeding-grounds. It wheeled round us at some distance and alighted on the ground about eighty yards ahead. We walked slowly up towards it, and stood for some time watching it busily employed in preening its feathers. By-and-by we sat down. It presently began to run towards us, stopping now and then to preen a feather or two ; then it turned back a few paces, and lifting its wings settled down, evidently on its nest. We gave it three minutes grace, to be quite sure, and then quietly walked up to the place, and sat down, one on each side of the eggs. The bird as quietly slipped off the nest, and began to walk about all round us, now and then pecking on the ground as if feeding, seldom going more than six feet from us, and often approaching within eighteen inches. It was a most interesting and beautiful sight. The tameness of the bird was almost ludicrous. We chatted and talked ; but the bird remained perfectly silent, and did not betray the slightest symptom of fear or concern, *until I touched the eggs*. She then gave a flutter towards me, apparently to attract my attention. I turned towards her, and she resumed her former unconcern. I stretched my hand towards her. She quietly retreated, keeping about two feet from my hand. She seemed so extremely tame that I almost thought for the moment that I could catch her, and, getting on to all fours, I crept quietly towards her. As soon as I began to move from the nest, her manner entirely changed. She kept about the same distance ahead of me; but instead of retreating, with the utmost apparent nonchalance, she did everything in her power to attract me still farther. She shuffled along the ground as if lame. She dropped her wings as if unable to fly, and occasionally rested on her breast, quivering her drooping wings and spread tail, as if dying. I threw one of my gauntlets at her, thinking to secure her without damage, but she was too quick for me. Piottuch then fired at her, and missed. He followed her for some distance; but she kept just out of range, and finally flew away. We waited about a quarter of an hour at the nest, talking and making no effort to conceal ourselves, when she flew straight up and alighted within easy shot, and I secured her.

The Little stint seems to be a very quiet bird at the nest, quite different from Temminck's stint. When you invade a colony of the latter birds, especially if they have young, the parents almost chase you from the spot —flying wildly round and round and crying vociferously, often perching upon a stake or a tree, or hovering in the air and trilling. We observed none of these habits in the Little stint. So far as we saw, only the female takes part in incubation, and only the female is seen near the nest. On our way back to the wreck we met with a party of sanderlings on the shore, and shot two of them. No doubt these birds were breeding somewhere in the district. After a good dinner of willow-grouse and a siesta of three hours, we started to take the nest that Piottuch had marked. Whilst we had slept the weather had changed. The mosquitoes had all gone. A smart gale was blowing from the north, and a heavy sea was breaking on the shore. It was cloudy, dark, and cold, with an attempt now and then at rain. The nest was a couple of miles off, very near the shore of the inland sea, but on somewhat similar ground—moss, cloudberry, grass, and the like. The eggs were intermediate in colour between those of the other two nests. On our return to our quarters we found that our Samoyede servant had caught a young Little stint, half-grown, a very interesting bird. Like the young of the dunlin, the first feathers are those of summer plumage. On comparing the young in down and half-grown birds of the dunlin with those of this bird, we noted that the legs of young dunlin in down were pale brown, whilst those of the half-grown and mature birds were nearly black ; the Little stint, on the other hand, seems to have nearly black legs and feet at all ages.

The Little stint is evidently much more nearly allied to the dunlin than to Temminck's stint, and ought to be called the Little dunlin. The birds are very similar in colour. Their eggs can hardly be mistaken for those of Temminck's stint, but are in every respect miniature dunlins' eggs. The young in down of Temminck's stint are quite grey compared with the reddish-brown of the young of the dunlin. The young in down of the Little stint are still redder, especially on the sides and the back of the neck.

The average size of the twenty eggs we obtained of the Little stint is about $1\frac{1}{16} \times \frac{3}{4}$ inch, a trifle smaller than the eggs of Temminck's stint usually are. The ground-colour varies from pale greenish-grey to pale brown. The spots and blotches are rich brown, generally large, and sometimes confluent at the large end. They probably go through every variety to which dunlins' eggs are subject. All the eggs which we found, with one exception, which would probably be a barren one, were very much incubated.

The following morning the gale from the north continued. It was a mosquitoless day, and very cold; a heavy sea still broke against the shore; ever and anon the sun shone, but masses of cloud kept drifting over the sky. We spent the day in exploring the tundra in the direction of Bolvanskaya Bay. Far as the eye could reach the country stretched before us, a gently undulating moor, an Arctic prairie, a Siberian tundra; no hills were on the horizon, save the short range of the Pytkoff Kamin. Plenty of lakes, large and small, gleamed upon the expanse; the banks of most of them were steep and of peat; others were flat, and covered with rushy grass; rarely were they sandy. Here and there the pools were almost dried up; some were so choked up by coarse grasses, rushes, and *carices* as to become swamps, holding a little space of open water in the centre. These were quite accessible, however, thanks to our waterproof boots; we sank some twelve to eighteen inches through water and mud, but reached a safe bottom, hard and level as a stone floor, a solid pavement of ice. We spent an hour or two wading round one of these open spaces of water, forming the centre of a choked-up lakelet. Upon a little island of firm ground, that raised its summit above the reeds, was the empty nest of some bird, probably a gull, and close to the open water was the nest of a black-throated diver, with one egg. The latter was placed upon a foundation of roots and dead grass, half turned to peat, raked up from the bottom of the swamp, and upon this was placed a lining of fresh green flaggy grass. The egg was very small; but both parent birds were flying overhead, often coming near enough for identification. On the open water phalaropes were swimming, and we frequently rose them from the grasses at our feet. Their behaviour plainly showed that they were breeding ; they circled round us wildly, uttering their usual cry. We secured three young in down, only recently hatched.

We spent another hour on the banks of a large lake, upon which swam two pairs of long-tailed ducks, each with its brood. After waiting and watching and stalking, we got hold of two old birds, two of the young in down of one brood, and six more grown-up young of the other. On the sandy margin of another lake, white with the seeds of the cotton-grass, we saw several ringed plover, and shot one Little stint. We came upon a few Buffon's skuas, and on their ground we found the grey plover abundant as usual. Returning home, I chose the lee shore for my route, and as I came along watched several glaucous and herring gulls, saw a pair of wheatears, and shot a shore-lark.

Meanwhile our Samoyede and our half-breed had made a long excursion into the tundra by the banks of the rivers Erisvanka and Eevka. They described the country as exactly the same as that which we already knew—moor, swamp, and bog, with plenty of lakes, large and small. They had met nothing of interest, except ducks, geese, and swans. These birds were now evidently leaving their breeding haunts and retiring into the tundra to moult. During this period of comparative helplessness and inability to fly, they are attacked by the Samoyedes on their way back from Varandai and the Bolshai Tundra. The Samoyedes have grand battues amongst the geese, and return to the Petchora laden with feathers and down, which they sell at the Pinega fair. Our men brought back with them but one bird. This was perhaps the most interesting of all to us—a Bewick's swan, shot on the banks of a great lake in company with four others.

On the morrow the storm continued, and rain fell during the morning; so we spent the hours inside our wreck, writing up our journals and examining the phalaropes.

The idle morning seemed a long one. After dinner we smoked a pipe, whiled away the time in chatting, and then retired, as I thought, very early to bed. I woke after some hours and got up, for I had had sleep enough, shouldered my gun, and went out, leaving all the others still deep in their slumbers. It was very windy, and ever and anon came gusts of rain, yet there were more birds than usual out feeding. "It's the early bird that catches the worm," I said to myself.

My first care was to seek out the Little stint ground. I saw several birds upon it, but no trace of a nest could I discover. Then I took a long stroll along the edge of the inland sea and by the banks of the river beyond. As I went along I constantly heard the clear, sharp, but not loud cry of the Little stint and phalarope—*wick*—but I had not yet learned to distinguish the one from the other, nor could I tell either from the cry of the sanderling. The spluttering note, *pt-r-r-r*, of the Temminck's stint is very distinct; so is the dunlin's thick hoarse cry of *peezh*, or its grating call-note—*trr*—as well as the noisy *too-it* of the ringed plover.

I had been out some hours when I met my companion, and hailed him with "Good morning." He answered with "Good evening." We both agreed the hour was seven, but we differed as to its being A.M. or P.M. I was convinced it was the morning of the morrow, whereas Harvie-Brown was persuaded it was yesterevening.   A never-setting sun plays strange pranks with one's reckoning of time.

Harvie-Brown had worked the Little stint ground, but had not seen a bird upon it. While with me, he shot a brace of grey plovers ; then we parted, and I returned to the Little stint feeding haunts. I secured a brace of them, a few dunlins, old and young, and a grey plover ; also some young Temminck's stints half-way between feathers and down. As I was picking up the latter I discerned in the distance the form of a great white bird, which seemed to me to alight upon a distant lake. Taking it to be a Bewick's swan, I put a slug-cartridge into my gun and walked rapidly on in its direction. Before I got within shot of it the bird rose, and I saw a snowy owl drop behind the sand-hills. I carefully stalked it, looked around, and after a time descried a white spot resting on the north twin cape, which, with the aid of my telescope, I discovered to be the owl. He, too, must have been watching me ; perhaps he took my sealskin cap for some new species of lemming, for presently he rose and flew across the water directly towards me. By the time he had reached the other twin cape he evidently discovered his mistake, and alighted on the beach about sixty yards in front of me. I rose and walked towards him ; he also rose, but before he had flown ten yards my shot reached him, broke one of his wings, and dropped him into the sea. As he lay struggling in the water a score of glaucous and herring-gulls came flying towards him, and sailed round and round him, making quite a small uproar with their cries. I was too anxious, how-ever, to secure my first snowy owl to pay any heed to them, especially as my cartridge extractor had got out of order ; I therefore plunged into the water, and, as it was shallow, I soon landed my prize.

My extractor was a complicated new-fangled patent invention, and already that day it had caused me to lose a pair of Buffon's skuas. I had shot a young dunlin on the muddy margin of the inland sea, breaking with the same barrel the wing of an old dunlin ; with the second barrel I killed a Little stint. The wounded bird lay a few yards off, when suddenly, down there flew upon it a couple of Buffon's skuas, who quarrelled over it and carried it off before—unable to reload—I could wade through the mud to the rescue.

After securing the owl, I carried my trophy home in triumph, overtaking my companion by the way. On reaching the wreck, we finally settled the question of evening or morning. We satisfactorily established that it was the former, so we dined and went to bed again.

The next day the gale continued, but there was some sunshine, and the cold kept the mosquitoes at bay. I spent my morning superintending the cooking of the swan our men had brought the preceding day. Meanwhile Harvie-Brown went out to the far end of the inland sea, and got a little distance from the spot where we had found the last nest of the Little stint. He came upon two more. We had by this time twenty of these birds' eggs ; all miniature dunlins' eggs, and like them, varying in colour. These two nests were not built on the tundra proper, but on the feeding-ground—a flat sandy strip of land on which grew short grass and bunches of a thick-leaved yellow-flowering plant, sprinkled here and there with dried-up or drying pools, and with drift-wood lying scattered about in all directions. The tundra stops at some 150 yards from the seashore, and this stretch of feeding ground lies between it and the water's edge.

After lunching on the baked breast of the swan, I

returned to the wreck, but by a different route from that which my companion had taken. I took the boat across to the north twin cape, and was an hour pulling half a verst against the heavy gale. I then skirted the margin of a long narrow inlet, exactly like the dried-up bed of a river, running some miles into the tundra, bending round almost behind the inland sea. I had not gone more than a mile when I heard the cackle of geese; a bend of the river bed gave me an opportunity of stalking them, and when I came within sight I beheld an extraordinary and interesting scene. At least one hundred old geese, and quite as many young ones, perhaps even twice or thrice that number, were marching like a regiment of soldiers. The vanguard, consisting of old birds, was halfway across the stream; the rear, composed principally of goslings, was running down the steep bank towards the water's edge as fast as their young legs could carry them. Both banks of the river, where the geese had doubtless been feeding, were strewn with feathers, and in five minutes I picked up a handful of quills. The flock was evidently migrating to the interior of the tundra, moulting as it went along.

On the top of the high embankment bordering the river I came upon a wooden monument, about a foot in height and width, and from two to three feet in length. The wood was entirely rotten, and I easily broke and tore open the lid that still covered it. Inside I found bones like those of a dog, a broken vessel of glazed earthenware, the rusty remains of an iron vase, and an abundance of mould. Outside were fragments of bleached bone, like the remains of an infant's skull. This was doubtless a Samoyede's tomb; but we could not determine if it was that of an infant, whose remains had been buried in the box, or that of an adult interred below.

After loitering some time about this spot I pushed on farther, crossing over a plateau of tundra, well covered in places with willows some three feet high. Here I found willow-grouse with young well able to fly, many willow-warblers, a few redpolls, and one blue-throated warbler.

MHF

OLD RUSSIAN SILVER CROSS

MIGRATION OF GEESE

CHAPTER XXII.

HOMEWARD BOUND.

On Short Commons—Bad Weather—A Foraging Party—Russian Super-
stitions—Return of the Steamer—Beautiful Flowers—Arrival at Alexievka
—Departure for Home—Thunderstorm—Water-spout—Sea-birds—Hard
Fare—Copenhagen—Summary of the Trip.

MATTERS were beginning to look somewhat serious in
our Robinson Crusoe encampment. The heavy gale
continued to blow unabated, and it was very probable
the steamer would not call for us until the sea grew
quieter. Meanwhile our larder was nearly empty. We
were reduced to half a loaf of bread, and to what birds
we could secure. We breakfasted on a grey plover a
brace of dunlins, and three duck's eggs, which, though
somewhat incubated, yet made a good omelette. There
was nothing, however, for dinner, so we all turned out

to provide for the pot. Harvie-Brown went south, and returned with only a few dunlins and a grey plover; he had chased a bar-tailed godwit for some distance near the seashore, but had not got within shot. I had met with no better luck, for although I had brought down a dozen dunlins and grey phalaropes as they fed on the margin of a lake I had been able only to secure three. At the first step I took in the direction of my prizes, I sank lower than knee-deep into the black mud. My gun also snapped at a willow-grouse within easy range. We returned to our quarters somewhat down-hearted; the gale was blowing more fiercely than ever, a thick mist covered the sea, and gusts of wind drove the rain into the wreck. We cooked ourselves a supper of fried dunlins, and allowed to each a weak basin of Liebig's extract-of-meat soup, and half a slice of bread. About midnight, as we smoked our pipes and listened to the howling and spitting of the wind and rain outside, our thoughts followed the forlorn-hope party we had sent out, and we doubted whether it would meet with better luck than we had. This party consisted of Cocksure, the Samoyede, and the half-breed. They had gone on what might be called, in a double sense, a wild-goose chase, in pursuit of the flock of geese I had seen the day before migrating across the water into the tundra. We went to bed hoping against hope, and were awakened towards four by the noisy arrival of our envoys, carrying back in triumph eleven old geese and five young ones. One of the party had taken the boat up the river upon which I had seen the flock. The other two followed, each keeping upon opposite banks. They came upon the geese a few versts higher up than the spot at which I had seen them, and falling upon them had made a grand haul of birds. The laying in of this stock of provisions lifted a burden off our minds.   We now proceeded to administer, with better grace than we could have before, a sound rating to our two lazy, good-for-nothing Russian servants. They were the only two who had grumbled during this time of perplexity ; for ever muttering that if the storm did not abate and the steamer come to our rescue, we should surely all be "*propal*" (lost).   We had ordered one to join the forlorn-hope party, but he had soon returned, and all the night he had done little but kneel in a state of abject fear, trembling, crossing himself, and crying, " *Gospodin, Gospodin, dai khleba* " (Lord, Lord, give us bread).   These poor dupes of the miserable Greek Church have not learnt the wholesome doctrine Cromwell taught his soldiers, to "trust in the Lord and keep their powder dry."   Like many other fanatics at home and abroad, they close their eyes to the truth that God *may* bless their work, but will *never* bless their idleness. As a just punishment for their sloth and cowardice, we condemned them to pluck the geese, on which we and the captors made a hearty meal.   While we regaled ourselves they had to look on, and feast upon leeks.

The larger number of geese, being in full moult, had been unable to fly.   Cocksure assured us that both old and young constantly hid themselves under the water, where some remained, just keeping their beaks above the surface, for ten minutes at a time.   He added that he had often observed the same thing in Mezén during the moulting season.

The gale exhausted its violence during the night, and gradually slackened and wore itself out during the day : when the following morning came, the weather was quite calm.   With ten geese in our larder, we considered our- selves entitled to a lazy day, so we wandered out in the tundra, making a small collection of the flowers that grow upon it, the bonnie bright Arctic blossoms that deck for a few weeks that region of ice. We shot an immature gull, and loafed about, feeling that we had exhausted the place, and hoping for the arrival of the steamer. A flock of what we took to be sandpipers, flying wildly overhead and uttering a note like that of the knot, roused our curiosity. When we at last succeeded in shooting one, the bird turned out to be a reeve. Another incident in this, our last day, was tracing the footprints of a swan in the mud, and identifying them as those of a Bewick's swan.

At two o'clock the following morning I was on our wreck's deck, chatting with Cocksure, when on the horizon we caught sight of the steamer. All our companions were asleep, except the half-breed, but five minutes later all were up and hard at work packing. By five o'clock we were on board, steaming over a sea smooth as glass towards Bolvanski Nos. At eight we went on shore at Stanavialachta to visit the peregrine's nest, where we expected to find a new lot of eggs. From a distance we could see the male bird sitting on the spot. He allowed us to approach to within ten or twelve yards, when suddenly he took the alarm and rose. We fired and dropped him on the beach below. There were no eggs in the nest. Probably the female bird was sitting on the other eyrie ; but we were dead-beat with fatigue, and the hillsides swarmed with mosquitoes, so we made our way back at once to the steamer, shooting a willow-grouse as we went, a male in fine summer plumage. The flowers on this part of the tundra were very beautiful, vividly coloured, and abundant ; especially lovely was a tall monkshood and a species of pink. On board the steamer we stretched ourselves on the sofa in the cabin and fell asleep, only to awake when the vessel stopped at Alexievka about noon.

The *Triad* was making ready to start on the morrow;
her cargo was to be about 8000 cubic feet of larch.   Our
stay in these Arctic latitudes was now fast drawing to an
end.   I spent the afternoon looking about the island,
directing my search especially for young of the yellow-
headed wagtail.   Scarcely a bird was to be seen out of
cover.   Grass nearly two feet high covered the ground,
and the willows were in full leaf.   It was difficult enough
to get a shot at a bird, and almost impossible to find it
when brought down.   At last I tried the coast, and found
plenty of birds feeding amongst the drift-wood and the
prostrate willows that had fallen with the crumbling away
of the banks.   Yellow-headed wagtails, red-throated pipits,
and reed buntings were here in abundance.   I could not
stay, however, for the sun was scorching hot, and the
mosquitoes were swarming.

I spent the night with Captain Taylor and Captain
Arendt on board the *Triad*, giving a helping hand in
superintending the loading of the schooner.   The heat
was so intense that I could scarcely bear the suffocation
of my mosquito-veil, and seldom put it on.   The consequence was that I was more bitten in those few hours than
I had been during the whole of my previous stay.   I did
not turn in till 6 A.M., but I woke at eleven, and spent my
day making out the bills of lading for Captain Arendt.
At five o'clock on Sunday, August 1, we finally bade
farewell to the tundra and to our wandering life, and
began our journey towards Europe and civilisation.   We
left Alexievka in tow of the steamer, reaching the bar
soon after midnight.   The cutter signalled ten feet of
water; as we were drawing so much we were soon
aground, as was to be expected.   I sat up with the
captain all night as we tediously manœuvred through the
shallow water.   We had just lit the fire to cook some

supper, when Engel suddenly heaving on the anchor, we got under way again. The captain took the helm, and I remained below cooking the steaks and making the coffee; but we were soon aground once more, and sat down to eat our meal in the cabin. For some hours we went on, sometimes aground, sometimes scraping the bank, until at last we crossed the bar; then Engel towed us until we sighted the beacon at Dvoinik. All sails were now set, and we steered N.E. by N. with a gentle breeze. All the following day and night we tacked from one bank of shoal water to another, with a head wind against us. The lead was kept constantly going, and as soon as the water under the keel was less than a foot, orders were immediately given to "'bout ship." By good luck or good management, we succeeded in getting out of the lagoon of the Petchora without running aground again, though Captain Taylor vowed that nothing should ever induce him a second time to risk a ship in such a dangerous and difficult river. We had scarcely cleared the banks more than half an hour before the wind dropped entirely; the sails flapped idly on the masts, and we sent the crew to bed. We were lounging on the after part of the ship, telling our adventures to the captain, when three curious clouds, like beehives, appeared to rise on the horizon. We were leaning over the bulwarks watching these unusual shapes in the sky, when our attention was caught by the sound of a distant rumbling. The sea was as smooth as glass, and we were debating whether the noise was not that of the Arctic ice, when the captain descried a distant ripple on the sea, and started up as if he had been shot. Hastily asking me to take the rudder, he ran to the hatchway and cried out, at the top of his voice, " All hands on deck!" Every possible exertion was made to haul down the canvas; but before this could be accomplished the gale came upon us, and the ship reeled as the squall struck her, first on the starboard and then on the port side. By the time the canvas had been taken in, the squall had become violent; the sea rose, peals of thunder followed each other rapidly, and rain came down in torrents. A still more extraordinary sight presented itself shortly afterwards—a waterspout. About half a mile from the ship the clouds came down in a funnel, and deluges of rain appeared to fall under it, the sea being lashed into foam as if ten thousand millstones had been suddenly hurled into it. It was some hours before the wind settled down again; but it proved to be a favourable one, and we made fair progress homewards through a Scotch mist from the Arctic ice.

For two days we had fog and fair wind, then came wind and sunshine. On the 3rd of August a few flocks of phalaropes passed overhead, and on the 4th a pair of snowy owls alighted on the ship. We saw also several kittiwake gulls and pomatorhine skuas. Then from the 8th of August to the 29th came three dreary weeks, during which the ship wearily toiled on, against heavy gales and contrary winds, but ever and anon came a fair breeze, to prevent us despairing altogether of ever reaching Elsinore. It seemed hopeless often enough. Various were the tacks the captain tried on the way. One day we would lie-to and let the good ship drift back with the heavy gale towards Kolguev Island, another we would tear along, blown forward by an equally fierce wind, which we welcomed, for it was bearing us homeward. Now we would lie motionless with sails idly flapping against the masts, and again we would be cutting the water with a favourable breeze impelling us on. As we approached the North Cape the weather grew wilder; it

seemed as if we could never round it; the bold promontory appeared to frighten away all fair winds. When we
were within eighty miles of Bear Island our search for
it was vain; it lay shrouded in impenetrable fogs. At
last we left the ill-starred land behind us. We passed
the wild peaks of the Lofodens; we left the storm-tossed
waves beating at their feet, and hailed the mountains
behind Christiansund in genial weather. During those
weeks we saw kittiwakes and Fulmar petrels almost
daily; now and then there passed a skua or a puffin or
two, but no bird on migration.

After another week of fair winds, head winds, calms,
and gales, we reached Elsinore on the thirty-fifth day.
All this time we had roughish fare on board. The
Triad had no provision for passengers. The first week
exhausted our stock of grog and fresh provisions, and
the remainder of the journey we had to put up with hard
captains' biscuits, Australian tinned meat, and coffee
with no milk and short rations of sugar. When we
landed at Elsinore we found that we had averaged
$2\frac{1}{2}$ knots per hour! Our first care was to order a good
dinner, which we all agreed was the most superb enter-
tainment to which we had ever sat down. For the last
fortnight we had dreamed of dining, but always woke
before the happy moment arrived. Our dinner at
Elsinore was enjoyed with an appetite which we never
hope to experience again. Taking the night train to
Copenhagen, we arrived there on the morning of Monday
the 6th of September. We were disappointed in our
efforts to find a steamer for England, so proceeded at
once to Hamburg, where my companion found a boat for
Leith; and I lost no time in putting myself and, not my
"sieben Sachen," but my "siebzehn Sachen," on board
a steamer for Hull.

I left Hamburg in the *Zebra* on Wednesday the 8th of September, and after a smooth passage landed in Hull on Saturday the 11th instant, having been away from home rather more than twenty-seven weeks. Of this time the journey out occupied about six weeks; another six weeks was spent in weary waiting for the arrival of spring; and the journey home took up a third period of six weeks, leaving only nine weeks in which the bulk of our ornithological work was done. Fortunately during this time we had twenty-four hours daylight, of which we frequently availed ourselves. By dint of hard work and long hours we succeeded in doing more in those nine weeks than we could possibly have expected. There can be no doubt that we were exceptionally fortunate in chancing upon the localities frequented by birds which appear to be extremely local during the breeding season.

OLD RUSSIAN SILVER CROSS

FROM MEKITZA TO KUYA ON A ROSPOSKI

CHAPTER XXIII.

RESULTS OF THE JOURNEY.

Results of the Trip—Summer in the Arctic Regions—Circumpolar Birds
—Birds Confined to the Eastern Hemisphere—Various Ranges of Birds—
Migration of Birds—Dates of Arrival—Probable Route—Conclusion.

THE results of our somewhat adventurous journey exceeded our most sanguine hopes.

Of the half-dozen British birds, the discovery of whose breeding-grounds had baffled the efforts of our ornithologists for so long, we succeeded in bringing home identified eggs of three—the grey plover,* the Little stint, and Bewick's swan. Of the remaining three, two—the sanderling and the knot—were found breeding

* Mr. Seebohm apparently overlooked the fact that Middendorff found the nest of the grey plover on the Taimyr peninsula in 1843, and figured the egg in his *Sibirische Reise*, Bd. II., Th. 2, plate 19, Fig. i. *Tringa minuta* was also found nesting, though its eggs were not figured, by the same traveller.—ED.

by Captain Fielden, in lat. 82°, during the Nares Arctic expedition, but the breeding-grounds of the curlew sand-piper still remain a mystery.* We added several birds to the European list, which had either never been found in Europe before, or only doubtfully so ; such as the Siberian chiffchaff, the Petchora pipit, the Siberian herring-gull, the Arctic forms of the marsh-tit and the lesser spotted woodpecker, the yellow-headed wagtail, and the Asiatic stonechat. We brought home careful records of the dates of arrival of the migratory birds which breed in these northern latitudes, besides numerous observations on the habits of little-known birds. Our list of skins brought home exceeded a thousand, and of eggs rather more than six hundred.

The number of species which we obtained was comparatively small, the whole of our collecting having been done north of latitude 65°. The Arctic regions are frost-bound for eight months out of the twelve, and buried under a mantle of snow varying in depth from three to six feet. During this time they are practically barren of ornithological life ; the small number of birds which remain within the Arctic circle forsake the tundras where they breed, to find feed in the pine-forests at or near the limit of forest growth, a few only remaining where the shelter of a deep valley or watercourse permits the growth of a few stunted willows, birches, and hazel bushes. Practically it may be said that there is no spring or autumn in the Arctic regions. Summer follows suddenly upon winter, and the forests and the tundra as suddenly swarm with bird-life. Although the number of species breeding within the Arctic circle is comparatively small, the number of individuals is vast beyond conception. Birds go to the

* Mr. H. Leybourne Popham afterwards obtained the eggs of the curlew sand-piper on the Yenesei, *vide* " Proc. Zoolog. Soc." 1897, p. 891, pl. li.—ED.

Arctic regions to breed, not by thousands, but by millions. The cause of this migration is to be found in the lavish prodigality with which Nature has provided food. Seed- or fruit-eating birds find an immediate and abundant supply of cranberries, crowberries, and other ground fruit, which have remained frozen during the long winter, and are accessible the moment the snow has melted ; whilst insect-eating birds have only to open their mouths to fill them with mosquitoes.

Of the 110 species which we obtained, the following are circumpolar birds, breeding both in the eastern and western hemispheres, being nearly one-third of the total number : —

Osprey.	Sanderling.
Peregrine Falcon.	Shoveller Duck.
Snowy Owl.	Pintail Duck.
Short-eared Owl.	Scaup Duck.
Raven.	Golden-eyed Duck
Pine Grosbeak.	Long-tailed Duck.
Mealy Redpoll.	Goosander.
Lapland Bunting.	Red-breasted Merganser.
Snow Bunting.	Arctic Tern.
Shore-lark.	Great Black-backed Gull.
Bohemian Waxwing.	Glaucous Gull.
Sand Martin.	Richardson's Skua.
Willow-grouse.	Buffon's Skua.
Grey Plover.	Red-throated Diver.
Red-necked Phalarope.	Black-throated Diver.
Dunlin.	

It will be observed that more than half of these species are water birds, showing that the communication between the Palæarctic and the Nearctic regions has been one of water rather than of land.

The following species are confined to the continents of Europe and Asia, and range throughout the Arctic regions of the eastern hemisphere from the North Cape to Bering's Strait. A few of these are occasionally found in Greenland and in Alaska, but are not found in the intermediate or Nearctic regions, though many of them are there represented by very nearly allied species, showing that the communication across the Pole has been interrupted at a comparatively modern geological epoch :—

White-tailed Eagle.	Skylark.
Hobby.	Red throated Pipit.
Merlin.	Green Wagtail.
Goshawk.	Blue-throated Warbler.
Sparrow-hawk.	Wheatear.
Hen-harrier.	Lapp Tit.
Eagle-owl.	Common Swallow.
Black Woodpecker.	Hazel Grouse.
Three-toed Woodpecker.	Little Ringed Plover.
Cuckoo.	Oystercatcher.
Magpie.	Greenshank.
Siberian Jay.	Wood Sandpiper.
Tree Sparrow.	Curlew Sandpiper.
Scarlet Bullfinch.	Spotted Redshank.
Brambling.	Common Sandpiper.
Reed-bunting.	Bar-tailed Godwit.
Ruff.	Teal.
Temminck's Stint.	Wigeon.
Common Snipe.	Tufted Duck.
Great Snipe.	Velvet Scoter.
Whimbrel.	Black Scoter.
Common Crane.	Smew.
Wild Swan.	Common Gull.
Bean-goose.	

From the length of this list it might be reasonable to assume that ornithologists are right in separating the Nearctic region from the Palæarctic region, and that it would be an error, even as far as Arctic birds only are considered, to unite the two together into one circumpolar region. A more minute examination of the list may, however, lead us to a different conclusion. It is not correct to speak of a bird as an Arctic species unless its breeding-grounds are principally within the Arctic circle. We must, therefore, eliminate from our list those species whose breeding-grounds are principally south of the Arctic circle, and only extend beyond it at the extreme northern limit of their range. This will dispose of thirty of the species we have enumerated, leaving only seventeen, of which at least two-thirds are represented in the Nearctic region by very closely allied species. Of the half-dozen species which may be said to belong especially to the eastern Polar region, every one is represented by a species in the western Polar region belonging to the same genus.

The following species range from Scandinavia eastwards as far as the watershed between the Yenesei and the Lena. The proportionate length of this list shows that this boundary is almost as important a one as Bering's Strait, especially when we consider that several enumerated in the second list cross over into Alaska. On the other hand, we must not forget that our knowledge of the birds of the country east of the Yenesei is very limited :—

Rough-legged Buzzard.	Redstart.
Hooded Crow.	Willow-warbler.
Jackdaw.	Sedge-warbler.
House Sparrow.	Capercailzie.
Northern Bullfinch.	Black Grouse.
Tree Pipit.	Golden Plover.
White Wagtail.	Dotterel.
Fieldfare.	Ringed Plover.
Redwing.	Little Stint.

The dotterel and the Little stint are the only species in this list of which it can be said that their principal breeding-grounds are north of the Arctic circle. The nearest relations of the former species are undoubtedly to be found in the southern Palæarctic region, whilst the genus to which the latter belongs is well represented in the Polar regions of both continents.

Two species only appear to range from Scandinavia eastwards as far as the valley of the Ob, but do not cross the watershed into the valley of the Yenesei :—

Rook.	Yellowhammer.

The Ural Mountains, although they are the boundary between political Europe and Asia, are by no means so geographically or ornithologically.   So far as we know, one species only of the Petchora birds recognises this chain as the eastern limit of its range, viz. :—

Meadow Pipit.

Four species ranging westward from Kamtschatka throughout Arctic Siberia and across the Ural Mountains, do not appear to advance farther into Europe, during the breeding season, than the valley of the Petchora :—

Siberian Pipit.	Siberian Stonechat.
Yellow-headed Wagtail.	Bewick's Swan.

Six species, ranging westward from Kamtschatka throughout Arctic Siberia and across the Ural Mountains, appear to extend beyond the valley of the Petchora as far as the White Sea, viz. :—

Siberian Lesser-spotted Woodpecker.	Marsh-tit (eastern form).
Little Bunting.	Terek Sandpiper.
Arctic Willow-warbler.	Siberian Herring-gull.

One bird only appears to be so restricted in its geographical range as to be found only in the valleys of the Petchora, the Ob, and the Yenesei, viz. :—

Siberian Chiffchaff.

Of the fourteen birds included in the last four lists, only four or five have their principal breeding-grounds within the Arctic circle, and these all belong to genera which are represented in the Nearctic region, with the exception of the Arctic willow-warbler, which has been obtained in Alaska.

The final conclusion to which we must therefore arrive, from a study of the geographical distribution of the birds found in the valley of the Petchora, is that a circumpolar region ought to be recognised : that so far as the Polar regions are concerned the division into Nearctic and Palæarctic is a purely arbitrary one.

The migration of birds is a subject which interests all naturalists, and is a very attractive one to a great number of persons who do not pretend to any scientific knowledge of ornithology. The dates and order of arrival of migratory birds present so many points of interest that, for the sake of comparison, the following list has been made of all those birds which we had reason to believe to be migratory in the Ust-Zylma district, leaving out those to which, from their rarity or localness, considerable doubt attaches as to their date of arrival :—

April	1.	Snow-bunting.
,,	1.	Mealy Redpoll.
May	4.	Hen-harrier.
,,	5.	Merlin.
,,	10.	Bean-goose.
,,	10.	Shore-lark.
,,	10.	Snowy Owl.
,,	11.	Wild Swan.
,,	11.	Bewick's Swan.
,,	11.	Siberian Herring-gull.
,,	12.	White Wagtail.
,,	12.	Redstart.
,,	12.	Meadow-pipit.
,,	13.	Pintail and other Ducks.
,,	13.	Peregrine Falcon.
,,	14.	Reed-bunting.
,,	15.	Common Gull.
,,	17.	Golden Plover.
,,	17.	Fieldfare.
,,	17.	Redwing.
,,	17.	Red-throated Pipit.
,,	17.	Green Wagtail.
May	18.	Lapland Bunting.
,,	18.	Whimbrel.
,,	18.	Teal.
,,	20.	Willow-warbler.
,,	20.	Wheatear.
,,	21.	Crane.
,,	22.	Siberian Chiff-chaff.
,,	22.	Siberian Stonechat.
,,	23.	Short-eared Owl.
,,	23.	Blue-throated Warbler.
,,	24.	Brambling.
,,	24.	Pine-grosbeak.
,,	26.	Oyster-catcher.
,,	26.	Ringed Plover.
,,	26.	Wood-sandpiper.
,,	26.	Temminck's Stint.
,,	26.	Common Swallow.
,,	31.	Little Bunting.
June	3.	Cuckoo.
,,	3.	Double Snipe.
,,	3.	Terek Sandpiper.
,,	3.	Black-throated Diver.

This list is necessarily very imperfect. In addition to the difficulty of ascertaining the date of arrival of rare or local birds, we had a still greater difficulty to contend with. There can be no doubt that Ust-Zylma lies somewhat out of the line of migration, which is probably determined largely by the direction of the great valleys.   Birds from the Mediterranean might fairly be supposed to reach the Volga *viâ* the Bosporus, the Black Sea, the Sea of Azov, and the river Don to Sarepta. The natural course of birds from India and Persia would be to the Volga by way of the Caspian Sea.   The line of migration would probably follow the Volga to Kasan,

OUR HEADQUARTERS AT UST-ZYLMA

and thence along the Kama to Perm and Cherdin, close to the source of the Petchora.   The course would then continue down the Petchora as far as its junction with the Ussa.   It would then be reasonable to conclude that the hardy species, which migrate early, would have plenty of time to go round by Ust-Zylma ; whilst the later arrivals would leave the Petchora at Ust-Ussa, and cross direct to the tundra.   For example, the snow-bunting, hen-harrier, merlin, bean-goose, shore-lark, snowy owl, wild swan, Bewick's swan, and herring-gull are probably amongst the earliest breeders on the tundra, and pass through Ust-Zylma, whilst the later breeders on the tundra are not there at all. The following birds are all summer migrants to the tundra, but were not seen passing through Ust-Zylma during migration :—

Yellow-headed Wagtail.	Dunlin.
Arctic Tern.	Richardson's Skua.
Siberian Pipit.	Dotterel.
Red-necked Phalarope.	Sanderling.
Long-tailed Duck.	Curlew Sandpiper.
Buffon's Skua.	Little Stint.
Grey Plover.	

Most of these are very late-breeding birds, but why they should breed late, or for what cause they seem to choose a different line of migration, seems at present inexplicable. Before a conclusion can be arrived at many more facts must be collected. The field of ornithological research is one in which any amount of work may be advantageously done, and possibly the perusal of the present narrative may help to arouse the enthusiasm of other adventurous ornithologists, and induce them to take up the running where we left it off.

OLD RUSSIAN SILVER CROSS

Map to illustrate the
author's journeys in
SIBERIA
1ˢᵗ Journey ——— 2ⁿᵈ Journey ·······

INDEX

INDEX

INDEX

INDEX

Marten, Beech, 282 (note)

Martin, Pallas's house-, 346, 385

Martes foina, -abietum, -sibirica, 282 (note) ; *-zibellina, -americana*, 283 (note)

Maydell, Baron, 127 (note)

Mealy redpoll, 19, 46 (note)

Mekitza, 208, *235*

Merganser, Red-breasted, 145

Merlin, 70, 71

Merula fuscata, 337, 423; *-atrigularis*, 451

Meves. M., 93

Mezén, 22 ; arrive at, 25 ; birds at, 26 ; leave. 27 ; its river scenery, 28 ; Samoyedes at, 49

Mezenski Pizhma, 28

Middendorff, 235 (note), 250; on crows, 272 ; on migratory routes, 427

Migration, times for, 188 ; night, *189;* swallows, 190 ; scientific theory of, 191 ; origin of, 192 ; cause of, 193 ; lines of, 195 ; Heligoland as resting-place, 196 ; affected by weather, 199 ; period of, 200, 201 ; moulting during, 201 ; mortality during, 201 ; hereditary impulse, 204 ; of geese, *226;* dates of arrival, 241 ; summer migrants, 243 ; to Kureika, 335, 340 ; great rush, 343, 357 ; dates of arrival of birds in valley of Yenesei, 374 ; study of continental, 416 ; during glacial period, 419 ; of grouse, 419 ; origin, 420 ; guided by reason, 425 ; autumn rushes in England, 426 ; course of in Yenesei valley, 426

Milvus ater, 456

Mongols, 431, 467

Moscow. Arrive at, 257 ; leave, 258 ; return, 485; leave, 486

Mosquitoes, 106 ; plague of, 163 ; clouds of, *164;* veil, *176*, 230, 377, 439, 441

Motacilla borealis, 84 ; *M. citreola*, 111 ; *M. melanope*, 339 ; *M. personata*, 459

N

NESTS (see also under Eggs), 149; swan's, *151;* duck's, 152; grey plover's, 176, 177 ; Little stint, *178*, 223

Nikandrina, Arrive at, 432; birds at, 432, 433

Nishni Novgorod, Arrive at, 258

Nordenskiöld, Prof., enters Kara Sea,

249 ; success of, 253 ; his goods at Yeneseisk, 460, 461

Nutcracker, 349

Nuthatch, 301

O

OB RIVER, 248; navigation of, 252; fishing station on, *273;* village on, *469*

Officials, at Ust-Zylma, 43; at Turukansk, 288–291

Omsk, 266 ; Kirghis arms at, 268 ; museum, 268

Ostiaks, of the Ob, *251;* cradle, *291;* interior of choom, *292;* exterior, *311;* wooden pipe, *298;* of the Yenesei, 299; baby and cradle, 300; their reindeer and snow-spectacles, dress, and habits, 305, 306; hairdressing, 306; head-coverings, 307; geographical distribution, 310; eating of raw flesh of birds, 312; physical characteristics, 313; costume, *319;* anchor, *334;* funeral, 338; pipe, *338;* drill, *340;* friendly nature, 347 ; arrow-heads, *348;* boats, *414;* choom on the Ob. *479*

Otocorys alpestris, 75

Outfit, for Siberia, 6

Ouzel, Dark, 372; dusky, 395; black-throated, 451

Owl, Eagle, 71; snowy, 75, 222; short-eared, 123; Tengmalm's, 123

Oyster-catcher, 96, 124

P

PALANDER, Capt., 253

Pallas, on Siberian ornithology, 498

Palmen, on migratory routes, 427

Parasites on reindeer, 50

Parus cinctus, 113; *P. borealis, P. camtchatkensis, P. japonicus, P. obtectus, P. palustris*, 500, 501

Pavoskas, 22, 52

Peacock, Dr., treats for scurvy, 466

Pelzam, Dr., visits Petchora, 5; at Kazan, 485

Peregrine falcon, 78, 86, 146, 147, 162

Perisoreus infaustus, 33

Perm, Arrival at, 479

Petchora, 5; visited by Schrenck, Keyserling, von Krusenstern, Dr. Pelzam, 5; Henke, Hoffmansegg, 6; first sight

INDEX

INDEX

INDEX